S0-CFM-367

LECTURES ON COMMUNICATION SYSTEM THEORY

Lectures on

Communication System Theory

EDITED BY

ELIE J. BAGHDADY, Sc. D.

Department of Electrical Engineering

Massachusetts Institute of Technology

McGRAW-HILL BOOK COMPANY, INC.

NEW YORK TORONTO LONDON

1961

LECTURES ON COMMUNICATION SYSTEM THEORY

Library of Congress Catalog Card Number 60-9835

03015

Contributors

Elie J. Baghdady
Department of Electrical Engineering and Research Laboratory of Electronics

Donald G. Brennan
Department of Mathematics and Lincoln Laboratory

Wilbur B. Davenport, Jr.
Department of Electrical Engineering and Research Laboratory of Electronics

Peter Elias
Department of Electrical Engineering and Research Laboratory of Electronics

Robert M. Fano
Department of Electrical Engineering and Research Laboratory of Electronics

Paul E. Green, Jr.
Lincoln Laboratory

Thomas Kailath
Research Laboratory of Electronics

Robert H. Kingston
Lincoln Laboratory

Robert M. Lerner
Lincoln Laboratory

Walter E. Morrow, Jr.
Lincoln Laboratory

Irwin Pollack
Air Force Command Control Division, Bedford Massachusetts

Robert P. Rafuse
Department of Electrical Engineering and Research Laboratory of Electronics

William L. Root
Lincoln Laboratory

Herbert Sherman
Lincoln Laboratory

William M. Siebert
Department of Electrical Engineering and Research Laboratory of Electronics

Arthur Uhlir, Jr.
Microwave Associates, Inc., Burlington, Massachusetts

Jerome B. Wiesner
Department of Electrical Engineering and Research Laboratory of Electronics

John M. Wozencraft
Department of Electrical Engineering, Research Laboratory of Electronics, and Lincoln Laboratory

Preface

This book is the outgrowth of a set of notes for a special summer program* on "Reliable Long-Range Radio Communication" which was offered at the Massachusetts Institute of Technology between August 17 and August 28, 1959, to a large group of practicing communication engineers. The main objective of the program was defined as "a well-integrated presentation of modern approaches to the development of new communication systems ..." in which "the application of basic models and mathematical techniques as guides in the design and evaluation of ... systems ... [is] stressed." The program was also intended to "provide an opportunity for members of the Electrical Engineering Department [M.I.T.] and of Lincoln Laboratory [M.I.T.] to present new results of their own research ... [as well as] personal interpretations of the work of others."

The outline of this book was drawn up by an editorial committee that consisted of D. G. Brennan, W. B. Davenport, Jr., W. E. Morrow, Jr., W. M. Siebert, with this writer as chairman. The original plans called for a distribution of the editorial load among the committee members. It soon became evident, however, that substantial rewriting and reorganization would be necessary, and that it would be preferable to have only one editor work closely with each and all of the contributors. The chairman undertook this task, vastly and optimistically underestimating what was lying ahead.

In its present form, the book includes the original notes, most of them completely rewritten, plus a large amount of material that was added during the editorial phase of the work. In several instances (of which two have been explicitly indicated against the editor's wishes) the rewriting was undertaken by this editor and almost all of the derivations and computations were checked in this process. But a great debt is owed to D. G. Brennan, W. B. Davenport, Jr., W. E. Morrow, Jr., and W. M. Siebert for their contributions to the editorial work. Their names do not appear on the title page by their own choice. I would like to acknowledge, in particular, my personal debt to Dr. Brennan for his valuable criticisms of my own Chapter 7.

In broad outline, the topics covered are:

(a) The mathematical representation of signals and disturbances. The basic concepts are introduced in Chapters 2 and 3, and the application of these concepts to individual circumstances is pursued throughout the remaining chapters. The emphasis here, as well as throughout the rest of the book, is on presenting the useful mathematical concepts

*"M.I.T. Offers Program in Reliable Long-Range Communication in August," *Proc. IRE*, vol. 47, p. 18A; July, 1959.

in engineering tutorial language. For example, in Chapter 2, Brennan formulates the communication engineer's concept of *probability* in an elegant mathematical framework, and analyzes critically the relevance of such items as the ergodic hypothesis in the context of the random-signal and noise models of communication-system engineering. In Chapter 3, Siebert presents a stimulating treatment of the use of exponential transforms in signal representation, and the place of this representation in the analysis of linear systems, with emphasis on the motivation for the choice of representation, which is made in a manner that should dispel some existing fundamental misconceptions about the use of Fourier-Laplace methods.

(b) Characterization of transmission channels in terms of observed behavior at the transmitting and receiving terminals. The various aspects of this characterization are treated in Chapters 4, 5, 6, and in a substantial part of Chapter 7. The contemporary viewpoint in the development of new communication systems recognizes the transmission medium as an integral and central part of the system. The disturbances and propagation characteristics of the medium must be taken into account in the process of signal selection at the transmitting end, and in the process of signal reproduction at the receiving end. Ideally, the message chosen for transmission must be expressed in a form that is most immune to disturbances encountered in transmission, and the processing of the corrupted signal at the receiver must take maximum advantage of the characteristics of the signal, as compared with the characteristics of the disturbance. The demands for precision, reliability, security, and efficiency of system utilization have increased to the point where existing knowledge of transmission channels is often inadequate, and specific measurements must precede the final design. Adequate models of channels are necessary to guide the course of measurements. The need here is not so much for physical models of propagation mechanisms as it is for system characterization in terms of observable parameters at the terminals of a black box.

(c) Discussion of various corrective measures and signal design and processing techniques aimed at combatting the multiplicative and additive disturbances introduced in the transmission channel. For example, the use of diversity to combat fading is discussed in Chapter 7; optimum-decision and matched-filter techniques are discussed in Chapters 8, 9, 11, and 12; coding and feedback from receiver to transmitter are discussed in Chapters 13 and 14; analog-modulation techniques are discussed in Chapter 19; and receiver-noise minimization techniques in Chapters 15, 16, and 17.

(d) Application of the background material to the synthesis of communication systems. In Chapters 1 and 21 Davenport and Morrow outline the various factors and criteria of communication system design. Performance criteria of speech systems are discussed by Pollack in Chapter 18. In Chapter 22, Wiesner presents a critical evaluation of the impact of earth satellites upon the future of long-range communication; and in Chapter 23, Fano highlights the important role that computers will play in the communication systems of the future.

Although the emphasis throughout the book is on tutorial presentation, almost every chapter contains new ideas and results that either were unpublished or developed especially in the writing of this volume. Many important unsolved research problems are pointed out in almost every area discussed. The book should therefore prove valuable not only as a reference book for practicing engineers or lecturers on the subject, but also as a textbook for students at the senior or graduate level. While no exercises per se are specifically provided, the reader should profit greatly from verifying derived conclusions, providing justification for unproven statements, or exploring extensions of arguments presented.

I wish to record a warm acknowledgment to Professor J. B. Wiesner, whose leadership, wisdom and hard work have been so instrumental in creating and sustaining a highly stimulating research environment at the Research Laboratory of Electronics at M.I.T. His enthusiastic endorsement of, and contribution to, this undertaking are sincerely appreciated. Professor Peter Elias's valuable participation and counsel in the planning of the course from which this book has evolved is also gratefully acknowledged.

Elie J. Baghdady

Table of Contents

CHAPTER 1

INTRODUCTION

Communication System Design

W. B. Davenport, Jr.

The need for reliable, rapid, and efficient means of communication has never been greater than it is today—nor is this need likely to diminish in the future. The increasing tempo of modern life places more and more emphasis on the need to communicate over greater and greater distances. Events capable of affecting the well-being of any nation, whether in the political or in the economic sphere, can occur at any time and at any place on the face of the earth today—and in outer space tomorrow. The problems of acquiring, transmitting, processing, and utilizing information pertaining to such events are among the most important problems facing communication engineers and scientists today.

In this book we shall attempt to present some of the methods of communication system analysis and synthesis. Parts of the presentation will be intuitive, while other parts will be quite analytic. In any case, emphasis will be primarily placed on the concepts involved, rather than upon detailed applications of the methods to specific communication problems. Also, we shall largely confine our attention to the problem of communicating between two points; in particular, to the designing of a single communications link. The problem of connecting a number of such links together to form an effective communication network is itself of considerable magnitude and cannot be treated here.

I. BASIC DESIGN FACTORS

There are many factors that enter into the determination of the design of a communication link. Basic amongst these are:

(a) the kind of signal to be transmitted,
(b) the transmission channels available,
(c) the ultimate criteria of performance, and
(d) the allowable cost.

Typical signals are speech, pictures, and numerical data; available channels might include an ionospheric-propagation channel in the high-frequency radio band, a channel over a submarine cable, and a channel utilizing an active repeater in an earth satellite; the criteria of performance might be fidelity of reproduction or probability of error; and allowable costs would include the annual costs of operation and maintenance as well as the costs of the initial design, development, construction, and installation.

The design of a communication link starts with the specification of the above basic factors. A change of any one generally results in a change of design. Thus, the design of a speech communication link in which fidelity of reproduction of the speaker's voice is deemed most important may well be quite different from that in which a low probability of error in reception of the spoken message is most important and the recognition of the speaker is unimportant. It should never be forgotten, however, that in any given case, the initial specification of the basic design factors may be incomplete or inconsistent and hence subject to change. For example, it might be asserted that the dominant criterion of performance is that a stated probability of error cannot be exceeded, only to find out later that the only designs capable of achieving that level of performance are ruled out on the basis of excessive cost. In such cases no link can be designed that will meet the initial specifications, and a decision must be made as to which, if any, of the specifications can be relaxed so as to enable a link design.

II. DESIGN PROCEDURE

After the kind of signals to be transmitted, the available channels, the criteria of performance, and the allowable cost have all been specified, the detailed design of a communication link can proceed. While communication theory has developed to a high degree over the past years, it is still true that there is often as much art in design as there is science; there are yet many problems which we do not know how to handle analytically. Although this book will emphasize some of the available analytic methods, it must be remembered throughout that in many practical cases these methods and their derived results can at best aid the intuition in developing a link design.

Perhaps the first step to be taken is to select the "best" of the available channels. Sometimes in order to do this an essentially complete design must be made for each of the available channels, in other cases a rough analysis of each will suffice. On occasion, none of the stated available channels will enable the design of a useful link, and effort must be made to find a new channel. The finding of a suitable new channel may well be the most difficult part of a link design.

The physical properties of the selected channel, (*e.g.*, the average total attenuation, the fading rates, the amount and kind of interference, the frequency characteristics, etc.) all determine which signals can best convey information through the channel. Unfortunately the signals appropriate to a given channel are rarely the same as those generated by the source of the information to be transmitted. Thus, at least a translation to the allocated frequency channel is required in most radio circuits, while in circuits subject to severe multipath and strong interfering signals rather more complex channel signals may be needed. The design of a communication link therefore generally requires the determination of appropriate channel signals and then the determination of methods of generating and detecting those signals.

The application of analytic methods to the design of a communication link requires the construction of a conceptual model of the link. Such a model forms a frame upon which to hang the analysis. The detailed structure of the model is determined partly by the physics of the situation and partly for analytic convenience. Since a "convenient" model may provide a poor replica of the real world, care must be taken not to throw away the essence of the problem when simplifying the model so as to facilitate the analysis. For example, while gaussian statistics provide the most convenient model of channel noise, in some cases this is such a poor model that analyses based upon its use will lead to fallacious results.

It is convenient to categorize communication *signals* as being either analog or digital. Thus speech and music are analog signals, while telegraph and teletype signals are digital. Similarly, it is convenient to categorize communication *systems* as either analog or digital. Thus the usual amplitude-modulated broadcast system is an analog system, while pulse-code modulation systems are digital. However, it is not necessarily true that analog systems are best for analog signals; for example, in some situations speech signals are best transmitted by pulse-code modulation systems.

A simple model of an analog communication link is shown in Fig. 1. The signal source might be a microphone, a television camera, or a pressure gauge. In addition to providing power amplification, the modulator performs the transformation from the given input signals to the signals suitable for transmission over the channel; it might simply use the input signal to modulate a radio-frequency carrier in amplitude or in frequency. The characteristics of the channel are concealed within the box labelled "Disturbed channel"; any detailed analysis of course requires a more detailed model of the channel. The detection of the channel signals, *i.e.* the transformation from the channel signals to signals suitable to the user, is performed by the demodulator. A criterion of performance for such a link is most often a fidelity criterion; say, for example, faithfulness of reproduction as judged by a human observer, or a least-mean-square error criterion, or uniformity of frequency response and level of harmonic or intermodulation distortion.

By suitably interpreting the actions of the modulator and the demodulator, Fig. 1 could also be used as a model of a digital communication link. However, it is desirable in the digital case to expand

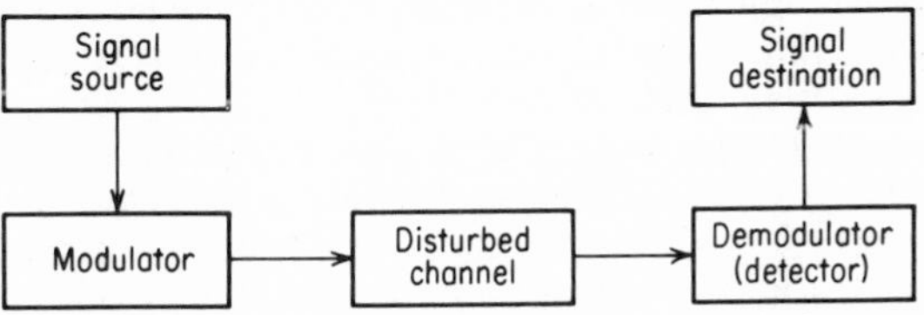

Fig. 1. An analog communication link

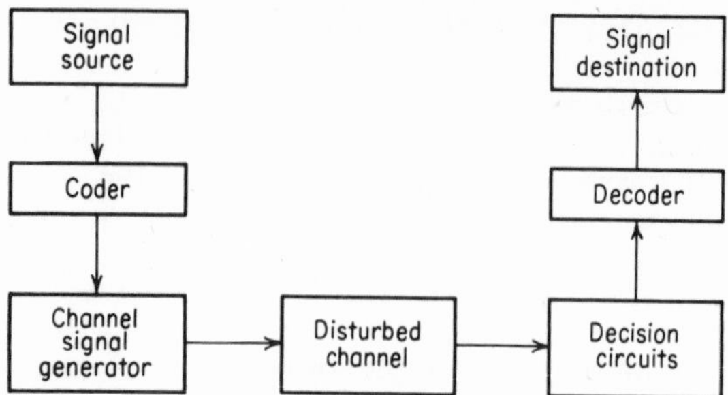

Fig. 2. A digital communication link

the detail of the model a bit and so arrive at Fig. 2. Here it is assumed that the signal source generates a sequence of symbols drawn from a finite set; *e.g.* a sequence of letters of the alphabet or a sequence of the binary digits zero and one. (Note that analog signals can be converted into digital form by sampling.)

The input symbol sequence must be transformed into a sequence of signals suitable for transmission over the given channel. It is often convenient to break this operation up into two parts: a coding operation and a signal-generation operation. Since the redundancies or constraints, if any, of the input symbol sequence may not be suitable for combatting the channel disturbances, it may be desirable to remove those constraints and to replace them with other constraints, which are suitable to the channel (*e.g.* by using error-correcting coding); this is the operation of the coder. The operation of transforming from the coded symbol sequence to a sequence of channel signals is then performed by the channel signal generator. The question as to how to allocate the effort between the coding and the signal generation operations can only be answered by reference to the details of the particular problem at hand. In some cases, it may be best to use a relatively simple set of signals in the channel (say, for example, a set of sine waves of different frequencies as in frequency-shift-keying systems) and a rather complicated coding operation; in other cases it may be desirable to put the greatest effort on channel-signal generation.

Once a waveform is received at the channel output, a decision must be made as to which of the possible channel signals it could have been; this is the function of the decision circuits. The ability to make a correct decision is a function of the level of interference in the channel. The coded sequence of symbols appearing at the output of the decision circuitry is then decoded and presented to the signal destination.

The advantage of a model, such as that shown in Fig. 2, is that it makes evident the basic functions which must be performed by the various elements of the communication link. The detailed structures of the various boxes in such a figure (*i.e.* the detailed methods of implementing those basic functions) depend, of course, upon the assumed characteristics of the link in question and upon the state of engineering development at the time of the design.

IV. STATISTICS AND THE COMMUNICATION LINK

It has been repeated many times so far in this introduction that the design of a communication link depends in detail upon the characteristics of the input signals and upon the characteristics of the given channel. It must be noted, however, that the detailed behavior of the signals and of the channel are not fixed for all time, but rather vary from instant to instant; to all intents and purposes they are unpredictable and "random" in nature. The input signal, in fact, must be unpredictable in some sense in order for it to be able to impart any information at all to the ultimate user. If the input signals were completely predictable, no communication link would be necessary! The randomness of the channel might, on the other hand, only be apparent and simply be due to the fact that not all the causal forces at work are known. Even in this case, though, the channel properties are random as far as the link designer is concerned.

While the characteristics of the input signals and of the channel are unpredictable in detail, their behavior is usually regular enough on the average that a useful link design can be based upon a knowledge of their statistical properties. Typical statistics of interest might be the probability of occurrence of the various possible input symbols in a digital system and the distribution of power with frequency of the output of a given channel in response to some specified test signal—say a sine wave.

It is of course a consequence of the random nature of the input signals and of the channel (and hence of basing the design of a communications link on their statistical properties), that the criteria of performance for the link must also be statistical in nature. Thus one can ask only that the average squared error be a minimum, or that the probability of error be below a certain bound.

V. THE BOOK

An attempt has been made in this chapter to introduce some of the basic concepts involved in the design of a communication link, and to point up their interrelationships. The ability to implement these concepts in practice is determined by the state of engineering development at the time of design. Today, we are much more able to state our problems than we are able to provide complete solutions for them. Nonetheless, significant advances have been made and guides for the future are available.

In the chapters that follow, the pertinent concepts and techniques of probability theory and statistics will be presented. These concepts and techniques will then be applied to the problems of characterizing signals and channels. Next, certain corrective reception and transmission techniques, and the closely related areas of channel-signal selection and detection and of symbol coding and decoding will be discussed. Finally, the application of these ideas to the synthesis of communication links for some channels of current interest will be discussed and illustrated.

CHAPTER 2

Probability Theory in Communication System Engineering

Donald G. Brennan

I. INTRODUCTION

It is impossible to predict in advance the precise signal and noise voltages on a communication circuit, the precise structure of the disturbances introduced by the transmission medium, or the precise nature of a message to be transmitted over the circuit. It is quite immaterial whether one regards the universe as fundamentally deterministic or not; the operational fact remains that we cannot predict such things in detail.

Yet we can and do predict certain facts about such systems; namely, certain statistical facts such as average values or probability distributions. The question of just what facts can be predicted, and with what degree of accuracy, is an experimental question that cannot be answered solely on the basis of any mathematical theory. The role of probability theory in the design of communication systems is (1) to provide theoretical frameworks for experimental observations, (2) to suggest new and possibly useful ways of finding and characterizing predictable statistical facts, (3) to enable the computation of theoretical performance of complicated systems on the basis of mathematical models that "imitate" the known or assumed properties of the system, and (4) to relate such theoretically computed performance to practical "verification" experiments in more-or-less specifiable ways. As with most of the subjects treated in this volume, probability theory is not at present in a very satisfactory state, especially with respect to objectives (3) and (4); we often have to use approximations with little or no information as to their accuracy, or employ assumptions for which little or no justification can be given. In the last analysis, radio communication systems are designed by "seat-of-the-pants" engineering—let no forest of formulae in this or other chapters of this book suggest otherwise. It is nevertheless possible to eliminate a great deal of the uncertainty in such design by the judicious use of probability theory, and there has been considerable progress in this field in the past three decades. There has been progress in the mathematical theory of probability, in the quantity and quality of available experimental information, and in our understanding of the relation between the two.

But it is quite impossible to exhibit more than a microscopic fraction of this progress in a single brief chapter, and it is advisable to indicate the scope of the present survey. To begin with, the purely mathematical theory of probability is a completely abstract discipline that has nothing to do with the design of communication systems, or any other kind of systems of a "real-life" variety. This theory as such will accordingly not concern us here, beyond noting, once and for all, that "probability" in this abstract framework is anything that satisfies a certain set of defining axioms, and the various kinds of "probability" we shall discuss below all satisfy these axioms.

However, we shall make use of the freedom permitted by the rigorous mathematical framework in the process of exhibiting various ideas and relationships, not all of which are well known. The basic objective of this chapter is to illuminate some relations between modern probability theory and communication system engineering. It is not particularly intended for beginners. We shall establish some connections between mathematical random variables and the ideas and experimental techniques employed by practicing communication system engineers. This will lead to a simple theorem relating experimental time averages to the moments of corresponding experimental distributions. This theorem in turn will later be used to clarify the role of ergodicity in mathematical random-process models for communication problems. The same setting for random variables will also lead (in Chapter 20) to a method of predicting certain types of results that cannot be predicted on the basis of conventional (and less explicit) models. We shall also include enough conventional material to provide a frame of reference. This will, however, be restricted to material that has been found to be most useful in the experimental characterization of disturbances in radio channels, in the statistical characterization of speech and other signal and noise voltages, in the design of communication systems and subsystems such as frequency-multiplex and diversity systems, and in understanding the coding results of information theory.

Even with this relatively restricted objective, it is not possible to do more than scratch the surface. We shall concentrate on the basic ideas and theorems only, omitting all derivations as well as machinery (such as characteristic functions) that is chiefly useful for computational purposes or the derivation of theorems. Readers with no previous acquaintance with probability theory would be well advised to master at least the material given in a highly readable tutorial paper of Bennett.[1] An introduction to the mathematical theory of probability may be found in the small book of Cramér[2] or, at a slightly more sophisticated (but not otherwise advanced) level, in Kolmogorov.[3] The standard elementary text on discrete mathematical probability is Feller.[4] The principal book treating applications of probability theory to communication systems is the text by Davenport and Root,[5] which is especially oriented to objective (3) in the second paragraph above. Advanced workers in communication theory often find the statistical material in the large book of Cramér[6] quite useful. The principal texts[7,8,9] used by mathematicians in probability theory would probably be of little interest to most readers of this volume.

II. RANDOM VARIABLES AND PROBABILITY DISTRIBUTIONS

2.1 Basic Definitions and Concepts

Since we cannot predict the performance of a communication system in precise detail, it is clear that the type of information that can (sometimes) be successfully predicted is, in some sense, an "abstract" of the complete situation. The most popular and successful devices used as "abstractors" are probability distribution functions and data derivable therefrom. We shall therefore begin by considering distribution functions.

It is possible, though completely unnatural, to treat almost the whole of probability theory by considering only properties of distribution functions, without ever saying what a distribution function "is". This procedure, however, is essentially never followed, and distribution functions are usually defined in connection with random variables. Specifically, a *distribution function* (occasionally abbreviated d.f.) $F(x)$ is defined as the probability that some random variable (occasionally abbreviated r.v.) is less than or equal to x. For example, if g is a random variable, the distribution function of g is

$$\begin{aligned} F(x) &= \text{Probability that } g \leqslant x \\ &= P(g \leqslant x), \end{aligned} \tag{1}$$

where we write $P(\ldots)$ for "the probability of $(\ldots)$". This is a one-dimensional distribution function, or "first-order" distribution function. The analogous distribution function for n random variables $g_1, g_2, \ldots, g_n$ would be a function of n variables $x_1, x_2, \ldots, x_n$, namely

$$F(x_1, x_2, \ldots, x_n) = P(g_1 \leqslant x_1 \text{ and } g_2 \leqslant x_2 \text{ and } \ldots \text{ and } g_n \leqslant x_n), \tag{2}$$

which is called an n-dimensional d.f. or the joint d.f. of the random variables g_i. For the time being, we shall primarily consider one-dimensional d.f.'s.

Evidently this shifts the burden of definition to the question of what a random variable is. On a primitive level, I suppose a random variable is anything that varies "randomly". The trouble with this is that one cannot do mathematics with a notion as fuzzy as the idea of "randomness". There are various ways out of this problem, but the way almost universally used in recent decades is to define a random variable as any kind of a mathematical function satisfying certain conditions. Without going into these conditions in detail, we may say that for our purposes, a *random variable* is any real-valued function defined on a probability space, where a "probability space" is any set with probabilities suitably affixed to it. Whether or not a random variable *qua* function is "random" in any sense whatever is a question that simply does not arise. For example, let us take a probability space consisting of a tribe of 10 Hottentots, whom we shall denote by ω_K, $K = 1, 2, \ldots, 10$, with each Hottentot having probability 1/10. Any real-valued function defined on this tribe of Hottentots is then a random variable; *e.g.*, the function that is equal to K on the Kth Hottentot, $g(\omega_K) = K$. Other, equally admissible random variables would be $\sqrt{K}$ or $\log K$ or $f(\omega_K) = \text{constant}$. For the random variable g that is equal to K on the Kth Hottentot, the distribution function (1) becomes

$$\begin{aligned} F(x) &= P(g \leq x) \\ &= \frac{1}{10}\,(\text{number of Hottentots } \omega_K \text{ for which } g(\omega_K) \leq x) \\ &= \frac{1}{10}\,[x],\ 0 \leq x \leq 10, \end{aligned} \tag{3}$$

where $[x]$ = greatest integer that is $\leq x$, and $F(x) = 0$ for $x < 0$, $F(x) = 1$ for $x > 10$.

The point to be illustrated by the example above is this: There are always a great many probability spaces and random variables that have the same distribution function. In the example, if π is any permutation of the integers 1, 2, ..., 10, the random variable g_π defined by $g_\pi(\omega_i) = g(\omega_{\pi(i)}) = \pi(i)$ has exactly the same distribution function (3); this gives 10! different random variables, just on the one probability space, with the *same* d.f. (3). (The reader should verify this if it is not already clear.) And, of course, a great many different probability spaces could have been chosen in place of the tribe of Hottentots; in the case of a probability space with infinitely many points, there would usually be infinitely many different random variables having a given d. f. However, the finite permutations considered above suggest a general fact: Random variables on a given probability space which differ from one another only by a suitable "shuffling" of the probability space all have the same distribution function.* Without explaining in detail what is meant by "suitable shuffling", we can nevertheless see that a d. f. "abstracts" certain information about a very large class of random variables.

This fact is the essence of the central role played by distribution functions in the design of communication systems. In practice, a somewhat more nebulous fact is generally of interest: For a fixed d. f., there is an even larger class of random variables than the one just described whose distribution functions all approximate the given d. f. This means that one can hope to find fixed model distribution functions that will, in some sense, "represent" or "abstract" the behavior of some part of a communication system in a regular and predictable way.

The definition of a distribution function given above is basic and applies to all types of random variables. For certain random variables, a derived function known as a "probability density function" may be defined. If the distribution function F of a random variable has a continuous first derivative, except possibly at the end points

*The converse of this fact is also true, as may be indicated by considering the example above.

$F = 0$ and $F = 1$, the random variable is said to be "of continuous type", and its probability density function p is defined by

$$p(x) = \frac{dF(x)}{dx},$$

i.e., as the derivative of the distribution function. It follows that $p(x) \geq 0$, and that

$$F(x) = \int_{-\infty}^{x} p(t)dt. \tag{4}$$

Moreover, for any function h for which the indicated integrals exist,

$$\int_{-\infty}^{\infty} h(t)dF(t) = \int_{-\infty}^{\infty} h(t)p(t)\,dt. \tag{5}$$

Not all random variables are of the continuous type. If the distribution function of a r.v. has a finite number of "jumps" in any finite interval, and is constant except for the "jumps", the r.v. is said to be "of discrete type". In this case, the r.v. takes on each of the discrete values at the "jumps" with positive probability (equal to the height of the "jump"). A r.v. of discrete type does not have a probability density function in the sense defined above, but the concept of a density function may be extended to discrete r.v.'s with the aid of Dirac delta-functions in such a way that the property (4) can be retained, and the property (5) can be retained for a restricted class of functions h. Random variables for which the distribution can be represented through a density function consisting of the sum of a continuous density function and a sequence of Dirac delta-functions are said to be of "mixed" type. There exist r.v.'s that are not of discrete, continuous, or mixed types; however, such r.v.'s are of no known importance for engineering applications.

A word of caution concerning this terminology may be in order. The phrases "discrete type" and "continuous type" refer to properties of *distributions*, not to properties of random variables *qua* functions. For certain kinds of probability spaces, it makes perfectly good sense to speak of continuous or discontinuous r.v.'s on the space. The trouble is that a continuous r.v. may be of discrete type and a discontinuous r.v. may be of continuous type; examples are easy to come by. Use of the terminology "continuous r.v." to mean a r.v. of continuous type, which is sometimes encountered, is therefore unfortunate. The correct terminology is given in Cramér,[6] among others.

2.2 "Fraction-of-Time" Distributions

Suppose we observe some function of time, $g(t)$, say the envelope of a fading radio wave, in an interval of total duration T, say from $t = t_1 - T$ to $t = t_1$. For any given value of x, we may ask: In what fraction of the interval of observation was $g(t) \leq x$? This question is evidently

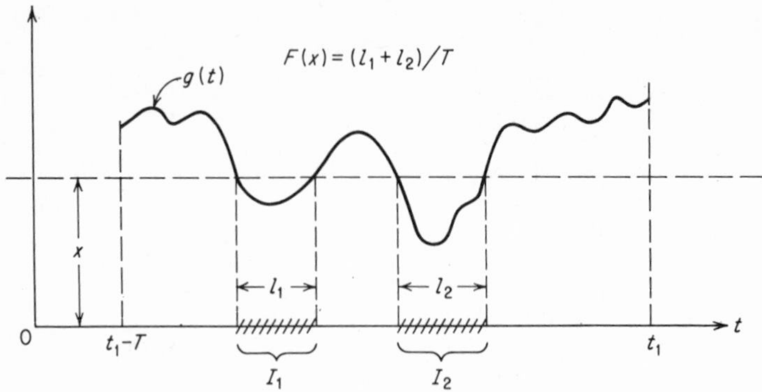

Fig. 1. Definition of $F(x)$ = fraction of the time of observation that $g(t) \leqslant x$.

meaningful for every value of x, and we denote the answer, which depends on x, by $F(x)$. The function $F(x)$ is determined as in Fig. 1. For values of x greater than the maximum value of g, we evidently have $F(x) = 1$. Similarly, if x is less than the minimum value of g, then $F(x) = 0$. For intermediate values of x, there will in general be several sub-intervals in which $g(t) \leqslant x$, with $g(t) > x$ elsewhere, and we simply add up the lengths of these intervals and divide by T to determine $F(x)$, as indicated in Fig. 1.

The point of this example is this: We may regard the interval $t_1 - T \leqslant t \leqslant t_1$ as a probability space, with the probability of any sub-interval given by $(1/T) \times$ (length of the sub-interval). The function g is then a random variable, and its distribution function is simply the fraction of time that $g \leqslant x$. In other words, the "probability" in the definition (1) can be taken to mean "the fraction of time". Such "fraction-of-time" distributions play a central role in the design of communication systems. For example, it is often found experimentally that for suitable values of T, usually on the order of a half hour, the fraction of time the envelope of a fading radio wave is $\leqslant x$ is quite well approximated by the Rayleigh distribution function

$$F(x) = \begin{cases} 1 - e^{-x^2}, & x \geqslant 0, \\ 0, & x < 0, \end{cases} \tag{6}$$

for which the associated probability density function $p(x) = dF/dx$ is

$$p(x) = \begin{cases} 2xe^{-x^2}, & x \geqslant 0, \\ 0, & x < 0, \end{cases} \tag{7}$$

where x is measured in units of the mean square value of the envelope during the interval of observation. The fixed model distribution (6) thus often serves as a predictable "abstractor" of certain complicated waveforms whose detailed behavior cannot be predicted at all.

Instruments for measuring such "fraction-of-time" distributions experimentally are known as "totalizers" or "level distribution re-

Fig. 2. Two "totalizers" or "level distribution recorders" that are in use at an experimental communication installation. The amount of time the signals spend below each of the (10) pre-set levels is displayed on the (cumulative) glow-tube counters, which are turned on and off by gates.

corders" (Fig. 2), and are widely used in the design and evaluation of communication systems. In the absence of these rather complicated instruments, such distributions are often determined by sampling the given waveform at closely spaced intervals, and taking $F(x)$ to be the fraction of the total number of sampled values that is $\leqslant x$; however, it is easy to see from Fig. 1 that this is essentially the same as a totalizer-type distribution.

One of the principal uses of such distribution functions is in computing time averages. If g is any function for which $F(x)$ is the fraction-of-time distribution function in the sense of Fig. 1, then all time-averages of g in the interval $t_1 - T \leqslant t \leqslant t_1$ can be computed from the d.f. $F(x)$. We shall endow this fact with a name, viz.

The Local-Ergodicity Theorem—Let $F(x)$ be the d.f. defined as in Fig. 1 for the function g in the interval $t_1 - T \leqslant t \leqslant t_1$. Then we have

$$\frac{1}{T}\int_{t_1-T}^{t_1} [g(t)]^n \, dt = \int_{-\infty}^{\infty} x^n dF(x) = \int_{-\infty}^{\infty} x^n p(x) dx, \tag{8a}$$

or, more generally, for essentially any function φ

$$\frac{1}{T}\int_{t_1-T}^{t_1} \varphi[g(t)] dt = \int_{-\infty}^{\infty} \varphi(x) dF(x) = \int_{-\infty}^{\infty} \varphi(x) p(x) dx. \tag{8b}$$

In other words, all time averages of g in the interval $t_1 - T \leqslant t \leqslant t_1$ are given by the corresponding moments of the distribution function $F(x)$. And, as indicated previously, there would be infinitely many different functions g that would have the same distribution function $F(x)$, and infinitely many more functions whose distribution functions would closely approximate the fixed d. f. $F(x)$. (The motivation for the name "local-ergodicity theorem" will become clear later. It is not particularly difficult to prove this theorem.)

Thus, the content of the local-ergodicity theorem is that whatever the actual d. f. of a given waveform in a given interval may be, the moments of this d. f. are related to the corresponding time averages of f via (8a) and (8b). This gives a powerful tool for computing, say, the average power of a radio-wave envelope from the model Rayleigh distribution function (6) under any circumstances when this model d. f. is a good approximation to the d. f. of the actual envelope.

Averages such as those in (8) are often endowed with a special notation and terminology. If X is a random variable with distribution function $F(x) = P(X \leqslant x)$, its average value is variously called the *average* or *mean* or *expectation* or *expected value* of X and variously written $\overline{X}$ or $E[X]$ or $\langle X \rangle$ or m_x, and is given by

$$E[X] = \int_{-\infty}^{\infty} x dF(x),$$

which may also be called the *first moment* of the distribution F. Sometimes the notation $\overline{X}$ or $\langle X \rangle$ is employed for different kinds of averages; but in contexts in which essentially only one kind of average is involved, the most sensible way of treating this plethora of notation is to use whichever seems most convenient for the expression at hand. Analogously to the first moment, the nth *moment* of a distribution is given by

$$E[X^n] = \langle X^n \rangle = \int_{-\infty}^{\infty} x^n dF(x).$$

The *n^{th} central moment* of a distribution is given by $E[(X-m_x)^n]$. A particularly important case is the second central moment, called the *variance*, σ_X^2,

$$\sigma_X^2 = \left\langle (X-\overline{X})^2 \right\rangle = \overline{X^2} - m_X^2,$$

where for the second equality we have made use of the facts that averaging is a linear operation and that the average of a constant is that constant. [For random variables and distributions given as in Fig. 1, these facts are an immediate consequence of the case $n = 1$ of the Local-Ergodicity Theorem (8a).]

Although the computation of averages is an important application of distribution functions, it is by no means the only important application. The direct interpretation of a d.f. as "the fraction of time that something is $\leqslant x$" is at least as important. For example, a very commonly specified design criterion for a communication system is that some designated signal-to-noise ratio (SNR) shall not fall below some specified value for more than (say) 1 per cent of some specified interval(s) of time. This information can evidently be obtained directly from the distribution function of the SNR in question—more specifically, it can be obtained approximately from a mathematical model d.f. that is thought likely to be a good approximation to the actual d.f. of the SNR in question. In digital systems, such as binary FSK, the "local" error probabilities in the digital data depend on the corresponding SNR, and, hence, the distribution of "local" error probabilities depends on the same SNR distribution; average error rates are obtained by integrating such "local" error rates.

2.3 "Population" Distributions

Although fraction-of-time distributions occupy a central position in the characterization of communication systems, it is by no means true that only distributions of this type are used in connection with such systems. Much of the analysis employed in the coding problems of information theory is of an essentially combinatorial character, in which the real-time dependence of the ultimate system does not usually enter explicitly. In order to illustrate this type of analysis, let us consider the problem of tossing a biased coin that has probability p of "heads" and probability $q = 1 - p$ of "tails". What is the probability that exactly k heads will turn up in a sequence of M tosses? If we let X be a random variable representing "number of heads", we are interested in the distribution of X. Now, the probability of any particular sequence of k "heads" and $M - k$ "tails" in M independent trials is $p^k q^{M-k}$. However, there are $\binom{M}{k} = M!/k!\,(M-k)!$ distinct ways of placing k "heads" in a sequence of M trials. Therefore,

$$P(X=k)=\binom{M}{k}p^k q^{M-k}=\frac{M!}{k!(M-k)!}p^k q^{M-k} \tag{9}$$

is the answer to our question. The distribution function of X is

$$F(x)=P(X\leqslant x)=\sum_{0\leqslant k\leqslant X}\binom{M}{k}p^k q^{M-k} \quad . \tag{10}$$

In particular,

$$F(M)=\sum_{k=0}^{M}\binom{M}{k}p^k q^{M-k}=(p+q)^M=1. \tag{11}$$

The form (11) indicates why the distribution (9) or (10) is called the *binomial distribution.* Note that the random variable X is of discrete type, in contrast to random variables of continuous type such as those with the Rayleigh distribution and density functions (6) and (7).

In applications of the binomial distribution to communication systems, the probability p is often taken to be the fraction of time something happens. For example, in the design of M-channel multiplex systems, the probability p might be the fraction of time any particular channel is actually in use—it is then called the "activity factor".[10] The distribution (9) then gives the fraction of time exactly k channels are in use (see, for example, Table III and Fig. 9 of reference 10).

2.4 Joint and Conditional Probabilities

To return explicitly to fraction-of-time distributions, an important extension of Fig. 1 is to the case in which several such functions of time (say, voltages) are given in a common interval of observation $t_1 - T \leqslant t \leqslant t_1$. Suppose we are given two voltages, say $f(t)$ and $g(t)$, in such an interval. Then, exactly as in Fig. 1, we may separately define the distribution functions $P_f(x)$ and $P_g(y)$ as the probability that f (respectively g) is less than or equal to x (respectively y). (Note that we shall sometimes use letters other than F for distribution functions.) However, we may also define a new function $P_{f,g}(x,y)$ as the probability that $f \leqslant x$ and $g \leqslant y$ *simultaneously*. $P_{f,g}(x,y)$ is the *joint distribution function* of the random variables f and g. Precisely, $P_{f,g}(x,y)$ is determined for each x and y by adding up the lengths of the sub-intervals on which both $f(t) \leqslant x$ and $g(t) \leqslant y$ hold. This is illustrated in Fig. 3, together with the relation of $P_{f,g}(x,y)$ to $P_f(x)$ and $P_g(y)$. It can be seen in the figure that $f(t) \leqslant x$ on the intervals denoted F_1, F_2, and F_3, that $g(t) \leqslant y$ on the intervals denoted G_1, G_2 and G_3, and that both $f(t) \leqslant x$ and $g(t) \leqslant y$ on the overlap of the F and G intervals, namely the intervals I_1 and I_2. If we write $\mu(F_k)$, $\mu(G_k)$, and $\mu(I_k)$ for the lengths of the F, G and I intervals, respectively (cf. Fig. 1, where $\mu(I_1)=l_1$, etc.), then

$$P_f(x)=[\mu(F_1)+\mu(F_2)+\mu(F_3)]/T, \tag{12}$$

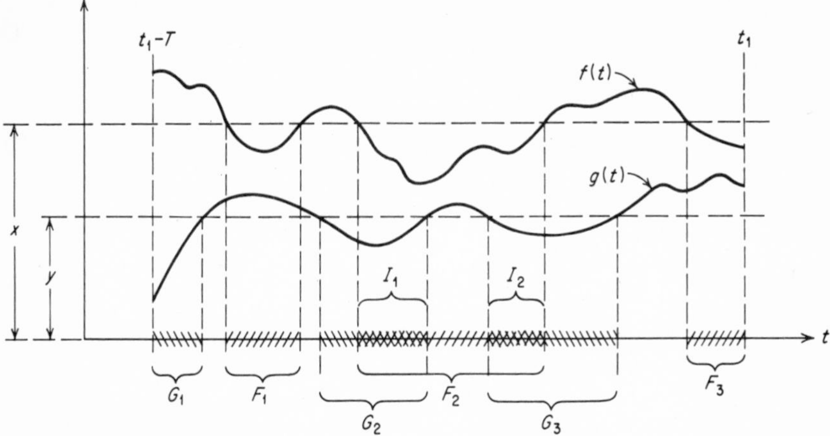

Fig. 3. Definition of the joint distribution function $P_{f,g}(x,y)$ = [(length of I_1) + (length of I_2)]/T.

$$P_g(y) = [\mu(G_1) + \mu(G_2) + \mu(G_3)]/T, \tag{13}$$

$$P_{f,g}(x,y) = [\mu(I_1) + \mu(I_2)]/T. \tag{14}$$

Equations (12) and (13) are simply restatements of the definition of a single distribution function given in Fig. 1; (14) defines the joint distribution function of f and g. It can be seen immediately that

$$P_{f,g}(x,\infty) = P_f(x), \tag{15}$$

$$P_{f,g}(\infty, y) = P_g(y). \tag{16}$$

A closely related concept is that of a conditional distribution function. Suppose it is known that $g(t) \leqslant y$, and we ask: What is the probability that $f \leqslant x$? We denote the answer by $P_f(x|g \leqslant y)$, which is called the *conditional distribution function* of f given that $g \leqslant y$. Now, the hypothesis $g \leqslant y$ is simply the assertion that we take as a new "interval" of observation the collection of intervals on which it is true that $g(t) \leqslant y$. In Fig. 3, this would be the collection of the intervals G_1, G_2 and G_3 taken together, and the total duration of this observation would be $\mu(G_1) + \mu(G_2) + \mu(G_3)$. Within *this* "interval," the total length of time that $f(t) \leqslant x$ is simply $\mu(I_1) + \mu(I_2)$. Thus, from our definition of probability, we have

$$P_f(x|g \leqslant y) = \frac{\mu(I_1) + \mu(I_2)}{\mu(G_1) + \mu(G_2) + \mu(G_3)}. \tag{17}$$

However, dividing the numerator and denominator of (17) by T and comparing with (13) and (14), we see that this is simply

$$P_f(x|g \leqslant y) = \frac{P_{f,g}(x,y)}{P_g(y)}, \tag{18}$$

and this explains why (18) is sometimes taken as the definition of $P_f(x|g \leqslant y)$. Of course, for (17) or (18) to make sense, we must have $P_g(y) \neq 0$; this is implicit in the hypothesis "it is known that $g(t) \leqslant y$". Considering (17), it is clear that the corresponding relation to (18) for $P_g(y|f \leqslant x)$ is

$$P_g(y|f \leqslant x) = \frac{P_{f,g}(x,y)}{P_f(x)} \tag{19}$$

and from (18) and (19), we have

$$\begin{aligned} P_{f,g}(x,y) &= P_f(x|g \leqslant y)\,P_g(y) \\ &= P_g(y|f \leqslant x)P_f(x). \end{aligned} \tag{20}$$

A concept of the utmost importance is that of *statistical independence*. Loosely speaking, we say that the function f is independent of g if statistical information about g provides no statistical information about f. A more precise way of formulating this is to require that $P_f(x|g \leqslant y) = P_f(x)$ for all values of x, and for all values of y for which $P_f(x|g \leqslant y)$ is defined. In this case, it is clear from (20) that we have $P_{f,g}(x,y) = P_f(x) \cdot P_g(y)$; *i.e.*, the joint distribution function is then simply the product of the separate distribution functions. Since this last relation makes sense for all values of x and y, we take this as our final definition: The functions f and g are independent if

$$P_{f,g}(x,y) = P_f(x) \cdot P_g(y) \tag{21}$$

for all values of x and y. The same must then be true of the joint density function $p_{f,g}(x,y) = \partial^2 P_{f,g}(x,y)/\partial x\,\partial y$; *i.e.*, if (21) holds, then

$$p_{f,g}(x,y) = p_f(x)p_g(y) \tag{22}$$

whenever (22) is applicable, and conversely.

Figure 3 can also be used to illustrate another important relation in probability theory. Suppose we let A and B denote events, and write $\mathbb{P}(A)$, $\mathbb{P}(B)$ for the probability of these events. As before, this refers to the fraction of some interval of observation during which A and B occur. Now, one is often interested in compound events such as "either A or B (or both) occurs", which is written $A \cup B$, or "both A and B occur", written $A \cap B$, and the probability $\mathbb{P}(A \cup B)$ of such compound events. Referring to Fig. 3, let A represent the event "$f \leqslant x$" and let B represent the event "$g \leqslant y$"; then $\mathbb{P}(A) = P_f(x)$, $\mathbb{P}(B) = P_g(y)$, and $\mathbb{P}(A \cap B) = P_{f,g}(x,y)$. What is $(A \cup B)$? It is not difficult to see that this is not given directly by $\mathbb{P}(A) + \mathbb{P}(B)$, because $\mathbb{P}(A) + \mathbb{P}(B)$ would "count" the event $A \cap B$ (namely, the intervals I_1 and I_2) twice. However, if the extra "count" is subtracted off, we obtain

$$\mathbb{P}(A \cup B) = \mathbb{P}(A) + \mathbb{P}(B) - \mathbb{P}(A \cap B). \tag{23}$$

It is not difficult to see that this relation actually holds for any events A and B, not only the events $f \leq x$ and $g \leq y$ depicted in Fig. 3.

Such events A and B are said to be "disjoint" if there is no value of the time t for which both A and B occur. In this case, $\mathbb{P}(A \cap B) = 0$, as is easily seen, and (23) becomes

$$\mathbb{P}(A \cup B) = \mathbb{P}(A) + \mathbb{P}(B).$$

Furthermore, if $A_1, A_2, \ldots, A_n$ is a collection of pairwise disjoint events, then

$$\mathbb{P}(A_1 \cup A_2 \cup \ldots \cup A_n) = \mathbb{P}(A_1) + \ldots + \mathbb{P}(A_n). \tag{24}$$

The practical importance of the relation (24) is that it is sometimes possible to express an event of interest as the union $A_1 \cup A_2 \cup \ldots \cup A_n$ of several disjoint events $A_1, A_2, \ldots, A_n$, the individual probabilities of which are known. Even if the events $A_1, A_2, \ldots, A_n$ are not disjoint, it always holds that

$$\mathbb{P}(A_1 \cup A_2 \cup \ldots \cup A_n) \leq \mathbb{P}(A_1) + \mathbb{P}(A_2) + \ldots + \mathbb{P}(A_n); \tag{25}$$

as is easy to see from Fig. 3. The result (25) is sometimes useful in setting bounds when more precise results cannot be achieved.

All of the foregoing material can easily be extended to the case in which more than two functions (random variables) are given in a common interval of observation. If $f_1, f_2, \ldots, f_n$ are n such functions (*e.g.*, voltages), their joint distribution function $P_{f_1, f_2, \ldots, f_n}(x_1, x_2, \ldots, x\ )$, which is the probability that $f_1 \leq x_1, f_2 \leq x_2, \ldots, f_n \leq x_n$ simultaneously, is simply defined as (the sum of the lengths of the sub-intervals in which this happens) divided by (the total duration of the interval of observation), exactly as shown in Fig. 3 for the case $n = 2$. The functions $f_1, f_2, \ldots, f_n$ are independent if $P_{f_1, f_2, \ldots, f_n}(x_1, x_2, \ldots, x_n) = P_{f_1}(x_1) P_{f_2}(x_2) \ldots P_{f_n}(x_n)$, and so on.

It may be useful to give an explicit example of a pair of independent random variables. This is done in Fig. 4, where the functions f and g

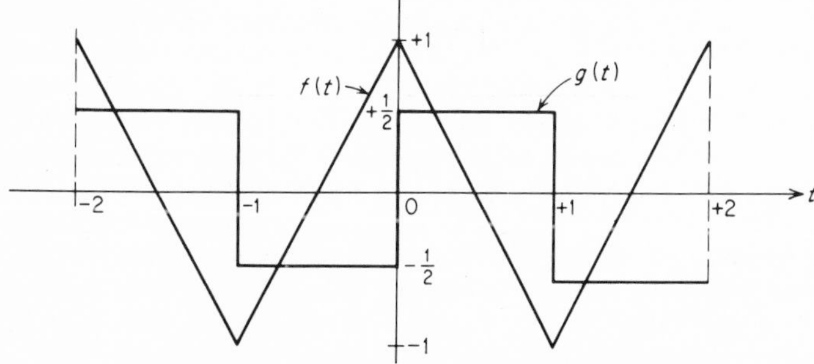

Fig. 4. Example of a pair of independent random variables.

are taken as random variables with "fraction-of-time" distributions on the interval $-2 \leq t \leq 2$. The distribution function of the variable f can easily be seen to be

$$P_f(x) = \begin{cases} 0, & x \leq -1; \\ \frac{1}{2}(1+x), & -1 \leq x \leq 1; \\ 1, & x \geq 1, \end{cases} \tag{26}$$

so that f has a rectangular distribution (*i.e.*, a constant density function) on the range -1 to 1. The variable g can take only the two values $+1/2$ and $-1/2$ with probability $1/2$ each, so its distribution function is

$$P_g(y) = \begin{cases} 0, & y < -\frac{1}{2}; \\ \frac{1}{2}, & -\frac{1}{2} \leq y < \frac{1}{2}; \\ 1, & y \geq \frac{1}{2}, \end{cases} \tag{27}$$

which is a distribution of discrete type. Now, $g = +1/2$ on the "interval" (= combination of two intervals) $-2 < t < -1$ and $0 < t < 1$, and it is trivial to see that on this "interval", the fraction-of-time distribution of f is precisely the same as the distribution (26) on the full interval $-2 \leq t \leq 2$; similarly if $g = -1/2$. That is to say, the conditional distribution of f, given that $g = +1/2$ (or $-1/2$), is the same as the distribution of f. Alternatively, if (a, b) is any interval in the range $(-1, 1)$ of f, and $I_{a,b}$ is the collection of (four) intervals in t determined by the condition $a < f < b$, then the distribution of g within $I_{a,b}$ is the same as the full distribution (27). Therefore, the random variables f and g in Fig. 4 are independent. [This can also be verified by directly computing the joint distribution function $P_{f,g}(x, y)$, and observing that it factors into the product $P_f(x)\,P_g(y)$.]

Some additional discussion of the situation in Fig. 4 may be in order. First of all, it should serve to emphasize our earlier point that random variables are simply any functions satisfying certain conditions, and whether or not they are "random" in some other sense is simply a question that does not arise. There is nothing at all mystical about random variables. Further, (statistically) independent random variables need not be "independent" in some other sense; for example, the r.v.'s f and g in Fig. 4 obviously satisfy the functional equation $g(t) = -f'(t)/4$; *i.e.*, they are functionally related, though we have just proved that they are (statistically) independent. The feature of random variables most often of importance for applications is not the r.v.'s themselves, but their distribution functions, which serve as *mathematical models* for experimental phenomena with which they may be associated—which phenomena may indeed be *physically* "random" in the sense of being more-or-less unpredictable. The distribution functions thus serve simultaneously as "abstractors" for both the underlying mathematical random variables and the phenomena the d.f.'s are modeling. (In this connection, the reader may find it instructive to convince himself that there are infinitely many different "pyramidal" or "sawtooth", or chopped-up sawtooth, functions with which the function f in Fig. 4 could be replaced without changing the distribution function (26).

But it is sometimes useful to go beyond the use of d.f.'s as models, and actually use mathematical random variables themselves as models for certain purposes. In such cases, the structure of the model r.v.'s may "imitate" certain properties of the "thing" to be modeled in a way that can lead to useful results. One may even "identify" the model r.v. with the "thing" to be modeled—as, *e.g.*, a fading radio wave. We have already done something of this sort in Figs. 1 and 3, where the model r.v.'s illustrated were deliberately chosen to "imitate" the sort of structure expected of a "random" waveform such as the envelope of a fading radio wave, or a speech waveform. The r.v.'s in Fig. 4 similarly "imitate" waveforms that might be expected from certain signal generators. It is desirable to be able to distinguish between model r.v.'s and d.f.'s on the one hand, and the waveforms and experimental distributions they are intended to model on the other. However, in cases (such as Fig. 1) where the structure of the model r.v. and the function to be modeled are so closely similar, little if any difficulty can arise from blurring the distinction and identifying them, provided it is clearly understood that there is nothing at all unique about the functions involved. (In section 3.2 of this chapter we shall discuss a situation in which the structures of the model and "modelee" are quite different, and in which such identification can and does lead to difficulties.)

One fact concerning several such functions is of such importance that it warrants a brief review in this context. Suppose that an adder circuit has two input voltages $f_1(t)$ and $f_2(t)$, such as those in Fig. 3, and we observe the two inputs and the output $f_1(t) + f_2(t)$ in the interval $t_1 \leq t \leq t_1 + T$. What is the distribution function of the sum $f_1(t) + f_2(t)$, given the joint distribution function $P_{f_1, f_2}(x, y)$? That is, we want the probability that $f_1 + f_2 \leq z$, $P_{f_1 + f_2}(z)$, in terms of purely statistical information about f_1 and f_2. In the particular but important situation in which f_1 and f_2 are independent, so that $P_{f_1, f_2}(x, y) = P_1(x) P_2(y)$, the result is

$$P_{f_1+f_2}(z) = \int_{-\infty}^{\infty} P_1(z-h)\,dP_2(h) = \int_{-\infty}^{\infty} P_2(z-h)\,dP_1(h). \tag{28}$$

(h is simply a dummy variable of integration in this equation.) If the distribution of one of the f_i, say f_1, is represented by a density function p_1, then $dP_1(h) = P_1'(h)\,dh = p_1(h)dh$, and (28) becomes

$$P_{f_1+f_2}(z) = \int_{-\infty}^{\infty} P_2(z-h)p_1(h)dh\,.$$

If also the distribution of f_2 has a density function p_2, then so does the distribution of $f_1 + f_2$, and

$$p_{f_1+f_2}(z) = \frac{d}{dz} P_{f_1+f_2}(z)$$

$$= \frac{d}{dz} \int_{-\infty}^{\infty} P_2(z - h) p_1(h)\, dh$$

$$= \int_{-\infty}^{\infty} \frac{\partial}{\partial z} P_2(z - h) p_1(h)\, dh$$

$$= \int_{-\infty}^{\infty} p_2(z - h)\, p_1(h)\, dh \,. \tag{29}$$

The distribution function or density function of the sum of independent voltages or currents is thus given by the convolution of the distribution or density functions of the summands.

In Chapter 20, we shall show how the analysis of model r.v.'s such as those in Fig. 4 can lead to engineering conclusions that could not be inferred on the basis of conventional models employing distribution functions alone.

2.5 Gaussian Distributions and Central Limit Theorems

The subject of sums of independent random variables brings us to one of the main theorems used in theoretical developments relating to probability theory in communication systems. This is the central limit theorem. Loosely speaking, this states that the distribution of the sum of a sufficiently large number of independent random variables is approximately normal (gaussian). A random variable X is said to be normal or gaussian if it has the density function

$$p(x) = \frac{1}{\sigma\sqrt{2\pi}}\, e^{-(x-\mu)^2/2\sigma^2} \tag{30}$$

for which the distribution function is

$$P(x) = P(X \leqslant x) = \frac{1}{\sigma\sqrt{2\pi}} \int_{-\infty}^{x} e^{-(t-\mu)^2/2\sigma^2} dt \,, \tag{31}$$

where $\mu = E[X] = \overline{X}$ and $\sigma^2 = E[(X-\mu)^2] = \overline{X^2} - \mu^2$.

There are actually several results that could reasonably be called central limit theorems; perhaps the most common form is the classical version that follows.

The Central Limit Theorem—Let $X_1, X_2, X_3, \ldots$ be a sequence of identically distributed, independent random variables with zero means ($\mu = 0$) and unit variances ($\sigma^2 = 1$). Then

$$\lim_{n \to \infty} P\left(\alpha < \frac{1}{\sqrt{n}} \sum_{k=1}^{n} X_k < \beta\right) = \frac{1}{\sqrt{2\pi}} \int_{\alpha}^{\beta} e^{-t^2/2} dt. \tag{32}$$

This theorem states that the distribution function of the *normalized* sum $\sum_{k=1}^{n} X_k)/\sqrt{n}$ is asymptotically gaussian.* In applications in radio engineering, one is most often interested in direct sums $\sum_{k=1}^{n} X_k$; for example, in the case of shot noise in vacuum tubes, where the X_k's would be the individual current pulses (due to individual electrons) in the plate circuit of the tube. The asymptotic "gaussianness" of such direct sums does not follow from the theorem above. However, under additional resistrictions on the X_k, it was proved by H. Cramer in 1937 and C. G. Esseen in 1945 that such non-normalized sums are in fact asymptotically gaussian. Let $F_n(x)$ denote the distribution function of the non-normalized sum,

$$F_n(x) = P\left(\sum_{k=1}^{n} X_k \leq x\right), \tag{33}$$

and let $\Phi_n(x)$ be the distribution function of a gaussian variable with zero mean and variance $\sigma^2 = n$,

$$\Phi_n(x) = \frac{1}{\sqrt{2\pi n}} \int_{-\infty}^{x} e^{-t^2/2n}\, dt. \tag{34}$$

The following statement is a consequence of Theorem 1, p. 217 in Gnedenko and Kolmogorov,[11] where more precise results are given.

Theorem (Cramér-Esseen)—Let $X_1, X_2, X_3, \ldots$ be a sequence of identically distributed, independent random variables with finite third moments, and (for convenience) zero means and unit variances. Then there is a constant B, independent of n and x, such that

$$|F_n(x) - \Phi_n(x)| \leq \frac{B}{\sqrt{n}} \tag{35}$$

for all x, for every n.

The constant B depends on the distribution F_1 of the X_k and sharp estimates are not usually easy to come by. This is one of the problems encountered in applications of the central limit theorem to engineering; it is usually difficult to tell how many summands are "enough" to make the right-hand side of (35) negligible. Another problem stems from the independence assumption; it often happens that random variables representing quantities that are "physically independent" (in the sense that no discernible cause-effect relation holds between them) are nevertheless statistically dependent in a mathematical sense. We may therefore list as two unsolved mathematical problems: (1) the determination of sharp estimates of the constant B in (35), and (2) the formulation of central-limit type theorems in which a suitable type of dependence is allowed.

Our consideration of several random variables has, so far, emphasized the case of independent random variables. However, some

*The assumptions that $\mu = 0$ and $\sigma^2 = 1$ are only to simplify the expressions; μ and σ^2 must exist, however.

of the most important applications of probability theory in radio engineering involve dependent random variables. The effect of such statistical dependence is very often estimated in terms of a parameter called the *correlation coefficient*. For two random variables f and g, this is defined by

$$\rho_{fg} = \frac{E[(f-\bar{f})(g-\bar{g})]}{\sigma_f \sigma_g} = \frac{\overline{fg}-\bar{f}\bar{g}}{\sigma_f \sigma_g}, \tag{36}$$

where σ_f^2 and σ_g^2 are the variances of f and g, assumed $\neq 0$. If f and g are independent, then $\overline{fg} = \bar{f}\bar{g}$, so in this case, $\rho_{fg} = 0$. The converse of this (that $\rho_{fg} = 0$ implies the independence of f and g) is not true in general, but is true in special cases. It always holds that $|\rho_{fg}| \leqslant 1$, and $\rho_{fg} = \pm 1$ if and only if $f = \pm ag + b$, where $a > 0$ and b are constants.

As an example of correlated variables, let Y_1 and Y_2 be two gaussian variables with zero means and unit variances. If the joint probability density function of Y_1 and Y_2 is of the form

$$p(y_1, y_2) = \frac{1}{2\pi(1-\rho^2)^{1/2}} \exp -\left[\frac{y_1^2 - 2\rho y_1 y_2 + y_2^2}{2(1-\rho^2)}\right] \tag{37}$$

then Y_1 and Y_2 are said to be *jointly normal* or *jointly gaussian* or *two-dimensional gaussian* or *bivariate gaussian.* The parameter ρ in (37) is the correlation coefficient of Y_1 and Y_2; it is assumed that $|\rho| < 1$. It is easy to see that if $\rho = 0$ in (37), the joint density function factors into the product of two one-dimensional densities, so that in this case, the vanishing of ρ implies the independence of Y_1 and Y_2. The importance of distributions [such as (37)] that are jointly normal is related to the fact that there is a two-dimensional form of the central limit theorem, analogous to (32) above, that states very general conditions under which normalized sums of independent *two-dimensional* variables are asymptotically jointly normal. (See Cramér,[6] pp. 285-287.) Similar facts are true of trivariate and higher-dimensional distributions.

III. RANDOM PROCESSES

3.1. Basic Discussion

Just as in the case of random variables, a random process is, as a mathematical matter, simply any function of a specified type. Specifically, a random process is a function of two variables $X(t,\omega)$, where ω ranges over a probability space and t ranges over a parameter set, usually taken as the real line $-\infty \leqslant t \leqslant \infty$ and thought of as the time. Another way of describing this situation is to say that a random process (sometimes called a "stochastic process") is an indexed family of random variables, indexed by t, so that for each t, $X(t,\omega)$ is a random variable in ω.

These objects are used as mathematical models for describing or predicting experimental systems in which the variability of the system with time plays an important role. The "thing" to be so described—as, for example, a fading radio wave—may itself be called a "random process", but in this case the term is used in a less formal sense. However, it is useful to bear in mind the distinction between the mathematical model and the system it is modeling.

Within the mathematical framework, there is a great deal of freedom and flexibility as to the structure of the model. The underlying probability space can be taken to be anything from a tribe of Hottentots to an interval of real numbers, as in the case of single random variables. For example, the function f in Fig. 1 could be defined on the entire real line and made into a random variable on each interval $[t-T, t]$, as in Fig. 1 for $t = t_1$. This would give a random variable for each t, *i.e.*, an indexed family of random variables, which is a random process. This in turn would be an example of a special type of random process called "translation processes". In some sense, translation processes are "natural" models for communication system engineering, as will be illustrated in some of the succeeding chapters. However, they are not the models most commonly used in theoretical developments, to which we now turn.

Instead of speaking of a random process $X(t, \omega)$ as a random variable in ω for each t, we could turn this around, and observe that for each fixed ω in the probability space, $X(t, \omega)$ is a function of the "time" t, called a "sample function" of the process. The collection of these sample functions, often called the "ensemble" of the process, essentially defines the process. This idea is illustrated in Fig. 5, where we have taken a simple probability space consisting of four points, denoted ω_1, ω_2, ω_3 and ω_4. If probabilities are defined for these points in any consistent manner, then the distribution function of the process at any particular time $t = t_0$, $F_{t_0}(x)$, is simply the probability $P\{X(t_0, \omega) \leq x\}$. In Fig. 5, if the points ω_k are equally

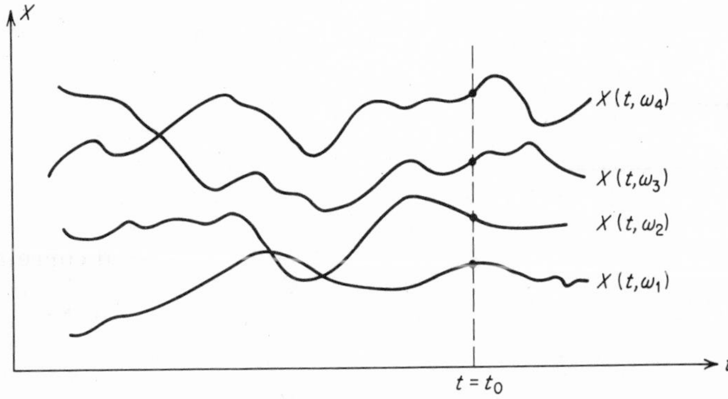

Fig. 5. Simple random process.

probable, this would simply be $F_{t_0}(x) = (1/4)$[number of points ω_k for which $X(t_0, \omega_k) \leq x$].

In general, one is interested in random processes with an uncountable infinity of sample functions, and joint distribution functions of the process at more than one value of the time. The general n-dimensional distribution function of a process at the times $t_1, t_2, \ldots, t_n$ would be

$$F_{t_1, \ldots, t_n}(x_1, x_2, \ldots, x_n) = P(X_{t_1} \leq x_1 \text{ and} \ldots \text{and } X_{t_n} \leq x_n), \tag{38}$$

where we have written X_{t_k} for $X(t_k, \omega)$. The corresponding joint density function $p_{t_1, \ldots, t_n}(x_1, \ldots, x_n)$ would be obtained by differentiating (38) with respect to each x_k, $k = 1, 2, \ldots, n$. As in the case of single random variables, there are a great many families of random variables that have a given multidimensional distribution; it is the distribution that serves as the "abstractor" which one hopes to be able to predict.

An important class of random processes is the class of stationary processes. These are the processes for which all distribution functions are invariant under a translation in time, *i.e.*, for which

$$F_{t_1+\tau,\, t_2+\tau, \ldots,\, t_n+\tau}(x_1, x_2, \ldots, x_n) = P_{t_1, t_2, \ldots, t_n}(x_1, x_2, \ldots, x_n)$$

for all $t_1, t_2, \ldots, t_n$ for every n and τ. In this case, the second-order moment

$$R(t_1, t_2) = \overline{X_{t_1} X_{t_2}} = \int_{-\infty}^{\infty}\int_{-\infty}^{\infty} x_1 x_2\, p_{t_1, t_2}(x_1, x_2)\, dx_1\, dx_2 \tag{39}$$

depends only on the difference $t_2 - t_1 = \tau$, so that $R = R(\tau)$ only. The function $R(\tau)$ is called a "correlation" or "auto-correlation" function, or, sometimes, a "covariance" function. At least in a loose sense, and sometimes in a very precise sense, it measures the degree of independence or dependence in the process at times separated by τ. The definition is often modified by subtracting out the square of the mean μ and dividing by the variance σ^2 of the process,

$$\rho(\tau) = \frac{R(\tau) - \mu^2}{\sigma^2}, \tag{40}$$

where $\mu = E[X_t]$ and $\sigma^2 = E[X_t^2] - \mu^2$ are independent of t by the assumed stationarity of the process. (It is assumed that $\sigma^2 > 0$.) The form (40) will be recognized as the correlation coefficient [defined in (36)] of the random variables X_t and $X_{t+\tau}$.

A more-or-less related idea is that of a time-averaged correlation. If f is any function defined on the line $-\infty < t < \infty$ for which the limit

$$R(\tau) = \lim_{T \to \infty} \frac{1}{2T} \int_{-T}^{T} f(t) f(t+\tau)\, dt \tag{41}$$

exists for every value of τ, the function $\mathcal{R}(\tau)$ gives the average product of f by itself under a lag τ. Sometimes an associated normalized function is defined as in (40). The function (41) is called a time-averaged auto-correlation function or simply an auto-correlation function. When a distinction between (39) and (41) is necessary we shall adopt the convention here of calling ensemble-averaged functions such as (39) [with or without normalization as in (40)] "ensemble correlation" functions, and time-averaged functions such as (41) (with or without normalization) "time correlation" functions. The relation between time correlation functions and the functions f from which they are computed is quite similar to the relation between distribution functions and their associated random variables; there are infinitely many different functions f having a given time auto-correlation function $\mathcal{R}(\tau)$. Therefore, a time correlation function is an "abstractor" of a large class of functions.

The principal theorem concerning ensemble and time correlation functions is the so-called Wiener-Khintchine theorem. This is actually two theorems, one of which refers to ensemble auto-correlation functions and one of which refers to time auto-correlation functions; these can be separately traced in the following statement by choosing the (first) (second) parentheses, respectively, throughout.

The Wiener-Khintchine Theorem-Let $[R(\tau)]$ $[\mathcal{R}(\tau)]$ be the (ensemble) (time) auto-correlation function of (a stationary random process) (any corresponding time function). Then $S(\omega) = \int_{-\infty}^{\infty} [R(\tau)]\,[\mathcal{R}(\tau)] e^{-j\omega\tau}\,d\tau$ is the power spectral density of (the process) (all corresponding time functions). If $H(\omega)$ is the complex frequency response of a linear system and $S_i(\omega)$ and $S_0(\omega)$ are the power spectral densities of the input and output (processes) (signals), respectively, then

$$S_0(\omega) = |H(\omega)|^2\, S_i(\omega). \tag{42}$$

It is clear that the essential intellectual content of the two theorems is closely similar, and there is no harm in lumping them together and calling them by a single name. In either case, the theorem extends classical ideas of power spectra to functions that do not have ordinary Fourier transforms. The original theorem of Wiener concerning time correlation functions is somewhat more general than the later adaptation by Khintchine to ensemble functions, in the sense that less structure is assumed in the Wiener setting. It is therefore perhaps the more appropriate in cases where the spectral properties alone of some class of functions are of primary interest. On the other hand, when probability-theoretic properties are simultaneously under consideration the ensemble-auto-correlation setting is perhaps more appropriate; in addition, stationary ensemble correlation functions are easier to manipulate.

To illustrate the ideas involved, suppose a noise signal $X(t)$ is to be subtracted from itself after a delay τ. What is the average power of the noise after subtraction? Let $X(t)$ either be represented by a stationary random process or be any function with an auto-correlation function, and let $S(\omega)$ be the power spectral density of X in either case. We use $\langle\ \rangle$ to represent either averages of the form (39) or (41), respectively, so that

$$\langle X \rangle = \lim_{T \to \infty} \frac{1}{2T} \int_{-T}^{T} X(t)\,dt \quad \text{or} \quad \int_{-\infty}^{\infty} y\,dP_X(y), \tag{43}$$

where P_X is the one-dimensional d.f. of the stationary-process representation. Let $\rho(\tau)$ be the normalized time or ensemble auto-correlation as the case may be. Now, the average square in question is

$$\begin{aligned} \left\langle [X(t+\tau)-X(t)]^2 \right\rangle &= \left\langle X^2(t+\tau) \right\rangle - 2\left\langle X(t+\tau)\,X(t) \right\rangle + \left\langle X^2(t) \right\rangle \\ &= 2\sigma^2[1-\rho(\tau)], \end{aligned} \tag{44}$$

where $\sigma^2 = \langle X^2 \rangle - \langle X \rangle^2$, and we have omitted the details in arriving at the last line of (44). The result (44) can then be evaluated in particular cases with the aid of the power density spectrum and the Wiener-Khintchine theorem. For example, suppose X is band-limited white noise of zero mean and with the power density spectrum

$$S(\omega) = \begin{cases} \dfrac{\pi}{W}\sigma^2, & -W \leqslant \omega \leqslant W, \\ 0, & |\omega| > W \end{cases} \tag{45}$$

Then

$$R(\tau) = \frac{1}{2\pi} \int_{-\infty}^{\infty} S(\omega)\, e^{j\omega\tau}\, d\omega = \sigma^2 \frac{\sin W\tau}{W\tau}, \tag{46}$$

so that (44) becomes

$$\left\langle [X(t+\tau)-X(t)]^2 \right\rangle = 2\sigma^2\left(1 - \frac{\sin W\tau}{W\tau}\right), \tag{47}$$

which is easily evaluated for any value of τ.

3.2 The Question of Ergodicity

Sometimes the question is raised as to the possible relation between the ensemble correlation function of a stationary process and the time correlation functions of the sample functions of the process, or more generally, between any moments of the joint distributions of the process and "corresponding" infinite time averages of sample functions of the process. It is not particularly difficult to construct stationary processes for which the time correlation functions of the sample functions of the process do not coincide with the ensemble correlation function of the process. However, if the process satisfies an additional condition called "ergodicity" or "metric transitivity," then almost all of the sample functions of the process have the same correlation function $\mathcal{R}(\tau)$, and it holds that $\mathcal{R}(\tau) = R(\tau)$. Sometimes this condition is called "the ergodic hypothesis", and there are two distinct senses in which it may be termed a "hypothesis." First, in physical systems involving a large number of particles in phase space, say the molecules of a gas, it is sometimes desirable to assume, without reference to a detailed mathematical model (such as a random process) for the system, that time averages of particular particles in particular orbits all coincide with the ensemble average of all the particles at an arbitrary time. This assumption is frequently termed "the ergodic hypothesis" by physicists. Second, when a random process is being used as a mathematical model for such a system, it may (and very often does) happen that it is very difficult to decide whether or not the mathematical process is metrically transitive, although the answer is determined, in principle, by the family of joint distributions of the process. In such cases, it may simply be assumed that the mathematical process is metrically transitive, and this assumption is sometimes called an "ergodic hypothesis." The classical setting of these considerations is given in a book by Khintchine[12] (see especially pp. 52-54).

In the literature of communication system theory, there is a good deal of discussion of ergodicity, and it may be useful to attempt some clarification of this subject. To begin with it must be emphasized that in the usual experimental environment of communication systems, there are *not* two separate types of things to be measured, viz., "time averages" and "ensemble averages." The experimental distributions in this environment are usually measured as fraction-of-time distributions, or "sampled" approximations thereto, and the fact that the moments of such distributions are one and the same thing as the corresponding time averages is simply the result (8a) of the local ergodicity theorem. (Although the result (8a) is stated only for one-dimensional distributions, analogous facts are true of multidimensional distributions.) Therefore, there cannot be two *different* things—"time averages" and "distribution averages"—in the experimental environment that may or may not be the same; they must be the same, and this fact must be kept in mind particularly when using mathematical random-process models in which the "time" and "distribution" averages of the *model* may or may not in fact be the same. This situation is depicted in Fig. 6. If the mathematical model is to have any engineering relevance at all, then *some* aspect of the model must "represent"—*i.e.*, approximate—something that could be measured experimentally. The usual route is to approximate the experimental distributions with the theoretical distributions on the probability space of the mathematical model, denoted approximation "A" in Fig. 6. If in any particular case this approximation is sufficiently accurate for the purpose at hand, then it is a consequence of the local-ergodicity theorem that the experimental time averages of interest will also be well approximated by the corresponding moments of the theoretical distributions of the model—whether the model is metrically transitive or not. Moreover, it does not matter which of the two approximations is originally intended in the synthesis of the model, because once one has an approximation for either the lower or upper part of the box on

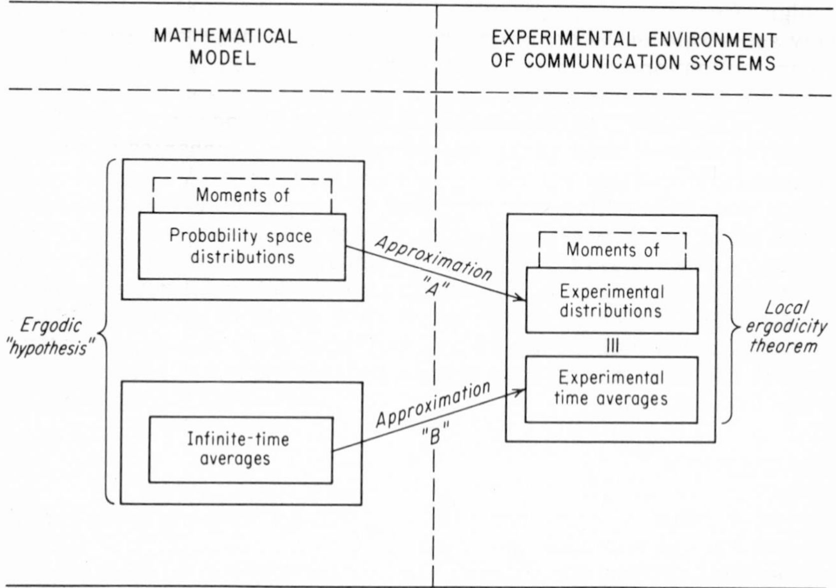

Fig. 6. Relation of general random-process model to communication systems.

the right, the local ergodicity theorem shows that the other part is determined, to within limits governed by the accuracy of the approximation.

It follows that the ergodic "hypothesis" does not play any operational role in the design of communication systems, or in other circumstances in which the distributions to be modeled are "fraction-of-time" distributions (or sampled approximations). The parameters of the model that are usually computed explicitly are the probability-space distributions, or the moments thereof, and the operational utility of the model stands or falls according as these distributions and moments are sufficiently good approximations (or "predictors") of the experimental distributions and moments; if they are, the same moments will also predict the experimental time averages, and if they aren't they won't. The "infinite-time" averages of the model cannot even be computed explicitly except in very trivial special cases (such as the sine process[1]) used as examples, and are therefore never used as predictors apart from the moments of the distributions of the model.

Much of the theoretical literature of communication systems does not reflect the fact that the structure of the distributions and averages to be predicted differs importantly from the structure of conventional random-process models. The basic problem in the design of a communication link is always the prediction of some measurable parameter(s) of that particular link.

Although the ergodic "hypothesis" plays no operational role in the design of communication systems, this is not to say that it may not play *some* role in the design of such system, or that there are not other applications in which it *does* play an operational role. Many of the theoretical mathematical models of noise theory—*e.g.*, the theory of shot noise—have, at least historically if not of necessity, been built up on the basis of arguments based on statistical mechanics and corresponding conventional random processes. Whether or not such a model is metrically transitive may then bear on the psychological credibility of the model as a good "predictor" for applications in communication systems. And statistical mechanics itself is, of course, an application in which the structure of the mathematical model is closely similar to the structure of the system being modeled, and in which the ergodicity or non-ergodicity of the model may reflect operationally measurable properties of the "modelee". But such applications are not the concern of this volume.

REFERENCES

1. W. R. Bennett, "Methods of Solving Noise Problems," *Proc. IRE*, vol 44, pp. 609-638, May, 1956.
2. H. Cramér, *The Elements of Probability Theory and Some of its Applications*, John Wiley & Sons, Inc., New York, 1955.
3. A. N. Kolmogorov, *Foundations of the Theory of Probability*, Chelsea, N.Y., 1956. (Translation of the German original edition published in 1933.)
4. W. Feller, *Probability Theory and its Applications*, John Wiley & Sons, Inc., New York, 1950 (first edition), 1957 (second edition).
5. W. B. Davenport, Jr. and W. L. Root, *Introduction to Random Signals and Noise*, McGraw-Hill Book Company, Inc., New York, 1958.
6. H. Cramér, *Mathematical Methods of Statistics*, Princeton University Press, Princeton, N.J., 1946.
7. J. L. Doob, *Stochastic Processes*, John Wiley & Sons, Inc., New York, 1953.
8. M. Loève, *Probability Theory*, D. Van Nostrand Company, Inc., Princeton, N.J., 1953.
9. U. Grenander and M. Rosenblatt, *Statistical Analysis of Stationary Time Series*, John Wiley & Sons, Inc., New York, 1957.
10. W. E. Morrow, Jr., C. L. Mack, Jr., B. E. Nichols, and J. Leonhard, "Single-Sideband Techniques in UHF Long-Range Communications," *Proc. IRE*, vol. 44, pp. 1854-1873, December, 1956.
11. B. V. Gnedenko and A. N. Kolmogorov, *Limit Distributions for Sums of Independent Random Variables*, Addison-Wesley Publishing Company, Reading, Massachusetts, 1954.
12. A. I. Khinchine, *Mathematical Foundation of Statistical Mechanics*, Dover Publications, New York, 1949. (Translation of original Russian edition published in 1938.)

CHAPTER 3

Signals in Linear Time-Invariant Systems

William M. Siebert

I. INTRODUCTION

An important part of communication theory is concerned with a pair of problems:

1. How to describe and analyze the behavior of models that represent parts of communication systems, and
2. How to describe or represent abstractly the signals that are operated on by these systems.

Clearly these problems are (or should be) related; the types of representations that are appropriate for the signals depend not only on the characteristics of the signals themselves but also on the properties of the device that is to process these signals. It would be foolish to describe the signals in such a way that the analysis of the effects of these signals was made inordinately difficult. The problem then is to find a representation for the signals that both emphasizes the salient features of the class of signals of interest and that also permits a ready analysis of the effect of these signals on the class of systems of interest. In general, of course, there is no reason to suppose that such a representation exists. But there is one important class of systems—*linear time-invariant systems*—and one group of methods of signal representation—the *Fourier* or *frequency method* is a typical example—that fit together beautifully. This chapter will explore this specific interrelation in some detail.

In particular we shall try to pin down the meaning (or perhaps it would be better to say *one* meaning) of the important concept of sinusoidal *frequency*, which so largely dominates the actions and thinking of every communication engineer. Just why the sinusoidal form of periodic process should have such special importance and wide usefulness is not exactly obvious to the uninitiated. And indeed the experienced communication engineer occasionally becomes so preoccupied with the notion of sinusoidal frequency that he fails to appreciate the limitations, disadvantages, and subtleties of the concept. These we shall try to emphasize—not only by stressing the relationship of sinusoidal frequency to linear time-invariant systems, but also by showing examples of cases in which other methods of representation and analysis are much more useful. Still the field of proper applications is so broad, and the methods of sinusoidal frequency analysis so powerful, both mathematically and conceptually, that enhanced understanding of frequency methods must be a continuing desire of every communication engineer.

II. LINEAR TIME-INVARIANT SYSTEMS

For our purposes we shall consider a *system* as a device, real or abstract, that interrelates an *input* (cause, stimulus, or given quantity) and an *output* (effect, response, or quantity to be found). This chapter will be exclusively concerned with that particular class of abstract systems which are both *linear* and *time-invariant*. Mathematically, this class is "interesting"—*i.e.*, there are many theorems that can be proved about such systems, or (to say very much the same sort of thing in another way) linear time-invariant systems are "easy to analyze." The utility of linear time-invariant systems as models for parts of physical communications systems is, of course, familiar. For our present purposes this class of systems is especially important because (as we shall show) it is for linear time-invariant systems, and (almost) *only* for such systems, that the concepts of sinusoidal frequency, frequency response, and spectral representation of signals have undeniable utility, unambiguous meaning, and undoubted justification.

Our first task will be to determine the general properties of the class of linear time-invariant systems and the method by which a particular member of this class may be identified. This, of course, is primarily a matter of definition, but it is useful to proceed with some care because there are various ways in which a linear time-invariant system can be specified, and the classes so defined are not identical nor are they equally suited to our purposes. For example, the most familiar method of specifying a linear time-invariant system is to say that it is characterized by a linear differential equation with constant coefficients. But differential-equation descriptions have certain disadvantages, particularly when one is trying to take a *system* view (as opposed to a detailed study component by component).

Most of the difficulties with differential equations arise from the fact that they are essentially *implicit* methods of description. Thus for the simple circuit of Fig. 1(a) Kirchoff's Voltage Law yields the differential equation

$$e(t) = Ri(t) + L\frac{di(t)}{dt} \tag{1}$$

which is implicit in the sense that it equates an operation on the (un-

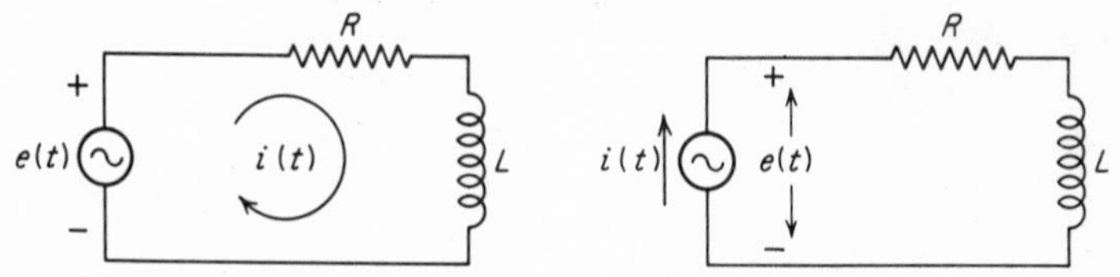

Fig. 1. Circuits for $e(t) = Ri(t) + L\dfrac{di(t)}{dt}$.

known) output $i(t)$ to the (known) input $e(t)$. (The same equation applies to the circuit of Fig. 1(b) except that here the equation gives the (unknown) output $e(t)$ in terms of an operation on the (known) input $i(t)$ and is thus, in this case, an *explicit* description of the system. Of course, for more general circuits, derivatives appear on both sides of Eq. (1) so that the description is implicit whichever quantity is considered as the input.) The trouble with an implicit differential-equation description, such as (1), is that *taken by itself*, it fails to define a *unique* response for each input. Or, in other words, the differential equation is not in itself a complete description of a system. To make it complete it is necessary in general to impose certain restrictions and to provide certain additional information; *e.g.*,

1. Restricting the *domain* of the solution to a finite or semi-infinite ($t \geq 0$) time interval, and
2. Specifying the *state* of the system at some finite time within this domain (*e.g.*, giving the "initial conditions" at $t = 0$), and
3. Limiting consideration to *realizable* systems (*i.e.*, those that do not respond before they are stimulated).

To say the least, such conditions are a nuisance for our present study. It is generally convenient to think about a communication system as being "in the stream of time" with all inputs $-\infty < t < \infty$ under our control (and not necessarily zero even if we go far back in time). And unrealizable systems are of considerable theoretical utility. Thus, if some other method is available, we should prefer not to define our systems in terms of differential equations.

In particular let us seek some *explicit* method of defining what we mean by linear time-invariant systems. Explicit methods all amount, in effect, to a *table of values* or a *formula*. Thus we choose a representative set of inputs $x_1(t)$, $x_2(t)$, $x_3(t)$, . . ., $x_n(t)$ and associate with each (or compute from the formula) its corresponding (unique) output $y_1(t)$, $y_2(t)$, $y_3(t)$, . . . , $y_n(t)$. This method (if such a naïve scheme deserves to be called a method) is completely general and is capable in principle of describing every possible system—linear time-invariant or not. To apply it to our problem we need to impose some restrictions on the $x_i(t)$ and $y_i(t)$; *i.e.*, we must define in terms of $x_i(t)$ and $y_i(t)$ what we mean by a linear time-invariant system. This we shall now do in terms of two postulates:

A. Superposition (Linearity) Postulate

If the input $x_1(t)$, $-\infty < t < \infty$, yields the output $y_1(t)$, $-\infty < t < \infty$, and if another input $x_2(t)$, $-\infty < t < \infty$, yields the output $y_2(t)$, $-\infty < t < \infty$, then for any constants a and b (including a and/or $b = 0$), the input $ax_1(t) + bx_2(t)$ yields the output $ay_1(t) + by_2(t)$, $-\infty < t < \infty$.

B. Time-Invariance Postulate

If the input $x(t)$, $-\infty < t < \infty$, yields the output $y(t)$, $-\infty < t < \infty$, then the input $x(t+\tau)$ yields the output $y(t+\tau)$ for every τ, $-\infty < \tau < \infty$.

These postulates are exceedingly strong; they place severe restrictions on the set of outputs $y_i(t)$ which can correspond to a given set of inputs $x_i(t)$. But they are sufficiently broad to include in the class of linear time-invariant systems not only the familiar lumped networks of elementary circuit theory but also distributed, active, and nonreciprocal systems as well.

Of course, we cannot long be satisfied with such a ridiculously cumbersome system-specification procedure as an infinite list of inputs and corresponding outputs. We must find some *formula* or *method of analysis* that permits us to generate the list at will. What sort of formula will be appropriate must be solely a consequence of our two postulates since these are the only restrictions we have imposed on our list. Let us then examine the consequences of our postulates in more detail.

The superposition postulate is by far the more powerful of the two and implies directly the central theme of linear-system analysis. Thus suppose that for each of a set of input time functions, $x_1(t)$, $x_2(t)$, $x_3(t)$, . . . , the corresponding outputs $y_1(t)$, $y_2(t)$, $y_3(t)$, . . . , are given. Then, from the first postulate, for any input $x(t)$ which can be represented as

$$x(t) = \sum_i a_i x_i(t) \tag{2}$$

the corresponding output is

$$y(t) = \sum_i a_i y_i(t). \tag{3}$$

This is a trivial observation (at least for finite sums). And yet it is profound. It really summarizes almost everything there is to be said about the analysis of linear systems and the related problem of signal representations—except, of course, an infinity of details! We can immediately deduce two important, and related conclusions. First, it is not necessary that the set of inputs for which we are given the outputs (the list of inputs and outputs which characterize the specific system) include *all* the inputs whose corresponding outputs we might like to know. It is merely necessary that the set of inputs for which we know the response be sufficiently *complete* that any other input whose response we desire can be represented as a weighted sum of the given inputs as in (2). And second, the representation of *signals* as weighted sums of other signals as in (2) is clearly appropriate and significant *if* the system that is going to operate on the signals is *linear*; the significance of a sum representation for a signal that is the input to a *non*-linear system has to be justified in each case. Moreover, a sum representation as in (2) is particularly appropriate if the $x_i(t)$ are time functions for which the response of the linear system is known. Thus the methods of signal representation are intimately tied to the methods of system analysis, as we have already suggested and will enlarge on in later sections.

For the moment our first conclusion is more important since it suggests that the method of analysis or formula describing a linear system depends critically on the selection of an appropriate set of characteristic inputs $x_i(t)$. We can easily list a number of desirable features for this set of $x_i(t)$.

1. The set of functions $x_i(t)$ should be *complete* in the sense that almost any "reasonably well-behaved" function $x(t)$ can be represented as in (2).

2. The set should be orthonormal over the infinite interval, *i.e.*,

$$\int_{-\infty}^{\infty} x_i(t)x_j(t)dt = \begin{cases} 1 \text{ if } i = j \\ 0 \text{ if } i \neq j \end{cases}. \tag{4}$$

This condition is not essential but it is very useful. Thus, if it is known that $x(t)$ can be represented as

$$x(t) = \sum_i a_i x_i(t)$$

and if the $s_i(t)$ are orthonormal, then

$$\int_{-\infty}^{\infty} x(t)x_j(t)\,dt = \int_{-\infty}^{\infty} \left[\sum_i a_i x_i(t)\right] x_j(t)\,dt = \sum_i a_i \int_{-\infty}^{\infty} x_i(t)x_j(t)\,dt = a_j \tag{5}$$

so that the coefficients a_i in the expansion of $x(t)$ can easily be found.

3. Both sets of functions $x_i(t)$ and $y_i(t)$ should be as easy to describe as possible.

This list is by no means sufficiently complete or precise to specify a unique set of functions, $x_i(t)$. But the last condition—coupled with the time-invariance postulate which we have not as yet used—goes a long way toward identifying a useful set of functions $x_i(t)$.

III. SPECIFICATION OF LINEAR TIME-INVARIANT SYSTEMS IN THE TIME DOMAIN

Suppose that one of the set of inputs $x_i(t)$—say $x_5(t)$—were identical with another—say $x_6(t)$—except for a shift in time origin, *i.e.*,

$$x_5(t) = x_6(t + \tau_0)\cdot \tag{6}$$

Then by the time-invariance postulate, the outputs would be similarly related, *i.e.*,

$$y_5(t) = y_6(t + \tau_0)\cdot \tag{7}$$

Of the two pairs of functions, $x_5(t) \leftrightarrow y_5(t)$ and $x_6(t) \leftrightarrow y_6(t)$, it would only be necessary to specify one pair and say that the other is the same except for a time shift. Now suppose that the *entire set* of $x_i(t)$ were merely time shifts of *one* basic function. The same would then be true of the output set $y_i(t)$, and it would be necessary to specify only *one* input function and *one* output function in order to specify

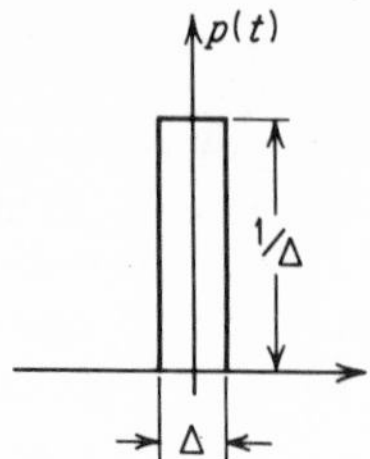

Fig. 2. The unit impulse as the limit of a pulse, $\delta(t) = \lim_{\Delta \to 0} p(t)$.

the *complete set* of inputs and outputs. This would be a tremendous simplification, and eminently desirable *if* we can find a set of functions $x_i(t)$ that are all time shifts of a single basic function *and* that are in some sense complete and orthonormal over the infinite interval.

One important set of such functions is the set of delayed *unit impulse functions*. The unit impulse function* (Dirac delta function) is specified by the conditions:

1. $\delta(t) = 0, \; t \neq 0$

2. $\int_{-\epsilon}^{\epsilon} \delta(t)\,dt = 1, \text{ all } \epsilon > 0$ (8)

We can represent a great many reasonably well-behaved functions in terms of delayed unit impulse functions; thus

$$x(t) = \int_{-\infty}^{\infty} x(\tau)\,\delta(t-\tau)\,d\tau \tag{9}$$

This may look a little silly; $x(t)$ is involved inside the integral so that it hardly seems to be a "representation" at all. But if (9) is compared with (2)—the integral replacing the sum, τ replacing the index variable i, $x(\tau)$ replacing a_i, and $\delta(t-\tau)d\tau$ replacing $x_i(t)$—the significance of (9) will become clearer. Or if we think of $\delta(t)$ as the

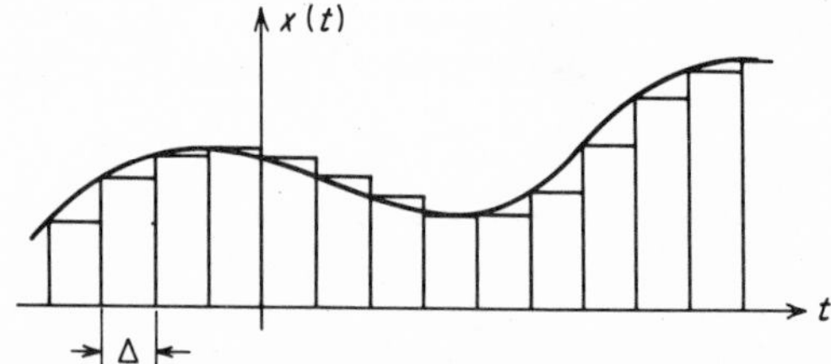

Fig. 3. Step-approximation to $x(t)$.

*Strictly speaking $\delta(t)$ is not a function over the interval $-\infty < t < \infty$ since it is not defined (infinite, if you like) for $t = 0$. But, with some care, it can be treated as if it were a function. And it is much too valuable to abandon merely because it is not "mathematically respectable" or because its use occasionally leads to difficulties.

limit of a narrow pulse (Fig. 2) as the width goes to zero, then we can consider (9) as the limiting form of the step-approximation to $x(t)$ shown in Fig. 3. The set of delayed impulse functions, at least in a limiting sense, satisfies the conditions of the preceding paragraph* and hence should be a very useful set of characteristic inputs. In particular, if the input $\delta(t)$ to a linear time-invariant system yields the output $h(t)$ then, by analogy with (3), an arbitrary input $x(t)$ should produce the output

$$y(t) = \int_{-\infty}^{\infty} x(\tau) h(t-\tau) d\tau . \tag{10}$$

This most important formula is called the *Superposition Integral*† and demonstrates that the impulse response $h(t)$ completely characterizes the behavior of a linear time-invariant system for any reasonably well-behaved input. Indeed, the Superposition Integral is so basic that the requirement that the system have a representation as in (10) rather than our two postulates is often taken as the definition of a linear time-invariant system.‡

The scheme of analysis described by the Superposition Integral can quite reasonably be called "time-domain analysis" since the input signal is represented by successive samples in time (Fig. 3). The analysis of the behavior of linear time-invariant systems in the "time-domain" is much more effective than is commonly realized. It is particularly useful for signals and impulse responses that can be described by such simple functions of time as pulses, steps, exponentials, etc. Thus the R-L circuit of Fig. 1(a) has the impulse response

$$h(t) = \begin{cases} \frac{1}{L} \exp[-Rt/L], & t \geq 0 \\ 0 & , t < 0, \end{cases} \tag{11}$$

*One should not try to carry this too far. The change from summation to integral formulation and the introduction of the impulse function have really changed the character of the problem, as can be seen by trying to carry out the limiting operations on the pulses and step-representation of Figs. 2 and 3. Perhaps the most sensible thing to do is merely to start over with (9) instead of (2), treating our preceding arguments as "suggestive" or "analogous."

†A somewhat more general form of the Superposition Integral applies to linear time-variant systems, viz.

$$y(t) = \int_{-\infty}^{\infty} x(\tau) h(t,\tau) d\tau \tag{10a}$$

where $h(t, \tau)$ is a function of *two* variables and is to be interpreted as the response at time t to an impulse applied at time τ. Equation (10a) includes (10), of course, since for a time-invariant system $h(t, \tau)$ would turn out to be merely a function of the difference $t - \tau$. We shall have little use in this chapter for the more general form (10a) since the notion of frequency is by no means as directly relevant to time-variant systems as it is to time-invariant systems.

‡By a trivial change of variable the Superposition Integral can be put in the form

$$y(t) = \int_{-\infty}^{\infty} h(\tau) x(t-\tau) d\tau \tag{10b}$$

which is slightly more convenient for some purposes.

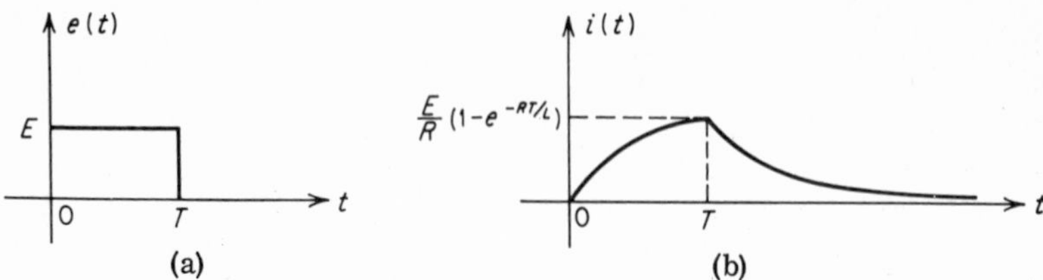

Fig. 4. (a) Excitation described by Eq. 12. (b) Response of RL circuit of Fig. 1(a).

as can be readily found from the differential equation (1) or (at least in principle) could be measured.* If the input $e(t)$ is a pulse (Fig. 4),

$$e(t) = \begin{cases} E, & 0 \leqslant t \leqslant T \\ 0, & \text{elsewhere} \end{cases} \tag{12}$$

then, from (10) the response is

$$i(t) = \int_{-\infty}^{\infty} e(\tau) h(t-\tau)\, d\tau .$$

For $t < 0$

$$i(t) = 0$$

For $0 \leqslant t \leqslant T$

$$i(t) = \int_0^t E \frac{1}{L} \exp\left[-R(t-\tau)/L\right] d\tau = \frac{E}{R}\left(1 - \exp\left[-Rt/L\right]\right)$$

For $t > T$,

$$i(t) = \int_0^T E \frac{1}{L} \exp\left[-R(t-\tau)/L\right] d\tau = \frac{E}{R}\left(\exp\left[RT/L\right] - 1\right) \exp\left[-Rt/L\right]$$

Therefore, the response of the R-L circuit of Fig. 1(a) to the excitation described in (12) has the form sketched in Fig. 4(b). The analysis of this problem in the time domain is neither longer nor more difficult than by any other method.

IV. SPECIFICATION OF LINEAR TIME-INVARIANT SYSTEMS IN THE FREQUENCY DOMAIN

Equation (10) represents a complete solution to the system analysis problem for linear time-invariant systems. But the set of delayed impulse functions is not the only set of characteristic imputs that lead to a simple description of a linear time-invariant system.

*From the "black box" point of view, since *some* characteristic of a system *has* to be measured, it might, in principle at least, just as well be the impulse response as the values of R, L, C, etc., in the circuit diagram.

Nor is the use of the impulse response and the Superposition Integral the most efficient computational method for all types of problems. Specifically, there is another set of characteristic inputs—the *exponential inputs*, e^{st}, $-\infty < t < \infty$, where s is a complex constant called the *complex frequency*—which have remarkable and useful properties. We can define a *set* of exponential inputs, $x_i(t)$, by varying the complex frequency, s, so that the input set is simply described by a single parameter. Furthermore, the outputs $y_i(t)$ can also be easily described and related to the corresponding inputs as a result of a remarkable and unique property of the exponential function, e^{st}. Specifically, the exponential function, e^{st}, is what is called an *eigenfunction* for linear time-invariant systems in the interval $-\infty < t < \infty$. In more prosaic language this means that if the *input* to a linear time-invariant system in the interval $-\infty < t < \infty$ *is of the form* e^{st} *then the output will also have the same form* (with the same value of complex frequency, s) except for a constant multiplier (independent of time but in general a function of s). This multiplier could be considered the *eigenvalue* for the system but it is more commonly called the *system function.* It characterizes the behavior of the system for any input of the form e^{st}, $-\infty < t < \infty$. Finally (this is where Fourier signal representation methods come in), since we can represent a large and useful class of inputs as a sum of terms of the form e^{st}, the *system function* provides an alternate (to the impulse response) method of characterizing a linear time-invariant system.

We can easily and elegantly prove directly from our two original postulates our assertion that an input of the form e^{st} yields an output of the same form. Thus, suppose that an input $x(t) = e^{st}$ yields some output, $y(t)$, whose structure we are trying to find. Then by the time-invariance postulate the input $x(t + \tau) = e^{s(t+\tau)}$ must yield the output $y(t + \tau)$. But we can write $e^{s(t+\tau)} = e^{s\tau}e^{st} = e^{s\tau}x(t)$ and by the superposition postulate the response to this excitation is also given by $e^{s\tau}y(t)$. Since the response is unique, it must be true that

$$y(t + \tau) = e^{s\tau}y(t)$$

for all t and τ. In particular setting $t = 0$ we have

$$y(\tau) = y(0)\,e^{s\tau}, \quad -\infty < \tau < \infty \,.$$

Thus $y(t)$ has the form of a constant times e^{st}, as was to be proved. This argument shows very clearly the way in which the significance of exponential signals (and thus of frequency) depends on the superposition and time-invariance postulates.

But we can also prove the same result in another way that has the additional merit of showing the relationship between the impulse-response and the frequency-response methods of characterizing the same system. Thus suppose our system is characterized by (10), i.e.,

$$y(t) = \int_{-\infty}^{\infty} x(\tau)\,h(t - \tau)\,d\tau$$

and suppose that we substitute $x(t) = e^{st}$. Then

$$y(t) = \int_{-\infty}^{\infty} e^{s\tau} h(t - \tau)\, d\tau$$

or making the change of variable $t - \tau = t'$,

$$y(t) = \int_{-\infty}^{\infty} e^{s(t-t')}\, h(t')\, dt' = \left[\int_{-\infty}^{\infty} h(t')e^{-st'}\, dt' \right] e^{st}$$

which again demonstrates that $y(t)$ has the form of a constant times e^{st}. But more significantly, it shows that the constant multiplier, or system function, to which we shall now give the symbol $H(s)$, is related to the impulse response $h(t)$ by

$$H(s) = \int_{-\infty}^{\infty} h(t)e^{-st}\, dt\,. \tag{13}$$

Equation (13) is a most important result, but our argument has been purely formal and the result must be handled with care. Let us examine the right-hand side of (13) for a particular case, *e.g.*, the $h(t)$ given by (11) for the R-L circuit of Fig. 1(a). Then

$$H(s) = \int_{-\infty}^{\infty} h(t)\, e^{-st}\, dt = \int_{0}^{\infty} \frac{1}{L}\, e^{-(R/L)t}\, e^{-st} dt$$

$$= \frac{1}{R + Ls} \left(1 - \lim_{t\to\infty} e^{-(R/L + s)t}\right) \tag{14}$$

If

$$\lim_{t\to\infty} e^{-(R/L + s)t} = 0 \tag{15}$$

then

$$H(s) = \frac{1}{R + Ls} \tag{16}$$

as we would expect from elementary circuit theory ($H(s)$ being, of course, the admittance of the circuit). But s is an arbitrary complex number, and it is clear that *(15) will be true if and only if*

$$\text{Re}[s] > -R/L. \tag{17}$$

Indeed for

$$\text{Re}[s] < -R/L$$

$H(s)$ as defined by (13) does not exist because the integral does not converge. In other words, *only for certain values of* s will the response of the circuit of Fig. 1(a) to e^{st} be $\frac{1}{R + Ls}\, e^{st}$ (specifically those values of s for which $\text{Re}[s] > -R/L$); for other values of s the response to e^{st} is infinite (undefined). This result holds in general. If and only if s lies in that region of the s-plane (*i.e.*, the plane whose axes are the real and imaginary parts of s) for which (13) converges

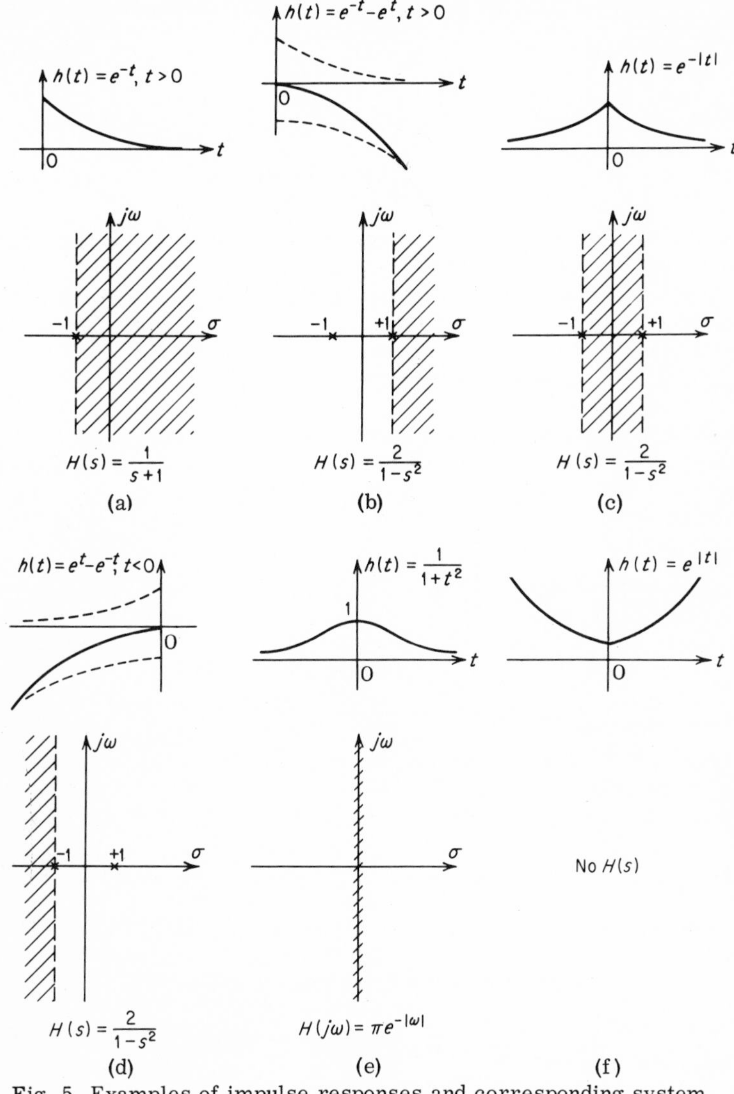

Fig. 5. Examples of impulse responses and corresponding system functions.

then the response to the input $x(t) = e^{st}$, $-\infty < t < \infty$, is $y(t) = H(s)e^{st}$, $-\infty < t < \infty$.

In general the region of the s-plane in which (13) converges is a *strip* parallel to the imaginary axis as shown by the examples in Fig. 5. There are a number of matters of interest that can be deduced from these examples. In the first place the domain of convergence of (13) can be a right half-plane [Figs. 5(a) and 5(b)]; a left half-plane [Fig. 5(d)], a strip of finite width [Fig. 5(c)], a single line

[Fig. 5(e)], or, may not even exist at all* [Fig. 5(f)]. Furthermore, although the formula for $H(s)$ may usually be evaluated by analytical continuation for values of s that lie outside the convergence strip for (13), the resulting values of $H(s)$ characterize the response of a *different* system. Thus the formulas for $H(s)$ for each of the three different systems of Figs. 5(b), 5(c) and 5(d) are all the same; only the regions of convergence are different. A linear time-invariant system is thus *not* uniquely defined† by simply giving a formula for $H(s)$ unless in addition a region (strip) is specified in the s-plane in which $H(s)e^{st}$ is to represent the response to an input equal to e^{st}. In this regard, it can be shown that if this strip is wider than a single line then $H(s)$ must be *analytic* in this (open) region. Specifically, if $H(s)$ is a rational function of s (the ratio of two polynomials in s) then the denominator of $H(s)$ can have no roots ($H(s)$ can have no poles) within the convergence region of (13).

V. STABILITY AND REALIZABILITY

Linear, time-invariant systems are often classified by two attributes—*realizability* and *stability*—which are variously defined in the literature and indeed often have, or appear to have, overlapping meanings. In the sense in which we shall use the word, realizability implies the notions of causality and of the unidirectional flow of time, but has nothing otherwise to do with the possibility of constructing the system from some specific class of elements. We shall thus define a system to be *realizable* if $h(t) \equiv 0$ for $t < 0$. It is easy to show that for a realizable system the domain of convergence of $H(s)$ is at least a right half-plane [Figs. 5(a) and 5(b)]. On the other hand we shall define a system to be *stable* if every bounded input yields a bounded output. A completely equivalent condition‡ is that a system is stable

*This merely means that frequency-domain methods of the simple type which we are discussing cannot be applied to such a system. This is no great loss, perhaps, since such systems are nearly always both unrealizable and unstable. A modified frequency representation similar to that which we shall use for some signals (Section VII, Example 5, below) can be devised if desirable.

†This result is closely related to our earlier comment that a differential equation does not yield a unique response for each input without further conditions.

‡See James, Nichols, and Phillips, *Theory of Servomechanisms*, McGraw-Hill, New York, Chap. 2 (1947). The proof is very simple. Since

$$|y(t)| = \left|\int_{-\infty}^{\infty} x(\tau)\, h(t-\tau)\, d\tau\right| \le \mathrm{Max}[x(t)] \int_{-\infty}^{\infty} |h(t)|\, dt < \infty$$

the condition (18) is clearly sufficient. Further, assume that (18) is not satisfied and let

1. $x(t) = 1$ for those t for which $h(-t) \ge 0$
2. $x(t) = -1$ for those t for which $h(-t) < 0$.

$x(t)$ is clearly bounded. However

$$y(0) = \int_{-\infty}^{\infty} x(\tau)\, h(-\tau)\, d\tau = \int_{-\infty}^{\infty} |h(t)|\, dt \to \infty$$

by hypothesis, so that the condition is necessary.

if and only if

$$\int_{-\infty}^{\infty} | h(t) | \, dt < \infty \tag{18}$$

i.e., if the impulse response is absolutely integrable. Again it is easy to show that if a system is stable the domain of convergence for $H(s)$ must include at least the imaginary axis $s = j\omega$ [Figs. 5(a), 5(c), 5(e)]. It should be observed that stability and realizability are completely independent attributes. However, if a system is *both* stable and realizable, then the domain of convergence of $H(s)$ is at least the entire right half-plane $\text{Re}[s] \geqslant 0$ and $H(s)$ will be analytic at least for $\text{Re}[s] > 0$ [Fig. 5(a)]. But unless realizability is implied, the statement that "an unstable system is one whose system function has a singularity in the right half-plane" is an oversimplification. See, for example, Fig. 5(c); this system is stable, and yet $H(s)$ has a pole at $s = +1$ (the system is unrealizable, of course).

VI. SPECTRAL REPRESENTATIONS OF SIGNALS; FREQUENCY ANALYSIS

In the preceding sections we have shown how a linear time-invariant system may be characterized explicitly in the frequency domain. Specifically, if the input is $x(t) = e^{st}$, $-\infty < t < \infty$, (where s is a complex number), then the output is $y(t) = H(s)e^{st}$ where $H(s)$, the system function, is given by (13) in terms of $h(t)$ and where s is restricted to a strip in the complex plane corresponding to the domain of convergence of (13). It remains to show how the frequency representation can be used to find the response to inputs that are not of the form e^{st}. The procedure, of course, is to represent such inputs, if possible, as sums of terms of the form e^{st}. Then, following the argument associated with (2) and (3), the output can be represented as a similar sum with e^{st} replaced by $H(s)e^{st}$. What kinds of inputs can be represented as weighted sums (or integrals) of terms like e^{st}? The answer is almost any input, but unfortunately there is no single theorem that quite says this. For most purposes, however, the following theorem suffices*:

If $x(t)$ is absolutely integrable in every finite interval and if

$$X(s) = \int_{-\infty}^{\infty} x(t) e^{-st} \, dt \tag{19}$$

exists for some $\sigma_0 = \text{Re}\,[s]$, then

$$x(t) \;(=)\; \frac{1}{2\pi j} \int_{\sigma_0 - j\infty}^{\sigma_0 + j\infty} X(s)\, e^{st} \, ds \,. \tag{20}$$

*D. V. Widder, *The Laplace Transform*, Princeton University Press, Princeton, New Jersey, 1946, Chap. 6.

The integral in (20) is a line or contour integral. The limits are intended to indicate that the path is the line Re $[s] = \sigma_0$; *i.e.*, (20) represents $x(t)$ in terms of a sum of e^{st} terms, *for all of which Re* (s) $= \sigma_0$. The amplitudes of these terms [analogous to the a_i in (2)] are proportional to $X(s)$ which is determined by (19) and is called the (bilateral) *Laplace Transform* or, as we shall call it to avoid confusion with the (unilateral) Laplace Transform, the *Exponential Transform* of $x(t)$, As a special case, if the conditions of the theorem are satisfied for $\sigma_0 = 0$ (a sufficient condition is that $\int_{-\infty}^{\infty} |x(t)|\, dt < \infty$), then $X(j\omega)$ is called the *Fourier Transform* of $x(t)$ and (20) may be simplified to

$$x(t) \; (=) \; \frac{1}{2\pi} \int_{-\infty}^{\infty} X(j\omega) e^{j\omega t} \, d\omega \tag{21}$$

which is a complex-valued ordinary integral in the real variable, ω.

The scheme for the analysis of linear time-invariant systems in the *"frequency domain"* should now be clear:

1. The input $x(t) = e^{st}$ yields the output $y(t) = H(s) e^{st}$ provided that s lies in that strip in which (13) converges.

2. Most arbitrary inputs, $x(t)$, can be represented as a sum of exponential terms, *i.e.*,

$$x(t) \; (=) \; \frac{1}{2\pi j} \int_{\sigma - j\infty}^{\sigma + j\infty} X(s) e^{st} \, ds,$$

provided that s lies in that strip in which (19) converges.

3. The strips in which (13) and (19) converge will in general be different. *If these two strips have in common at least one line*, say Re $[s] = \sigma_0$, then

$$y(t) \; (=) \; \frac{1}{2\pi j} \int_{\sigma_0 - j\infty}^{\sigma_0 + j\infty} X(s) H(s) e^{st} \, ds, \tag{22}$$

or in other words, the Exponential Transform of $y(t)$ is given by

$$Y(s) = X(s) H(s). \tag{23}$$

VII. EXAMPLES

Example 1

Suppose that the input is a unit impulse, *i.e.*,

$$x(t) = \delta(t).$$

$X(s)$ is then, by (19),

$$X(s) = \int_{-\infty}^{\infty} \delta(t) e^{-st} dt = 1$$

throughout the entire s-plane. [This is an example of a general result—the Exponential Transform of any pulse-type signal (an absolutely integrable signal of finite duration) is an *entire function, i.e.,* defined and analytic for all finite s.] Hence from (22)

$$y(t) = h(t) \;(=)\; \frac{1}{2\pi j} \int_{\sigma_0 - j\infty}^{\sigma_0 + j\infty} H(s)\, e^{st}\, ds \tag{24}$$

where σ_0 lies in the strip for which $H(s)$ is defined. Equation (24) provides a general method for going back from the system function $H(s)$ to the impulse response $h(t)$, thus inverting (13) and demonstrating that the specification of $H(s)$ *and the strip in the* s-*plane* in which the response to e^{st} is supposed to be $H(s)e^{st}$ is completely *equivalent* to the specification of $h(t)$. But the importance of specifying the strip of convergence of (13) in addition to $H(s)$ cannot be overemphasized, as our next two examples illustrate.

Example 2

Let us apply (24) to the $H(s)$ of Fig. 5(c); *i.e.,*

$$H(s) = \frac{2}{1 - s^2},\; -1 < \mathrm{Re}\,[s] < +1 .$$

We may choose σ_0 in (24) to be zero so that $h(t)$ should be given by

$$h(t) \;(=)\; \frac{1}{2\pi j} \int_{-j\infty}^{j\infty} \frac{2}{1 - s^2}\, e^{st}\, ds . \tag{25}$$

Integrals of this type are most conveniently evaluated by the method of residues. Extending analytically the domain of the integrand to the entire plane,* we have poles of the the integrand at $s = +1$ and $s = -1$ with residues $-e^t$ and e^{-t} respectively. Closing the contours to the right for $t < 0$ and to the left for $t > 0$ (see Fig. 6) the contributions of the semi-circles to the integral vanish in the limit (Jordan's Lemma)† and we obtain

$$h(t) = \begin{Bmatrix} e^t, & t < 0 \\ e^{-t}, & t > 0 \end{Bmatrix} = e^{-|t|},\; -\infty < t < \infty .$$

*There is nothing inconsistent here with our previous attitude that $H(s)$ is defined only in a strip. For the purpose of evaluating the integral in (25) it is of course permissible to continue analytically the integrand (equal to $H(s)e^{st}$ in the strip) wherever we wish and can. It is only the *significance* of $2/1-s^2$ as an *output-input ratio* that we deny outside the strip; we may certainly evaluate the *function* $2/1-s^2$ for other values of s than those in the strip $|\mathrm{Re}[s]| < 1$.

†Copson, *Theory of Functions of a Complex Variable*, Oxford University Press, London, 1935, p. 137.

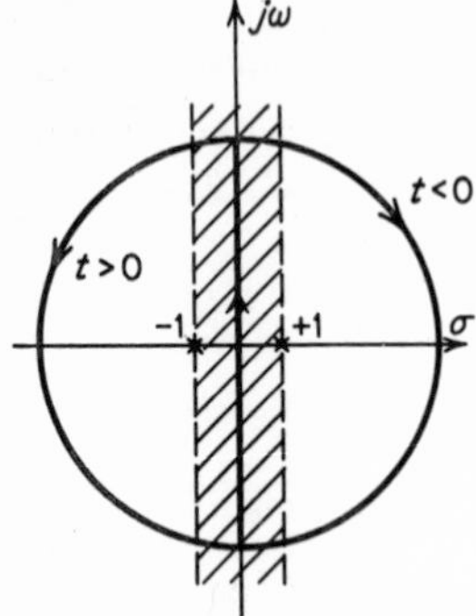

Fig. 6. s-plane sketch for Example 2.

This result is precisely the $h(t)$ we started from to obtain $H(s)$ in Fig. 5(c).

Example 3

Suppose again we apply (24) to the $H(s)$ of Fig. 5(b); *i.e.*,

$$H(s) = \frac{2}{1-s^2}, \ \mathrm{Re}\,[s] > 1$$

which is identical with the preceding example, except for the domain of definition of $H(s)$. We now choose σ_0 in (24) to be, say, 2 so that

$$h(t) \ (=) \ \frac{1}{2\pi j} \int_{2-j\infty}^{2+j\infty} \frac{2}{1-s^2} \, e^{st} \, ds \, . \tag{26}$$

Closing the contours as before, we have poles and residues as before, but the contour is in a different place (see Fig. 7) so that

$$h(t) = \begin{cases} e^{-t} - e^{t}, \ t \geqslant 0 \\ 0 \qquad\quad , \ t < 0 \end{cases}$$

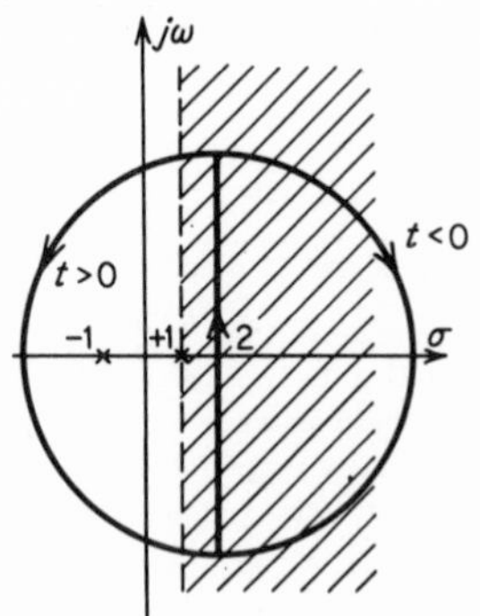

Fig. 7. s-plane sketch for Example 3.

as it should. We should note, incidentally, that even though the function $\frac{2}{1-s^2}$ may be analytically continued from the region $\mathrm{Re}[s] > 1$ to yield uniquely the function $\frac{2}{1+\omega^2}$ for $s = j\omega$ and even though the (Fourier) integral $\frac{1}{2\pi j}\int_{-j\infty}^{j\infty} \frac{2}{1+\omega^2} e^{j\omega t}\, d(j\omega)$ converges to a perfectly definite time function, this time function is not the $h(t)$ corresponding to $H(s) = \frac{2}{1-s^2}$, $\mathrm{Re}[s] > 1$. (It is instead the $h(t)$ corresponding to $H(s) = \frac{2}{1-s^2}$, $-1 < \mathrm{Re}[s] < 1$, of Example 2.) Thus statements like "Fourier transforms are merely Laplace transforms with $j\omega$ substituted for s" are seen to be oversimplifications, at least unless stability and realizability are assumed.

Example 4

To illustrate the methods of frequency analysis in a rather typical case, consider the stable unrealizable filter

$$h(t) = \begin{cases} e^{-3t}, & t \geqslant 0 \\ e^{3t}, & t < 0 \end{cases} ; \quad H(s) = \frac{6}{9-s^2}, \ -3 < \mathrm{Re}[s] < 3$$

(similar to Fig. 5c) with the input

$$x(t) = \begin{cases} e^{t}, & t \geqslant 0 \\ 0, & t < 0 . \end{cases}$$

From (19)

$$X(s) = \int_0^\infty e^t e^{-st}\, dt = \frac{1}{s-1}, \ \mathrm{Re}[s] > 1.$$

Choosing $\sigma_0 = 2$, *i.e.*, in the region common to the defined regions for *both* $H(s)$ and $X(s)$ (see Fig. 8)

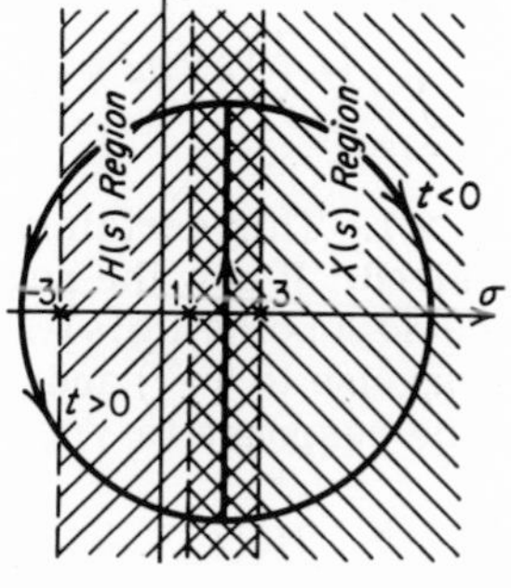

Fig. 8. s-plane sketch for Example 4.

$$y(t) \; (=) \; \frac{1}{2\pi j} \int_{2-j\infty}^{2+j\infty} \frac{6}{(9-s^2)(s-1)} e^{st} \, ds .$$

Evaluating by residues after closing the contours as in Fig. 8, we obtain

$$y(t) = \begin{cases} (1/2)\, e^{3t} & , t \leqslant 0 \\ -(1/4)\, e^{-3t} + (3/4)\, e^{t}, & t > 0 \end{cases}$$

Example 5

As a final example consider an input

$$x(t) = \begin{cases} 1 , & t \leqslant 0 \\ e^{t}, & t > 0. \end{cases}$$

Although $x(t)$ is absolutely integrable in every finite interval, $X(s)$ as given by (19) does *not* exist for *any* σ_0. We need not, however, admit defeat quite yet. The essence of the frequency method is to represent a signal as a sum of terms of the form e^{st}. There is no requirement that all of these terms must have the *same* value of Re $[s]$; merely that the values of Re $[s]$ must lie in the appropriate strip. Thus suppose we break up $x(t)$ into two parts,

$$x(t) = x_1(t) + x_2(t)$$

where, say,

$$x_1(t) = \begin{cases} 1, & t \leqslant 0 \\ 0, & t > 0 \end{cases} \qquad x_2(t) = \begin{cases} 0 , & t \leqslant 0 \\ e^{t}, & t > 0. \end{cases}$$

We find then easily from (19) that

$$X_1(s) = -\frac{1}{s} , \text{ Re}[s] < 0; \; X_2(s) = \frac{1}{s-1}, \text{ Re}[s] > 1$$

so that

$$x(t) \; (=) \; \frac{1}{2\pi j} \int_{\sigma_1 - j\infty}^{\sigma_1 + j\infty} \left(-\frac{1}{s}\right) e^{st} \, ds + \frac{1}{2\pi j} \int_{\sigma_2 - j\infty}^{\sigma_2 + j\infty} \frac{1}{s-1} e^{st} \, ds$$

where $\sigma_1 < 0$, $\sigma_2 > 1$. This certainly represents $x(t)$ as a sum of e^{st}-terms as desired. If now the region of definition of $H(s)$ is broad enough to include *both* some Re$[s] < 0$ and Re$[s] > 1$, then in effect by finding the response to $x_1(t)$ and $x_2(t)$ separately and adding the results we find the response to $x(t)$. For example, if

$$H(s) = \frac{6}{9-s^2} , \; -3 < \text{Re}[s] < 3,$$

as in Example 4, then

$$y(t) = \frac{1}{2\pi j} \int_{-1-j\infty}^{-1+j\infty} \frac{6}{s(s^2-9)} e^{st} ds + \frac{1}{2\pi j} \int_{2-j\infty}^{2+j\infty} \frac{6}{(9-s^2)(s-1)} e^{st} ds.$$

The evaluation is left to the reader.

VIII. SPECIAL INPUT SIGNALS; BAND-LIMITED SIGNALS AND THE SAMPLING THEOREM

In the preceding sections we have presented two explicit methods for describing the behavior of linear time-invariant systems and for representing the input and output signals of such systems. The essence of both methods was to represent the input as a sum (integral) of characteristic signals (impulses or complex exponentials) for each of which the response of the system could be easily given [by $h(t)$ or $H(s)$]. In both cases the set of characteristic signals was sufficiently complete that almost *any* reasonable input signal could be represented as a weighted sum of these characteristic inputs.

However, there are many important problems in communication engineering in which we are interested in only some *restricted* class of inputs to a linear system. In such cases there is often an advantage in choosing as characteristic inputs some set of signals other than impulses or complex exponentials. Previously, we have been concerned solely with the choice of signal representations that are suited to linear time-invariant systems; we shall now consider, in addition, the effect of certain special types of *signals* upon the choice of representation.

As an illustration, suppose that the set of input signals in which we are interested consists of "stepped" signals with equally spaced discontinuities. One such waveform is shown in Fig. 9(a). Such signals can be represented in terms of the set of delayed pulse signals [Fig. 9(b)]

$$\varphi_n(t) = \varphi(t - nT), \quad n = 0, \pm 1, \pm 2, \ldots$$

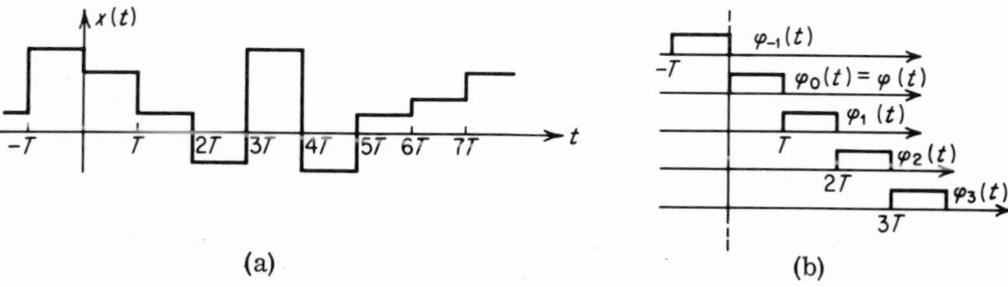

Fig. 9. Example of a stepped waveform, (a), and corresponding suitable set of characteristic signals, (b).

as

$$x(t) = \sum_{-\infty}^{\infty} a_n \varphi_n(t) = \sum_{-\infty}^{\infty} a_n \varphi(t - nT).$$

The set of $\varphi_n(t)$ make an excellent set of characteristic inputs to a linear time-invariant system since they are identical except for a delay. If the response of the system is known or given for any one $\varphi_n(t)$ it is known for all. Thus, if the response to $\varphi_0(t) = \varphi(t)$ is $p(t)$, then the response to $\varphi_n(t)$ is $p(t - nT)$ and the response to $x(t)$ is

$$y(t) = \sum_{-\infty}^{\infty} a_n p(t - nT).$$

Thus, $p(t)$ characterizes the behavior of the system for any "stepped" input of the form illustrated in Fig. 9(a).

A much more important, but similar, example is the *band-limited* input signal which can be defined by the property that

$$X(j\omega) = \int_{-\infty}^{\infty} x(t) e^{-j\omega t}\, dt \tag{27}$$

exist in some sense and that

$$X(j\omega) \equiv 0 \text{ for } |\omega| > 2\pi W. \tag{28}$$

Band-limited signals have a number of interesting properties of which the most important for our present purposes is the *Sampling Theorem.*

Formally the Sampling Theorem states that if $X(j\omega)$ satisfies (28), *i.e.*, if $x(t)$ is (low-pass) band-limited to the band $|\omega| < 2\pi W$, then $x(t)$ may be represented as

$$x(t) = \sum_{-\infty}^{\infty} x\left(\frac{n}{2W}\right) \frac{\sin 2\pi W\left(t - \frac{n}{2W}\right)}{2\pi W\left(t - \frac{n}{2W}\right)}. \tag{29}$$

A formal proof of (29) is easily given. An equivalent formula to (29) is

$$x(t) = \int_{-\infty}^{\infty} \left[\sum_{-\infty}^{\infty} x(\tau)\delta\left(\tau - \frac{n}{2W}\right)\right] \left[\frac{\sin 2\pi W(t-\tau)}{2\pi W(t-\tau)}\right] d\tau \tag{29a}$$

as may be shown by interchanging integration and summation, and carrying out the integration. Comparison of (29a) with the Superposition Integral (10) suggests the interpretation of $x(t)$ as the response of a filter characterized by

$$h(t) = \frac{\sin 2\pi Wt}{2\pi Wt}, \quad -\infty < t < \infty \tag{29b}$$

to the excitation $\sum_{-\infty}^{\infty} x(t)\,\delta(t - n/2W)$ which is a train of impulses

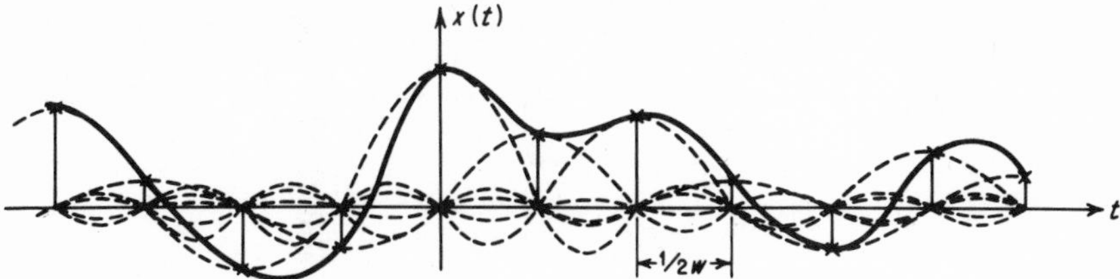

Fig. 10. Band-limited waveform.

spaced $1/2W$ apart in time. If $X(j\omega)$ is band-limited as in (28), then the Fourier transform of this impulse-train excitation is easily seen to be $X(j\omega)$ repeated *periodically* in frequency. (This is the dual of the more familiar line spectrum corresponding to a periodic time function.) The Fourier transform of $h(t)$ of (29b) is 1 over the band $|\omega| < 2\pi W$ and zero elsewhere, so that the spectrum of $x(t)$ is simply the first cycle of the periodic spectrum of the impulse train, *i.e.*, simply $X(j\omega)$, which justifies (29).

Equation (29) represents $x(t)$ in terms of *samples* taken $1/2W$ seconds apart, the values in between being interpolated by the $\sin 2\pi Wt/(2\pi Wt)$ term (see Fig. 10). Any (low-pass) band-limited signal can be specified, then, in terms of a set of characteristic

signals $\dfrac{\sin 2\pi W\left(t - \frac{n}{2W}\right)}{2\pi W\left(t - \frac{n}{2W}\right)}$ which once again, are identical except

for delay. If the response of a linear time-invariant system to the input $\sin 2\pi Wt/(2\pi Wt)$ is $s(t)$ then the response to the band-limited input $x(t)$ is

$$y(t) = \sum_{-\infty}^{\infty} x\left(\frac{n}{2W}\right) s\left(t - \frac{n}{2W}\right). \tag{30}$$

A similar sampling theorem and system analysis procedure holds for band-pass band-limited signals, *i.e.*, those for which $X(j\omega) \equiv 0$ except for $\omega_0 - 2\pi W < |\omega| < \omega_0 + 2\pi W$, $\omega_0 > 2\pi W$, except that both the envelope and phase of the carrier (or equivalent) must be sampled at the times $n/2W$. This theorem is discussed in Chapters 6 and 12.

In addition to yielding useful results, the discussion of this section provides an excellent example of the relationship between the methods of signal representation and system analysis on the one hand, and the type of signals and systems to be analyzed on the other. A sum representation for the signal is strongly suggested by the linearity of the system. But among all the various possible sum representations, that of (29) is especially simple and permitted only because of the special character of the signal. And the signal representation of (29) is particularly appropriate since it permits us to exploit the time-

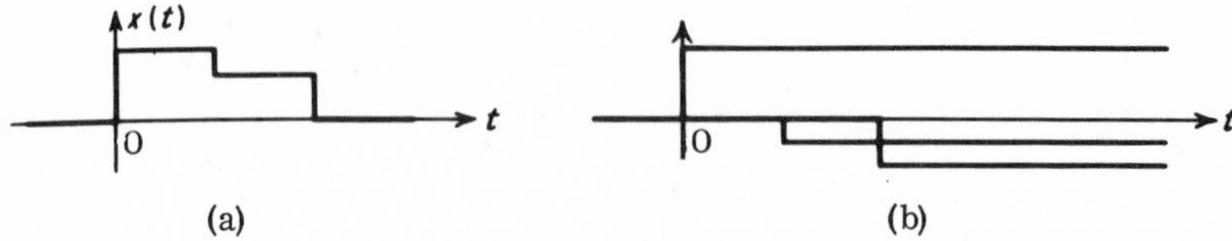

Fig. 11. Stepped waveform.

invariance of the system to yield the simple analysis result of (30). We should always be aware of the variety available in the methods of signal representation or system analysis; we should never become so attached to one method (*e.g.*, Laplace transforms, or the whole idea of sinusoidal frequency representations for that matter) that we are not prepared to exploit some special feature of our specific problem. The problem of the band-limited signal into a linear time-invariant system *can* be represented and analyzed by means of the Superposition-Integral (impulse response) or Exponential-Transform (system function) methods if desired, but it is often easier and more illuminating to use the Sampling Theorem method of this section. Similarly the waveform of Fig. 11(a) as an input to the *R-L* circuit of Fig. 1(a) can be described and analyzed by frequency methods, but it is certainly more appropriate to represent it [as in Fig. 11(b)] as a sum of delayed step-functions for each of which the response of the *R-L* circuit can be easily found and the results summed to yield the complete response.

IX. RANDOM INPUTS; BAND-LIMITED WHITE GAUSSIAN NOISE

In view of the importance of random-signal models in communication theory, we cannot close this chapter on signals in linear systems without at least a brief discussion of random inputs. One of the most useful random-input models is the band-limited white gaussian random process which may be defined in the following way. Let each sample function of the random process have the form

$$x(t) = \sum_{-\infty}^{\infty} x_n \frac{\sin 2\pi W\left(t - \frac{n}{2W}\right)}{2\pi W\left(t - \frac{n}{2W}\right)} \tag{31}$$

where the x_n are statistically independent gaussian-distributed random variables with zero mean and variance σ^2. This is clearly a gaussian process since the weighted sum of any number of gaussian processes is a gaussian process. Furthermore, the correlation function is

$$E[x_t x_{t+\tau}] =$$

$$\sum_{-\infty}^{\infty}\sum_{-\infty}^{\infty} E[x_n x_m] \frac{\sin 2\pi W\left(t - \frac{n}{2W}\right) \sin 2\pi W\left(t + \tau - \frac{m}{2W}\right)}{4\pi^2 W^2 \left(t - \frac{n}{2W}\right)\left(t + \tau - \frac{m}{2W}\right)} \tag{32}$$

This series can be summed to yield

$$E[x_t x_{t+\tau}] = \sigma^2 \frac{\sin 2\pi W\tau}{2\pi W\tau} = R_x(\tau), \tag{33}$$

which, it should be observed, is independent of t (as also is $E[x_t]$) so that $x(t)$ is (at least) wide-sense stationary. Furthermore, the power spectral density $S_x(\omega)$, is given by

$$S_x(\omega) = \int_{-\infty}^{\infty} R_x(\tau) e^{-j\omega t} d\tau = \begin{cases} \frac{\sigma^2}{2W}, & |\omega| < 2\pi W \\ 0, & \text{elsewhere} \end{cases} \tag{34}$$

which justifies both the statement that $x(t)$ is band-limited and that it is white (*i.e.*, has a constant power spectral density over the band). Letting $\sigma^2 = 2WN_0$ where N_0 is the power spectral density (watts/cycle per second) we have

$$S_x(\omega) = \begin{cases} N_0, & |\omega| < 2\pi W \\ 0, & \text{elsewhere} \end{cases} \tag{35}$$

and

$$R_x(\tau) = N_0 \frac{\sin 2\pi W\tau}{\pi\tau}. \tag{36}$$

If $x(t)$ is the input to a stable linear time-invariant filter characterized by $H(j\omega)$, then it is easy to argue formally that

$$S_y(\omega) = |H(j\omega)|^2 S_x(\omega) \tag{37}$$

and

$$R_y(\tau) = \frac{1}{2\pi}\int_{-\infty}^{\infty} S_y(\omega) e^{j\omega t} d\omega. \tag{38}$$

If $x(t)$ is a white band-limited gaussian process, then $y(t)$ will also be a band-limited gaussian process but, of course, will not in general be white. In particular if W is so large that $|H(j\omega)|^2$ is negligible for $|\omega| > 2\pi W$ then

$$S_y(\omega) = N_0 |H(j\omega)|^2 \tag{39}$$

$$R_y(\tau) = \frac{N_0}{2\pi}\int_{-\infty}^{\infty} \left|H(j\omega)\right|^2 e^{j\omega t} d\omega. \tag{40}$$

The average power in the output process is simply

$$R_y(0) = \frac{N_0}{2\pi}\int_{-\infty}^{\infty} \left|H(j\omega)\right|^2 d\omega = N_0 \int_{-\infty}^{\infty} h^2(t)\, dt \tag{41}$$

where the last equality follows from Parseval's Theorem.

X. CONCLUSION

In this chapter we have tried to show the ways in which the methods of linear time-invariant system description and analysis, and the methods of representation for the signals that are the inputs and outputs of such systems, are intimately related. In some respects the unique properties of the linear time-invariant systems are dominant—*e.g.*, they suggest that representations of the signals in terms of *sums* of more elementary signals are highly appropriate, and they suggest further that the description or characterization of the specific system of interest will be simplest if the elementary signals are exponentials (sinusoids) or are all delayed replicas of some basic signal such as an impulse, pulse, or sin t/t function. But the selection of what particular set of elementary signals to employ in a given problem depends about equally on the character of the specific system to be analyzed and on the character of the specific signals that are the inputs to the system. Still in the final analysis the choice in the majority of cases falls on the exponential signals, *i.e.*, on frequency methods. The reasons are many:

1. The method is quite general—capable of dealing (with differences only in ease of manipulation) with almost any signal and almost any linear time-invariant system.

2. Often the signal in which we are interested (for example, narrow-band signals) and the systems with which we are concerned (for example, lumped R-L-C circuits) can be described with greater simplicity and efficiency in terms of frequency than in any other way. This point surely needs no amplification for any practicing engineer. But we should be careful that this does not become a chick-and-the-egg type of argument, *i.e.*, we should beware of choosing both systems and signals primarily *because* they can be easily analyzed in frequency terms.

3. Many communication problems involve sharing some channel or medium (the atmosphere, ionosphere, cable, amplifier, etc.) with a number of other users located, perhaps, at widely separated geographic sites. Often the channel is at least approximately linear and time-invariant. Thus if the signals employed by the various transmitters have non-overlapping *spectra, i.e.*, if they are *frequency multiplexed,* the received signals will also have non-overlapping spectra (because sinusoids are eigenfunctions of linear time-invariant systems) and can be separated easily. This property of disjointness, furthermore, is independent of the timing (synchronization) of the various signals. Other forms of multiplexing generally require synchronization. The use of the frequency concept is thus often unavoidable.

By changing the variable of integration in the Superposition Integral or from observation of the corresponding frequency relation

$$Y(s) = H(s)X(s),$$

it is clear that, for linear time-invariant systems, the input signal and the system description (which is intimately related to the system analysis procedure) play completely symmetrical, indeed indistinguishable roles. Signal representation methods and system analysis methods are thus merely different interpretations of one basic set of methods.

CHAPTER **4**

Channel Characterization: Basic Approach

Walter E. Morrow, Jr.

I. INTRODUCTION

The design of reliable long-range radio systems requires precise knowledge of the channel through which one desires to transmit signals. Long-range radio circuits, and for that matter, some short-range ones also, have many different types of disturbances that affect the transmitted signals.

In this chapter, we shall attempt to show how these various disturbances can be characterized in a generalized model of a channel. If this model is sufficiently general and flexible, a communication engineer may be able to represent any particular channel by a judicious selection of model parameters. No attempt will be made to describe the physics of the various types of channels by means of a mathematical model because of the difficulty encountered in representing different physical processes. The discussions will be restricted to the development of a general channel model with one or two illustrative examples to show how the model can be used to represent typical channels.

The different types of channels over which communication may be desired are numerous and quite varied in nature. The following list is typical of some of the different types that have been used in the past or are under consideration for future use.

(a) Open-wire transmission systems
(b) Land and undersea coaxial-cable systems
(c) Acoustical or underwater sound systems
(d) Ground-wave systems
(e) Line-of-sight systems
(f) Systems employing reflection from the ionosphere
(g) Ionospheric-scatter systems
(h) Meteor-trail-reflection systems
(i) Beyond-line-of-sight systems employing diffraction
(j) Tropospheric-scatter systems
(k) Systems employing scattering from artificial satellites
(l) Space communication through ionized gas plasmas.

The transmission characteristics of these channels have, in some cases, enormous differences. Thus, the multipath time delay encountered on a microwave line-of-sight path may be only a few hundredths of a microsecond, while over a long distance ionospheric path, differential time delays of many tens of milliseconds may be observed. It will be noticed that channels other than strictly radio have been included. This was done because although these channels employ sound waves and transmission along lines, they have problems similar to those of radio channels. It should also be noted that in some cases channels may have more than one input or output (space-diversity antenna systems, for example). In addition to the above variations, it is also possible to consider radio channels that may or may not include antennas. If the antennas are not included in the channel, adequate characterization may require representation of the angular dispersion of the received signals—energy may be transmitted from one point to another by a variety of different paths separated in angle (as, for example, in the case of signals scattered from a number of aircraft).

Under these circumstances one may well ask whether it is possible to achieve a single representation of all the different possible channels. One may also well ask what the value of a single representation is. It should be evident that optimum transmission techniques deduced for this generalized channel would have enormous value since they could be applied to any channel.

What then do these various channels have in common? First, it is evident that all have inputs into which power in the form of various input signals may be fed, and outputs from which power is received. Second, observations have shown that, for the most part, the channels may be considered as linear. That is, the outputs obtained are simply the sum of the inputs—cross-product output signals, if observed, are practically always small compared with the other output signals. Notable exceptions to linearity may occur (Luxemburg Effect and nonlinearity in telephone-line repeating amplifiers, for instance); however, for the purposes of this study, linearity will be assumed. Third, there is present in the output of the channels some power (interference) even in the absence of an input. Fourth, the signals transmitted through the channels require a finite time for transmission and are attenuated in various ways that may range from simple fixed losses to complicated time-variant losses.

In summary, the common characteristics of the various types of channels are:

(a) They have input(s) and output(s).
(b) They are linear.
(c) There are additive disturbances in the outputs.
(d) The inputs are delivered at the outputs after a time delay with a loss that may be time variant.

These characteristics suggest that time-variant linear networks with two or more terminal pairs can be used to characterize the various types of channels. With such models the effects of a transmission channel on a given signal can be determined.

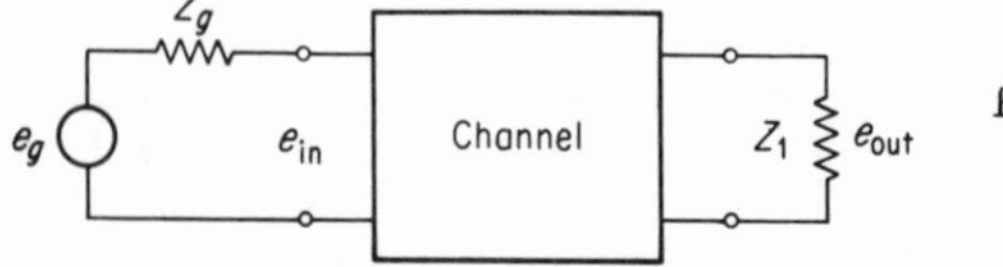

Fig. 1. Two-terminal-pair channel.

II. GENERAL MODEL OF CHANNELS

The communication engineer is interested in characterizing a channel by means of a generalized mathematical model which he can employ to determine the effects of radio propagation on the signals that he wishes to transmit. The study of such a model may lead to the selection of suitable signals to insure that the transmission disturbances are minimized. It is not essential to represent the actual physics of radio propagation in this model, although a knowledge of the physics is quite useful. It is sufficient to obtain a mathematical representation of the physical channel for such studies, and it is of little importance from the point of view of signal design how the energy is physically transmitted from the input to the output of the channel.

The simplest type of channel that can be encountered is the two-terminal-pair channel, illustrated in Fig. 1, that has an input into which signals are sent and an output at which signals are received. The output from this channel can be expressed in the form

$$e_{\text{out}}(t) = K(t)e_{\text{in}}(t) + e_N(t) \tag{1}$$

It will be noticed that the channel may operate on the transmitted signal in a *multiplicative* fashion by $K(t)$, and it may also *add* to the signal a certain amount of noise disturbance, e_N. The effects of the channel are thus divided into two major categories: multiplicative disturbances* and additive disturbances. These will be treated separately in the discussions that follow.

Many times the communication engineer is faced with a more complicated channel than the single-input-single-output channel described above. These more complicated channels may have one or more input pairs and one or more output pairs, and they become of importance in diversity reception and in the study of the operation of antenna systems when the received signals come from a number of sources separated in angle. A practical example of such a channel might be a tropospheric-scatter system with two transmitting and two receiving antennas for the purpose of obtaining space-diversity protection against signal fading. Figure 2 shows symbolically such a channel which is often described as a multi-terminal-pair channel. The equations describing the transmissions through this channel are more complicated than in the two-port case. They can be represented as follows:

$$\left.\begin{aligned}
e_{\text{out},1}(t) &= K_{11}(t)e_{\text{in},1}(t) + K_{12}(t)e_{\text{in},2}(t) + \dots + K_{1k}(t)e_{\text{in},k}(t) + e_{N1}(t)\\
e_{\text{out},2}(t) &= K_{21}(t)e_{\text{in},1}(t) + K_{22}(t)e_{\text{in},2}(t) + \dots + K_{2k}(t)e_{\text{in},k}(t) + e_{N_2}(t)\\
&\cdots\cdots\cdots\cdots\cdots\cdots\cdots\cdots\cdots\cdots\\
e_{\text{out},m}(t) &= K_{m1}(t)e_{\text{in},1}(t) + K_{m2}(t)e_{\text{in},2}(t) + \dots + K_{mk}(t)e_{\text{in},k}(t) + e_{N_m}(t)
\end{aligned}\right\} \tag{2}$$

*In most channels, an explicit representation of the multiplicative disturbances requires a much more complex form that is shown in Eq. (1). In spite of the fact that these representations are not simple multiplications in the time domain, it is customary to refer to all channel effects that are not purely additive as multiplicative disturbances.

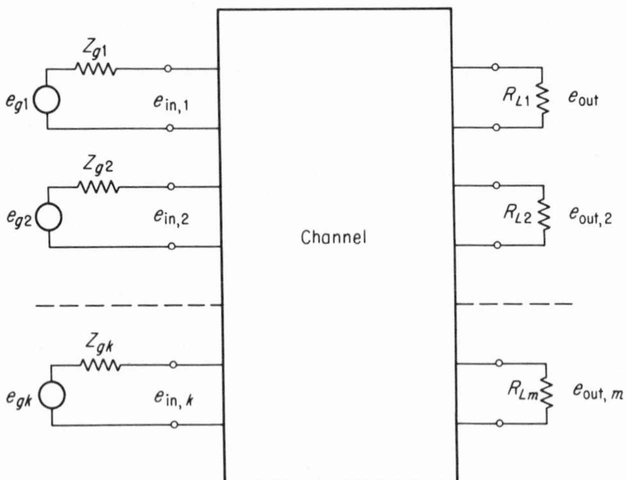

Fig. 2. Multi-terminal-pair channel.

where $K_{mn}(t)$ are the multiplicative disturbances

$e_{Nm}(t)$ are the additive disturbances.

It is generally necessary to use a separate function to describe the relationship between each output and input. In addition, it is necessary to employ a separate additive disturbance at each output.

It will be noticed that Eqs. (1) and (2) imply that the signals are transmitted through a linear system (*i.e.*, no terms in powers of e_{in}). The multiplicative factors usually are functions of time. It has become customary to separate the time variations in multiplicative disturbances into two components, one describing the long-term variations and the other describing the short-term variations. Thus each multiplicative factor can be expressed as a product of two terms

$$K(t) = K_L(t) \times K_S(t)$$

where $K_L(t)$ describes the long-term variation in received signal strength and $K_S(t)$ describes the short-term variations.

The division of the multiplicative factor into these two terms is made for practical reasons in order to simplify system design. In general, the long-term variations occur at all frequencies in the band of interest and affect equally the signals received at locations many hundreds of wavelengths apart. The short-term second-to-second variations of received signals are generally uncorrelated at different frequencies and at different receiving locations. Thus it is possible to devise techniques to reduce the effects of this short-term fading (*e.g.*, space and frequency diversity, etc.). As an example, the diurnal and yearly variations of received signal strength are usually called long-term. The communication engineer has no control over these variations other than raising the mean received signal strength through the use of more powerful radio equipment. The long-term variations are usually associated with changes in the propagation conditions such as are caused by the difference in the ionosphere between daylight and night or the difference in the temperature and moisture content of the troposphere from summer to winter. The short-term multiplicative disturbances are in general associated with various forms of changing multipath propagation over a circuit. In addition to producing rapid fluctuations in the signal strength at a particular frequency, these changes also cause frequency-selective fading, *i.e.*, uncorrelated fading at different frequencies, and in the time domain they can cause distortion of short pulses.

In addition to the multiplicative disturbances, each output of the channel will have a certain amount of additive disturbance that may be produced by receiver front-end noise, man-made interference, or noise pickup from a number of natural sources such as lightning, cosmic noise, and atmospheric absorption. The additive disturbances on the various outputs of the channel may or may not be independent depending on the source of the interference. For example, lightning noise in one output may often be highly correlated with that in the other output terminals, whereas front-end noise in one output is certainly independent of noise generated in other front-ends and appearing in the other outputs.

III. ADDITIVE DISTURBANCES

Additive disturbances are present in the output even in the absence of a desired input signal and they may be caused by a wide variety of natural and man-made sources. The additive noise disturbances can take on many different forms and can therefore be quite difficult to characterize. Traditionally, these disturbances are divided as follows:

(a) Interference from other signals;
(b) Impulse noise from natural and man-made sources, such as lightning and ignition interference;
(c) Gaussian-distributed random noise from receiver front ends or from antenna pickup of natural sources, such as cosmic noise.

A knowledge of the characteristics of these various types of additive disturbances is important in any analysis of the performance of a radio system. Such characterizations have particular importance when it is desired to calculate precisely the received signal-to-noise ratio in analog transmission systems or the probability of error in digital transmission systems.

It was shown in the preceding section that the additive channel disturbances can be represented as functions of time that are added into the output of a channel. These functions can be described in a statistical manner through the use of the following:

(a) The probability density function or the probability distribution function of the disturbance.

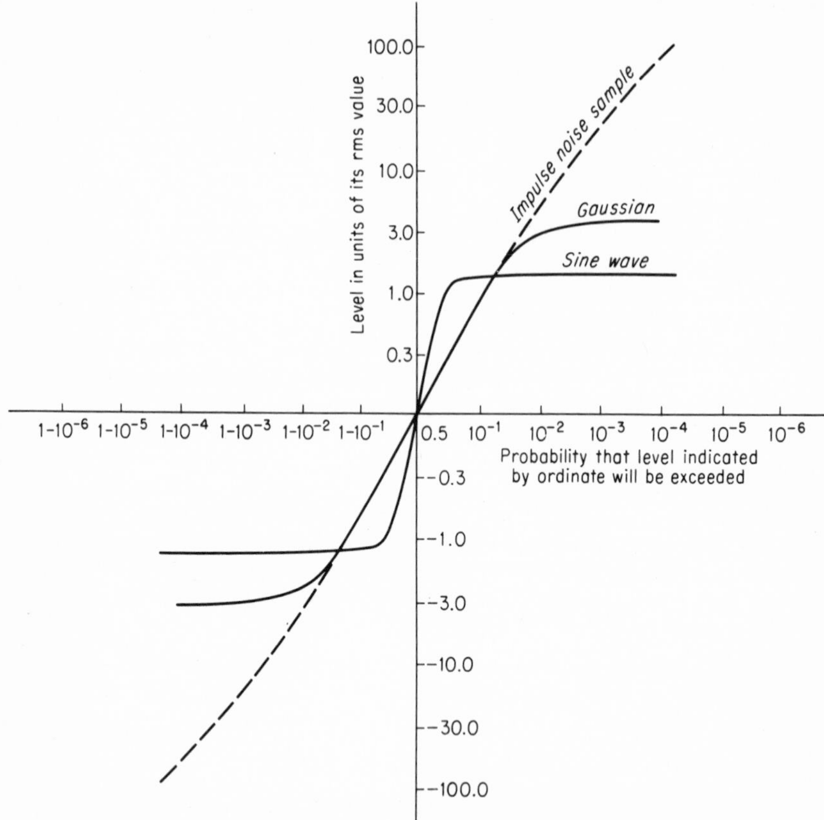

Fig. 3. Probability distribution functions of various types of interference.

(b) The power spectral density or its Fourier transform, the auto-correlation function, of the disturbance.

The probability distribution function gives the percentage of time that the associated additive disturbance may be expected to exceed a certain value. It is also possible to derive a value for the mean power of the additive disturbance from a knowledge of this distribution function.

The probability density function for a sine wave is given by

$$p(x) = \frac{1/\pi}{\sqrt{1 - x^2/2}}$$

and for a gaussian-distributed variable by

$$p(x) = \frac{1}{\sqrt{2\pi}}\, e^{-x^2/2}$$

where x is the instantaneous value of the disturbance measured in

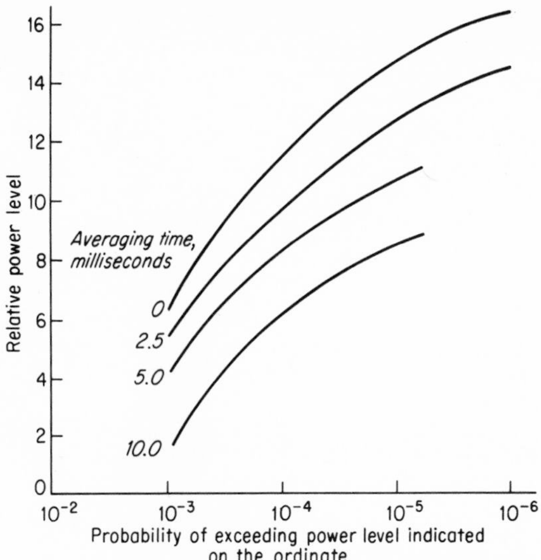

Fig. 4. Probability distribution function of a sample of telephone-line impulse noise averaged over different time intervals.

units of its rms value. The probability distribution functions

$$P(x) = \int_{-\infty}^{x} p(x)\,dx$$

of these two types of disturbance are plotted in Fig. 3 along with the probability distribution function of a sample of impulse noise of the type encountered on a telephone line. It is interesting to note that impulse noise amplitudes much greater than the rms value can occur quite often. In cases where large numbers of similar interfering disturbances, such as impulsive radiations or sinusoidal disturbances of different frequencies or identical current pulses are added together in a random manner, the probability distribution of the resultant disturbance approaches the gaussian distribution function. This result follows from the central limit theorem.

In the case of impulse noise, it is important to know not only the probability distribution function of the noise but also the probability distribution function of the noise power averaged over an interval of time that is comparable with the duration of the signal elements being used; *i.e.*

$$F\left(\frac{1}{T}\int_{0}^{T} e_N^2(t)\,dt\right)$$

A measurement of the probability distribution function of impulse noise in a wide bandwidth often shows very high peak values with a small probability. If the signal symbols being transmitted are appreciably longer than the reciprocal of the bandwidth, then the very high peak values of impulse noise may not be effective in causing confusion at the receiver. But instead of the peak values, one must calculate the average impulse power received over the duration of the signal symbol. In the case of sine-wave interference, the mean power is constant for any signal duration. But for impulse noise the mean power distributions are affected by the length of time over which the interference power is averaged. Figure 4 shows the probability distribution function of a sample of impulse noise power averaged over various time intervals.

In the case of channels with multiple outputs it is important to know whether noises appearing at the different outputs are correlated. Cross-correlation of the various additive signals in the channel outputs can be used to make the necessary measurements. If the output noises are correlated, it is often possible to improve the signal-to-noise ratio by a linear combination of the various outputs which results in a partial cancellation of the noise.

Another characteristic of the additive disturbance which is of great interest is the power spectral density $S(\omega)$. In most cases of gaussian noise, $S(\omega)$ is relatively constant over the frequency band of interest. This is usually the case because the noise is introduced by the receiver front end or by pickup from local or galactic sources. However, the additive disturbances sometimes arrive at the channel output after transmission through some portion of the channel. Under these circumstances, the power spectral density may not be flat and careful measurements of $S(\omega)$ are of great interest in the design of appropriate receiving systems.

IV. LONG-TERM MULTIPLICATIVE VARIATIONS

The characterization of the long-term variations of the multiplicative channel disturbances is obtainable from experimental measurements of the transmission loss of a given radio or wire circuit. In some cases it may be possible to predict statistically the variations in this transmission loss from a knowledge of the propagation theory and of the variations in the parameters that enter into this theory. For example, in the case of a wire circuit, the transmission-loss variations can be predicted from a knowledge of the dependence of the transmission loss on temperature and humidity along the circuit together with a knowledge of the expected variations in these parameters. For most radio circuits empirical measurements are used to obtain adequate characterization of the transmission loss. It may thus be possible to develop empirical formulas for the prediction of the statistical behavior of the variations on a given circuit if knowledge is available concerning the significant parameters and their variations. It is customary in measurements of transmission loss to average the received power over a time interval that is long com-

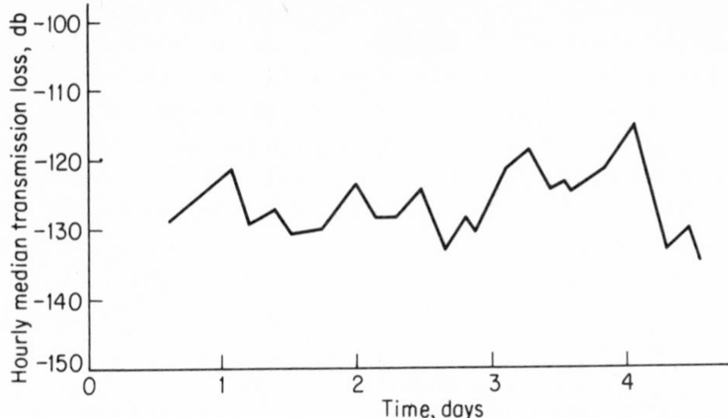

Fig. 5. Typical long-term variation of hourly median transmission loss encountered in tropospheric scatter.

pared with the transmission fluctuations caused by such effects as varying multipath. The averaging time must, of course, be less than the period of time in which the basic transmission loss can vary significantly, and averaging times of a few minutes to an hour are customarily used. These transmission loss measurements yield a function of time that can fluctuate up and down in a random or a periodic fashion when observed over periods of several hours to a day or days.

Figure 5 shows a typical presentation of data concerning long-term variations. In order to make such a function of time useful for the prediction of system performance, it is necessary to characterize the data in a statistical fashion. For this purpose, it is most convenient to compute the probability density or the probability distribution function of the measured quantity. Typical plots of these functions for the transmission-loss data shown in Fig. 5 are presented in Figs. 6 and 7. It will be noticed that the probability

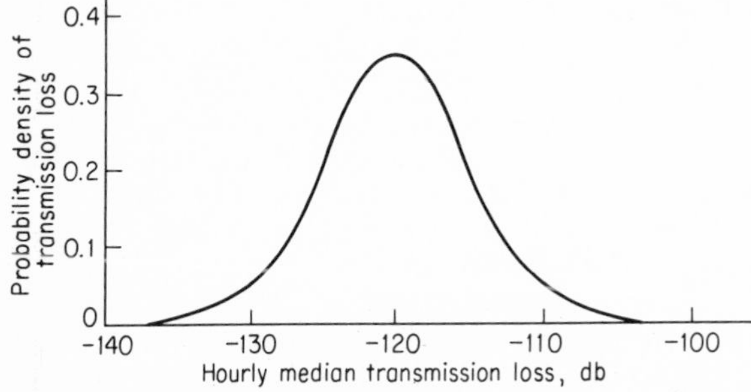

Fig. 6. Typical probability density function of hourly median transmission loss encountered in tropospheric scatter.

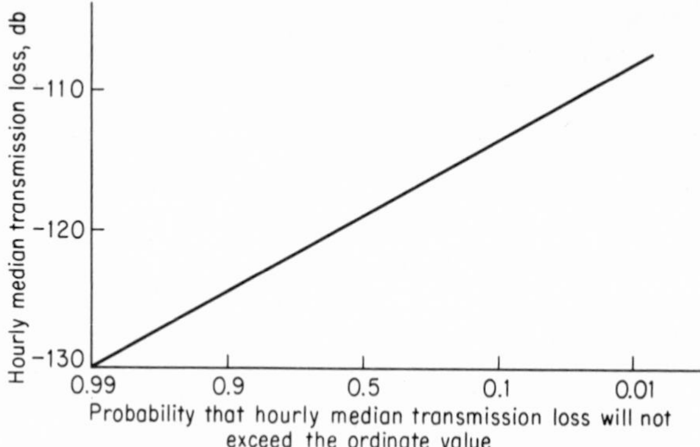

Fig. 7. Typical probability distribution function of hourly median transmission loss encountered in tropospheric scatter.

distribution function in Fig. 7 is plotted against the logarithm of the transmission loss and that on normal probability paper it plots as almost a straight line. This illustrates that in some cases it is possible to use simple analytic representations for these distributions which greatly simplify the calculations on the performance of radio systems, particularly for systems having tandem links. In many cases, however, it is not possible to obtain simple analytic representations. A typical example of a probability distribution function that cannot be simply represented is shown in Fig. 8. Distribution functions of this type are often encountered in measurements of the transmission loss of high-frequency, ionospheric-reflection radio circuits.

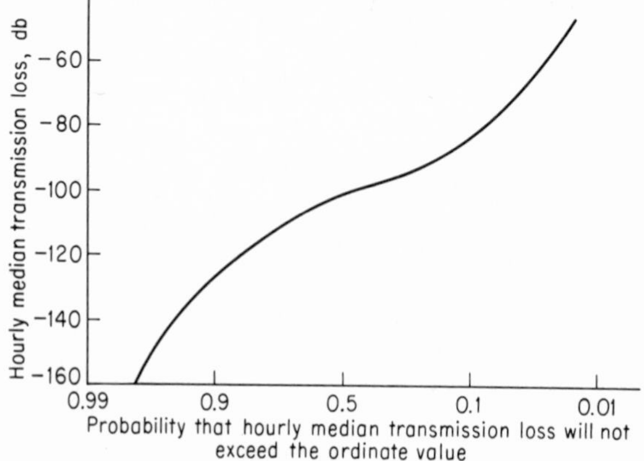

Fig. 8. Typical probability distribution function of hourly median transmission loss encountered in ionospheric reflection of HF signals.

The importance of obtaining an accurate statistical representation of the long-term variations cannot be overemphasized when high communication reliability is required. If reliabilities of 99.9 per cent are required over long periods of time, then probability distributions of the long-term variations accurate to 99.9 or 99.99 per cent are absolutely necessary.

The short-term or rapid fluctuations will be discussed in some detail in Chapters 5, 6, and 7.

CHAPTER 5

Channel Characterization: Rapid Multiplicative Perturbations

Herbert Sherman

I. INTRODUCTION

The preceding chapter has dealt with the characterization of additive noise in a transmission channel and with the long-term variations of the channel characteristics. This chapter will deal with the characterization of channels whose parameters change more rapidly, but not so rapidly that important changes are perceived when observations are made over time intervals of the order of the duration of the longest message element. If the variations can be perceived in the duration of a message element, then the variations of the channel will cause received signal changes that may be indistinguishable from those caused by transmitted messages. The medium may then be incapable of carrying usable signals. If the variations occur very much more slowly than the slowest signal, these changes will be considered as long-term variations that may be taken into account by changes in transmitter power. These somewhat ill-defined extremes will bound the channels discussed in this chapter.

A great deal has been published on the statistical variations of transmission media like the ionosphere and the troposphere. Merely listing and organizing the published data is a monumental task that will not be undertaken here. Channel characterization must be appropriate to the application and little of the data taken meets all of the needs of signaling analysis or synthesis. The approach to be used here will give the description of the channel as a multiterminal-pair network, the terminal-pairs in the case of radio systems being those of the transmitting and the receiving antennas. The emphasis will be on deriving the system response characteristics starting from elementary physical models. Operational understanding will be stressed in preference to mathematical rigor.

II. LINEAR, TIME-VARIANT CHANNELS

It was pointed out in the preceding chapter that transmission media are essentially linear. Unfortunately, in all significant cases the media can rarely be characterized as also being time-invariant. Whether one observes ionospheric reflections, tropospheric scatter, or signals arriving by moon reflection, the common denominator is a time variation in transmission characteristics. In fact, one must search perseveringly for the case in which time invariance of the transmission medium has been wholly acceptable as an operating premise.

Let us consider the transmission medium as being accessible only through pairs of antenna terminals at two spatially separated points. The antennas at transmitting and receiving points may be elaborate directional arrays or isotropic radiators; in either event the influence of the antenna on the communication system is reflected as a change in the terminal-to-terminal measurements.

Consider the measurement of transmission systems by the usual linear-system techniques; namely, apply a signal and measure the response of the system to this signal. Zadeh[1] has extended the classical techniques described in Chapter 3 to allow for time variations of the system and his techniques will be used here. The output of the system is measured as a function of the usual running time variable, t. The input signal is inserted at an absolute time ξ where

$$\xi = t - a \text{ .}$$

The "age" variable a represents the difference between the time of observation t and the signal insertion time ξ, and, as the name implies, it represents the antiquity of the applied signal.*

The response of the network, $h(t,a)$, to an impulse $\delta(t - \xi)$ applied at time $(t = \xi)$ differs from the commonly used impulse response in that it is a function of both the absolute time, t, at which the response is being observed, and the age of the applied impulse.

Since the network has been assumed to be linear, the response of the network to any $x(t-a)$ can be found by superposing the responses of the system to a weighted series of impulses whose sum is equal to $x(t-a)$. Thus

$$y(t) = \int_{-\infty}^{\infty} h(t,a)\, x(t-a)\, da \text{ .} \tag{1}$$

where $h(t,a) = 0$ for $a < 0$ and $x(t-a) = 0$ for $t < a$. Using the Fourier representation

$$x(t-a) = \int_{-\infty}^{+\infty} X(j\omega)\, e^{j\omega(t-a)} \frac{d\omega}{2\pi}$$

one can substitute for $x(t-a)$ and invert the order of integration to obtain

$$y(t) = \int_{-\infty}^{+\infty} \frac{d\omega}{2\pi} X(j\omega)\, e^{j\omega t} \int_{-\infty}^{+\infty} da\, h(t,a)\, e^{-j\omega a} \tag{2}$$

*While this notation is similar to that of Zadeh, the formulation of all equations will be in terms of t and a, rather than t and ξ, in order to lay the groundwork for later chapters on the canonical representation of time-variant networks in which the "age" variable takes on physical significance in the representation (Chapters 6 and 12).

One must now define a quantity $H(j\omega;\, t)$,* which will be termed the system function,

$$H(j\omega;\, t) = \int_{-\infty}^{+\infty} h(t, a)\, e^{-j\omega a}\, da \tag{3}$$

and which is the Fourier transform of the impulse response of the network. Introduction of $H(j\omega;\, t)$ into Eq. (2) leads to

$$y(t) = \int_{-\infty}^{+\infty} X(j\omega)\, H(j\omega;\, t) e^{j\omega t}\, \frac{d\omega}{2\pi}. \tag{4}$$

If one attempts to complete the usual convolution theorem by taking the Fourier transform of $y(t)$, it will be evident that the conventional product $X(j\omega) H(j\omega;\, t)$ is *not* equal to $Y(j\omega)$.

It is useful to give an operational definition of the system function in a form that is different from the Fourier transform of the impulse response of the network. This may be accomplished by exciting the network with the monochromatic spectral line

$$X(j\omega) = 2\pi\,\delta(\omega - \omega_0); \qquad x(t) = e^{j\omega_0 t}, -\infty < t < \infty.$$

The output $y(t)$ for such an input is, from Eq. (4),

$$y(t) = H(j\omega_0;\, t)\, e^{j\omega_0 t}.$$

Thus, $H(j\omega;\, t)$ can also be defined as the output $y(t)$ for an exponential input

$$H(j\omega;\, t) = \left.\frac{y(t)}{x(t)}\right|_{x(t) = e^{j\omega t}, -\infty < t < \infty} \tag{5}$$

Zadeh[1] has discussed the behavior of the time-variant system function for the special cases in which the variations are slow compared to the impulse response and the variations are periodic.

Some of the simpler time-variant channels suggested by the expression for $y(t)$ rarely occur in pure form in nature. For example, no instances are known in which there is only a transmission loss that varies with time and the channel is characterized by an impulse response $h(t)\,\delta(a)$, so that

$$y(t) = \int_{-\infty}^{\infty} h(t)\,\delta(a)\, x(t-a)\, da = h(t) \int_{-\infty}^{\infty} \delta(a) x(t-a)\, da = h(t) x(t)$$

This is the familiar amplitude modulator which, it should be noted, is a *linear* operator. The closest illustrations may be a tumbling

*Because the channel is treated as a linear operator acting on (or "multiplying") the input signal, the term "multiplicative noise" has been frequently used in discussions of randomly varying channels.

satellite with a non-isotropic antenna in which the effective transmission loss is a function of the tumbling rate and phase, but here the effect is usually coupled with a doppler shift. Another illustration is the VOR (*V*ery-High-Frequency-*O*mnidirectional *R*ange) in which the antenna pattern is deliberately modulated to give angular reference information. Other cases can be cited, but the variation in transmission loss is usually accompanied by variations in transmission delay.

Transmission delay is another familiar channel phenomenon in which the input signal appears at the output with a delay that varies as a function of time:

$$y(t) = x\{t - \tau(t)\}$$

The system function for this phenomenon is that of the "shift" function

$$H(j\omega;\, t) = e^{-j\omega\tau(t)}$$

which will be familiar from the shift theorems of linear systems.[2] In nature, such a phenomenon is usually accompanied by transmission loss variations.

A special case of transmission-delay channels is one in which the transmission delay varies linearly with time, as in the case of any communication system in which the transmitting and receiving points are in relative motion with a continuing change of intervening path length. The output signal from such a channel is then

$$y(t) = x(t + kt) = x\{(1 + k)t\}$$

where k is usually v_r/v_c, v_r = radial velocity component* and

*The doppler shift experienced by a narrow-band signal in a receiver that moves with vector velocity $\mathbf{V}$ and receives a wave traveling in vector direction $\mathbf{n}_T$ from a transmitter (as illustrated in the sketch below) is $(-\mathbf{V}\cdot\mathbf{n}_T)\omega_0/v_c$ (assuming $|\mathbf{V}| \ll v_c$).
If it is re-radiated in a new vector direction $\mathbf{n}_R$ as illustrated below (e.g., by specular reflection), the narrow-band signal will receive a further doppler shift of $(-\mathbf{V}\cdot\mathbf{n}_R)\omega_0/v_c$ in addition to any phase changes at the re-radiator.

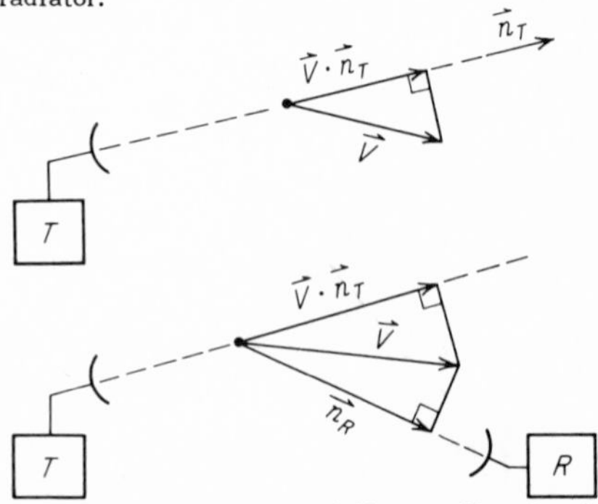

The total doppler shift ω_D will therefore be $\omega_D = (-\mathbf{V}\cdot\mathbf{n}_T + \mathbf{V}\cdot\mathbf{n}_R)\omega_0/v_c$ where ω_0 is the carrier frequency. In the radar case with a target having only radial velocity, this reduces (taking account of the defined directions of $\mathbf{n}_T$ and $\mathbf{n}_R$) to $\omega_D = 2(v_r/v_c)\omega_0$, where $v_r > 0$ for targets with increasing path lengths.

v_c = velocity of propagation in the medium.

In the frequency domain this has the effect of changing the frequency scale by the factor $1/(1+k)$ with an attendant change in amplitude that is usually neglected. If one is concerned with signals whose bandwidth occupancy is small compared with the carrier frequency, ω_0, this change of the frequency scale can, with excellent approximation, be considered as a linear shift of $-k\omega_0$ in frequency across the entire signal bandwidth.* This is the well-known doppler effect.

Channels with doppler shift are already familiar to the radar designer and are becoming of increasing importance to the communication designer as the speed of vehicles increases and as the intervening medium begins to include reflecting bodies with high-velocity components.

In the case of a specular reflector moving away with velocity v along the extension of the straight line through the transmitter and receiver (but not between them), the system function for the channel is

$$H(j\omega;\, t) = \exp\left[-j\omega(2v_r/v_c)t\right] .$$

Thus, the carrier is introduced at one frequency and it comes out with a doppler shift. It might be incidentally noted that this is another case of a linear system that produces frequencies other than those present in the input, because of its time-variant character.

III. INPUT-OUTPUT TRANSFORMATION OF STATISTICS

Returning now to the general significance of the system function defined in Eq. (3), we note from Eq. (4) that for every input signal, $x(t)$, the output signal $y(t)$ can be found uniquely and the problem of system characterization is complete. While this is true for determinate signals whose values can be prescribed at every point in time, one should also consider the case in which the signal may be taken from an ensemble of signals about which only certain statistical parameters are known. This will be particularly important when one seeks to exploit the channel to its limits. Furthermore, natural channels are themselves subject to unpredictable variations that can only be described by statistical means. Ideally, one would like to find a means for taking a complete statistical description of the input signal and a complete statistical description of the channel and determining from these a complete statistical description of the output signal. Unfortunately the mathematical tools for dealing with this

*When using the frequency shift approximation to the doppler effect, it should be noted that the positive and negative frequency components must be shifted in equal *and opposite* directions in order that the shifted signal retain the frequency symmetry needed to insure that the corresponding time function has no complex components.

mapping from input statistics to output statistics are not yet at hand in any useful fashion except for a very limited class of statistical ensembles.[3]

As has been pointed out in Chapter 2, one must frequently be content with a modest description of a random process in the form of suitable abstractions. In the treatment of transmission perturbations whose rapidity is comparable with the rapidity of the signaling, the first-order probability distributions are not wholly adequate for describing the channel. The inadequacy of the first-order distribution functions arises because these functions ignore the relatedness in the channel behavior from instant to instant. The first-order distribution functions are usually generated by taking some parameter of the system as measured over a period of time and sorting this parameter into bins. The relative frequency with which the parameter x falls into the bin $(x + dx)$ is called the probability density $p(x)$ and is measured with total disregard for the time dependence of the events x. If the parameters change so slowly that we can depend on the fact that x will remain in the bin $(x + dx)$ for a relatively long time, the first-order distributions are completely satisfactory, as in the discussion of long-term channel variations. However, if the channel parameter x changes more rapidly than the message changes, and particularly if the changes from sample to sample are unrelated, then the first-order distributions are again completely satisfactory. This chapter is concerned with channel changes lying between these extremes which therefore must be characterized in a manner that insures consideration of the relatedness of adjoining samples of channel behavior.

In addition to the distribution and density functions, averages are usually extremely useful abstractors of random processes. A most useful average that takes account of the time-relatedness of a pair of random variables is the time correlation function

$$R_x(\tau) = \lim_{T \to \infty} \frac{1}{2T} \int_{-T}^{T} x(t)x^*(t - \tau)\,dt \tag{6}$$

where $x^*(t)$ is the complex conjugate of $x(t)$. A stationary gaussian process is completely described by the correlation function. Since the gaussian process is frequently a good model for many phenomena found in nature, this is a most important and natural average to know. Fortunately, there exists a convenient relationship between the input and output correlation functions of a statistically stationary time-variant network[4,5] whose statistics are independent of the input. Define a system correlation function as†

†Later on in this chapter system functions will be used that are functions of space as well as time. For these it should be noted that the system correlation function is *not* defined by the time average of the system function and its *conjugate*, but exactly as in Eq. (7).

$$R_H(j\omega;\tau) = \lim_{T\to\infty} \frac{1}{2T} \int_{-T}^{+T} H(j\omega;t)\, H(-j\omega;t-\tau)\, dt \tag{7}$$

where τ should be taken as a constant parameter rather than a variable. For $\tau = 0$, $R_H(j\omega;\,0)$ is the average-power transmission function. In terms of this system correlation function, one can express the output correlation function as the output of a fictitious network whose input is the correlation function of the input signal and whose system function is the system correlation function of the original network. Thus, with reference to Fig. 1, we have

$$R_y(\tau) = \frac{1}{2\pi} \int_{-\infty}^{+\infty} R_H(j\omega;\,\tau) S_x(j\omega) e^{j\omega\tau}\, d\omega \tag{8}$$

where

$$S_x(j\omega) = \int_{-\infty}^{\infty} R_x(\tau) e^{-j\omega\tau}\, d\tau = \text{power spectral density of the input.}$$

Since

$$S_y(j\omega) = \int_{-\infty}^{\infty} R_y(\tau) e^{-j\omega\tau} d\tau$$

where $S_y(j\omega)$ is the power spectral density of the output, we have

$$S_y(j\omega) = \frac{1}{2\pi} \int_{-\infty}^{\infty} \Gamma(j\omega;\, j\omega') S_x(j\omega')\, d\omega' \tag{9}$$

where

$$\Gamma(j\omega;\, j\omega') = \int_{-\infty}^{\infty} R_H(j\omega';\,\tau) e^{j\omega'\tau}\, e^{-j\omega\tau}\, d\tau\,. \tag{10}$$

For passive, time-invariant networks

$$S_y(j\omega) = R_H(j\omega;\,0)\, S_x(j\omega)$$

which is the expected formula for power transmission through such networks.

One further step in rounding out an "algebra" of correlation functions is an expression for the correlation function of summed

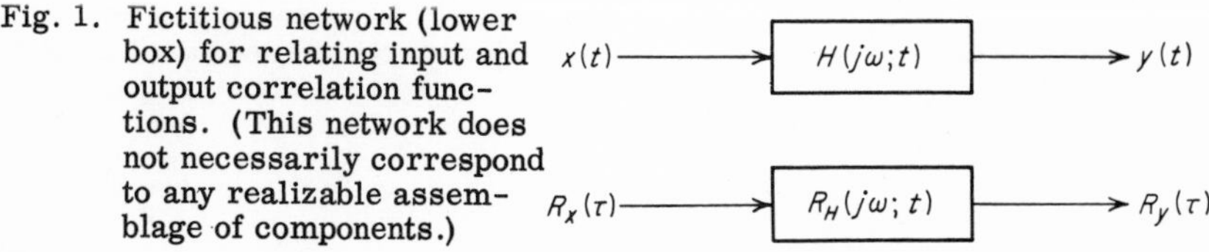

Fig. 1. Fictitious network (lower box) for relating input and output correlation functions. (This network does not necessarily correspond to any realizable assemblage of components.)

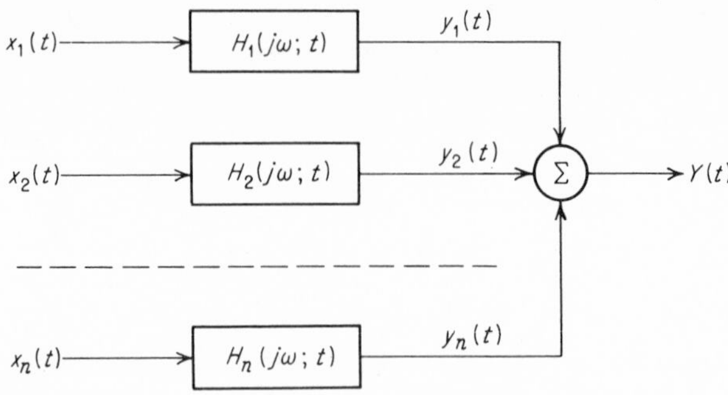

Fig. 2—Summation of *n* channel outputs.

channels.[6] With reference to Fig. 2, the correlation function for $Y(t)$ can be shown* to be

$$R_Y(\tau) = \sum_{i,k=1}^{n} R_{ik}(\tau) . \tag{11}$$

If the channel variations are much slower than the signal variations, we can show that†

$$R_{ii}(\tau) = \frac{1}{2\pi} \int_{-\infty}^{+\infty} R_{H_i}(j\omega;\tau)\, S_{x_i}(j\omega)\, e^{j\omega\tau}\, d\omega \tag{12}$$

and

$$R_{ik}(\tau) = \frac{1}{2\pi} \int_{-\infty}^{+\infty} R_{H_iH_k}(j\omega';\tau)\, S_{x_ix_k}(j\omega')\, e^{j\omega'\tau}\, d\omega' \tag{13}$$

with

$$S_{x_ix_k}(j\omega') = \int_{-\infty}^{+\infty} R_{x_ix_k}(\tau)\, e^{-j\omega'\tau}\, d\tau \tag{14}$$

and

$$R_{H_iH_k}(j\omega';\tau) = \lim_{T\to\infty} \frac{1}{2T} \int_{-T}^{+T} H_i(j\omega';t) H_k(-j\omega';t-\tau)\,dt . \tag{15}$$

*See Appendix at the end of this chapter.

†Although they hold under more general conditions, these relations are stated in the manner that is most suited to our processes here, and that is consistent with the view (see Chapter 2) that "probability" in channel measurements is a "fraction of an interval of time of observation." See Appendix at the end of this chapter.

Since the time correlation function is taken as an average over all time, and because of the conventional usage of the transform relationship, the results are applicable only to systems having stationary statistics. If the statistics are not stationary, this theory is not immediately applicable.

IV. MODELS FOR SOME SIMPLE CHANNELS

If the physics of the propagation medium is well understood, then one can, at least in principle, synthesize the channel characteristics to be expected from the physical model. It is instructive to consider some simple models for illustration even though these models have not been found to characterize realistic channels adequately under all possible conditions.

The classical model for perturbed signals received via ionospheric channels over short distances has included a directly received ground wave and a sky wave specularly reflected from an ionospheric layer. If the reflection were truly specular, then this channel might be diagrammatically represented as in Fig. 3. The output signal and its Fourier transform are given by

$$y(t) = a_1 x(t - \tau_1) + a_2 x(t - \tau_2)$$

and

$$Y(j\omega) = X(j\omega)\left[a_1 e^{-j\omega\tau_1} + a_2 e^{-j\omega\tau_2}\right] .$$

The system function for this model is therefore

$$H(j\omega) = \left[a_1 e^{-j\omega\tau_1} + a_2 e^{-j\omega\tau_2}\right] .$$

A phasor construction of $H(j\omega)$ is shown in Fig. 4. The resultant phasor in Fig. 4 operates on the transmitted signal. Zeros of transmission will occur if

$$a_1 = a_2$$

and

$$\omega\tau_1 = \omega\tau_2 + (2n + 1)\pi$$

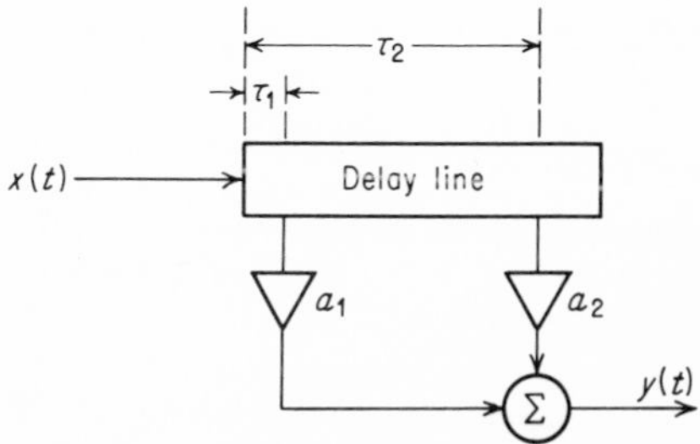

Fig. 3. Simple model of short-distance ionospheric channel.

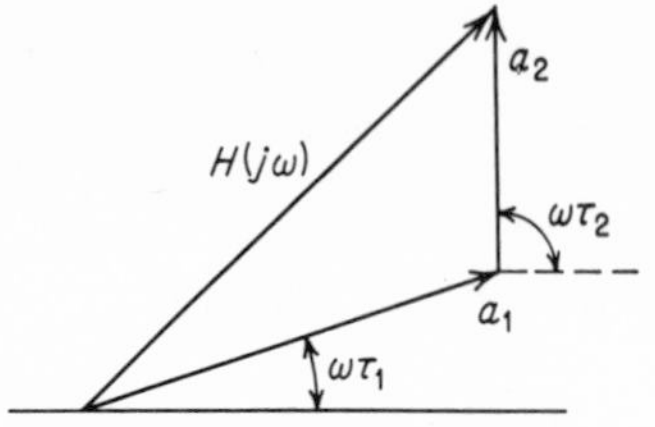

Fig. 4. Phasor diagram for simple ionospheric channel.

or

$$\omega = \frac{(2n + 1)\pi}{(\tau_1 - \tau_2)} \quad .$$

With changes in delay times and additional paths, one obtains the classical selective fading effects of the ionosphere. This model has also been useful for microwave links in which specularly reflecting objects such as calm water are illuminated. Experimental examination of ionospheric sky-wave signals and sea-reflected signals has shown that the usual reflected signals exhibit short-term variations that suggest more complex physical models.

Let us now consider a situation in which there is a direct ray and a ray reflected from a moving object (such as an aircraft in the beam of the microwave link). This is a simple example of a time-variant channel. Here

$$y(t) = a_1 x(t - \tau_1) + a_2 x(t - kt) \quad .$$

If the linear phase shift with time is treated as any other phase shift, the system function is

$$H(j\omega; t) = a_1 e^{-j\omega\tau_1} + a_2 e^{-j\omega kt} \quad .$$

A phasor representation of this is shown in Fig. 5. Note that the channel now causes phase and amplitude modulation of the signal in the presence of a specular mode of transmission. In the absence of the specular mode, or in case the specular component is of nearly the same amplitude as the component reflected from the moving object, the phase variation speeds up near phase opposition causing sharp changes in frequency.

Next, as an illustration of a channel having random elements, let us consider the case in which there is a multiplicity of scatterers each having the system function

$$H(j\omega; t) = \exp\left[j\omega(2v/v_c)t\right] \quad .$$

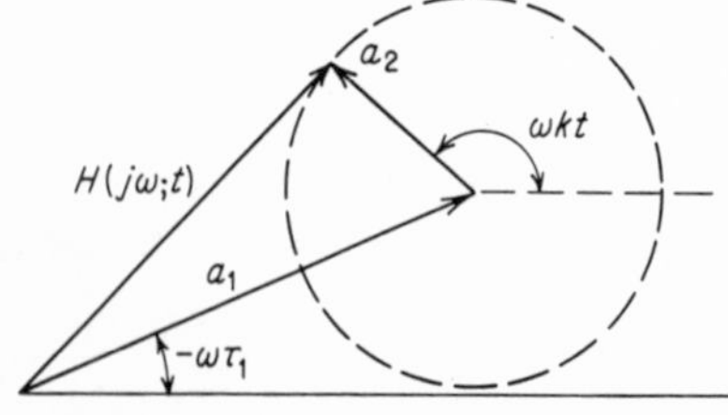

Fig. 5. Phasor diagram for channel with moving reflector.

Assume that the reflections from the scatterers are all equal and that the re-radiated components arising from multiple scattering (*e.g.*, a re-radiated wave from one scatterer impinging upon another) may be neglected. Assume further that the scatterers have a gaussian-density distribution of radial velocities

$$p(v) = \frac{1}{\sqrt{2\pi\sigma_v^2}} \exp\left[-(v - v_0)^2/2\sigma_v^2\right]$$

where

σ_v^2 = mean square radial velocity of the scatterers

and v_0 = average radial velocity of the scatterers.

If the transmission delay from each of the scatters having velocities between v and $v + dv$ is random, then the returned signal from each will be incoherently added to the rest. The returned signal will be of a frequency between

$$\omega' = \omega\left(1 + \frac{2v}{v_c}\right)$$

and

$$\omega' + d\omega' = \omega\left(1 + \frac{2v}{v_c}\right) + \frac{2\omega}{v_c}\, dv \ .$$

The amplitude at this point will be random because of the incoherent addition of the components and therefore the effective system functions can only be described in statistical terms. A suitable average over all paths, such as the average of the system correlation functions of the paths, would be desirable. Thus, if we assume that the amplitude of the returned signals in the band v and $v + dv$ is proportional to the number of scatterers in this range, the system correlation function averaged* over the radial velocities will be

$$\overline{R_H(j\omega;\ \tau)} = \lim_{T\to\infty} \frac{1}{2T} \int_{-T}^{+T} \int_{-\infty}^{+\infty} p(v) H(j\omega; t; v) H[-j\omega; (t - \tau); v]\, dv\, dt$$

$$= \frac{1}{\sqrt{2\pi\sigma_v^2}} \int_{-\infty}^{+\infty} \exp\left[-(v - v_0)^2/2\sigma_v^2\right] \exp\left[j\omega\,(2v/v_c)\,\tau\right] dv$$

$$= \exp\left[-(2\sigma_v^2/v_c^2)\,\omega^2\tau^2\right] \exp\left[j\,(2v_0/v_c)\,\omega\tau\right]$$

where we have used pair 705.1 and pair 206 in Ref. 2. The resulting expression has the form of a carrier having a gaussian-shaped envelope and a frequency of $(2v_0/v_c)\omega$ rad/sec.

From the system correlation function, the correlation function of the output can be found if one is given the correlation function of the

*In this averaging process, it is assumed that there is no contribution from scatterers of different velocities.

input. For example, for $x(t) = e^{j\omega_0 t}$ the input power spectral density is

$$S_x(j\omega) = 2\pi\,\delta(\omega - \omega_0)$$

and

$$R_y(\tau) = \frac{1}{2\pi}\int_{-\infty}^{+\infty} \overline{R_H(j\omega;\,\tau)} S_x(j\omega)\, e^{j\omega\tau}\, d\omega$$

$$= \int_{-\infty}^{+\infty} \exp\left[-(2\sigma_v^2/v_c^2)\,\omega^2\tau^2\right]\delta(\omega - \omega_0)\exp\left[j(1 + 2v_0/v_c)\omega\tau\right]d\omega$$

$$= \exp\left[-(2\sigma_v^2/v_c^2)\omega_0^2\tau^2\right]\exp\left[j\omega_0(1 + 2v_0/v_c)\tau\right] .$$

If one is interested in the power spectral density of the output, then

$$S_y(j\omega) = \int_{-\infty}^{+\infty} R_y(\tau)\, e^{-j\omega\tau}\, d\tau$$

$$= A\frac{v_c}{\sigma_v\omega_0}\ \exp\left\{-(v_c^2/8\sigma_v^2)\cdot\left[(\omega/\omega_0) - (1 + 2v_0/v_c)\right]^2\right.$$

The proportionality constant A is determined by the transmission loss in the channel. The significance of the result is that the spectral-line input is spread into a gaussian-shaped spectrum whose width is proportional to the carrier frequency ω_0 and to σ_v/v_c. This model has been proposed by Ratcliffe[7] and by Booker *et al.*[8] to explain the fading of single-hop ionospheric radio waves, with further experimental evidence from McNicol.[9] It has also been used by Rice[10] to explain fading phenomena in tropospheric scatter propagation and by Lawson and Uhlenbeck[11] to describe radar returns from chaff.

This scattering model is not very successful in explaining the behavior of real channels and caution should be exercised in applying it. Brennan and Phillips[12] have made an exhaustive study of medium-frequency ionospheric transmission and they have found that correlation functions exhibit great variability and rarely fit this model.

There is one other physical model that may lead to better representations of particular physical situations. This is a channel with a specular signal superimposed on a background of scatterers in random motion.[7,9,12] In addition, one might consider a combination of several waves that fade in some dependent fashion. For some situations it may be useful to consider time-dependent behavior such as randomly excited exponentially decaying time functions (perhaps meteor ionization trails). Much work remains to be done to formulate physical models that represent the behavior of real channels adequately.

The models that we have described thus far may be combined in a variety of ways. Moreover, the delay-line model may have a number of taps. Each of the taps may have a randomly varying gain associated with it. The modeling of doppler-shifted sources by a delay line with static taps requires an infinity of such taps with varying gains although other artifices may appear more feasible. A canonical set of models under suitable restrictions is considered in Chapter 6.

V. MULTI-TERMINAL-PAIR CHANNELS

In a number of practical situations, one seeks economical ways of either transmitting and/or receiving signals in such a way that the signal is never completely lost as a result of propagation disturbances. Ideally one would like to find transmission methods that are negatively correlated in the sense that the loss of signal in one channel is compensated by the guaranteed appearance of signal in another. This very nearly occurs in some diversity systems, for example those that utilize antennas at different elevations above the reflecting ground plane (such as the sea) in order to minimize lobing.

In diversified transmission techniques, one hopes that the fluctuations of signal in each channel are more or less uncorrelated with those in other channels and the simultaneous loss of signal will occur with low probability over a multiplicity of such channels. In order to make this probability of signal loss as low as possible, an effort is made to find many channels that are either statistically independent or negatively correlated. For this purpose it is occasionally possible to use two different polarizations on the receiving antennas, or receivers at several different angles of arrival for the electromagnetic wave front, or to place antennas in several different spatial locations or to transmit the signal over several disparate carrier frequencies. Signal-diversification techniques and methods of combining signals from a number of such channels will be discussed in the next chapter. In this section, the problems of interdependence of such multiport channels will be discussed.

Assume that a number of terminal pairs is available for different output signals $y_i(t)$ from one or more input signals $x_k(t)$. When frequency (or time) diversity is used, there is no mathematical distinction between a set of multi-terminal-pair channels, each centered on the different carriers (or different times) and a single channel whose system function encompasses all frequencies (or all times) in use. In practice, since one may use physically different receivers, the use of

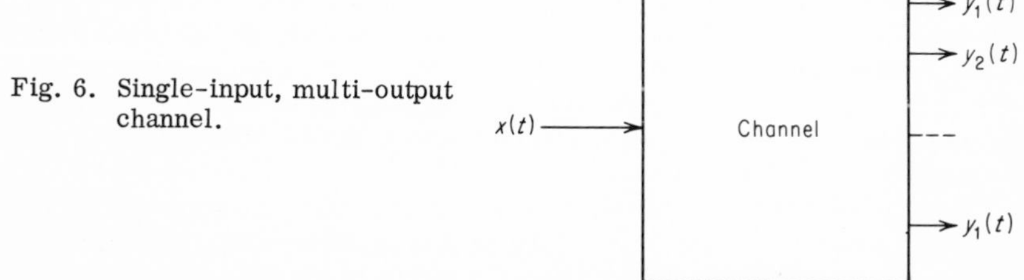

Fig. 6. Single-input, multi-output channel.

separate system functions to characterize the outputs from each receiver is useful. If space diversity is used, one may be concerned with the system function that depends upon the spatial position as a continuous variable.

The cross-correlation function between the outputs of two diversity channels when the channels are both excited by the same signal $x(t)$ is given by Eq. (13). Thus,

$$R_{kl}(\tau) = \frac{1}{2\pi} \int_{-\infty}^{+\infty} R_{H_k H_l}(j\omega'; \tau) S_x(j\omega') e^{j\omega'\tau} d\omega'$$

where, from (15),

$$R_{H_k H_l}(j\omega'; \tau) = \lim_{T \to \infty} \frac{1}{2T} \int_{-T}^{+T} H_k(j\omega'; t) H_l(-j\omega'; t-\tau) dt \ .$$

Thus the cross-channel correlation is fully determined by a complete knowledge of the system functions for each channel alone. In view of the random nature of the channels, the most that can be done to provide this knowledge in practice is to determine the joint statistical properties of the channels.

The signal diversification techniques mentioned above do not all lead to independent results. One must therefore, recognize those diversification techniques that are dependent in order to avoid trying to "squeeze juice out of an already dehydrated orange." For example, one cannot apply both frequency *and* time diversity to the same channel in any wide sense. In fact an argument might be made that complete distinction between frequency and time diversity may be wholly artificial, since the signal designer usually has a given time-bandwidth product available to him that he must exploit in conjunction with the channel characteristics.

Another pair of diversity channels that are not necessarily independent of each other are distinguished as angular diversity and space diversity channels. Consider an array of n isotropic antennas that are spaced a sufficient distance so that the mutual impedances between antennas can be ignored. If the transmission characteristics of the medium are measured between the transmitting-antenna terminals and the terminals of each of the n receiving antennas, then n channel system functions will result, each of which is associated with one of the spatially dispersed antennas. If the antenna outputs are added through a phase-shifting network the resultant array will have a receiving pattern that can be adjusted by changing the phase shifting network to exhibit preferences for a variety of different angles of arrival. The problem of combining the outputs of the array through appropriate phase shifters, in order to achieve major lobes that are directed at favorable angles of arrival would be considered a problem in angular diversity, while the problem of combining the outputs of the elements in order to obtain a resultant signal whose qualities are superior to those of the individual outputs is normally considered as the problem of space-diversity combining, yet both can lead to the same end result. The accent is on the space-diversity outlook when the phase front is a random function of space and/or time.

In order to exhibit the interrelationships between space and angle diversity more quantitatively, consider the functional relationship of the antenna excitation and the polar diagram given by[15]

$$\mathcal{E}(\beta S, t) = \int_{-\infty}^{+\infty} E_z(0, z, t)\, e^{j\beta S z}\, dz \tag{17}$$

where $\mathcal{E}(\beta S, t)$ = the polar diagram of the antenna in the Fraunhofer (or far) region,

$E_z(0, z, t)$ = the excitation of an antenna which has an aperture along $x = 0$,

β = propagation coefficient, assumed constant in the space $x > 0$,

and $S = \sin \Theta$.

This relationship is subject to the following restrictions:

1. The antenna is excited by (or is receiving) a single frequency of wavelength $\lambda = \dfrac{2\pi}{\beta}$ in the medium $x > 0$.
2. The field is assumed to be two-dimensional and is independent of y.
3. For simplicity, it is assumed that $E_y = E_x = H_z = H_x = 0$.
4. Θ is measured from the x axis in the xz plane, as illustrated in Fig. 7.

The fact that the relation in Eq. (17) is a Fourier transformation has led Booker and Clemmow[15] to interpret $\mathcal{E}(\beta S, t)$ as an "angular spectrum" of plane waves each arriving at an angle Θ with the x axis and having an amplitude and a phase given by the value of $\mathcal{E}(\beta S, t)$ taken at Θ. The time dependence of this angular spectrum is particularly pronounced in such situations as scatter. If the received signal were composed of a group of plane waves, each with the amplitude and phase given by $\mathcal{E}(\beta S, t)$ at the appropriate angle,

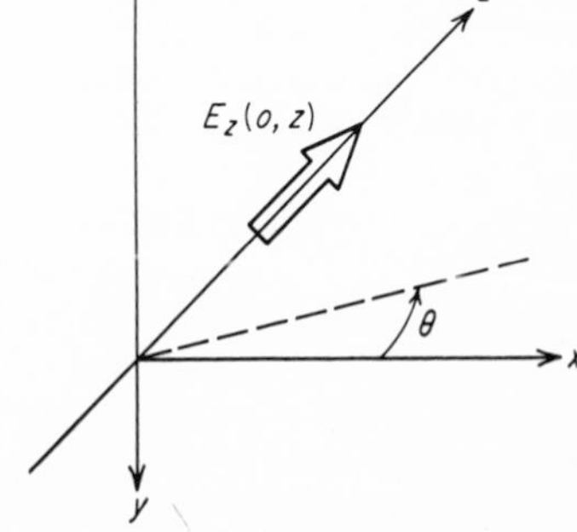

Fig. 7—Coordinate system for antenna.

then the aperture excitation would be

$$E_z(0, z, t) = \frac{1}{2\pi} \int_{-\infty}^{+\infty} \mathcal{E}(\beta S, t)\, e^{-i\beta S z}\, d(\beta S) \; .$$

For purposes of illustrating the dependence between angle correlation and space correlation, consider an antenna system that consists of two isotropic antennas placed along the z axis at $z = \pm z_1$. The voltages induced in these antenna will be

$$E_{+z_1}(t) = \frac{1}{2\pi} \int_{-\infty}^{+\infty} \mathcal{E}(\beta S, t)\, e^{-i\beta S z_1}\, d(\beta S)$$

$$E_{-z_1}(t) = \frac{1}{2\pi} \int_{-\infty}^{+\infty} \mathcal{E}(\beta S, t)\, e^{i\beta S z_1}\, d(\beta S)$$

The cross-correlation between these two voltages will be

$$R_{+z_1, -z_1}(\tau) = \lim_{T \to \infty} \frac{1}{2T} \int_{-T}^{+T} E_{+z_1}(t)\, E^{*}_{-z_1}(t - \tau)\, dt$$

$$= \frac{1}{(2\pi)^2} \int_{-\infty}^{+\infty} \int_{-\infty}^{+\infty} \lim_{T \to \infty} \frac{1}{2T} \int_{-T}^{+T} \mathcal{E}(\beta S, t)\, \mathcal{E}^{*}(\beta S', t - \tau)$$

$$\times\, e^{-i\beta(S - S')z_1}\, d(\beta S)\, d(\beta S')$$

Consider now the same pair of antennas and introduce phase shifters at the terminals of each. With appropriate phasing, the antennas can be connected to act as an interferometer with a beamwidth determined by the distance between antennas. The polar acceptance diagram of such an antenna will be limited by the large side lobes (equal in gain to the main beam), but the width of the main lobe of the antenna pattern will be comparable to that of any antenna having the same effective aperture length. Furthermore, the main lobe can be steered by choosing the correct phase shift between antennas. Assume first that the phasing gives the received signal a phase shift proportional to the distance z (*i.e.*, multiplies it by e^{-jaz}). The sum of the phased voltages will be

$$E_1(t) = \{e^{-jaz_1} + e^{jaz_1}\} \frac{1}{2\pi} \int_{-\infty}^{+\infty} \mathcal{E}(\beta S, t)\, e^{-i\beta S z_1}\, d(\beta S) \; .$$

If a second proportionality constant a' is chosen to steer the antenna beam in a different direction, Θ', the correlation between the voltages appearing at the terminals of each phase shifter will be

$$R_{\Theta\Theta'}(\tau) = \lim_{T\to\infty} \frac{1}{2T} \int_{-T}^{+T} E_1(t) E_2^*(t-\tau)\, dt$$

$$= \frac{4}{(2\pi)^2} \int_{-\infty}^{+\infty} \int_{-\infty}^{+\infty} \lim_{T\to\infty} \frac{1}{2T} \int_{-T}^{+T} \mathcal{E}(\beta S', t)\, \mathcal{E}^*(\beta S', t-\tau)\, dt$$

$$\times\, e^{-j\beta(S-S')z_1} d(\beta S)\, d(\beta S')\cos az_1 \cos a'z_1 \; .$$

If we assume that the transmission medium is uniform and compare this expression with the previous expression for the space correlation, we find that

$$R_{\Theta\Theta'}(\tau) = 4R_{+z_1,-z_1}(\tau)\cos az_1 \cos a'z_1 \; .$$

Thus *the space correlation function is directly proportional to the angular correlation function for the simple antenna system under consideration, provided the transmission medium is uniform.*

The Fourier transform relationship in Eq. (17) is identical to the time-frequency transform with the following identifications:

$t \to -z$
$f(t) \to E_z(0, z, t)$
$\omega \to \beta S$
$F(\omega) \to \mathcal{E}(\beta S, t)$

Since both the aperture excitation and polar diagram are complex, the Fourier transform is between two complex domains.

With the Fourier relationship between aperture excitation and polar diagram a number of the usual signal concepts may be applied. For example, if the pattern is of interest for small angles off the broadside (or x) axis, then

$$S = \sin\Theta \approx \Theta$$

and the transform relationship becomes

$$\mathcal{E}(\beta\Theta, t) = \int_{-\infty}^{+\infty} E_z(0, z, t)\, e^{j\beta\Theta z}\, dz \tag{18}$$

and

$$\mathcal{E}(\beta[\Theta - \Theta_0], t) = \int_{-\infty}^{+\infty} E_z(0, z, t)\, e^{j\beta(\Theta-\Theta_0)z}\, dz \; .$$

Thus, for small angles off the broadside, the Fourier shift theorem may be interpreted as a linear phase shift of value $\exp(-j\beta\Theta_0 z)$ applied to the aperture excitation causing a change in the direction of the beam pattern.

The sampling theorem for band-limited signals also has a counterpart for anglewidth-limited antenna patterns. Thus, consider an antenna pattern $\mathcal{E}(\beta S, t)$ whose amplitude is substantially limited to the angular range $\pm\Theta_1$. From the sampling theorem we might expect that this pattern could be reproduced by taking samples across the aperture at space intervals of $1/(2\beta S_1)$, where $S_1 = \sin\Theta_1$. These samples may be complex (namely, having both magnitude and nonzero phase). Accordingly, the antenna excitation $E_z(0,z,t)$ can be expressed in the form

$$E_z(0,z,t) = \sum_{n=0}^{\pm 2\beta S_1 z_1} E_z(0, n/2\beta S_1, t)\,\frac{\sin\pi(2\beta S_1 z - n)}{\pi(2\beta S_1 z - n)}$$

where it has been assumed that the contributions from samples off the aperture ($|z| > |z_1|$) may be neglected (recognizing the usual qualifications on the impossibility of functions with simultaneous limitations on aperture and angle width of polar diagram). Each of the samples must be a point sampling of the aperture excitation. The polar diagram is then

$$\mathcal{E}(\beta S, t) = \int_{-\infty}^{+\infty} \sum_{n=0}^{\pm 2\beta S_1 z_1} E_z(0, n/2\beta S_1, t)\,\frac{\sin\pi(2\beta S_1 z - n)}{\pi(2\beta S_1 z - n)}\,e^{i\beta S z}\,dz$$

$$= \sum_{n=0}^{\pm 2\beta S_1 z_1} E_z(0, n/2\beta S_1, t)\int_{-\infty}^{+\infty} \frac{\sin\pi(2\beta S_1 z - n)}{\pi(2\beta S_1 z - n)}\,e^{i\beta S z}\,dz\,. \tag{19}$$

The integral represents an angle-shifted pulse function.

Another interesting observation can be derived from the equivalent beam pattern of a linear array of discrete antennas spaced by intervals of $1/(2\beta S_1)$ whose phasing and amplitude weightings are known and whose mutual impedances are negligible. Assume that this array is used for receiving purposes. In such a case the voltage at each pair of terminals of the elements of the array may be corrupted by internal noise $N_i(t)$ where the index i is the same index as that of the antenna element. Since this noise is assumed to be generated internally (*e.g.*, by the receiver front end attached to each of the sampling antennas) the noises in the various antennas may be considered independent. The apparent polar diagram $\mathcal{E}'(\beta S, t)$ in the presence of internal noise is therefore

$$\mathcal{E}'(\beta S, t) = \sum_{n=0}^{\pm 2\beta S_1 z_1} \left[E_z(0, n/2\beta S_1, t)\int_{-\infty}^{+\infty} \frac{\sin\pi(2\beta S_1 z - n)}{\pi(2\beta S_1 z - n)}\,e^{i\beta S z}\,dz + N_n(t)\right]$$

$$= \mathcal{E}(\beta S, t) + \sum_{n=0}^{\pm 2\beta S_1 z_1} N_n(t)$$

$$= \mathcal{E}(\beta S, t) + \mathcal{E}_N(t) \tag{20}$$

The effect of the internal noise is to generate an equivalent additive noise $\mathcal{E}_N(t)$ that may be indistinguishable from an angularly independent external cosmic and galactic noise added to the desired signal $\mathcal{E}(\beta S, t)$.[16] This is another example of the close interrelationships between angular and space characterizations of antenna systems.

The concept of "angular spectrum" introduced by Booker and Clemmow in viewing $\mathcal{E}(\beta S, t)$ can be exploited in a manner that parallels the more familiar frequency-spectrum approach to time signals. Consider first the problem of extracting the maximum signal energy relative to angular-noise energy from a linear array that is excited by some angular spectrum corrupted by spectrally flat (*i.e.*, omnidirectional) angle noise. One seeks an "angle" filter analogous to the optimum frequency filter. If the "angle" spectrum of the desired signal is an impulse, that is if it comes from a single direction in space, then the optimum "angle" filter (*i.e.*, the optimum phasing of the antenna array) comes directly from the energy optimization techniques in time-frequency domain filtering.

To state it more formally, consider a point source at a great distance from an aperture along the z axis. Assume that this source is radiating a monochromatic signal of angular frequency ω_0. Since the wave incident upon the aperture will be a plane wave, the aperture excitation can be found from the angular spectrum

$$\mathcal{E}(\beta S, t) = \delta(\beta S - \beta S_1) \exp j\omega_0 t$$

and it is given by

$$E_z(0, z, t) = \frac{1}{2\pi} \int_{-\infty}^{+\infty} \delta(\beta S - \beta S_1)\, e^{j\beta S z} \cdot e^{j\omega_0 t}\, d(\beta S)$$

$$= \frac{1}{2\pi}\, e^{j\beta S_1 z} \cdot e^{j\omega_0 t}$$

If the angular spectral noise were white, then the optimum space filter (in the sense of maximizing the ratio of angular signal to angular noise) by analogy with the time-frequency domain, would be one whose response along the aperture was matched or, in this case, the complex conjugate of the angle spectrum.

In the case of a monochromatic excitation of angular frequency ω_0, $E_z(0, z, t)$ may also be recognized as being proportional to the system function of the transmission path between the source and the sample taken at $(0, z)$ along the aperture, multiplied by $\exp j\omega_0 t$.

VI. CONCLUDING REMARKS

In this chapter the channel has been characterized as a linear time-variant network with the analytical basis for including the antennas and transmission medium into a concatenation of devices that operate on the signals being transmitted. While some simple physical models have been analyzed here from this point of view, it was repeatedly emphasized that none of these models is wholly satisfactory. In general it is necessary that the characteristics of the channel be measured under the conditions of use.

Since many practical transmission channels are neither static nor deterministic, they must be characterized in some statistical fashion. The only tractable statistic that is presently known to relate input, channel, and output is the time correlation function and this has been shown to be an extension of the power transmission function of the channel. While the system correlation function suffices for gaussian channels, experimental demonstration should be used to check whether any given channel can be described by gaussian statistics.

In Chapter 6, more general canonical descriptions of the linear time-variant network will be given. Statistical characterization and analytical manipulations with this more general channel are subject to the same qualifications that we have made here. Despite these limitations, such models can suggest techniques for characterizing and dealing with many types of transmission difficulty. More work remains to be done on the methods of measurement of the system function of the channel, on the characterization of channels with non-stationary statistics, and on the statistical characterization of non-gaussian channels.

APPENDIX

by Elie J. Baghdady

Derivation of Equations (11), (12), and (13) of the Text

With reference to Fig. 2, the autocorrelation function of $Y(t)$ is

$$R_Y(\tau) = \lim_{T\to\infty} \frac{1}{2T} \int_{-T}^{T} Y(t)\, Y^*(t-\tau)\, dt$$

$$= \lim_{T\to\infty} \frac{1}{2T} \int_{-T}^{T} [y_1(t) + y_2(t) + \cdots + y_n(t)]$$

$$\times [y_1^*(t-\tau) + \cdots + y_n^*(t-\tau)]\, dt$$

$$= \sum_{i,k=1}^{n} R_{ik}(\tau) \tag{A1}$$

where

$$R_{ik}(\tau) = \lim_{T\to\infty} \frac{1}{2T} \int_{-T}^{T} y_i(t)\, y_k^*(t-\tau)\, dt, \quad i,k = 1, 2, \ldots, n\,. \tag{A2}$$

In order to derive expressions (12) and (13) of the text, we first note from Eq. (4) that

$$y_i(t) = \frac{1}{2\pi} \int_{-\infty}^{+\infty} H_i(j\omega; t) X_i(j\omega)\, e^{j\omega t}\, d\omega$$

and

$$y_k^*(t-\tau) = \frac{1}{2\pi} \int_{-\infty}^{+\infty} H_k(-j\omega'; t-\tau)\, X_k(-j\omega')\, e^{-j\omega'(t-\tau)}\, d\omega'$$

$$y_i(t)\, y_k^*(t-\tau) = \frac{1}{4\pi^2} \int_{-\infty}^{+\infty} \int_{-\infty}^{+\infty} H_i(j\omega; t) H_k(-j\omega'; t-\tau) X_i(j\omega) \times X_k(-j\omega')\, e^{j[(\omega-\omega')t+\omega'\tau]}\, d\omega\, d\omega'$$

Therefore

$$R_{ik}(\tau) = \frac{1}{2\pi} \int_{-\infty}^{\infty} \frac{1}{2\pi} \int_{-\infty}^{\infty} \left[\lim_{T\to\infty} \frac{1}{2T} \int_{-T}^{T} H_i(j\omega; t) \times H_k(-j\omega'; t-\tau)\, e^{j(\omega-\omega')t}\, dt \right] \times X_i(j\omega) X_k(-j\omega')\, d\omega\, d\omega' \tag{A3}$$

We now draw a distinction between the time variations of the input signals and the time variations of the channel system functions, and assume that the channel properties fluctuate much more slowly than the signal. In this way, the time average in (A3) may be carried out in two stages: first, we average with respect to the signal over an interval whose duration is considered to become essentially infinite on the time scale of the signal when this interval becomes long enough to encompass a typical behavior pattern of the signal. But during this interval, the channel system functions do not change noticeably, according to our assumption regarding relative rates of channel and signal variations. Only the relatively slow channel fluctuations therefore remain after this first averaging process. Second, the result of the first averaging process is averaged with respect to the channel fluctuations, the averaging interval now being chosen to be sufficiently long to encompass a typical behavior pattern of the channel. This second averaging interval is clearly much longer than the first. According to this reasoning, we may write

$$\lim_{T\to\infty} \frac{1}{2T} \int_{-T}^{T} H_i(j\omega; t)\, H_k(-j\omega'; t-\tau)\, e^{j(\omega-\omega')t}\, dt =$$

$$= \left[\lim_{T \to \infty} \frac{1}{2T} \int_{-T}^{T} H_i(j\omega;\, t)\, H_k(-j\omega';\, t-\tau) dt \right]$$

$$\times \left[\lim_{T \to \infty} \frac{1}{2T} \int_{-T}^{T} e^{j(\omega-\omega')t} dt \right] .$$

The second factor in brackets is the unit impulse $\delta(\omega - \omega_0)$. Substitution into (A3) leads to

$$R_{ik}(\tau) = \frac{1}{2\pi} \int_{-\infty}^{\infty} \frac{1}{2\pi} \int_{-\infty}^{\infty} \left\{ \lim_{T \to \infty} \frac{1}{2T} \int_{-T}^{T} H_i(j\omega;\, t) H_k(-j\omega';\, t-\tau)\, dt \right\}$$

$$\times X_i(j\omega) X_k(-j\omega')\, \delta(\omega - \omega')\, d\omega\, d\omega' .$$

Integration with respect to ω leads to

$$R_{ik}(\tau) = \frac{1}{2\pi} \int_{-\infty}^{\infty} \left\{ \lim_{T \to \infty} \frac{1}{2T} \int_{-T}^{T} H_i(j\omega';\, t) H_k(-j\omega';\, t-\tau)\, dt \right\}$$

$$\times \left[\frac{1}{2\pi} X_i(j\omega') X_k(-j\omega') \right] d\omega' . \tag{A4}$$

The factor in braces is defined as being $R_{H_iH_k}(j\omega';\, \tau)$ in Eq. (15) of the text. The factor in brackets can be shown to be the cross-spectral density $S_{x_ix_k}(j\omega')$ as follows. First, note that

$$R_{x_ix_k}(\tau) = \lim_{T \to \infty} \frac{1}{2T} \int_{-T}^{T} x_i(t) x_k^*(t-\tau)\, dt$$

$$= \lim_{T \to \infty} \frac{1}{2T} \int_{-T}^{T} \frac{1}{2\pi} \int_{-\infty}^{\infty} \frac{1}{2\pi} \int_{-\infty}^{\infty} X_i(j\omega)\, e^{j\omega t}$$

$$\times X_k(-j\omega')\, e^{-j\omega'(t-\tau)}\, d\omega\, d\omega'\, dt$$

$$= \frac{1}{2\pi} \int_{-\infty}^{\infty} \left\{ \frac{1}{2\pi} \int_{-\infty}^{\infty} X_i(j\omega) X_k(-j\omega') \right.$$

$$\left. \times \left[\lim_{T \to \infty} \frac{1}{2T} \int_{-T}^{T} e^{j(\omega-\omega')t}\, dt \right] d\omega \right\} e^{j\omega'\tau}\, d\omega'$$

$$= \frac{1}{2\pi} \int_{-\infty}^{\infty} \left\{ \frac{1}{2\pi} X_i(j\omega') X_k(-j\omega') \right\} e^{j\omega'\tau}\, d\omega' .$$

Therefore

$$S_{x_i x_k}(j\omega') = \int_{-\infty}^{\infty} R_{x_i x_k}(\tau)\, e^{-j\omega'\tau} d\tau$$

$$= \frac{1}{2\pi} X_i(j\omega') X_k(-j\omega') \ . \tag{A5}$$

Finally, substitution from (15) and (A5) into (A4) yields

$$R_{ik}(\tau) = \frac{1}{2\pi} \int_{-\infty}^{\infty} R_{H_i H_k}(j\omega'; \tau) S_{x_i x_k}(j\omega')\, d\omega'$$

which is Eq. (13). A similar argument holds for Eq. (12).

The argument we have presented to derive the preceding formulas is one that is most suited to our processes here, and that is consistent with the view (see Chapter 2) that "probability" in channel measurements is a "fraction of an interval of time of observation." But the theorem embodied in these results can be made more general by removing the stated restriction on the relative rates of channel and signal variations. If the argument is carried out entirely in terms of *ensemble* averages then the signal and the channel are assumed to belong to statistically stationary and independent ergodic random processes.

REFERENCES

1. L. A. Zadeh, "Frequency Analysis of Variable Networks," *Proc. IRE,* vol. 38, pp. 291-299, March, 1950.
2. G. A. Campbell and R. M. Foster, *Fourier Integrals for Practical Applications,* D. Van Nostrand Company, Inc., Princeton, N.J., 1947, pair 207.
3. W. B. Davenport, Jr., and W. L. Root, *Introduction to Random Signals and Noise,* Lincoln Laboratory Publications, McGraw-Hill Book Company, Inc., New York, 1958, p. 190.
4. L. A. Zadeh, "Correlation Functions and Power Spectra in Variable Networks," *Proc. IRE,* vol. 38, pp. 1342-1345, November, 1950.
5. L. A. Zadeh, "Correlation Functions and Spectra of Phase and Delay-Modulated Signals," *Proc. IRE,* vol. 39, p. 425, April, 1951.
6. Davenport and Root, p. 109.
7. J. A. Ratcliffe, "Diffraction from the Ionosphere and the Fading of Radio Waves," *Nature,* vol. 162, pp. 9-11, July 3, 1948.
8. H. G. Booker, J. A. Ratcliffe and D. H. Shinn, "Diffraction from an Irregular Screen with Applications to Ionospheric Problems," *Phil. Trans. Roy. Soc. (London),* Ser. A, vol. 462, no. 856, p. 579, September, 1950.

9. R. W. E. McNicol, "The Fading of Radio Waves at Medium and High Frequencies," *Proc. Inst. Elec. Engrs. (London),* Pt. III, vol. 96, no. 44, p. 517, October, 1949.
10. S. O. Rice, "Statistical Fluctuations of Radio Field Strengths for Beyond the Horizon," *Proc. IRE,* vol. 41, pp. 274-281, February, 1953.
11. J. L. Lawson and G. E. Uhlenbeck, *Threshold Signals,* Radiation Laboratory Series, vol. 24, McGraw-Hill Book Company, Inc., New York, 1950, p. 125 et seq.
12. D. G. Brennan and M. L. Phillips, "Phase and Amplitude Variability in Medium Frequency Ionospheric Transmission," Technical Report No. 93 (ASTIA No. 110016), Lincoln Laboratory, Massachusetts Institute of Technology, September 16, 1957.
13. Davenport and Root, p. 158 et seq.
14. R. Price, "Statistical Theory Applied to Communication Through Multipath Disturbances," Research Laboratory of Electronics, Massachusetts Institute of Technology, Report No. 266 (Lincoln Laboratory Report No. 34), p. 21, September 3, 1953.
15. H. G. Booker and P. C. Clemmow, "The Concept of an Angular Spectrum of Plane Waves and its Relation to that of Polar Diagram and Aperture Distribution," Institute of Electrical Engineers, Radio Section Paper No. 922, 621.396.11, 1.11.
16. R. Manasse, "An Analysis of Angular Accuracies from Radar Measurements," Group Report 32-24, Lincoln Laboratory, Massachusetts Institute of Technology, Dec. 6, 1955; and E. R. Hiller, Jr., "Available Source Information from Receiving Apertures," Technical Report No. 3, Research Laboratory of Electronics, Massachusetts Institute of Technology, United States Navy Bureau of Ordnance, (NOrd 14632) and Massachusetts Institute of Technology Lincoln Laboratory (DDL-B-157), Sept. 1, 1956.

CHAPTER 6

Channel Characterization: Time-Variant Dispersive Channels

Thomas Kailath

I. INTRODUCTION

The chief obstacles to obtaining reliable signal transmission through the ionosphere are atmospheric noise and time-variant multipath propagation. The characteristics of atmospheric noise, which is largely caused by lightning discharges, have been extensively studied.[1,2,3] The main defense against it is sufficiently large signal power. Atmospheric noise is an additive disturbance and therefore, in a sense, is extrinsic to the actual physical communication medium. On the other hand, multipath disturbances—manifested most commonly as selective fading, frequency distortion, and intersymbol interference—directly involve the channel itself. Multipath problems are the result of dispersive propagation by paths of different electrical (and/or physical) lengths.

We can regard the channel as a time-variant filter with additive noise superimposed on the output. In these general terms, of course, little of a specific nature can be said about the problem. But in communication systems there are certain additional constraints present: Signals are of finite time-bandwidth product, the channel is nearly linear, and so forth. Introducing these constraints into the problem should enable us to obtain restricted, but simpler, models for the filter—models that are more useful for our purposes. These models will imitate the operation of the filter under the imposed constraints but may not bear any physical resemblance to the original filter and may not imitate the filter under other operating conditions. This chapter is devoted to methods of obtaining such models under the constraints of linearity and limited bandwidth or limited duration of channel memory. Some properties and methods of description and analysis of such models are also studied.

II. CHARACTERIZATION OF LINEAR TIME-VARIANT NETWORKS

A time-variant network is one whose input-output relationship is not invariant under translations in time. If, in addition, the superposition principle holds for the network, we have a linear time-variant network. In communications engineering linear time-variant

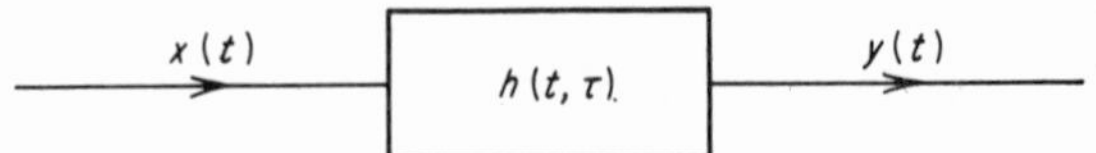

Fig. 1. Linear time-variant network.

networks have long been in use, especially as modulators and oscillators. Such systems, which usually contain only a single variable element, have been widely investigated, chiefly by mathematicians, and several theories and methods of solution[4,5]—Floquet theory, Mathieu functions, the WKB method, for examples—have been developed, although these are not yet in the most suitable form for engineering application. In present-day communication theory, however, interest has shifted to time-variant systems of a more general nature, the behavior of which is governed by linear, and not necessarily differential, operators. The most commonly used methods of characterizing such linear time-variant networks are the impulse response of the network and the corresponding time-variant system function introduced by Zadeh.[6]

2.1 The Impulse Response and the System Function

The impulse response of a linear time-variant network (Fig. 1) is defined as $h_1(t, \tau)$, the output measured at time t in response to a unit impulse applied at time τ. For a physically realizable network, $h_1(t, \tau)$ is zero for $t < \tau$.

Since the input $x(t)$ can be regarded as being composed of weighted impulses,

$$x(t) = \int_{-\infty}^{t} x(\tau)\,\delta\,(t - \tau)\,d\tau \ , \tag{1}$$

we can write, by virtue of linearity,

$$y(t) = \int_{-\infty}^{t} x(\tau) h_1(t, \tau)\,d\tau \tag{2}$$

which, for a realizable network, can also be written

$$y(t) = \int_{-\infty}^{\infty} x(\tau) h_1(t, \tau)\,d\tau \tag{3}$$

because $h_1(t, \tau) = 0$ for $t < \tau$.

The system function is defined[6] by the relation

$$H_1(j\nu, t) = \int_{-\infty}^{\infty} h_1(t, \tau)\, e^{-j2\pi\nu(t-\tau)}\, d\tau \tag{4}$$

where ν is the frequency in cps. Using Eq. (3) we can write this as

$$H_1(j\nu, t) = \frac{\text{response of the network to } \exp(j\,2\pi\nu t)}{\exp(j\,2\pi\nu t)} \,. \tag{5}$$

By virtue of linearity, it is then easily deduced that

$$y(t) = \int_{-\infty}^{\infty} H_1(j\nu, t) X(j\nu)\, e^{j2\pi\nu t}\, d\nu \,. \tag{6}$$

Zadeh[6] further defines a bifrequency function

$$\Gamma(j\nu, j\mu) = \int_{-\infty}^{\infty}\int_{-\infty}^{\infty} h_1(t, \tau)\, e^{j2\pi\nu\tau}\, e^{-j2\pi\mu t}\, d\tau dt \,. \tag{7}$$

For later comparisons, it is convenient to introduce

$$\mathcal{H}_1(j\nu, j\mu) = \int_{-\infty}^{\infty} H_1(j\nu, t)\, e^{-j2\pi\mu t}\, dt \tag{8}$$

so that (as is easily verified)

$$\Gamma(j\nu, j\mu) = \mathcal{H}_1[j\nu, j(\mu - \nu)] \,. \tag{9}$$

In a time-invariant network, $h_1(t, \tau)$ would be a function of $(t - \tau)$ only, and not of t or τ separately, and $H_1(j\nu, t)$ would be independent of t. We shall note later on that in the time-variant case, it is reasonable to regard the frequency variable μ as corresponding to the rate of change of the system characteristics and to associate ν with frequencies in the network excitation.

2.2 Other Forms for the Impulse Response and Frequency Functions

In the function $h_1(t, \tau)$ the realizability condition is that the response be identically zero for $t < \tau$. This constraint involves both t and τ, and therefore is often inconvenient to use. In the alternate forms of impulse response now to be described, the realizability condition involves only one variable. Furthermore, in section III, we shall have to impose frequency and time restrictions on the impulse response and the frequency functions, and this is not conveniently done with $h_1(t, \tau)$ in all cases. Thus, for example, if we have a restriction on the output frequency range of the linear time-variant network or on the duration of the impulse response of the network, it is not immediately clear how these are reflected in $h_1(t, \tau)$. The forms that we shall introduce will turn out to be more convenient for such restrictions. Another feature is that these forms will exhibit direct Fourier transform relationships between the frequency and impulse response functions.

We define

$h_2(z, \tau)$ = response measured at time $t = \tau + z$ to a unit impulse applied at time τ.

$h_3(y, t)$ = response measured at time t to a unit impulse applied at time $t - y$.

The distinction between $h_2(z, \tau)$ and $h_3(y, t)$ is in reality one of a "frame of mind" that is set by the choice of time reference. Thus, the notation of $h_2(z, \tau)$ can be said to emphasize the "impulse *response*" character of the quantity described, z measuring "elapsed time" since the application of the impulse. The $h_3(y, t)$ notation emphasizes the "*weighting* function" character, y measuring the "antiquity" or "age" of the input. The realizability conditions are zero response for $z < 0$ and $y < 0$, respectively.

Of course, $h_1(t, \tau)$, $h_2(z, \tau)$, and $h_3(y, t)$ must all be related. The rules governing transformation from one form to another are given in subsection 2.3. They are derived from the relations $z = t - \tau = y$ between the time-domain variables z, t, τ, and y.

2.2A The Form $h_2(z, \tau)$

In terms of $h_2(z, \tau)$, the operation of the linear time-variant network can be conveniently pictured as in Fig. 2, which displays on a (z, τ) plane several network responses to impulse inputs at different times, T. Notice, again, that the variable z in $h_2(z, \tau)$ refers to the time elapsed since the application of the input time function. If we had a fixed network, the response to a unit impulse at time T_1 would be the same as the response to a unit impulse at time T_2. In terms of Fig. 2, then, it would appear that the variation of $h_2(z, \tau)$ with τ, for fixed z, would be a measure of the rate of variation of the system. We could find the Fourier transform of $h_2(z, \tau)$ with respect to τ for fixed z,

$$H_2(z, j\mu) = \int_{-\infty}^{\infty} h_2(z, \tau)\, e^{-j2\pi\mu\tau}\, d\tau \tag{10}$$

and the variable μ would be a frequency-domain measure of the variation of the system. If μ were confined to low values, the system would be varying slowly; it would be varying rapidly if there were high frequencies in the μ domain. We shall see later (in subsection 2.4A) that this interpretation of μ is consistent with the one

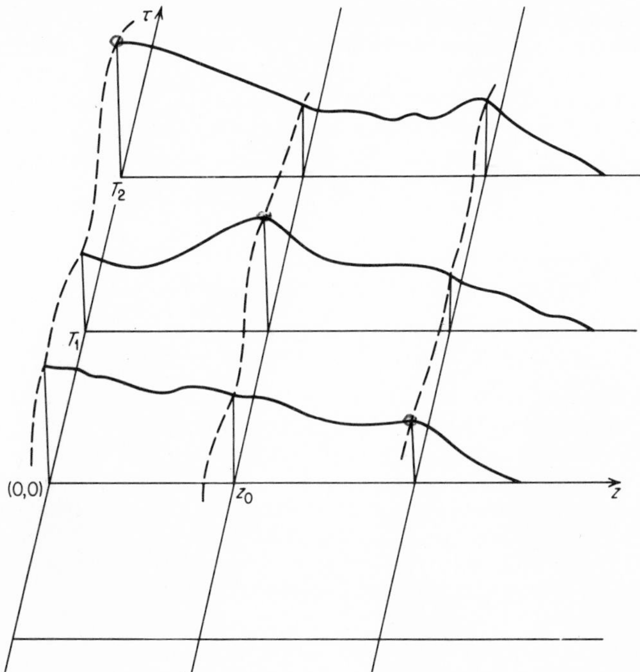

Fig. 2. The impulse response $h_2(z, \tau)$.

previously given in the case of $\mathcal{H}_1(j\nu, j\mu)$ and also with other interpretations of system variation that we shall obtain. Therefore the variable μ here has the same significance that it had in $\mathcal{H}_1(j\nu, j\mu)$.

We may also define Fourier transforms with respect to z, keeping τ fixed:

$$H_2(j\eta, \tau) = \int_{-\infty}^{\infty} h_2(z, \tau)\, e^{-j2\pi\eta z}\, dz \tag{11}$$

and

$$\mathcal{H}_2(j\eta, j\mu) = \int_{-\infty}^{\infty} H_2(j\eta, \tau)\, e^{-j2\pi\mu\tau}\, d\tau \tag{12}$$

$$= \int_{-\infty}^{\infty} H_2(z, j\mu)\, e^{-j2\pi\eta z}\, dz \tag{13}$$

$$= \int_{-\infty}^{\infty} \int_{-\infty}^{\infty} h_2(z, \tau)\, e^{-j2\pi\eta z}\, e^{-j2\pi\mu\tau}\, dz\, d\tau \,. \tag{14}$$

We shall show later that the variable η can be associated with the frequencies in the output waveform.

2.2B The Form $h_3(y, t)$

Similarly, for $h_3(y, t)$ we obtain by direct Fourier transformation the set of functions

$$H_3(j\nu, t) = \int_{-\infty}^{\infty} h_3(y, t)\, e^{-j2\pi\nu y} dy \tag{15}$$

$$H_3(y, j\mu) = \int_{-\infty}^{\infty} h_3(y, t)\, e^{-j2\pi\mu t} dt \tag{16}$$

$$\mathcal{H}_3(j\nu, j\mu) = \int_{-\infty}^{\infty} H_3(j\nu, t)\, e^{-j2\pi\mu t} dt \tag{17}$$

$$= \int_{-\infty}^{\infty} H_3(y, j\mu)\, e^{-j2\pi\nu y}\, dy \tag{18}$$

$$= \int_{-\infty}^{\infty} \int_{-\infty}^{\infty} h_3(y, t)\, e^{-j2\pi\nu y}\, e^{-j2\pi\mu t}\, dy\, dt \tag{19}$$

The last two functions are exactly equivalent to $H_1(j\nu, t)$ and $\mathcal{H}_1(j\nu, j\mu)$. This is because, using Eq. (3), we can write

$$H_3(j\nu, t) = \frac{\text{response of network to } \exp\,(j2\pi\nu t)}{\exp\,(j2\pi\nu t)}$$

$$= H_1(j\nu, t)$$

and therefore, by virtue of Eqs. (8) and (17),

$$\mathcal{H}_3(j\nu, j\mu) = \mathcal{H}_1(j\nu, j\mu) \,.$$

Thus the frequency variables for $h_3(y, t)$ have the same significance as those for $h_1(t, \tau)$, and, therefore, we have used the same symbols, ν and μ, in both cases. However, note that $H_3(j\nu, t)$ and $h_3(y, t)$ are related directly by a Fourier transform, which is not true of $H_1(j\nu, t)$ and $h_1(t, \tau)$. [Cf. Eq. (4)].

Finally, the form of the input-output relation

$$y(t) = \int_0^\infty h_3(y, t)\, x(t - y)\, dy$$

suggests that $h_3(y, t)$ can be interpreted as a weighting function by which the signal inputs in the past must be multiplied to determine their contributions to the present output. The realizability condition, $h_3(y, t) = 0$ for $y < 0$, thus reflects the fact that the filter cannot weight portions of the input that have yet to occur.

2.3 Summary of Relations Involving the Different Forms of Impulse Response and Frequency Functions

For convenience, we now list the relationships between the various forms of impulse and frequency response that we have introduced and also give the convolution integral formulas connecting the input and output functions.

a. Transformations between $h_1(t, \tau)$, $h_2(z, \tau)$, $h_3(y, t)$. The relations among the various representations of the impulse response follow from $z = t - \tau = y$. Thus, let us consider a unit impulse input to the network at time τ. The response of the network after z seconds is identically the same as the response at time $z + \tau$. Therefore,

$$h_2(z, \tau) = h_1(z + \tau, \tau)$$

Similarly, we have

$$h_1(t, \tau) = h_2(t - \tau, \tau) \tag{20}$$

$$\left.\begin{aligned} h_2(z, \tau) &= h_3(z, z + \tau) \\ h_3(y, t) &= h_2(y, t - y) \end{aligned}\right\} \tag{21}$$

$$\left.\begin{aligned} h_3(y, t) &= h_1(t, t - y) \\ h_1(t, \tau) &= h_3(t - \tau, t) \end{aligned}\right\} \tag{22}$$

It is helpful to point out that in all functions (h, H, $\mathcal{H}$) with subscripts 2 and 3, the independent variables are arranged so that what follows the comma is always associated with system variations and what precedes it is related to output quantities (for 2) or input quantities (for 3). For example, in $h_3(z, z + \tau)$, if z is held constant, h_3 as a function of τ reflects the system variations, just as $h_2(z, \tau)$ does for constant z (see Fig. 2).

b. Input-output relations—time domain. Starting from Eq. (2), let $\tau' = t - \tau$, $d\tau' = d\tau$, and later drop the prime on τ, to obtain

$$y(t) = \int_{-\infty}^{t} h_1(t, \tau)\, x(\tau)\, d\tau = \int_0^\infty h_1(t, t - \tau)\, x(t - \tau)\, d\tau \tag{23}$$

In a similar way, we can show that

$$y(t) = \int_{-\infty}^{t} h_2(t - z, z)\, x(z)\, dz = \int_{0}^{\infty} h_2(z, t - z)\, x(t - z)\, dz \tag{24}$$

$$= \int_{-\infty}^{t} h_3(t - y, t)\, x(y)\, dy = \int_{0}^{\infty} h_3(y, t)\, x(t - y)\, dy \tag{25}$$

c. **Transformation between** $\mathcal{H}_1(j\nu, j\mu)$, $\mathcal{H}_2(j\eta, j\mu)$, $\mathcal{H}_3(j\nu, j\mu)$

We have

$$\mathcal{H}_1(j\nu, j\mu) = \int_{-\infty}^{\infty}\int_{-\infty}^{\infty} h_1(t, \tau)\, e^{-j2\pi\nu(t-\tau)}\, e^{-j2\pi\mu t}\, d\tau\, dt$$

$$= \int_{-\infty}^{\infty}\int_{-\infty}^{\infty} h_2(t - \tau, \tau)\, e^{j2\pi\nu\tau}\, e^{-j2\pi(\nu+\mu)t}\, d\tau\, dt$$

Let $t - \tau = z$; then $dt = dz$, and

$$\mathcal{H}_1(j\nu, j\mu) = \int_{-\infty}^{\infty}\int_{-\infty}^{\infty} h_2(z, \tau)\, e^{-j2\pi\nu z}\, e^{-j2\pi\mu z} e^{-j2\pi\mu\tau}\, d\tau\, dz$$

$$= \mathcal{H}_2[j(\nu + \mu), j\mu] \tag{26}$$

$$= \mathcal{H}_3(j\nu, j\mu)$$

Simple rearrangements of the preceding relations lead to

$$\mathcal{H}_2(j\eta, j\mu) = \mathcal{H}_3[j(\eta - \mu), j\mu] = \mathcal{H}_1[j(\eta - \mu), j\mu] \tag{27}$$

$$\mathcal{H}_3(j\nu, j\mu) = \mathcal{H}_1(j\nu, j\mu) = \mathcal{H}_2[j(\nu + \mu), j\mu] \tag{28}$$

d. **Input-output relations—frequency domain**

We have

$$y(t) = \int_{-\infty}^{\infty} h_1(t, \tau) x(\tau)\, d\tau$$

$$= \int_{-\infty}^{\infty}\int_{-\infty}^{\infty} h_1(t, \tau)\, e^{j2\pi\nu\tau}\, X(j\nu)\, d\nu\, d\tau$$

$$= \int_{-\infty}^{\infty} H_1(j\nu, t)\, e^{j2\pi\nu t}\, X(j\nu)\, d\nu$$

Therefore

$$Y(j\mu) = \int_{-\infty}^{\infty} \int_{-\infty}^{\infty} H_1(j\nu, t)\, X(j\nu)\, e^{j2\pi\nu t}\, e^{-j2\pi\mu t}\, d\nu\, dt$$

$$= \int_{-\infty}^{\infty} \mathcal{H}_1[j\nu, j(\mu - \nu)]\, X(j\nu)\, d\nu \tag{29}$$

From Eqs. (26), (27), and (28), it follows that

$$Y(j\mu) = \int_{-\infty}^{\infty} \mathcal{H}_2[j\mu, j(\mu - \eta)]\, X(j\eta)\, d\eta \tag{30}$$

$$= \int_{-\infty}^{\infty} \mathcal{H}_3[j\nu, j(\mu - \nu)]\, X(j\nu)\, d\nu \tag{31}$$

e. Interpretations of the variables: definitions of variables and their physical significance

Time Domain

- t: variable corresponding to instant of observation of response
- τ: variable corresponding to instant of application of impulse excitation
- z: variable corresponding to elapsed time since application of input
- y: variable corresponding to age of input

Frequency Domain

- μ: variable corresponding to system variation
- ν: variable corresponding to input frequencies
- η: variable corresponding to output frequencies

Throughout this chapter, μ, ν, and η are understood to be in cycles per second.

2.4 Bandwidth Relations in Linear Time-Variant Networks

When we study the frequency behavior of linear time-variant networks the time-variant character of the network is usually evidenced by a frequency spread, or a frequency shift, or both. Thus if we put in a sine wave of frequency ν_0, the output is usually a band of frequencies centered about ν_0, or a single sine wave of a different value, or a band of frequencies centered about a frequency ν that is different from ν_0.

In the first case we can use the frequency spread as a measure of the rate of variation of the system; a small spread indicates a relatively slow variation, and a large spread a rapid variation. The amount of spread produced may depend on the particular frequency of the input excitation. Therefore we shall pick the largest spread, for all possible input frequencies, as a measure of the system variation. We shall denote this by W_s and call it the filter (system or network) bandwidth. This first case is often encountered in scatter-multipath situations.

The second case usually arises in amplitude modulation or in doppler radar. Thus, for example, in doppler radar, a sine wave of frequency ν_0 has a new frequency, after reflection from a body moving away from it at v meters per second, of $[(c+v)/(c-v)]\,\nu_0$ cps where c is the velocity of propagation in the medium. In such cases the amount of frequency shift, $\Delta\nu$, can be regarded as a measure of the time-variation of the system. When both frequency shift and frequency spreading are present, neither W_s nor $\Delta\nu$ by itself will be, in general, an adequate measure of the system variation. It would be more appropriate to consider some combination of W_s and $\Delta\nu$ as a proper measure, but the nature of the combination would depend on the particular situation considered. In this chapter, we shall be concerned only with situations of the first type—simple frequency spreading.

2.4A The Filter Variation and the Variable μ

We pointed out earlier that it seemed reasonable to associate the variable μ with the variation of the system. We shall now show that this interpretation is consistent with the notion of filter bandwidth.

Using Eqs. (29), (30), and (31), we see that if $x(t)$ is a sinusoid of frequency ν_0—that is, if $x(t) = \exp(j2\pi\nu_0 t)$ and $X(j\nu) = \delta(\nu - \nu_0)$, then the output is given by

$$Y(j\mu) = \mathcal{H}_1[j\nu_0, j(\mu - \nu_0)] \tag{32}$$

$$= \mathcal{H}_2[j\mu, j(\mu - \nu_0)] \tag{33}$$

$$= \mathcal{H}_3[j\nu_0, j(\mu - \nu_0)] \tag{34}$$

Therefore $Y(j\mu)$ is nonzero for the range W_s of μ-values over which $\mathcal{H}_1(j\nu, j\mu)$, $\mathcal{H}_2(j\eta, j\mu)$, $\mathcal{H}_3(j\nu, j\mu)$ are nonzero, and therefore the maximum μ-bandwidth of $\mathcal{H}_1(j\nu, j\mu)$, $\mathcal{H}_2(j\eta, j\mu)$, $\mathcal{H}_3(j\nu, j\mu)$ is defined by W_s for all ν. Therefore if filter bandwidths W_s—that is, measures of the rate of variation of the system—are specified, the appropriate frequency variable to consider is μ. Note, also, from relations (32) and (34) and the convolution formulas (29) and (31), that an input of bandwidth W_i to a linear time-variant network of filter variation bandwidth W_s results in an output of bandwidth greater than or equal to W_i but not greater than $W_i + W_s$.

2.4B Input Bandwidth and the Variable ν

We have found that

$$\mathcal{H}_1(j\nu, t) = \mathcal{H}_3(j\nu, t) = \frac{\text{response of linear time-variant network to } \exp(j2\pi\nu t)}{\exp(j2\pi\nu t)}$$

Therefore, if we are interested in determining the response of the linear time-variant network to an input whose spectrum is nonzero only over particular frequency ranges, we need only consider $\mathcal{H}_1(j\nu, j\mu)$ and $\mathcal{H}_3(j\nu, j\mu)$ for values of ν in these ranges. Thus, if input bandwidth restrictions are specified, the appropriate frequency variable to consider is ν.

2.4C Output Bandwidth and the Variable η

We know that if we have an input, bandlimited to $(-W_i, W_i)$, to a linear time-variant network with filter-variation bandwidth $2W_s$, the bandwidth of the output signal is restricted to $(-W_s - W_i,\ W_s + W_i)$. Thus if we examine the arrangement of variables in

$$\mathcal{H}_1(j\nu, j\mu) = \mathcal{H}_2[j(\nu + \mu), j\mu]$$

$$\mathcal{H}_2(j\eta, j\mu) = \mathcal{H}_1[j(\eta - \mu), j\mu]$$

we notice that in the first equation we have

$$\mathcal{H}_1\left[\begin{pmatrix}\text{input}\\ \text{frequencies}\end{pmatrix}, \begin{pmatrix}\text{system}\\ \text{frequencies}\end{pmatrix}\right]$$

$$= \mathcal{H}_2\left[\underbrace{\begin{pmatrix}\text{input}\\ \text{frequencies}\end{pmatrix} + \begin{pmatrix}\text{system}\\ \text{frequencies}\end{pmatrix}}_{\text{output frequencies}}, \begin{pmatrix}\text{system}\\ \text{frequencies}\end{pmatrix}\right]$$

and in the second

$$\mathcal{H}_2\left[\begin{pmatrix}\text{output}\\ \text{frequencies}\end{pmatrix}, \begin{pmatrix}\text{system}\\ \text{frequencies}\end{pmatrix}\right]$$

$$= \mathcal{H}_1\left[\underbrace{\begin{pmatrix}\text{output}\\ \text{frequencies}\end{pmatrix} - \begin{pmatrix}\text{system}\\ \text{frequencies}\end{pmatrix}}_{\text{input frequencies}}, \begin{pmatrix}\text{system}\\ \text{frequencies}\end{pmatrix}\right]$$

Thus it seems reasonable to associate the bandwidth in terms of the variable η in $\mathcal{H}_2(j\eta, j\mu)$ with the bandwidth of the output of the linear time-variant network. Furthermore, in section III we shall find that physical networks derived on the basis of such an interpretation do actually have output bandwidths restricted by the range of η in $\mathcal{H}_2(j\eta, j\mu)$.

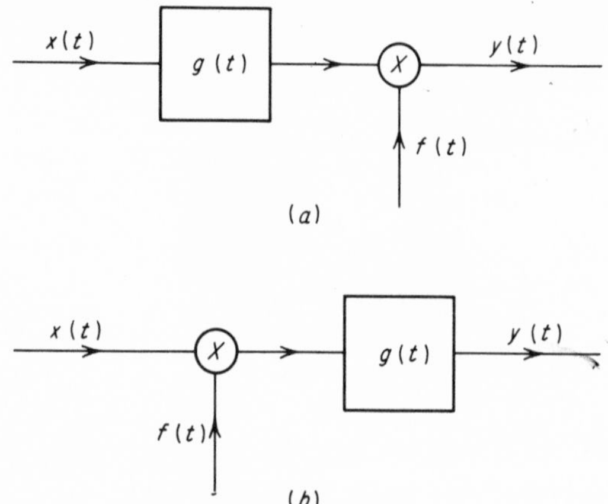

Fig. 3. Two elementary time-variant networks: (a) Type I; (b) Type II.

2.5 Separable Time-Variant Systems

Two elementary forms of linear time-variant networks are of special interest, because of their simplicity and usefulness in constructing more complicated linear time-variant networks. It has also been found that the solution to a large class of optimization problems in automatic control and communication involves such elementary networks.[7,8]

These networks are shown in Fig. 3. In the first network (Type I) the input $x(t)$ is passed through the linear time-invariant filter $g(t)$, and then multiplied by the function $f(t)$ to give the output $y(t)$. In the second network (Type II) the input is first multiplied by $f(t)$ and then passed through the time-invariant network.

The impulse response of the Type I network is given by

$$\left.\begin{aligned} &h_1(t, \tau) = g(t-\tau)\, f(t) \\ \text{or}\quad & \\ &h_2(z, \tau) = g(z)\, f(\tau + z) \\ \text{or}\quad & \\ &h_3(y, t) = g(y)\, f(t) \end{aligned}\right\} \tag{35}$$

Notice that these three expressions are of the form

$$\text{impulse response} = g\begin{pmatrix}\text{time elapsed since}\\ \text{application of input}\end{pmatrix} f\begin{pmatrix}\text{instant at which}\\ \text{output is observed}\end{pmatrix}$$

Similarly the impulse response of the Type II network can be expressed in the generic form

$$\text{impulse response} = f\begin{pmatrix}\text{instant at which}\\ \text{input is applied}\end{pmatrix} g\begin{pmatrix}\text{time elapsed since}\\ \text{application of input}\end{pmatrix}$$

which, in particular, becomes

$$\left.\begin{array}{l} h_1(t,\tau) = f(\tau)g(t-\tau) \\ \text{or} \\ h_2(z,\tau) = f(\tau)g(z) \\ \text{or} \\ h_3(y,t) = f(t-y)g(y) \end{array}\right\} \tag{36}$$

Because of the form of Eqs. (35) and (36) for $h_3(y,t)$ and $h_2(z,\tau)$, these will be called separable networks.

The frequency functions for these networks also assume a simple form.

For Type I:

$$\begin{aligned} \mathcal{H}_1(j\nu, j\mu) &= G(j\nu)F(j\mu) = \mathcal{H}_3(j\nu, j\mu) \\ \mathcal{H}_2(j\eta, j\mu) &= G(j\eta - j\mu)F(j\mu) \end{aligned} \tag{37}$$

For Type II:

$$\begin{aligned} \mathcal{H}_1(j\nu, j\mu) &= G(j\nu - j\mu)F(j\mu) = \mathcal{H}_3(j\nu, j\mu) \\ \mathcal{H}_2(j\eta, j\mu) &= G(j\eta)F(j\mu) \end{aligned} \tag{38}$$

From Eq. (34) we see that Type II network has its output frequency range governed by $G(j\omega)$. If $G(j\omega)$ is restricted to $(-W_0, W_0)$ the output frequencies for Type II network will never fall outside this range regardless of the input.

For Type I network, the output range is a little harder to define; but if μ is restricted to $(-W_s, W_s)$ and ν is restricted to $(-W_i, W_i)$, then, from Eq. (33), $\eta - \mu$ is restricted to $(-W_i, W_i)$ for all μ, and therefore η is restricted to $(-W_s - W_i, W_s + W_i)$.

III. SAMPLING THEOREMS FOR LINEAR TIME-VARIANT FILTERS

We have said that in general a communication channel can be regarded as a time-variant filter with constraints imposed on it. If we assume the filter to be linear it can be described conveniently by impulse and frequency response functions. Additional constraints on the filter can now be represented as constraints on these functions. The constraints presented in this section will be in the form of bandwidth or time-duration restrictions on filter inputs and outputs. The use of sampling analysis is at once suggested, and we shall, in fact, derive appropriate sampling theorems for various sets of restrictions. Such restrictions may arise in two forms. For example, with a bandwidth constraint, it may be that the filter itself transmits only a certain range of frequencies; or we may be interested solely in the filter behavior over a particular range of frequencies. In the latter case, we may consider the actual filter to be replaced by another having the same frequency response over the specified range of interest but having zero response outside it. This situation is thus reduced to the first case. In any case, input or output restrictions will be suitably reflected in the impulse and/or frequency response of the linear time-variant network and we shall derive sampling results for such modified networks. These results will then hold either for arbitrary filters under the specified constraints on the input and output signals or for constrained filters under arbitrary operating conditions. Different types and sets of restrictions can be studied, but we shall consider only the following, which we consider most significant.

Case I: Restriction on input frequencies of signal (or filter)

Case II: Restriction on output frequencies of signal (or filter)

Case III: Restriction on filter memory, with potential limitation on range of (a) input frequencies and (b) output frequencies.

From the discussion of the last section we find that in each case there is a most convenient form of the impulse response to use in deriving the sampling theorems. Having used this form for the derivation, we can obtain the theorems for the other forms by use of the transformations given in subsection 2.3. In Case I and Case II we shall consider two different situations: in one, the frequency range of interest is a lowpass region; in the other, it is a bandpass region. In none of the cases is any restriction on the filter variation necessary. However, it is often useful to consider situations in which the filter variation bandwidth is limited, to W_s, say. Therefore we shall develop theorems for both μ (the filter-variation frequency variable) restricted and μ unrestricted.

3.1 Sampling Theorems

The method of deriving sampling theorems differs according to whether the region of interest is a lowpass region or a bandpass region. In both cases, however, it is convenient to use Woodward's compact notation and method of sampling analysis.[9] This method can be regarded as a translation into compact analytical form of the point of view that regards sampling as being obtained by impulse modulation.[10] With this fact in mind a physical interpretation of the steps in the following derivations is more readily seen.

We shall need a pair of definitions for studying Fourier transforms of periodic functions[9]

$$\text{rep}_T\, h(t) = \sum_{n=-\infty}^{\infty} h(t - nT) \tag{39}$$

$$\text{comb}_T\, h(t) = \sum_{n=-\infty}^{\infty} h(nT)\delta(t - nT) \tag{40}$$

By using a Fourier-series expansion of $\text{rep}_T\, h(t)$, it is easily shown that

$$\mathcal{F}\{\text{rep}_T\, h(t)\} = \frac{1}{T}\, \text{comb}_{1/T} H(jf) \tag{41}$$

where $\mathcal{F}$ denotes the Fourier transform. That is to say, if a non-periodic function $h(t)$, which has a transform $H(jf)$, is shifted in time by all integral multiples of T, and the results are added together, the spectrum of the resulting periodic function will be obtained by picking out the values of $H(jf)$ at intervals $1/T$. Conversely,

$$\mathcal{F}\{\text{comb}_T\, h(t)\} = \frac{1}{T}\, \text{rep}_{1/T} H(jf) \tag{42}$$

Another useful pair of transforms consists of the rectangular function and its spectrum. Woodward uses the convenient notation, which we shall adopt,

$$\text{rect}\; t = \begin{cases} 1 & |t| < 1/2 \\ 0 & |t| > 1/2 \end{cases} \tag{43}$$

for the pulse, and

$$\text{sinc}\; f = \frac{\sin \pi f}{\pi f} \tag{44}$$

for its spectrum.

Case I: Band-limited inputs—In this case the frequency range of the input signals is restricted. Since we are concerned with input frequencies, the appropriate variable to consider is ν, and we might consider it in $H_1(j\nu, t)$, or in $H_3(j\nu, t)$, to be restricted to a lowpass region $(-W_i, W_i)$ or a bandpass region $(\omega_c - W_i/2,\ \omega_c + W_i/2)$. It is simpler to use $H_3(j\nu, t)$ because of its direct Fourier transform relationship to $h_3(y, t)$—a fact that is not true of $H_1(j\nu, t)$ and $h_1(t, \tau)$. We shall consider first the lowpass case.

(a) In the *lowpass case*, ν is restricted to $(-W_i, W_i)$ and μ is either restricted to $(-W_s,\ W_s)$, or is unrestricted. Then we can write

$$H_3(j\nu, t) = \text{rep}_{2W_i}\ H_3(j\nu, t)\ \text{rect}\, \frac{\nu}{2W_i}\, .$$

Transforming both sides gives

$$h_3(y, t) = \text{comb}_{1/2W_i} h_3(y, t) * \text{sinc}\ 2W_i\, y$$

in which the star denotes convolution. Therefore

$$h_3(y, t) = \int_{-\infty}^{\infty} \sum_{n=-\infty}^{\infty} h_3(s, t)\, \delta\left(s - \frac{n}{2W_i}\right)\ \text{sinc}\ 2W_i\,(y - s)\, ds$$

$$= \sum_{n=-\infty}^{\infty} h_3\left(\frac{n}{2W_i}, t\right)\ \text{sinc}\ 2W_i\left(y - \frac{n}{2W_i}\right)\, . \tag{45}$$

This is the lowpass sampling theorem for μ unrestricted.

Next, in terms of the variable μ we can write

$$H_3(y, j\mu) = \text{rep}_{2W_s} H_3(y, j\mu) \text{ rect } \frac{\mu}{2W_s}$$

and, as before, we obtain

$$h_3(y, t) = \sum_{m=-\infty}^{\infty} h_3\left(y, \frac{m}{2W_s}\right) \text{sinc } 2W_s\left(t - \frac{m}{2W_s}\right) \quad . \tag{46}$$

Substituting for $h_3(y, m/2W_s)$ from Eq. (45) we obtain the lowpass sampling representation

$$h_3(y, t) = \sum_{m,n=-\infty}^{\infty} h_3\left(\frac{n}{2W_i}, \frac{m}{2W_s}\right) \text{ sinc } 2W_i\left(y - \frac{n}{2W_i}\right) \times \text{ sinc } 2W_s\left(t - \frac{m}{2W_s}\right) \tag{47}$$

which applies when μ is restricted to $(-W_s, W_s)$. If use is made of the relations between the different forms of the impulse response, this can also be written

$$h_1(t, \tau) = \sum_{m,n=-\infty}^{\infty} h_1\left(\frac{m}{2W_s}, \frac{m}{2W_s} - \frac{n}{2W_i}\right) \times \text{ sinc } 2W_i\left(t - \tau - \frac{n}{2W_i}\right) \text{ sinc } 2W_s\left(t - \frac{m}{2W_s}\right) \quad . \tag{48}$$

(b) In the *bandpass case*, ν is restricted to the region $(\omega_c - W_i/2, \omega_c + W_i/2)$ and, as before, μ is either unrestricted or is confined to $(-W_s, W_s)$.

We first define the analytic complex function (see section II, Chapter 12)

$$u_3(y, t) = h_3(y, t) + j\hat{h}_3(y, t)$$

where

$$\hat{h}_3(y, t) = \frac{1}{\pi} \int_{-\infty}^{\infty} \frac{h_3(r, t)}{y - r}\, dr \tag{49}$$

is the Hilbert transform of $h_3(y, t)$. If we apply the procedure in (a) to $u_3(y, t)$, the final result when μ is restricted to $(-W_s, W_s)$ is

$$h_3(y, t) = \left[\sum_{m,n=-\infty}^{\infty} h_3\left(\frac{n}{W_i}, \frac{m}{2W_s}\right) \text{ sinc } 2W_s\left(t - \frac{m}{2W_s}\right) \times \text{ sinc } W_i\left(y - \frac{n}{W_i}\right) \cos \omega_c\left(y - \frac{n}{W_i}\right)\right]$$

$$-\left[\sum_{m,n=-\infty}^{\infty} \hat{h}_3\left(\frac{n}{W_i}, \frac{m}{2W_s}\right) \text{sinc } 2W_s\left(t - \frac{m}{2W_s}\right)\right.$$

$$\left.\times \text{ sinc } W_i\left(y - \frac{n}{W_i}\right) \sin \omega_c\left(y - \frac{n}{W_i}\right)\right]. \tag{50}$$

When μ is unrestricted, this reduces to

$$h_3(y, t) = \left[\sum_{n=-\infty}^{\infty} h_3\left(\frac{n}{W_i}, t\right) \text{sinc } W_i\left(y - \frac{n}{W_i}\right) \cos \omega_c\left(y - \frac{n}{W_i}\right)\right]$$

$$-\left[\sum_{n=-\infty}^{\infty} \hat{h}_3\left(\frac{n}{W_i}, t\right) \text{sinc } W_i\left(y - \frac{n}{W_i}\right) \sin \omega_c\left(y - \frac{n}{W_i}\right)\right]. \tag{51}$$

Case II: Band-limited outputs—Here, recalling the discussion in section II, the appropriate variable to use is η, with the associated functions $h_2(z, \tau)$ and $H_2(j\eta, j\mu)$. As before, we consider a lowpass and a bandpass case.

(a) In the *lowpass case,* the output frequency variable is restricted to $(-W_0, W_0)$, and μ may either be restricted to $(-W_s, W_s)$ or may be unrestricted. Using a procedure similar to the procedure in Case I, we have

$$H_2(j\eta, \tau) = \text{rep}_{2W_0}\, H_2(j\eta, \tau) \text{ rect } \frac{\eta}{2W_0}$$

and transforming this, we have

$$h_2(z, \tau) = \sum_{n=-\infty}^{\infty} h_2\left(\frac{n}{2W_0}, \tau\right) \text{sinc } 2W_0\left(z - \frac{n}{2W_0}\right) \tag{52}$$

which is the sampling theorem for unrestricted μ. Similarly,

$$H_2(z, j\mu) = \text{rep}_{2W_s}\, H_2(z, j\mu) \text{ rect } \frac{\mu}{2W_s}$$

and

$$h_2(z, \tau) = \sum_{m=-\infty}^{\infty} h_2\left(z, \frac{m}{2W_s}\right) \text{sinc } 2W_s\left(\tau - \frac{m}{2W_s}\right). \tag{53}$$

Substituting in Eq. (53) from Eq. (52) yields finally

$$h_2(z, \tau) = \sum_{m,n=-\infty}^{\infty} h_2\left(\frac{n}{2W_0}, \frac{m}{2W_s}\right) \text{sinc } 2W_0\left(z - \frac{n}{2W_0}\right)$$

$$\times \text{ sinc } 2W_s\left(\tau - \frac{m}{2W_s}\right) \tag{54}$$

or

$$h_1(t, \tau) = \sum_{m,n=-\infty}^{\infty} h_1\left(\frac{n}{2W_0} + \frac{m}{2W_s}, \frac{m}{2W_s}\right)$$

$$\times \text{ sinc } 2W_0\left(t - \tau - \frac{n}{2W_0}\right) \text{ sinc } 2W_s\left(\tau - \frac{m}{2W_s}\right) . \qquad (55)$$

b. In the *bandpass case,* η is restricted to $(\omega_c - W_0/2,\ \omega_c + W_0/2)$. The appropriate sampling theorems, with restricted μ, are

$$h_2(z, \tau) = \left[\sum_{m,n=-\infty}^{\infty} h_2\left(\frac{n}{W_0}, \frac{m}{2W_s}\right) \text{ sinc } W_0\left(z - \frac{n}{W_0}\right)\right.$$

$$\left.\times \text{ sinc } 2W_s\left(\tau - \frac{m}{2W_s}\right)\cos \omega_c\left(z - \frac{n}{W_0}\right)\right]$$

$$-\left[\sum_{m,n=-\infty}^{\infty} \hat{h}_2\left(\frac{n}{W_0}, \frac{m}{2W_s}\right) \text{ sinc } W_0\left(z - \frac{n}{W_0}\right)\right.$$

$$\left.\times \text{ sinc } 2W_s\left(\tau - \frac{m}{2W_s}\right) \sin \omega_c\left(z - \frac{n}{W_0}\right)\right] \qquad (56)$$

or

$$h_1(t, \tau) = \left[\sum_{m,n=-\infty}^{\infty} h_1\left(\frac{n}{W_0} + \frac{m}{2W_s}, \frac{m}{2W_s}\right) \text{ sinc } W_0\left(t - \tau - \frac{n}{W_0}\right)\right.$$

$$\left.\times \text{ sinc } 2W_s\left(\tau - \frac{m}{2W_s}\right) \cos \omega_c\left(t - \tau - \frac{n}{W_0}\right)\right]$$

$$-\left[\sum_{m,n=-\infty}^{\infty} \hat{h}_1\left(\frac{n}{W_0} + \frac{m}{2W_s}, \frac{m}{2W_s}\right) \text{ sinc } W_0\left(t - \tau - \frac{n}{W_0}\right)\right.$$

$$\left.\times \text{ sinc } 2W_s\left(\tau - \frac{m}{2W_s}\right)\sin \omega_c\left(t - \tau - \frac{n}{W_0}\right)\right] . \qquad (57)$$

Here, $\hat{h}_2$ and $\hat{h}_1$ are the Hilbert transforms of h_2 and h_1 with respect to z and τ, respectively. The theorems for unrestricted μ can be obtained from Eqs. (56) and (57) by changing $m/2W_s$ to τ, dropping the sinc $2W_s(\tau - m/2W_s)$ factors, and omitting the summations on m.

Case III: Duration-limited impulse response—When the channel memory is limited in time, the appropriate variable to consider is y. Recall that $h_3(y, t)$ acts as a weighting function on past values of the input. Therefore if the weighting is zero after a certain range of y, say 0 to Y, for any t, channel inputs of age greater than Y seconds are "forgotten"; in other words the channel has a memory of only Y seconds. We can similarly show that, if $h_2(z, \tau) = 0$ for $z > Z$, the memory of the filter is Z seconds. However, as we explained in the discussion of **Cases I and II**, the variables y and z are most appropriate when considering input and output frequencies, respectively.

Thus, if we limit the input frequency range, we shall use the variable y and define $h_3(t, y) = 0$ for $y > Y$. Application of the frequency sampling theorem (given in the Appendix) yields

$$h_3(y, t) = \sum_{l=-\infty}^{\infty} H_3\left(\frac{jl}{Y}, t\right) \exp\left(\frac{j2\pi ly}{Y}\right) \quad \text{for } 0 \leqslant y \leqslant Y$$

$$= 0 \quad \text{elsewhere}. \tag{58}$$

If, in addition, μ is restricted to $(-W_s, W_s)$ we have

$$H_3(t, j\mu) = \text{rep}_{2W_s}\, H_3(y, j\mu) \text{ rect } \frac{\mu}{2W_s}$$

and transforming, we obtain

$$h_3(y, t) = \sum_{m=-\infty}^{\infty} h_3\left(y, \frac{m}{2W_s}\right) \text{sinc } 2W_s\left(t - \frac{m}{2W_s}\right) \tag{59}$$

and

$$H_3(j\nu, t) = \sum_{m=-\infty}^{\infty} H_3\left(j\nu, \frac{m}{2W_s}\right) \text{sinc } 2W_s\left(t - \frac{m}{2W_s}\right). \tag{60}$$

Substituting into Eq. (58) we get,

$$h_3(y, t) = \sum_{l,m=-\infty}^{\infty} H_3\left(\frac{jl}{Y}, \frac{m}{2W_s}\right) \text{sinc } 2W_s\left(t - \frac{m}{2W_s}\right) \exp\left(\frac{j2\pi ly}{Y}\right)$$

$$\text{for } 0 \leqslant y \leqslant Y$$

$$= 0 \quad \text{elsewhere}. \tag{61}$$

In terms of $h_1(t, \tau)$ this is

$$h_1(t, \tau) = \sum_{l,m=-\infty}^{\infty} H_1\left(\frac{jl}{Y}, \frac{m}{2W_s}\right) \text{sinc } 2W_s\left(t - \frac{m}{2W_s}\right) \exp\left[\frac{j2\pi l(t-\tau)}{Y}\right]$$

$$\text{for } 0 \leqslant y \leqslant Y$$

$$= 0 \quad \text{elsewhere}. \tag{62}$$

In the treatment of band-limited outputs, the appropriate variable is z, and if the response $h_2(z, \tau)$ is zero after Z seconds z ranges over $(0, Z)$. We may note that this is effectively a restriction on the duration of the output waveform, because it requires that the output never last for more than Z seconds beyond the duration of the input.

Again, the frequency sampling theorem gives

$$h_2(z, \tau) = \sum_{l=-\infty}^{\infty} H_2\left(\frac{jl}{Z}, \tau\right) \exp\left(\frac{j2\pi lz}{Z}\right) \quad \text{for } 0 \leqslant z \leqslant Z$$
$$= 0 \text{ elsewhere.} \tag{63}$$

If, in addition, we assume that μ lies within $(-W_s, W_s)$ we have

$$h_2(z, \tau) = \sum_{l,m=-\infty}^{\infty} H_2\left(\frac{jl}{Z}, \frac{m}{2W_s}\right) \exp\left(\frac{j2\pi lz}{Z}\right) \text{sinc } 2W_s \left(\tau - \frac{m}{2W_s}\right) \tag{64}$$

or

$$h_1(t, \tau) = \sum_{l,m=-\infty}^{\infty} H_1\left(\frac{m}{2W_s}, \frac{m}{2W_s} - \frac{jl}{Z}\right) \exp\left[\frac{j2\pi l(t-\tau)}{Z}\right]$$
$$\times \text{ sinc } 2W_s \left(\tau - \frac{m}{2W_s}\right). \tag{65}$$

3.2 Discrete Models

We can use the sampling theorems derived in the previous sections to construct discrete models for suitably restricted linear time-variant filters or, equivalently, for linear time-variant networks to be used with restricted inputs. Before proceeding to do this, however, we note that the summation over n in the various theorems need run only from 0 to ∞, provided the (modified) networks are made approximately realizable by allowing appropriate delays to make their impulse response substantially zero for z or y less than zero. We shall therefore use the range $(0,\infty)$ for n because it makes the models easier to comprehend, although for theoretical analyses such a restriction is unnecessary. However, m and l range over all the integers $(-\infty, \infty)$.

In each case the models are obtained by rearranging the appropriate sampling theorems as sums of simple separable networks of the type considered in subsection 2.5. Linearity is used to rearrange the resulting networks in more convenient form.

It is important to note that the models given are not the only ones that can be derived from the sampling theorems; it is often possible to recast these theorems in other forms that lead to different physical models. The only requirement is that all of these models have the required number of degrees of freedom as specified by the appropriate sampling theorems.

Case I. Limited input frequency range

(a) *Lowpass case—*

From Eq. (47) we can write

$$h_3(y, t) = \sum_{n=-\infty}^{\infty} f_n(t)\, g\left(y - \frac{n}{2W_i}\right) \tag{66}$$

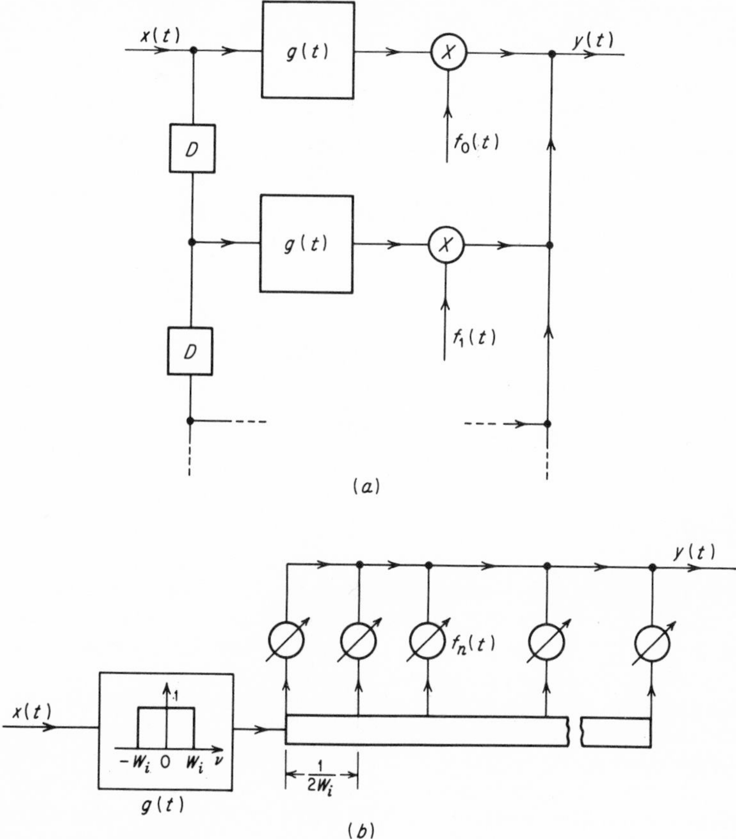

Fig. 4. A model for Case I. Lowpass restriction on input frequencies.

where

$$f_n(t) = \frac{1}{2W_i} \sum_{m=-\infty}^{\infty} h_3\left(\frac{n}{2W_i}, \frac{m}{2W_s}\right) \text{ sinc } 2W_s \left(t - \frac{m}{2W_s}\right)$$

and

$$g(y) = 2W_i \text{ sinc } 2W_i y \ .$$

If we now refer to subsection 2.5 and Fig. 3a, we see that we can synthesize $h_3(y, t)$ as shown in Fig. 4a where the boxes marked D provide pure delays in time of $1/2W_i$ seconds each. Furthermore, $g(t)$ is recognized as a filter with a flat passband from $-W_i$ to W_i. By virtue of linearity, we can transfer the $g(t)$ across the delay boxes, and combine the boxes into a delay line with taps and associated tap functions, or tap gains, $f_n(t)$. The resulting model is shown in Fig. 4b. The rectangular filter is assumed to have zero phase shift.

Theoretically, the delay line should have infinite length because

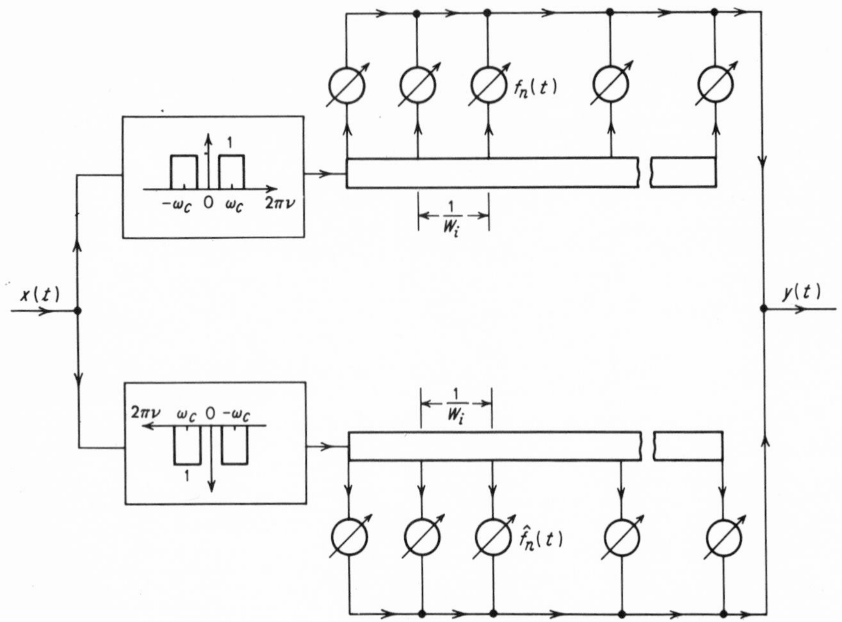

Fig. 5. A model for Case I. Bandpass restriction on input frequencies.

$h_3(y, t)$ has finite bandwidth; this is indicated by the broken lines in Fig. 4b. However, since the set of sinc functions used in the sampling theorem (which may also be regarded as a series expansion) form a complete set, we see that a finite length can be used, at the cost of an error that can be made arbitrarily small by lengthening the line sufficiently. Finally, referring to the last paragraph in subsection 2.5, we note that if the input to our filter has bandwidth $2W_i$ and the system bandwidth is $2W_s$, then the output bandwidth with our model is not greater than $(2W_i + 2W_s)$.

(b) In the *bandpass case*, a similar procedure leads to the model shown in Fig. 5. Here the top filter has zero phase shift; the lower filter has phase shift $\pi/2$ in the negative frequency band and $-\pi/2$ in the positive frequency band. The impulse response of the top filter is $2W_i$ sinc $W_i t$ cos $\omega_c t$, and that of the lower one is $-2W_i$ sinc $W_i t$ sin $\omega_c t$.

In the bandpass case we note that the sampling theorem, Eq. (46), can be rewritten in many different forms (*e.g.*, envelope and phase sampling), and different models can be derived. Since the basic procedure is the same as that just described, we shall not consider all of these possibilities.

(c) If μ is unrestricted, we now have for the tap gains

$$f_n(t) = \frac{1}{2W_i} h_3\left(\frac{n}{2W_i}, t\right) \quad \text{in Fig. 4}$$

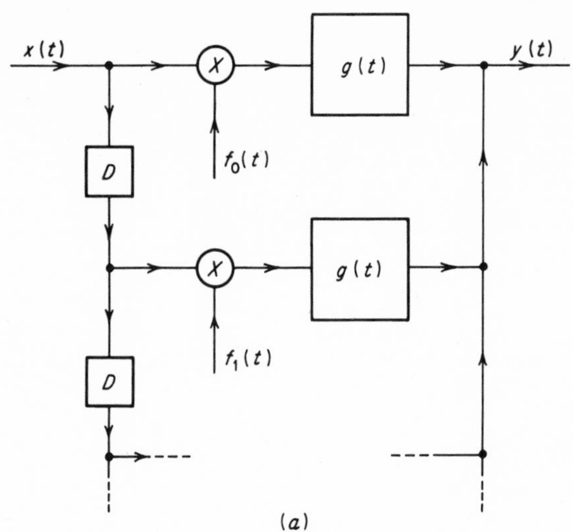

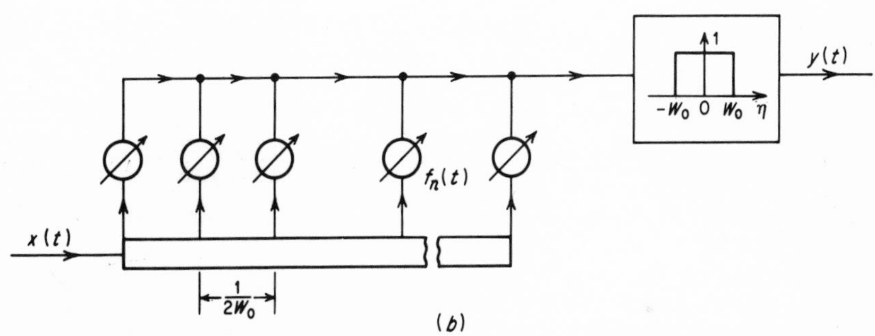

Fig. 6. A model for Case II. Lowpass restriction on output frequencies.

and

$$\left.\begin{aligned} f_n(t) &= \frac{1}{2W_i}\, h_3\!\left(\frac{n}{W_i},\, t\right) \\ \hat{f}_n(t) &= \frac{1}{2W_i}\, \hat{h}_3\!\left(\frac{n}{W_i},\, t\right) \end{aligned}\right\} \quad \text{in Fig. 5}$$

Case II. Limited output frequency range
(a) Lowpass case—
Here it is convenient to rewrite Eq. (54) as

$$h_2(z, \tau) = \sum_{n=-\infty}^{\infty} f_n\left(\tau + \frac{n}{2W_0}\right) g\left(z - \frac{n}{2W_0}\right) \tag{67}$$

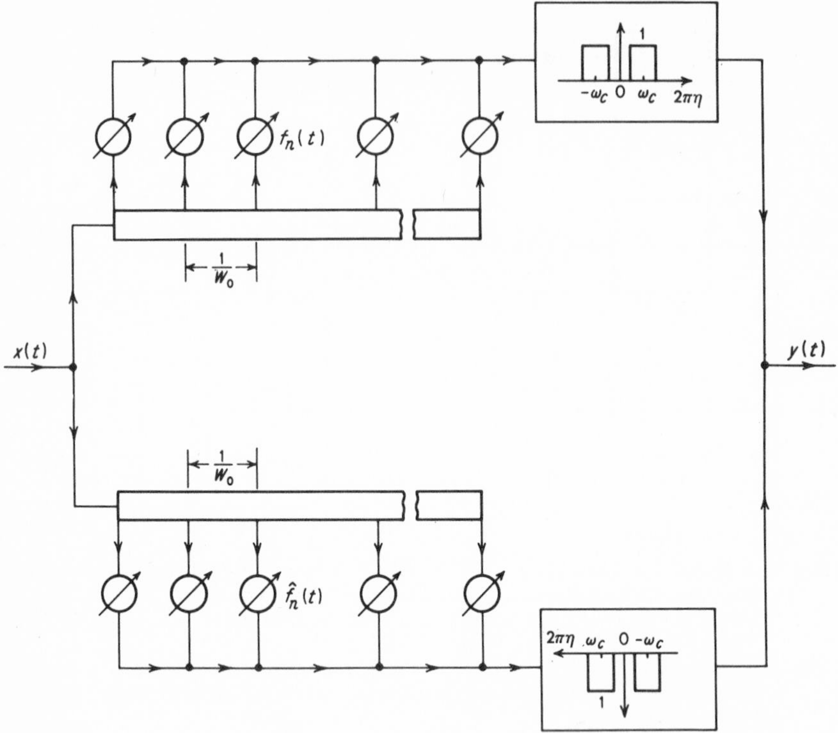

Fig. 7. A model for Case II. Bandpass restriction on output frequencies.

where

$$f_n(t) = \frac{1}{2W_0} \sum_{m=-\infty}^{\infty} h_2\left(\frac{n}{2W_0}, \frac{m}{2W_s}\right) \text{sinc } 2W_s \left(t - \frac{m}{2W_s}\right)$$

and

$$g(z) = 2W_0 \text{ sinc } 2W_0 z \text{ .}$$

Referring to subsection 2.5 and Fig. 3b we note that $h_2(z, \tau)$ can be synthesized as shown in Fig. 6a. By steps similar to those used above, this can be reduced to Fig. 6b.

(*b*) *Bandpass case—*

The model for the bandpass case is derived in similar fashion and is shown in Fig. 7. We can make the same comments on line length, filter phase shifts, frequency relations (*i.e.*, output has bandwidth no greater than $2W_0$ regardless of the input), and different bandpass models, that we made in connection with Fig. 5.

(*c*) If μ is unrestricted, we have for the tap gains

$$f_n(t) = \frac{1}{2W_0} h_2\left(\frac{n}{2W_0}, t\right) \qquad \text{in Fig. 6}$$

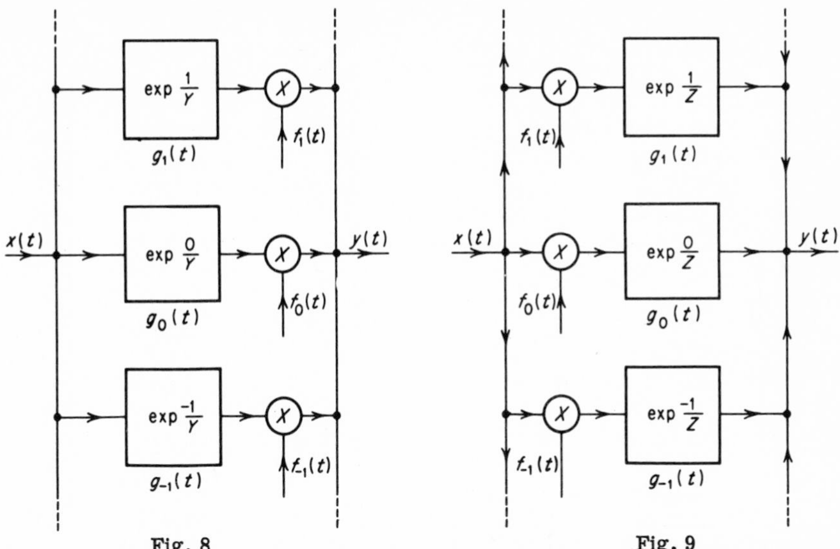

Fig. 8 Fig. 9

Fig. 8. A model for Case IIIa. Limited filter memory (or duration of impulse response) with potential restriction on input frequency range. The notation exp (l/Y) denotes a filter with impulse response exp $[(j2\pi l y)/Y]$ $\cdot$ rect $[(y/Y) - (1/2)]$.

Fig. 9. A model for Case IIIb. Limited filter memory (or duration of impulse response) with potential restriction on output frequency range. Same notation as in Fig. 8.

and

$$\left.\begin{aligned} f_n(t) &= \frac{1}{2W_0} h_2\left(\frac{n}{W_0}, t\right) \\ \hat{f}_n(t) &= \frac{1}{2W_0} \hat{h}_2\left(\frac{n}{W_0}, t\right) \end{aligned}\right\} \quad \text{in Fig. 7}$$

Case IIIa. Duration-limited impulse response and band-limited inputs

In this case we can rearrange Eq. (61) in the form

$$h_3(y, t) = \sum_{l=-\infty}^{\infty} f_l(t) g_l(y) \tag{68}$$

where

$$f_l(t) = \sum_{m=-\infty}^{\infty} H_3\left(\frac{jl}{Y}, \frac{m}{2W_s}\right) \operatorname{sinc} 2W_s\left(t - \frac{m}{2W_s}\right)$$

and

$$g_l(y) = \exp\left(\frac{j2\pi l y}{Y}\right) \operatorname{rect}\left(\frac{y}{Y} - \frac{1}{2}\right) .$$

Recognizing that the $g_l(y)$ represent envelope-integrating filters (with a finite integration time Y) at the frequencies l/Y and recalling the Type I network of subsection 2.5, we can construct a model for this case, as shown in Fig. 8. Another interpretation for the operation of the filters $g_l(y)$, which is perhaps less obvious, is that they represent filters that continuously extract a signal that would be the lth Fourier component of a periodic waveform, each period of which duplicates the last Y seconds of the input to the filters. (Such filters are used in the Kineplex communication system[11] where they are operated as "integrate-and-quench" filters.) Theoretically we should have an infinite bank of filters, but if we impose a bandwidth restriction on the frequency range of the input signals, a finite number of filters will be sufficient.

Case IIIb. Duration-limited impulse response and band-limited outputs

The sampling theorem of Eq. (63) can be written as

$$h_2(z, \tau) = \sum_{l=-\infty}^{\infty} f_l(\tau)\, g_l(z) \tag{69}$$

where

$$f_l(t) = \sum_{m=-\infty}^{\infty} H_2\left(\frac{jl}{Z}, \frac{m}{2W_s}\right) \operatorname{sinc} 2W_s \left(t - \frac{m}{2W_s}\right)$$

$$g_l(z) = \exp\left(\frac{j2\pi l z}{Z}\right) \operatorname{rect}\left(\frac{z}{Z} - \frac{1}{2}\right) .$$

The $g_l(z)$ represent, as before, integrating filters at the frequencies l/Z, and we now use networks of Type II (Fig. 3b) to construct the model shown in Fig. 9. Again, theoretically we should have an infinite bank of such filters, unless we impose a bandwidth restriction on the output frequency range of the signals, in which case a finite number will suffice.

Finally, we may point out that in both Case IIIa and Case IIIb we can combine the terms $f_{-l}\,g_{-l}$ and $f_{+l}\,g_{+l}$ to obtain a representation in terms of filter banks together with amplitude and phase controls.

IV. CONCLUDING REMARKS

The development of mathematical models for communication channels has been the subject of much research since the advent of statistical communication theory. Although channels with additive random disturbances—such as the binary symmetric channel and the gaussian channel—have been studied in some detail, less work has been done on channels with nonadditive disturbances, of which multipath and scatter channels are important examples. The notable work in this area has been done by Price[12,13] and Turin.[14,15] While their studies have yielded considerable insight into the problem and have aided the development of a successful system to combat multipath,[16] the models they have used are not quite general, since several assumptions about the path structure of the channel are made. Price considers only statistically independent paths with Rayleigh-distributed strengths and known delays. In Turin's model knowledge of path delays is not required; moreover, he considers more general path statistics, but he is forced to assume that the paths are resolvable and time-invariant.

The models proposed in this chapter are not, as they stand, models for multipath channels, chiefly because no statistical information has been taken into account in their formulation. The determination of appropriate statistical distributions for the time-variant tap gains in our models is an interesting topic that has not been adequately investigated. However, we feel that a significant feature of the models presented here is the operational, or phenomenological, point of view adopted in their derivation: Our delay-line and filter-bank models have been based on assumptions concerning the limitations of signal-generating and measuring equipment. Thus consider, for example, the delay-line model for the situation in which the output-signal frequency range is limited: The actual channel structure may have either a discrete or a continuous structure, or have randomly varying paths, and so forth, but the model summarizes all this information into the form of a delay line with taps at fixed intervals. These models may therefore be regarded as canonical forms for the linear time-variant network under the different constraints imposed on it.

We may note in passing that the operational models we have derived are similar in form to the delay-line model used in the Rake system[16] and the filter-bank model used in the Kineplex system.[11] Our analysis may be considered as establishing the sufficiency of such models. Further discussion of these models and their application to the description of the Rake and Kineplex systems is presented in Chapter 12.

APPENDIX

The Sampling Theorem in the Frequency Domain

Consider a time function $h(t)$ limited to $T = T_2 - T_1$. We can write

$$h(t) = \text{rep}_T\, h(t) \text{ rect } (t - T_0)/T$$

$$H(jf) = \text{comb}_{1/T}\, H(jf) * \text{sinc } fT \exp(-j2\pi f T_0)$$

$$= \sum_{n=-\infty}^{\infty} H\left(j\frac{n}{T}\right) \text{ sinc } T\left(f - \frac{n}{T}\right) \exp\left[-j2\pi T_0\left(f - \frac{n}{T}\right)\right] \quad \text{(A-1)}$$

where $T_0 = (T_1 + T_2)/2$. This is one form of sampling representation.

Another can be derived as follows: Transform both sides of Eq. (A-1):

$$h(t) = \sum_{n=-\infty}^{\infty} H\left(j\frac{n}{T}\right) \int_{-\infty}^{\infty} \text{sinc}\; T\left(f - \frac{n}{T}\right) \exp\left[-j2\pi T_0 \left(f - \frac{n}{T}\right)\right]$$

$$\times \exp\,(j2\pi f t)\, df$$

$$= \sum_{n=-\infty}^{\infty} H\left(j\frac{n}{T}\right) \exp\left(\frac{j2\pi n T_0}{T}\right) \int_{-\infty}^{\infty} \text{sinc}\; T\left(f - \frac{n}{T}\right)$$

$$\times \exp\,[\,j2\pi f(t - T_0)]\, df$$

$$= \sum_{n=-\infty}^{\infty} H\left(j\frac{n}{T}\right) \exp\left(\frac{j2\pi n T_0}{T}\right) \exp\left[\frac{j2\pi n}{T}(t - T_0)\right] \;\text{rect}\;(t - T_0)/T$$

$$= \sum_{n=-\infty}^{\infty} H\left(j\frac{n}{T}\right) \exp\left(\frac{j2\pi n t}{T}\right), \quad T_1 \leq t \leq T_2$$

$$= 0 \quad \text{elsewhere} \tag{A-2}$$

which we recognize as the Fourier series expansion of $h(t)$ over the interval (T_1, T_2). This form also gives $2TW + 1$ degrees of freedom for a (W, T) function.

REFERENCES

1. H. A. Thomas and R. E. Burgess, *Survey of Existing Information and Data on Radio Noise in the Frequency Range, 1-30 mc*, Special Report 15, Radio Research Board, H.M. Stationery Office, London, England, 1947.
2. S. V. C. Aiya, "Atmospheric Noise Interference to Short-wave Broadcasting," *Proc. IRE*, vol. 46, pp. 580-588, August, 1955.
3. *Ionospheric Radio Propagation*, Circular 462, National Bureau of Standards, Washington, D.C., June 25, 1948.
4. L. A. Pipes, "Four Methods for the Analysis of Time-variable Circuits," *Trans. IRE*, CT-2, pp. 4-11, March, 1955.
5. W. R. Bennett, "A General Review of Linear Variable Parameter and Nonlinear Circuit Analysis," *Proc. IRE*, vol. 38, pp. 259-263, March, 1950.
6. L. A. Zadeh, "Frequency Analysis of Variable Networks," *Proc. IRE*, vol. 38, pp. 291-299, March, 1950.
7. J. S. Bendat, *Principles and Applications of Random Noise Theory*, John Wiley & Sons, Inc., New York, 1958.
8. J. H. Laning and R. H. Battin, *Random Processes in Automatic Control*, McGraw-Hill Book Company, Inc., New York, 1956.
9. P. M. Woodward, *Probability and Information Theory with Ap-*

plications to Radar, McGraw-Hill Book Company, Inc., New York, 1953.

10. W. K. Linvill, "Sampled-data Control Systems Studied through Comparison with Amplitude Modulation," *Trans. AIEE*, vol 70, pp. 1779-1788, 1951.
11. M. L. Doelz, E. T. Heald, and D. L. Martin, "Binary Data Transmission Techniques for Linear Systems," *Proc. IRE*, vol. 45, pp. 656-661, May, 1957.
12. R. Price, *Statistical Theory Applied to Communication through Multipath Disturbances*, Technical Report 266, Research Laboratory of Electronics, M.I.T., Sept. 3, 1953.
13. R. Price, "Optimum Detection of Random Signals in Noise, with Application to Scatter-multipath Communication, I," *Trans. IRE*, IT-2, pp. 125-135, 1956.
14. G. L. Turin, *Communication through Noisy, Random-multipath Channels*, Technical Report 116, Lincoln Laboratory, Massachusetts Institute of Technology, Cambridge, Massachusetts, May, 1956.
15. G. L. Turin, "A Review of Statistical Multipath Communication Theory," Paper presented at the Second National Symposium on Global Communications, St. Petersburg, Florida, Dec. 3-5, 1958.
16. R. Price and P. E. Green, Jr., "A Communication Technique for Multipath Channels," *Proc. IRE*, vol. 46, pp. 555-570, March, 1958.

CHAPTER 7

Diversity Techniques

Elie J. Baghdady

I. INTRODUCTION

The discussions of the characteristics of transmission media bring out a most important realization: In the synthesis of a reliable communication link, the system must be planned around the chosen transmission medium. The disturbances and propagation characteristics of the medium must be taken into account in the process of signal selection at the transmitting end, and in the process of message extraction at the receiving end. Once a satisfactory characterization of the anticipated difficulties has been made, the message chosen for transmission must be expressed in a form that the disturbances cannot imitate or mutilate beyond recognition at the receiving end. With a corrupted message (whose important characteristics are known in advance) at its hands, the receiving system must be prepared to operate continuously in the presence of the disturbances and to take maximum advantage of the basic differences between the characteristics of messages and of disturbances.

Starting with the present chapter, we shall explore the various approaches that are presently believed to be fruitful in combating troublesome disturbances. In this chapter we assume that the form in which the message is to be transmitted *has been chosen,* and that this chosen form has been transformed into a radio-frequency signal by an appropriate modulation technique (for example, by varying some distinguishable parameter of a sinusoidal carrier). Improvements in system performance can only be realized through the utilization of appropriate corrective signal-processing techniques. Of primary interest here will be what is widely known as diversity techniques for combating the effects of fading resulting from multipath interference that changes with time. In the succeeding chapters, optimum-decision and waveform-reproduction systems will be discussed, as well as the problem of signal selection, the application of coding and decoding theory, and the use of channel-estimation techniques without and with feedback from receiver to transmitter.

II. PRELIMINARY CONSIDERATIONS

Diversity is defined here as a general technique that utilizes two or more copies of a signal with varying degrees of disturbance to achieve, by a selection or a combination scheme, a consistently higher degree of message-recovery performance than is achievable from any one of the individual copies separately. Although diversity is commonly understood to be aimed at improving the reliability of reception of signals that are subject to fading in the presence of random noise, the significance of the term will be extended here to cover conceptually related techniques that are intended for other difficulties.

The first problem in diversity is the procurement of the "diverse" copies of the disturbed signal, or, if only one copy is available, the operation on this copy to generate additional "diversified" copies. When the signal is disturbed by a combination of multiplicative and additive disturbances, as in the case of fading in the presence of additive random noise, the transmission medium can be tapped for an ever-available supply of diversified copies in any desired numbers.

As pointed out in the preceding chapters, propagation media are generally time variant in character and this causes transmitted signals to fluctuate randomly with time. These fluctuations are usually of three types:

(a) Rapid fluctuations, or fluctuations in the instantaneous signal strength, whose cause can be traced to interference among two or more slowly varying copies of the signal arriving via different paths. This may conveniently be called *multipath-interference fading*. This type of fading often leads to a complete loss of the message during time intervals that are long even when compared with the slowest components of the message. It is observed, however, that if widely spaced receiving antennas are used to pick up the same signal, then the instantaneous fluctuations in S/N ratio at any one of the receiving sites is almost completely independent of the instantaneous fluctuations experienced at the other sites. In other words, at times when the signal at one of the locations is observed to fade to a very low level, the same signal at some other sufficiently distant site may very probably be at a much higher level compared to its own ambient noise. Signals received at widely spaced time intervals or widely spaced frequencies also show almost completely independent patterns of instantaneous fading behavior. Nearly uncorrelated multipath-interference fading has also been observed with signal waves differing only in polarization. It will be evident that by appropriate selection or combination techniques it should be possible to obtain from such a diversity of signals a better or more reliable reception of the desired message than is possible from processing only one of the signals all the time.

(b) The instantaneous fluctuations in signal strength occur about a mean value of signal amplitude that changes relatively so slowly that its values must be compared at instants separated by minutes to hours before any significant differences can be perceived. These changes in short-term (or "hourly") mean signal amplitude are usually attributable to changes in the attenuation in the medium which signals will experience in transit between two relatively small geographical or space locations. No significant random spacial variations in the received mean signal amplitude are usually perceived in receiving localities, that could be utilized for diversity protection against this *attenuation fading*. Nor are there sufficient, and sufficiently random, differences in the attenuation fading at different frequencies or different polarizations that could be utilized in diversity reception in the radio spectrum in use at present. However, it is possible to combat this type of fading by a feedback operation in which the receiver informs the transmitter about the level of the received mean signal amplitude, thus instructing it to radiate an adequate amount of power. The Janet system (see Chapter 14) is an extreme example of this operation. But the usual practice is to anticipate the greatest attenuation to be expected at the design stage and counteract it by appropriate antenna design and adequate transmitter power.

(c) A type of attenuation fading that is much slower than that just described. The "hourly" mean signal levels are different from day to day, just as they are from hour to hour in any one day. The mean signal level over one day changes from day to day and from month to month. The mean signal level for a period of one month changes from month to month and from season to season, and then there are yearly variations, and so on. As in the case of the "hourly" fluctuations in (b), the long-term fluctuations are generally caused by changes in the constitution of the transmission medium, but the scale and duration of these changes for the long-term fluctuations are vastly greater than those for the "hourly" changes. Diversity techniques *per se* are ineffective here.

In addition to the instantaneous-signal diversification that can be achieved by seeking two or more separate channels between the transmitting and receiving antennas, certain types of useful diversification can also be achieved by appropriate design of the patterns of two or more receiving antennas placed essentially in the same location, or by operations in the receiver on only one of the available replicas of a disturbed signal. The usefulness of "receiver diversification" of a disturbed signal will be demonstrated in Chapter 19 for the case in which the disturbance is impulsive and the case of interference from some other undesired signal source or (under certain circumstances) from a delayed replica of the desired signal arriving via a different path.

The second problem in diversity is the question of how to utilize the available disturbed copies of the signal in order to achieve the least possible loss of information in extracting the desired message. The techniques that have thus far been developed can be classified into (a) switching, (b) combining, and (c) a combination of switching and combining. These operations can be carried out either on the noisy modulated carriers (pre-detection) or on the noisy, extracted modulations that carry the message specifications (post-detection).

In any case, if K suitable noisy waveforms described by $f_1(t)$, $f_2(t)$, ..., $f_K(t)$, are available, let the kth function be weighted by the factor a_k, and consider the sum

$$f(t) = \sum_{k=1}^{K} a_k f_k(t). \tag{1}$$

In the *switching techniques* only one of the a_k's is different from zero at any time. In one of these techniques, called *scanning diversity*, the available waveforms are tried one at a time, in a fixed sequence, until one is found whose quality exceeds a preset threshold. That one is then delivered for further processing in order to extract the desired message, until its quality falls below the preset threshold as a result of fading. It is then dropped and the next one that meets the threshold requirement in the fixed sequence is chosen. In scanning diversity, the signal chosen is often not the best one available. A technique that examines the K available signals simultaneously and selects only the best one for delivery is conceptually (though not always practically) preferable. Such a technique will be referred to as *optimal-selection diversity*.

In the combining techniques, all of the available noisy waveforms, good and poor, are utilized simultaneously as indicated in Eq. (1); *i.e.*, the a_k's are all nonzero all the time. Of all the possible choices of nonzero a_k's, only two are of principal interest. First, on the assumption that there is no *a priori* knowledge or design that suggests that some of the $f_k(t)$'s will always be poorer than the others, all of the available copies are weighted equally in the summation of Eq. (1) irrespective of the fluctuations in quality that will be experienced. Thus, equal mean values of signal level and equal rms values of noise being assumed, the choice $a_1 = a_2 = \dots = a_K$ is made, and the technique is known as *equal-weight* or *equal-gain* combining. The second possible choise of nonzero weighting factors that is of wide interest is one in which a_k depends upon the quality of $f_k(t)$ and during any short time interval the a_k's are adjusted automatically to yield the maximum signal-to-noise ratio for the sum $f(t)$. This is known as *maximal-ratio combining*.

In the *alternate-switching-and-combining technique* a number of the a_k's up to $K-1$ can be zero during certain time intervals because some of the available signals are dropped when they become markedly noisier than the others. This approach is based upon the fact that the performance of an equal-gain combiner will approximate that of the maximal-ratio combiner as long as the signal-to-noise ratios of the various channels are nearly equal. But if any of the signal-to-noise ratios become significantly inferior to the others, the overall signal-to-noise ratio can be kept closer to the maximum ratio obtainable if the inferior signals are dropped out of the sum $f(t)$.

III. STATISTICAL CHARACTERIZATION OF FADING SIGNALS

Illustrative sample recordings of the envelopes of fading signals are shown in Fig. 1. A combined time and frequency, three-dimensional presentation is pictured in Fig. 2. Our interest here centers on a single carrier with a relatively slow message modulation so that the radio-frequency space occupied is too narrow to encompass any important differences in the fading of the sinusoidal components contained in it. For analytical purposes, waveforms of the type illustrated in Fig. 1 are usually treated as describing a random variable

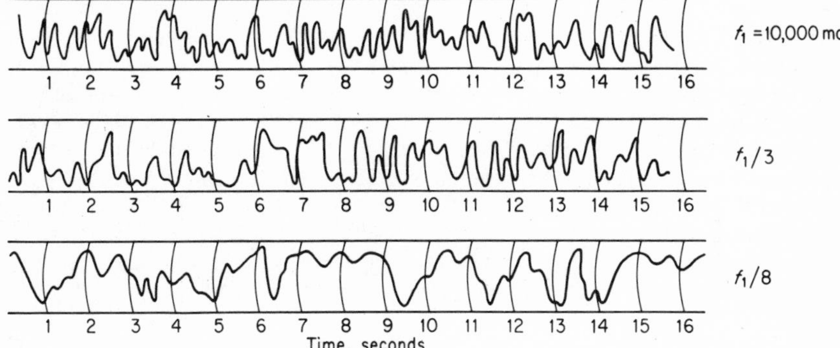

Fig. 1. Sample recordings illustrating the effect of changing multipath-interference fading upon received envelope of sinusoidal carrier for three widely different frequencies. (Typical for tropospheric scatter.)

whose statistical properties are determined from fraction-of-time distributions and are hence intimately related to the duration of the interval of observation. As pointed out by Brennan,[1,2] the probability distribution functions of such random variables can be considered to characterize a type of stochastic process, called translation process, for which the Local-Ergodicity Theorem (see section 2.2 of Chapter 2) applies. According to this theorem, time and distribution averages of random variables described by fraction-of-time distributions are one and the same thing, and they can be used interchangeably depending on expediency.

It is important to note here that although the rate at which the envelope of a received carrier fluctuates may often appear to be high, it is usually quite slow in comparison with the slowest expected variations in the message waveform. That is to say the envelope of the carrier is usually approximately constant when observed over intervals of time that extend over the duration of the longest message element, or over a few periods of the lowest-frequency component in the message spectrum. On the time scale of the fading envelope, such time intervals (henceforth denoted by T_{short}) are then too short for any significant changes in the envelope to occur but not so short

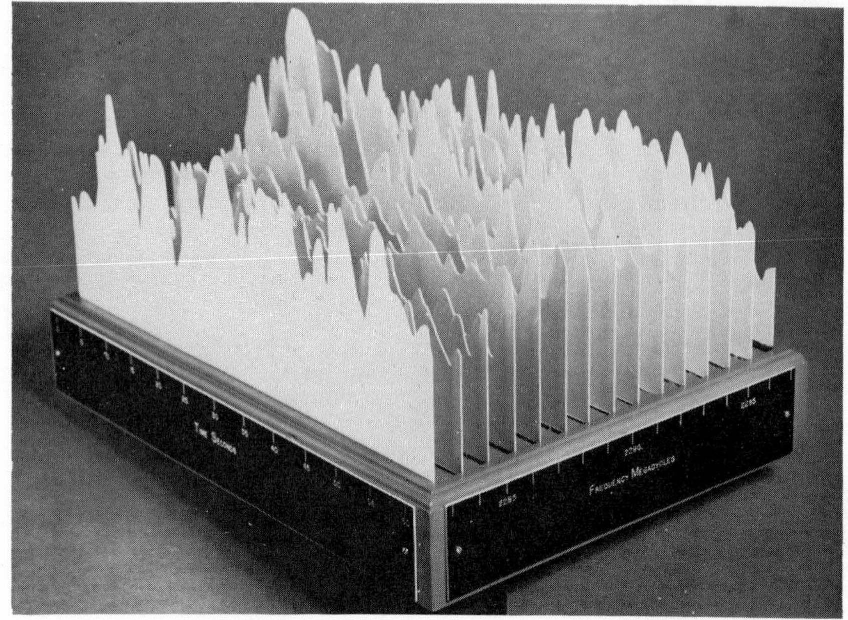

Fig. 2. A combined time and frequency presentation of the fading envelopes of sinusoidal carriers whose frequencies differ by small fractional amounts. (Courtesy of J. H. Chisholm and J. F. Roche, M.I.T. Lincoln Laboratory.)

that the details of the message waveform are perceived in averaging over the interval. Typical values of T_{short} are always below a few milliseconds. Time averages over such intervals lead to so-called "local" statistics, or short-time statistics. Among these we cite the local mean-square value of the signal $s_k(t)$ and the local mean-square value of the noise $n_k(t)$, which are defined by

$$S_k^2(t) = \frac{1}{T_{\text{short}}} \int_{t-(1/2)T_{\text{short}}}^{t+(1/2)T_{\text{short}}} s_k^2(\tau)\, d\tau \tag{2}$$

and

$$N_k^2(t) = \frac{1}{T_{\text{short}}} \int_{t-(1/2)T_{\text{short}}}^{t+(1/2)T_{\text{short}}} n_k^2(\tau)\, d\tau . \tag{3}$$

It is clear that such local statistics will in general depend upon the locality on the time scale, t, about which the interval T_{short} is centered. This accounts for the explicit indication that the quantities represented by S_k^2 and N_k^2 are functions of t. It is clear from the oscillograms of Fig. 1, for example, that as the locality of T_{short}

is changed, S_k^2 changes, and so should the local signal-to-noise mean-square (or power) ratio

$$r_k(t) = \frac{S_k^2(t)}{N_k^2(t)} . \tag{4}$$

In fact, if $r_k(t)$ is plotted as a function of t, a time function results which can be considered to characterize a random variable whose (fraction-of-time) probability distributions over suitable time intervals in turn characterize a translation process.

The fraction-of-time distribution functions of fading carrier envelopes and of the associated local signal-to-noise power ratios, $r_k(t)$, when each of these is observed over time intervals that extend over many times the subinterval T_{short}, are of extreme importance in the study of diversity techniques. On the time scale of the fading envelope, such time intervals (henceforth denoted by T_{int}, and generally satisfying the condition $T_{\text{int}} \gg T_{\text{short}}$) are neither too short for the important instantaneous envelope variations to occur in them nor are they so long as to encompass significant variations in the mean or median value of the carrier envelope. The subscript "int" stands for "intermediate." The mean and the median of the envelope will change with time over long time intervals $T_{\text{long}} \gg T_{\text{int}}$. The median, rather than the mean, is the quantity that is usually presented in experimental studies of fading envelopes because the median can be read directly from the probability distribution function that is determined by a level-distribution recorder. The presentation is typified by the illustration in Fig. 3. On the time scale of this figure, the interval T_{int} must be sufficiently short for the assumption of constant median envelope to apply, but on the time scale of Fig. 1 T_{int} must be sufficiently long to sample a typical structure or behavior of the fading envelope. Inasmuch as the detailed character of the envelope functuations will depend, among other things, upon the

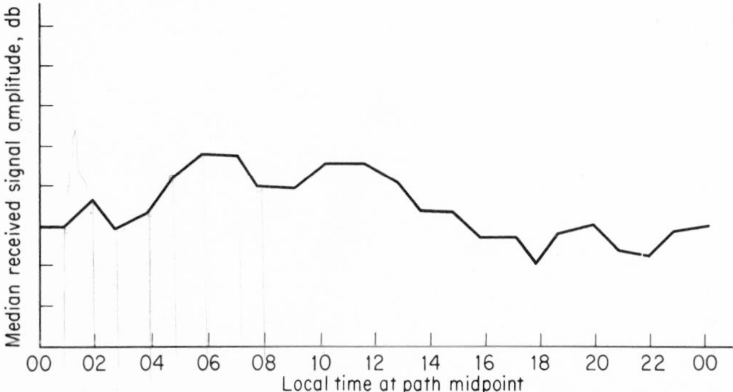

Fig. 3. A typical presentation of data showing the diurnal variation of median signal level in a time interval of duration T_{int} (here hourly median for ionospheric scatter).

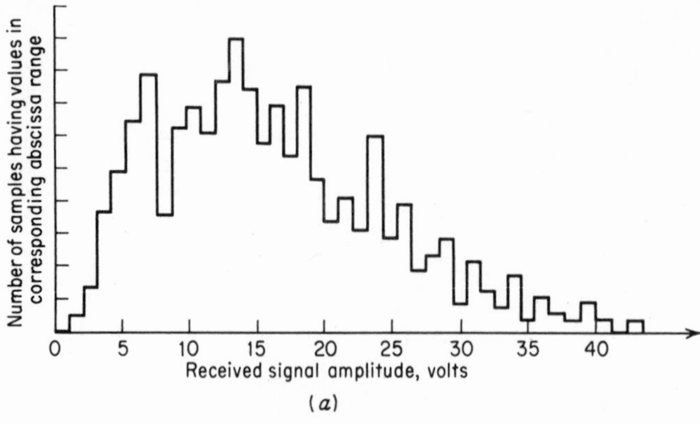

(a)

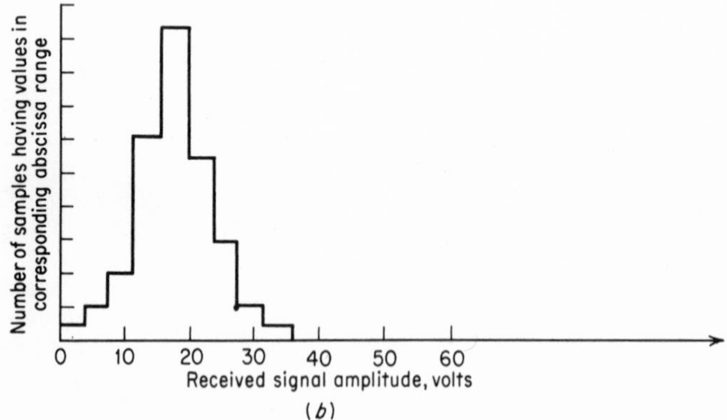

(b)

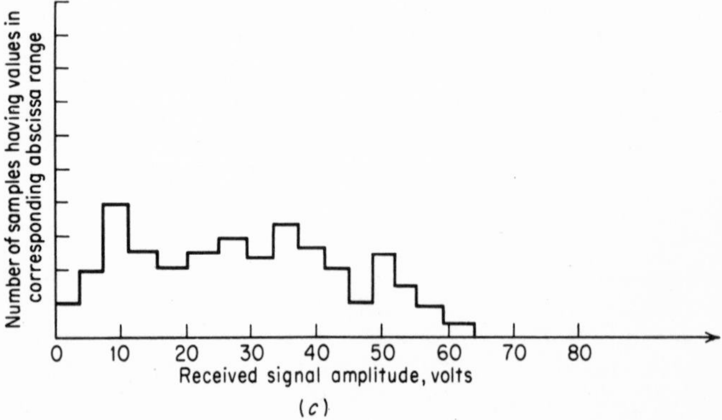

(c)

Fig. 4. Histographic study of the distribution of the values of received signal amplitude in intervals of duration T_{int}.

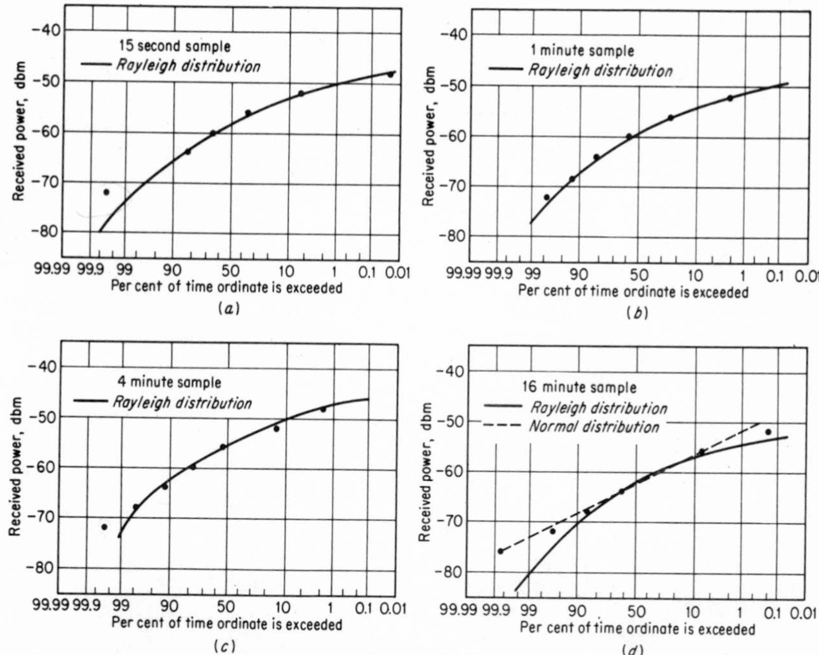

Fig. 5. Per-cent-of-time distribution of signal level received via a 188-mile tropospheric scatter path at 3670 mc for various observation intervals. Results show effect of choice of duration of observed sample upon the per-cent-of-time distribution of the signal envelope. Best choice indicated for T_{int} is a few minutes. (Courtesy of J. H. Chisholm, M.I.T. Lincoln Laboratory.)

carrier frequency, the transmission distance, the specific propagation mechanism, and the receiving antenna pattern, no one specific value can be assigned to T_{int} in advance. Values used by various investigators to suit their individual circumstances have ranged from a few minutes to a few hours, but data described by "hourly median" is encountered most often.

The probability distribution of a fading envelope is usually determined from samples of duration T_{int} and the results are presented in histograms (illustrated in Fig. 4), and by curves (illustrated in Fig. 5). Such histograms and curves are invariably compared with simple mathematical curves such as the Rayleigh density and distribution functions or some other functions whose shapes resemble the appearance of the experimental presentations. The fit of the experimental distributions to the Rayleigh distribution is most often excellent for long-range SHF and UHF tropospheric transmission, quite often so for short-range UHF and for ionospheric scatter and reflection of VHF and HF, and almost infrequent for ionospheric transmission at medium frequencies[3,4] and for line-of-sight VHF and SHF transmissions.

Accordingly, the Rayleigh-fading model is almost always assumed in theoretical treatments, although it is well-known that serious deviations from it arise in some situations. According to this model, if a sinusoid of frequency ω_c is radiated at the transmitting end, it will reach a receiver in the form

$$e(t) = V(t) \cos [\omega_c t + \phi(t)] \tag{5}$$

where $V(t)$ is a slowly fluctuating envelope (or instantaneous amplitude) whose possible values have a probability density function

$$\begin{aligned} p(V) &= \frac{2V}{v^2} e^{-V^2/v^2} \quad \text{for } V \geqslant 0 \\ &= 0 \quad \text{otherwise,} \end{aligned} \tag{6}$$

where v^2 is the mean-square value of V during an interval of duration T_{int}. The Rayleigh density function is sketched as curve a in Fig. 6. No explicit assumptions are usually made concerning the phase $\phi(t)$ beyond the fact that its fluctuations, like those of $V(t)$, are slow compared to the slowest expected variations in the message waveform. But one possible and sometimes convenient assumption to make is that $\phi(t)$ fluctuates in a random manner and can assume all values between 0 and 2π in accordance with the probability density function

$$\begin{aligned} p(\phi) &= 1/2\pi \quad \text{for } 0 \leqslant \phi \leqslant 2\pi \\ &= 0 \quad \text{otherwise.} \end{aligned} \tag{7}$$

The convenience that results from the assumption of a uniformly distributed phase is due to the fact that $e(t)$ of Eq. (5) can now be viewed as a sample function of a narrow-band gaussian process with zero mean and variance $\sigma_e^2 = v^2/2$. This immediately places a whole body of well-developed mathematical theory at the disposal of the analyst.[5,6] According to this theory, if we express $e(t)$ in the form

$$e(t) = e_c(t) \cos \omega_c t - e_s(t) \sin \omega_c t, \tag{8}$$

then $e_c(t)$ and $e_s(t)$ are gaussian random variables that characterize the random fluctuations of the envelope

$$V(t) = \sqrt{e_c^2(t) + e_s^2(t)} \,.$$

The gaussian variables $e_c(t)$ and $e_s(t)$ are independent, and they have zero means and variances that equal $\sigma_e^2 = v^2/2$. In the next section shall make use of this model to justify an important assumption in diversity theory. An excellent example of the application of the theory of the gaussian process to the solution of certain important problems in maximal-ratio combining theory is provided in publications by Packard[7] and by Pierce and Stein.[8]

The "narrow-band" attribute of a narrow-band gaussian process does not affect the basic mathematical theory of this process. It enters the picture only insofar as it influences the analyst's "frame of mind'' or attitude toward the meaning of $V(t)$ and $\phi(t)$. The properties that one would wish to associate with $V(t)$ and $\phi(t)$ in the solution of communication problems can be substantiated in the laboratory only when the width of the spectrum of the process constitutes a small fraction of the center frequency. In application of the theory, the words "narrow-band" serve as a reminder about the restriction of the spectrum to a small range around the center frequency, and this is important when the manipulations end and the interpretations of the practical significance of the results start.

According to the Rayleigh-fading law, the probability that the received signal amplitude will (during any time interval that fits our description of T_{int}) fall at or below some specified level V' is given by

$$P(V \leqslant V') = \int_0^{V'} \frac{2V}{v^2} e^{-V^2/v^2}\, dV$$

$$= 1 - e^{-(V'/v)^2} \tag{9}$$

The value of signal amplitude that is exceeded half the time is that value V_M for which $P(V \leqslant V_M) = 1/2$. For the Rayleigh distribution, $V_M^2 = (\ln 2)\, v^2 \cong 0.693\, v^2$, which shows that the median V_M is about 1.6 db delow the rms value v. It is often convenient to express the Rayleigh probability distribution function (Eq. 9) in the form

$$P(V \leqslant V') = 1 - e^{-0.693(V'/V_M)^2} \tag{10}$$

Two possible non-Rayleigh probability density functions are also sketched in Fig. 6. The first, marked b, corresponds to a relatively mild type of fading usually described as being "shallow." Here, deep fades are relatively infrequent and of short duration, and the envelope

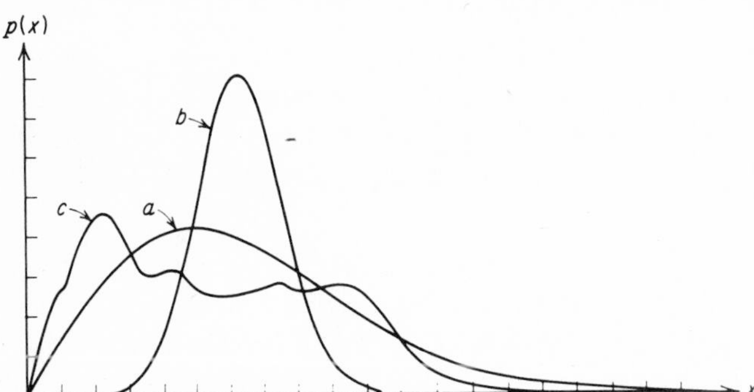

Fig. 6. Illustrative probability density functions for fading envelopes. Curve a is suggested by histogram in Fig. 4(a), curve b corresponds to Fig. 4(b), and curve c corresponds to Fig. 4(c). (Courtesy of D. G. Brennan, M.I.T. Lincoln Laboratory.)

lingers in the vicinity of its median value most of the time. The second density function, marked c, indicates another "near extreme" condition in which the fluctuations cover a wide range and deep fades are relatively frequent and persistent. Histograms that suggest these two types of density functions are presented in Fig. 4. Such histograms are encountered in ionospheric transmission at medium and high frequencies.[3,4]

IV. DIVERSIFICATION OF FADING SIGNALS

The usefulness of diversity reception techniques depends fundamentally upon the possibility of obtaining two or more independently fading copies of the same signal. The less dependent the fading patterns of the available copies, the less likely it is that they will all fade simultaneously below the threshold of message extractability, and hence the more ideal the conditions for improving reception with diversity. Even more desirable is the situation (in dual diversity) in which there is complete negative correlation between the fading patterns so that when one signal is too weak to be useful another is almost certainly of sufficient strength. It is therefore important to examine the criterion for ascertaining the degree of statistical dependence between randomly fluctuating copies of a desired signal, and to discuss the ways in which the desired condition can be approached.

Assume that a sinusoid $A_c \cos \omega_c t$ is transmitted, and is received in the two forms

$$\begin{aligned} e_1(t) &= V_1(t) \cos [\omega_c t + \phi_1(t)] \\ &= e_{c1}(t) \cos \omega_c t - e_{s1}(t) \sin \omega_c t \end{aligned} \tag{11}$$

and

$$\begin{aligned} e_2(t) &= V_2(t) \cos [\omega_c t + \phi_2(t)] \\ &= e_{c2}(t) \cos \omega_c t - e_{s2}(t) \sin \omega_c t\,. \end{aligned} \tag{12}$$

The dependence between the two envelopes V_1 and V_2 is usually specified in terms of their correlation coefficient. This specification is generally open to question, but we shall now show that it is complete in situations in which the narrow-band gaussian model is a satisfactory representation for the randomly fading signals.

For the two random variables V_1 and V_2 with variances σ^2_{V1} and σ^2_{V2} and means m_{V1} and m_{V2}, we recall from Eq. (36) of Chapter 2 that the correlation coefficient is given by

$$\rho_{V_1V_2} = \frac{E[V_1 V_2] - m_{V1} m_{V2}}{\sigma_{V1}\sigma_{V2}} \tag{13}$$

It can be shown[5] that the value of $\rho_{V_1V_2}$ will always fall in the range $-1 \leqslant \rho_{V_1V_2} \leqslant 1$, where the values ± 1 signify that $V_2 = \pm a V_1 + b$, $a > 0$. If $E[V_1 V_2] = m_{V1} m_{V2}$, then $\rho_{V_1V_2} = 0$ and V_1 and V_2 are said to be uncorrelated. Two random variables that are statistically independent are also uncorrelated, but two uncorrelated random variables are not necessarily statistically independent. Jointly gaussian variables are an exception to the latter statement. This exception is one of the many convenient properties that jointly gaussian variables enjoy, and it offers the basis for the validity of utilizing $\rho_{V_1V_2}$ as an index of the statistical dependence of Rayleigh-distributed fluctuating envelopes, as we now proceed to show.

We first assume that the functions $e_1(t)$ and $e_2(t)$ of Eqs. (11) and (12) are sample functions of narrow-band, individually and jointly gaussian processes with zero means and the same variance σ_e^2, and covariances that are given by

$$E[e_{ck}e_{sk}] = 0, \; k = 1, 2$$

$$E[e_{c1}e_{c2}] = E[e_{s1}e_{s2}] = \mu_c < \sigma_e^2 \tag{14}$$

$$E[e_{c1}e_{s2}] = E[e_{c2}e_{s1}] = \mu_{cs} < \sigma_e^2. \tag{15}$$

The joint probability density function for the envelopes V_1 and V_2 is given by

$$p(V_1, V_2) = \frac{V_1V_2}{B} I_0\left(\frac{V_1V_2}{B}\sqrt{\mu_c^2 + \mu_{cs}^2}\right) e^{-\frac{\sigma_e^2}{2B}(V_1^2 + V_2^2)} \qquad \text{if } V_1, V_2 \geqslant 0$$

$$= 0 \qquad \text{otherwise,} \tag{16}$$

where $I_0(x)$ is the modified Bessel function of the first kind and zero order, and

$$B = \sigma_e^4 - (\mu_c^2 + \mu_{cs}^2) > 0. \tag{17}$$

Note that if $\mu_c = \mu_{cs} = 0$, then $p(V_1, V_2)$ factors out into the product of the Rayleigh density functions for V_1 and V_2, which is the condition for the statistical independence of V_1 and V_2 and hence for $\rho_{V_1V_2} = 0$. This simply confirms the expectation that if the cosine and sine components of $e_1(t)$ are uncorrelated with (and hence statistically independent of) those of $e_2(t)$, then V_1 and V_2 must be statistically independent.

Our problem is now to show that the hypothesis $\rho_{V_1V_2} = 0$ (*i.e.*, V_1 and V_2 uncorrelated) is a sufficient condition for the statistical independence of V_1 and V_2 because it necessarily means that $\mu_c = \mu_{cs} = 0$. In section AI of the Appendix (at the end of this chapter) we show that

$$\rho_{V_1V_2} = \frac{1}{4(4-\pi)} \sum_{n=1}^{\infty} \left[\frac{\Gamma(n-1/2)}{n!}\right]^2 \left(\frac{\mu_c^2 + \mu_{cs}^2}{\sigma_e^4}\right)^n \tag{18}$$

which converges for all $(\mu_c^2 + \mu_{cs}^2)/\sigma_e^4 < 1$. The coefficients in this expansion are all *positive real* numbers. Moreover, since $e_1(t)$ and

$e_2(t)$ are *real*, $(\mu_c^2 + \mu_{cs}^2)/\sigma_e^4$ is always real and positive. Therefore Eq. (18) expresses $\rho_{V_1V_2}$ as an infinite sum of *positive real* terms (which incidentally shows that $\rho_{V_1V_2}$ must be non-negative). Such a sum can vanish only if the individual terms vanish separately, and these in turn can be zero only when $\mu_c = \mu_{cs} = 0$. We therefore conclude that the only solution that satisfies $\rho_{V_1V_2} = 0$ is $\mu_c = \mu_{cs} = 0$, which means that $\rho_{V_1V_2} = 0$ is a sufficient (as well as necessary) condition for the statistical independence of V_1 and V_2.

It is important to remember that the preceding conclusion is based completely upon the assumption of a narrow-band gaussian model for the fading signals. In general, it cannot be demonstrated strictly for other possible models of the signals.

Now let the transmitted sinusoid be received in K different forms $e_1(t), e_2(t), \ldots, e_K(t)$ which can be considered as being sample functions of N corresponding narrow-band jointly gaussian processes. Then, for investigating the question of statistical dependence among these copies, it is sufficient to consider the correlation coefficients of the various signals taken *two at a time*. This is based upon another convenient property of jointly gaussian variables: the expectation of the product of K such variables is expressible completely in terms of the expectations of products of the variables taken *two at a time*.

There are several known techniques for obtaining copies of the same signal with low degrees of correlation among the fading envelopes. The most widely used method is known as *spaced-antenna diversity*. If two or more similar antennas are used at the receiving end, the correlation between the envelope fluctuations of the received signals can be decreased by spacing the antennas vertically, horizontally along the circumference of the great circle that passes through the transmitting and receiving locations, horizontally along the normal to this circle, or in some direction that combines all three. For brevity, we refer to the orthogonal directions that we have specified in the horizontal plane as "horizontally along" and "horizontally normal." The spacing between antennas is most often specified in units of one wavelength, and the separation at which $\rho_{V_1V_2} = 1/e \cong 0.37$ is sometimes called the diversity or correlation distance. We shall see later on (section VIII) that the effect of correlation between the signals can be neglected for practical purposes if $\rho_{V_1V_2}$ lies in the range $0 < \rho_{V_1V_2} < 1/e$.

In order to illustrate the type of variation of $\rho_{V_1V_2}$ with antenna spacing that is encountered in practice, we reproduce samples of published data in Fig. 7. In scatter systems, it is generally observed that the correlation coefficient decreases with increased antenna separation at a faster rate vertically and in the horizontally normal direction than in the horizontally along direction. In microwave line-of-sight links, only vertical spacing of antennas will result in signals

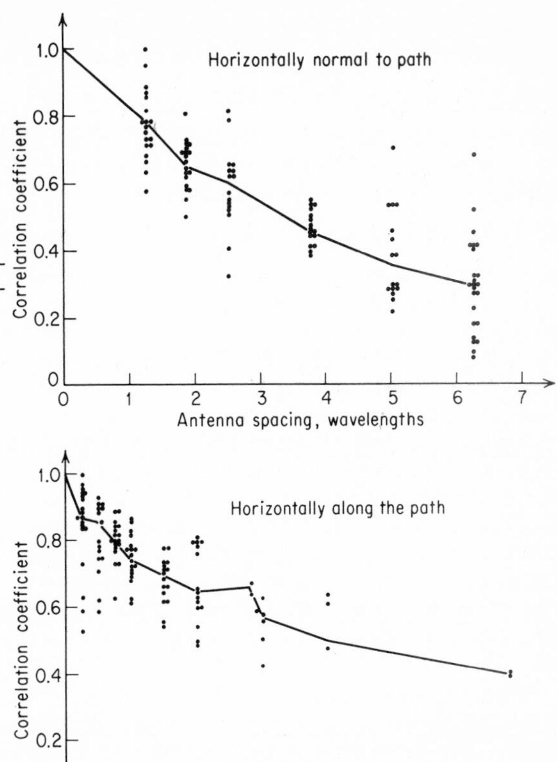

Fig. 7. Experimental data showing the variation of correlation coefficient with antenna spacing: (a) Data from experiment on ionospheric scatter over a 1243-km path at 49.8 mc. Curves pass through medians of observed values. (After G. R. Sugar, *Proc. IRE,* vol. 43, pp. 1432-1436; October, 1955.) (b) Data from experiment on tropospheric scatter over a 93-mile path at 2780 mc. (After Y. Kurihara, *Proc. IRE,* vol. 43, pp. 1362-1368; October, 1955.)

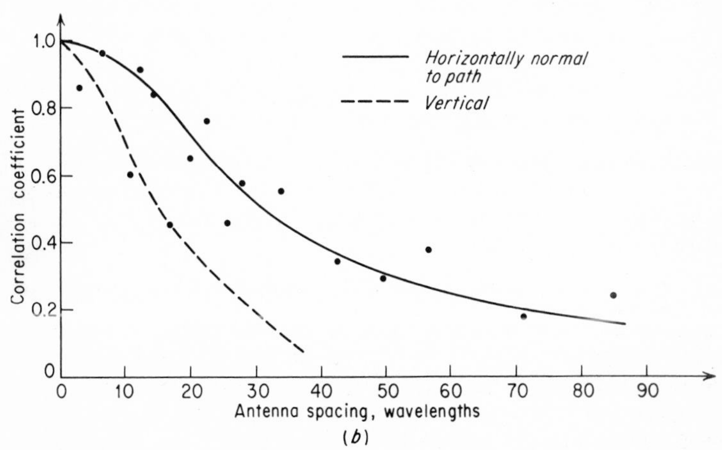

whose fading has a useful measure of independence without going to excessive and impractical separations.

An important type of space diversity that does not utilize spaced antennas is embodied in the Rake system that will be discussed in Chapter 12. In this system, delayed replicas of the same signal, arriving at the receiving antenna via a multiplicity of transmission paths, are sorted out and treated as channel-diversified copies of the same signal with negligible correlation between their noise components and individual fading patterns. Appropriate time repositioning and recombination of these signals offsets the destructive interference between them and enhances the signal-to-random-noise ratio.

Sometimes the fading is due in part to changes of polarization as the signal traverses the transmission medium. In fact, in normal ionospheric transmission of signals in the HF range, the transmitted signal acquires horizontally and vertically polarized components whose envelope fluctuations are approximately independent. Under such circumstances two copies of the disturbed signal which are suitable for diversity reception can be produced by means of two closely situated but independent dipole antennas whose relative orientation makes them respond to different polarization components of the incident wave. Such signals have been observed to obey the Rayleigh-fading law with reasonable independence,[9,10] and polarization diversity has even been deemed preferable to dual space diversity for transatlantic HF transmissions.[10] But no such results have been observed in tropospheric scatter and line-of-sight propagation of UHF and SHF, in which cases very little depolarization appears to be produced. Even when horizontally and vertically polarized components were deliberately transmitted, the received components appeared to fade in approximate synchronism.[11]

If the correlation coefficient of $V(t)$ and $V(t + \tau)$ is denoted by $\rho_V(\tau)$, then $\rho_V(0) = 1$, $\rho_V(\tau)$ decreases toward zero as τ is increased, and $\rho_V(\tau) \leqslant 1/e$ for $\tau \geqslant \tau_d$ where τ_d may be termed the diversity time spacing. Thus segments of the same received signal spaced in time by more than τ_d will exhibit almost independent fading patterns. This is the basis of so-called time diversity. The utilization of time diversity requires repetitive transmission of the same information over appropriately spaced time frames. This imposes obvious limitations on the speed of message delivery and on the number of different pieces of information that can be transmitted. In HF ionospheric transmission τ_d is of the order of seconds.[3,4,10] In radar application, the signal received during one scan would be stored and added to the signal received during the next scan to reinforce the message component.

In a similar manner, the correlation coefficient of the received envelopes of two independent sinusoids decreases as their frequency difference is increased. This is illustrated in Fig. 8. Consequently, another kind of diversity can be utilized in which the same message is transmitted on a number of carriers whose frequencies are suit-

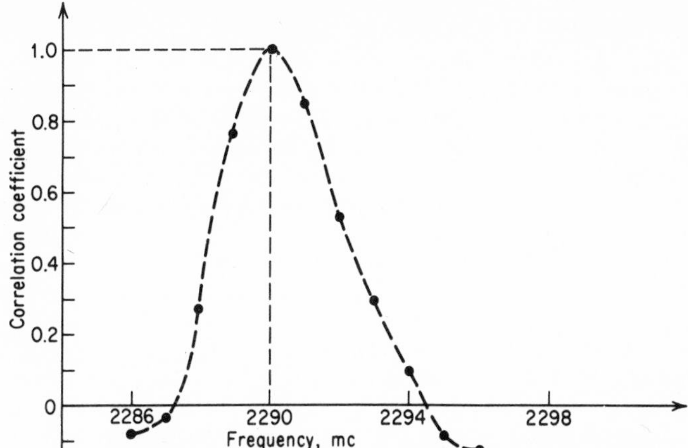

Fig. 8. Experimental plot of envelope correlation coefficient of two carriers as a function of their frequency separation. Data from tropospheric scatter experiment over a 188-mile path. (After J. H. Chisholm *et al.*, Ref. 13.)

ably spaced. However, the extravagant use of frequency space has so far discouraged the use of frequency diversity where other alternatives were readily available, particularly in scatter systems. But for microwave line-of-sight systems, frequency diversity offers important economical advantages over space diversity, and under certain conditions may even promise greater reliability.

Under certain circumstances, it is possible to distinguish between copies of the desired signal on the basis of angle of arrival. Utilization of this technique is known as angle diversity. For example, in scatter communication, a system of antenna-beam diversity which receives replicas of the signal from energy scattered by separate or partially overlapping parts of the scattering volume can be realized with one parabolic reflector. Two or more separate, isolated feeds that are slightly displaced from the focus of the reflector can provide highly directive beams whose center lines are oriented to form appropriate angles of separation. If the width of each beam is small in comparison with the angle subtended by the scattering volume, the desired separation of the beams can be achieved without moving any of the beams so far from the direction giving maximum signal that a great sacrifice in the level of received signal power is incurred. Bolgiano *et al.*[12] have presented a computed curve of correlation coefficient of the envelopes of received signals as a function of the angular separation between two beams. This curve with two experimental points superimposed by Chisholm *et al.*[13] is reproduced in Fig. 9. Another interesting example is afforded by the MUSA system.[14] In this system, angular diversity is realized by means of directive arrays that capitalize on differences in the angles of arrival

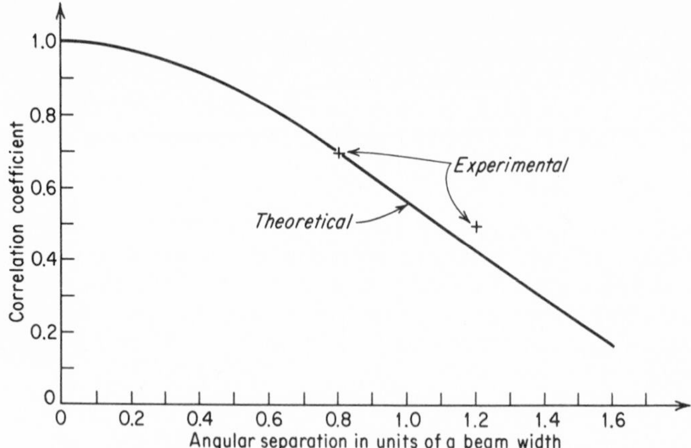

Fig. 9. Envelope correlation coefficient of two copies of the same carrier as a function of the azimuthal separation of the receiving antenna beams. Experimental points obtained in a tropospheric scatter experiment over a 188-mile path at 2290 mc. (From J. H. Chisholm *et al.*, Ref. 13.)

of ionospheric-reflected replicas of the signal arriving via different paths.

The preceding techniques constitute basic approaches to the problem of obtaining diversified replicas of the disturbed signal. These techniques need not, however, be viewed merely as alternative, inasmuch as suitable combinations of them may be advantageous.

V. EVALUATION OF THE SELECTION AND COMBINING TECHNIQUES

Having briefly described the ways in which a number of suitable replicas of the disturbed signal can be obtained, we now consider the ways in which we can utilize these signals. In the introduction, we have described a few signal utilization techniques as special cases of the operation indicated in Eq. (1). It will become evident presently that if observations of $f(t)$ in Eq. (1) are made over intervals that satisfy the description of T_{short} in section II, then the operation indicated in Eq. (1) will appear to be essentially linear for all of the possible choices of the weighting factors that were listed in the introduction. This accounts for Brennan's description of these techniques as "linear diversity combining techniques."[2] This "local linearity" of the techniques is a direct consequence of the "local constancy" of the weighting factors a_k. Operations on the signals, $f_k(t)$, that cannot be described as being "locally linear" can be readily dismissed on several accounts, not the least important of which are the detrimental effects of the resulting cross-modulation among the signal components and the noise components. Accordingly, we shall only be concerned here with the so-called locally linear operations listed in the introduction.

We start by assuming that the time function, $f_k(t)$, which describes the output of the kth diversity channel, is expressible in the form

$$f_k(t) = s_k(t) + n_k(t) \tag{19}$$

where $s_k(t)$ is the desired signal and $n_k(t)$ is the noise. We shall also assume that $s_k(t)$ and $n_k(t)$ are independent, except in the discussion of optimal selection where this is not needed. If we are combining the signals at r-f or i-f (*i.e.*, pre-detection), then over any interval of duration T_{short} (as described in section II), $s_k(t)$ is expressible in the form

$$s_k(t) = V_k \cos\left[\omega_c t + \phi_k\right] \tag{20}$$

where V_k and ϕ_k are substantially constant. With the exception of those parts of the discussion where we shall specify otherwise, the fading in the channel will be assumed to cause V_k and ϕ_k to be uncertain and to have the statistics of the instantaneous amplitude and instantaneous phase of a narrow-band gaussian process. As we have explained in section II, the experimental determination of such statistics would be carried out on the basis of samples of duration T_{int} ($\gg T_{\text{short}}$). This duration for the samples is chosen to bring out a typical behavior of the instantaneous amplitude while, at the same time, the median amplitude maintains a substantially constant value. Thus V_k and ϕ_k will be different for the different channel outputs (different k) and the signals must be appropriately phased before they are combined in order to assure maximum signal enhancement. In predetection combining we can always assume that the sum of signal and noise will encounter only linear processing prior to the combination of the various channel outputs, and therefore the noise component in $f_k(t)$ can be assumed to be completely independent of the signal component if the noise is largely receiver noise or, in the case of noise from external sources, if this is the condition that prevails in the transmission channel between transmitter and receiver.

But in post-detection combining, the assumption of independence between $s_k(t)$ and $n_k(t)$ is quite restrictive. It is justified for all signal-to-noise ratios only when the demodulation process is *linear* (*i.e.*, amounts to a distortionless translation of the spectrum), as in product demodulation of AM signals. Otherwise, the assumption of $n_k(t)$ independent of $s_k(t)$ necessarily restricts the validity of the argument to the range of r-f signal-to-noise ratios for which the inevitable interaction between signal and noise in the demodulator results in a negligible $S \times N$ term. In conventional FM and AM demodulation, this restriction means that only high values of S/N ratios at the intermediate frequency are of interest (see Chapter 19).

Post-detection combining brings in another important issue. In AM and related systems, we can generally assume that the amplitude of the signal component is directly proportional to the instantaneous amplitude of the r-f or i-f signal. Therefore, we can write

$$s_k(t) = V_k m(t), \quad k = 1, 2, \ldots, K \tag{21}$$

where $m(t)$ is the same for all channels, and V_k is a real and non-negative amplitude factor whose fluctuations (as a result of fading) follow those of the r-f or i-f signal envelope exactly. But this assumption cannot be made for FM, and the related pulse-time modulation systems. In these systems, as long as the threshold-drive requirements of the demodulator are satisfied, the signal level at the output of the demodulator is completely independent of the input signal level. But the signal-to-noise power ratio at the output of the demodulator is directly proportional to the signal-to-noise power ratio at the intermediate frequency for FM and pulse-time modulation systems, as well as for AM and related systems, as long as the ratio at the intermediate frequency exceeds a threshold value that is peculiar to the system and to the particular demodulator (product demodulators excepted). It is also interesting to note that a piecewise direct-proportionality relationship between the i-f and the low-frequency ratios does hold in some instances below the threshold because the low-frequency ratio can be closely approximated by a piecewise linear function of the i-f ratio.

There are various ways in which we can estimate the effect of a diversity technique upon the overall system performance. The criteria that are often chosen are (a) the "outage time," *i.e.*, the percentage of time that the communication will be interrupted as a result of signal fading below the threshold of message extractability; (b) the percentage of time that the local signal-to-noise ratio ($r(t)$ of Eq. (4)) will exceed a specified level; (c) the average value of $r(t)$; and (d) the error rate in the reception of digital signals. Error probabilities will not be considered in this chapter.

It must be emphasized here that any advantages gained from diversity will apply strictly to expected performance in any time interval of duration T_{int}, during which noise levels, thresholds, and median signal levels remain substantially constant. The long-term fluctuations in these "constants" will cause the overall performance of the system to fluctuate whether or not diversity is applied because:

(a) Fluctuations in median signal levels are usually identical for all receivers in a given locality and are the same for different frequencies, polarizations, and time intervals that do not exceed T_{int};

(b) Many possible types of fluctuation in noise level and thresholds do not possess a sufficient degree of statistical regularity to enable the designer to predict in advance the nature of the provisions that must be incorporated into the system design in order to combat these fluctuations.

5.1 Optimal Selection

Of the two switching techniques that we have listed in the introduction, the optimal selection technique is in principle (though not necessarily in practice) the more desirable. We shall therefore discuss only this technique in detail.

In an optimal-selection diversity system the outputs of the channels are observed simultaneously and only the best signal is connected to the output of the system.

With reference to Eq. (19), we note initially that whatever the nature of the noise component $n_k(t)$, the reception of the desired message will be interrupted, or the signal will be unusable, whenever the amplitude of $s_k(t)$ falls below some threshold (or least usable level) V_{th} set by the noise $n_k(t)$. Such thresholds are usually more sharply defined for FM and the related pulse-time modulation systems than they are for systems of the AM variety. For example, if $n_k(t)$ is a sinusoidal carrier of some fixed amplitude, then V_{th} for a conventional FM demodulator is very nearly equal to the amplitude of $n_k(t)$. If $n_k(t)$ is a sample function of a random white-noise process, then $V_{th} = bN_k(t)$, where b is a constant whose numerical value for most conventional FM receivers exceeds the peak factor of the noise (see Chapter 19). In the case in which $N(t)$ can be considered constant over the interval T_{int}, V_{th} will be constant, and if narrow-band gaussian statistics are attributed to the fading signals, the fraction of the time that the signal in the kth channel will be useless is given by

$$P_1(V \leqslant V_{th,k}) = 1 - e^{-0.693(V_{th,k}/V_{Mk})^2} \tag{22}$$

where $V_{th,k}$ is the threshold and V_{Mk} is the median signal amplitude for the kth channel. This result is a measure of the reliability of communicating through one fading channel. In contrast, if the selection is made from the outputs of K statistically independent channels, the fraction of the time that none of the signals will be useable and suitable for selection is given by

$$\prod_{k=1}^{K} \left[1 - e^{-0.693(V_{th,k}/V_{Mk})^2}\right]. \tag{23}$$

If the ratio of threshold-to-median signal amplitude is different for the different available channels, the channels will not be equally reliable. The ratio V_{th}/V_M may be different for the different channels because V_{th} and/or V_M are different for the different channels. The medians can be different, in particular, for polarization diversity and for angle diversity as a result of uncontrollable antenna design considerations. The thresholds can be different, for example, if post-detection selection is made and the different receivers have different sensitivities and different susceptibilities to interference and other disturbances.

In any case, it is easy to show that the product (23) is least when all the V_{th}/V_M ratios are *equal* to the *least* available ratio. For example, if $K = 2$ and $V_{th_1}/V_{M_1} = x$ while $V_{th_2}/V_{M_2} = qx$ where $q \geqslant 1$, then

$$\left[1 - e^{-0.693x^2}\right]\left[1 - e^{-0.693q^2x^2}\right] \geqslant \left[1 - e^{-0.693x^2}\right]^2$$

because, for fixed x, the second factor on the left-hand side increases monotonically with increasing q.

The percent outage time of a single channel is given by 100 times $P_1(V \leqslant V_{th})$ in Eq. (22), that of a K-fold selection diversity system by 100 times the product in (23).

Let us now consider the probability distribution function for the signal-to-noise power ratio obtainable with a K-fold optimal selection system and compare it with the distribution function for the ratio obtainable from the best available channel. We shall assume here that the local mean-square values of the noise components (as defined in Eq. 3) are all equal to N^2_{rms}, say, and that they do not change appreciably over intervals of duration T_{int}. Otherwise, we need no explicit statement as to whether or not the noise components of the various channels are correlated with one another or with the signal components. The fading patterns of the K available signals are also assumed to be uncorrelated (and hence statistically independent). Under these circumstances, the fluctuations in

$$r_k(t) = S^2_k(t)/N^2_{rms}$$

are caused only by the envelope fading. For predetection selection, $s_k(t)$ is given by Eq. (20). For post-detection selection, $s_k(t)$ is given by Eq. (21) where we now add the assumption that

$$\frac{1}{T_{short}} \int_{t-(1/2)T_{short}}^{t+(1/2)T_{short}} m^2(\tau)\,d\tau = 1/2 \tag{24}$$

for convenience only. For either of these two possibilities, we can now write that

$$S^2_k(t) = \frac{V^2_k}{2} \tag{25}$$

and, hence,

$$r_k(t) = \frac{V^2_k}{2N^2_{rms}} \tag{26}$$

With Rayleigh statistics assumed for V_k, we have

$$\begin{aligned} P_1(r_k \leqslant R_k) &= P_1(V_k \leqslant \sqrt{2N^2_{rms}\,R_k}\,) \\ &= 1 - e^{-R_k/(v^2/2N^2_{rms})}. \end{aligned} \tag{27}$$

This can also be written in the forms

$$P_1(r_k \leqslant R_k) = 1 - e^{-R_k/(\sigma_e/N_{rms})^2} \tag{28a}$$

$$= 1 - e^{-0.693 R_k/R_{M,k}} \tag{28b}$$

where σ^2_e is the variance of the narrow-band gaussian model of the fading signal and $R_{M,k}$ is the median value of R_k. If we now set

$$y_k = r_k/(\sigma_e/N_{\text{rms}})^2 = 0.693\, r_k/R_M \tag{29}$$

where y_k has the significance of r_k measured in units of $(\sigma_e/N_{\text{rms}})^2$, then

$$P_1(y_k \leqslant Y_k) = 1 - e^{-Y_k} \tag{30}$$

Henceforth y_k will be referred to as the "normalized S/N power ratio."

In optimal selection diversity, the signal with the highest value of Y_k is chosen all the time. If this largest value of Y_k is $\leqslant y$, then $Y_k \leqslant y$ for every channel. Hence, the probability that the normalized S/N power ratio, y, at the output of the K-fold optimal selection system is $\leqslant Y$ is the same as the probability that each of the individual channel ratios is $\leqslant Y$ at the same time. The assumption of statistically independent V_k enables us to write the latter probability as the product of the individual probabilities. Therefore,

$$P_K(y \leqslant Y) = [1 - e^{-Y}]^K \tag{31}$$

where the subscript K refers to K-fold diversity whereas the subscript 1 in Eq. (30) refers to one channel.

The average value of the realized, normalized S/N local power ratio, y, is

$$E_K[y] = \int_{-\infty}^{\infty} y p_K(y)\, dy$$

$$= \int_0^{\infty} yK(1 - e^{-y})^{K-1} e^{-y}\, dy. \tag{32}$$

This integral was evaluated by Brennan[2] who found the remarkably simple expression

$$E_K[y] = \sum_{k=1}^{K} \frac{1}{k} \tag{33}$$

$$\cong \ln K \text{ for large } K.$$

Note that $E_1[y] = 1$, and that adding the Kth channel increases $E_K[y]$ only by adding $1/K$ to it.

5.2 Combining Techniques

In switching diversity, $K - 1$ of the K available signals are totally rejected in favor of the best one, as in optimal selection, or in favor of the first-encountered one that happens to meet a preset requirement on quality, as in scanning diversity. The advantage of utilizing all of the available signals in order to achieve a better performance than is obtainable from any of the individual channels was pointed out by L. R. Kahn.[15] His conclusions were based on a simple analysis of a dual diversity system with constant and equal mean-square values for the noise components in the channels. C. L. Mack[16] followed with a system that applied for situations in which the mean squares of the noises were different, but the mean squares of the signal components were the same. But the general theorem that covered maximal K-fold linear combination for the case of arbitrary mean squares for signals and for noises was stated and proved by D. G. Brennan.[17] Kahn, Mack, and Brennan pointed out the advantage of maximal-ratio combining, but Altman and Sichak[18] pointed out that equal-weight (or equal-gain) combining will often outperform optimal selection and approximate the performance of maximal-ratio combining.

Before we consider maximal-ratio and equal-gain combiners, let us establish Brennan's theorem. To this end, we combine Eq. (1) and Eq. (19) and write

$$f(t) = \sum_{k=1}^{K} a_k s_k(t) + \sum_{k=1}^{K} a_k n_k(t). \tag{34}$$

The first sum represents a resultant signal component which we denote by $s(t)$, the second a resultant noise $n(t)$. The local mean-square value of each resultant component is again found by averaging the square over a time interval of duration T_{short}. For the signal component, we have from Eqs. (20), (21), and (24) that in either predetection or postdetection combining we can write

$$s_k(t) = V_k g(t) \tag{35}$$

where $g(t)$ is independent of k, and has a square whose mean value over any interval of duration T_{short} is 1/2. Moreover, we recall that in describing T_{short} we have specified that V_k must remain substantially constant during such a time interval. Therefore

$$s(t) = \sum_{k=1}^{K} a_k s_k(t) = g(t) \sum_{k=1}^{K} a_k V_k \tag{36}$$

and the local mean-square value of $s(t)$ is the local mean-square value of $g(t)$ weighted by $\left(\sum_{k=1}^{N} a_k V_k\right)^2$; *i.e.*,

$$S^2(t) = (1/2)\left[\sum_{k=1}^{K} a_k V_k\right]^2 = \left[\sum_{k=1}^{K} a_k (V_k/\sqrt{2})\right]^2. \tag{37}$$

If the noise components $n_k(t)$ are assumed to be random, uncorrelated, and to have zero means, the local mean square of their weighted sum is equal to the weighted sum of their local mean squares. Therefore the local mean-square value of the resultant noise component is

$$N^2(t) = \sum_{k=1}^{K} a_k^2 N_k^2(t) \tag{38}$$

where $N_k^2(t)$ is defined in Eq. (3). The ratio of the mean-square signal and noise in $f(t)$ is thus

$$r(t) = S^2(t)/N^2(t) = \frac{\left[\sum_{k=1}^{K} a_k(V_k/\sqrt{2})\right]^2}{\sum_{k=1}^{K} a_k^2 N_k^2}\,. \tag{39}$$

This ratio can be expressed in terms of the local ratios, $r_k(t) = V_k^2/2N_k^2$, of the various channels by noting that

$$\begin{aligned} a_k(V_k/\sqrt{2}) &= a_k N_k \left(\frac{V_k/\sqrt{2}}{N_k}\right) \\ &= a_k N_k r_k^{1/2}. \end{aligned}$$

Thus

$$r(t) = \frac{\left[\sum_{k=1}^{K} a_k N_k r_k^{1/2}\right]^2}{\sum_{k=1}^{K} a_k^2 N_k^2}\,. \tag{40}$$

But from the Schwarz inequality we know that

$$\left[\sum_{k=1}^{K} (a_k N_k) r_k^{1/2}\right]^2 \leqslant \left[\sum_{k=1}^{K} a_k^2 N_k^2\right]\left[\sum_{k=1}^{K} r_k\right].$$

Substitution in Eq. (40) and cancellation of common factors between numerator and denominator leads to

$$r(t) \leqslant \sum_{k=1}^{K} r_k(t). \tag{41}$$

This states that the maximum possible S/N power ratio that is obtainable from the sum (34) is given by the sum of the S/N power ratios of the individual channel outputs. This is the first part of Brennan's theorem. If in Eq. (40) we set

$$a_k N_k = \beta r_k^{1/2} \tag{42}$$

where β is some arbitrary proportionality factor that is independent of k, then

$$r(t) = \frac{\left[\beta \sum_{k=1}^{K} r_k\right]^2}{\beta^2 \sum_{k=1}^{K} r_k} = \sum_{k=1}^{K} r_k(t). \tag{43}$$

We therefore conclude that for the choice of the weighting factors a_k indicated in Eq. (42) (namely $a_k = \beta S_k/N_k^2$ where S_k is the local rms value of $s_k(t)$) the equality sign in (41) applies, and hence the maximum possible value for $r(t)$ is achieved. This is the second part of Brennan's theorem.

5.2A Maximal-Ratio Combining

A maximal-ratio combiner, by definition, delivers the maximum value of S/N power ratio obtainable from any locally linear combination of the available signals. In any time interval of duration T_{short}, the weighting factor a_k is automatically adjusted to have a value that is directly proportional to the rms value of the kth signal component and inversely proportional to the mean-square value of the noise in the kth channel. The proportionality factors are the same for all channels.

The simplest criterion to consider here is the mean value of the local normalized output S/N ratio y. From Eq. (43) we have that the output S/N power ratio is always equal to the sum of the channel ratios. Consequently,

$$y = \sum_{k=1}^{K} y_k \tag{44}$$

where y_k is the normalized power ratio for the kth channel. The mean of y is therefore the sum of the means of the y_k's; *i.e.*,

$$E_K[y] = \sum_{k=1}^{K} E_1[y_k] = K \tag{45}$$

where we have substituted the value $E_1[y_k] = 1$ obtainable from Eq. (33) for each individual channel. The mean value of y is seen to increase linearly with K for maximal ratio combining, whereas a much slower dependence upon K is indicated in Eq. (33) for optimal selection.

Next we seek an expression for the outage probability, or the percentage of time that the communication will be interrupted. We assume that the envelope V of the resultant signal component $s(t)$ must exceed or equal some threshold value V_{th} in order for the message to remain extractable. We also assume for simplicity that the local mean squares of the noise components in the various channels are all constant and equal to N_{rms}^2 for any interval of duration T_{int}. The resultant local S/N power ratio can therefore be written as

$$r(t) = \sum_{k=1}^{K} \left(\frac{V_k/\sqrt{2}}{N_{\text{rms}}}\right)^2 \tag{46}$$
$$= V^2/2N_{\text{rms}}^2$$

where

$$V^2 = \sum_{k=1}^{K} V_k^2 . \tag{47}$$

This shows that if the mean-square noise is the same for all channels, then to within a constant multiplier (that is the same for the resultant signal and the resultant noise) the amplitude of the resultant signal component out of a maximal-ratio combiner is given by the square-root of the sum of the squares of the amplitudes of the signal components of the various channels and, in comparison, the resultant mean-square noise is equal to the mean-square noise of one channel. Stated backward, this says that if the mean-square value of the output noise is scaled down to the value of the input noise, the corresponding resultant signal will have an amplitude whose square equals the sum of the squares of the amplitudes of the input signals. In effect, the signals add on "a mean-square basis" rather than on a "rms basis."

From Eq. (47), the outage probability is

$$P_K(V \leqslant V_{\text{th}}) = P\left(\sum_{k=1}^{K} V_k^2 \leqslant V_{\text{th}}^2\right). \tag{48}$$

If the V_k's are assumed to be independent Rayleigh-distributed variables with equal mean squares given by v^2, then from

$$P_1(V_k \leqslant V_k') = P_1(V_k^2 \leqslant V_k'^2)$$
$$= 1 - e^{-V_k'^2/v^2}$$

we have

$$p_1(V_k'^2) = d[1 - e^{-V'^2/v^2}]/d(V'^2)$$
$$= (1/v^2)\, e^{-V_k'^2/v^2},\ k = 1, 2, \ldots, K. \tag{49}$$

In order to evaluate the right-hand member of Eq. (48), we therefore seek the probability density function of the sum of K independent random variables each of which has a known probability density function given in Eq. (49). In section 2.4 of Chapter 2 it was shown that the probability density function of the sum of two independent random variables is given by the convolution integral of the individual density functions. This result can be applied here as follows. First convolve $p_1(V_1^2)$ and $p_1(V_2^2)$ in order to obtain $p_2(V_1^2 + V_2^2)$. Now, if $p_2(V_1^2 + V_2^2)$

is convolved with $p_1(V_3^2)$, $p_3(V_1^2 + V_2^2 + V_3^2)$ results, and so on. The density function $p_K\left(\sum_{k=1}^{K} V_k^2\right)$ finally results from convolving the two density functions $p_{K-1}\left(\sum_{k=1}^{K-1} V_k^2\right)$ and $p_1(V_K^2)$. If we set

$$\lambda_K = \sum_{k=1}^{K} V_k^2$$

then, it turns out that

$$P_K(\lambda_K) = \frac{1/v^2}{(K-1)!}\left(\frac{\lambda_K}{v^2}\right)^{K-1} e^{-\lambda_K/v^2} \tag{50}$$

Now

$$\begin{aligned} P_K(\lambda_K \leqslant \lambda_K') &= \int_0^{\lambda_K'} p(\lambda_K)\, d\lambda_K \\ &= \frac{1}{(K-1)!} \int_0^{\lambda_K'/v^2} x^{K-1} e^{-x}\, dx. \end{aligned} \tag{51}$$

The function

$$\gamma_n(u) = \frac{1}{n!} \int_0^u x^n e^{-x}\, dx$$

is known as the incomplete Γ function and it is tabulated.[19] In terms of this function we can write

$$P_K(\lambda_K \leqslant \lambda_K') = \gamma_{K-1}(\lambda_K'/v^2).$$

In section AII of the Appendix, an expression is derived for the incomplete Γ function. This enables us to write

$$P_K(\lambda_K \leqslant \lambda_K') = 1 - \left[\sum_{k=0}^{K-1} \frac{(\lambda_K'/v^2)^k}{k!}\right] e^{-\lambda_K'/v^2} \tag{52}$$

Therefore we conclude that

$$\begin{aligned} P_K(V \leqslant V_{\text{th}}) &= \gamma_{K-1}(V_{\text{th}}^2/v^2) \\ &= 1 - \left[\sum_{k=0}^{K-1} \frac{(V_{\text{th}}^2/v^2)^k}{k!}\right] e^{-V_{\text{th}}^2/v^2} \qquad (53) \\ &= \left[\sum_{k=K}^{\infty} \frac{(V_{\text{th}}^2/v^2)^k}{k!}\right] e^{-V_{\text{th}}^2/v^2}. \qquad (54) \end{aligned}$$

From (54), an approximate expression which holds for $V_{\text{th}}^2/v^2 \leqslant (K+1)/10$ is given by

$$P_K(V \leqslant V_{\text{th}}) \cong \frac{(V_{\text{th}}/v)^{2K}}{K!}\, e^{-(V_{\text{th}}/v)^2}\,. \tag{55}$$

The per cent outage time is 100 $P_K(V \leqslant V_{\text{th}})$.

The preceding derivation also gives us the probability distribution function for the normalized local S/N power ratio y. Thus, if we replace V_{th}^2/v^2 by y, we obtain

$$P(y \leqslant Y) = 1 - \left[\sum_{k=0}^{K-1} \frac{Y^k}{k!}\right] e^{-Y} \tag{56}$$

$$\cong \frac{Y^K}{K!}\, e^{-Y} \text{ for } Y \leqslant (K+1)/10.$$

5.2B Equal-Gain Combining

In an equal-gain combiner, the K diversity-channel outputs are added together with equal weighting for all, good and poor. In order to ensure this equal weighting in practice, all receiver signal-processing circuits through which the signals are channeled before superposition must have identical transfer characteristics. Among other things, this requirement usually necessitates that the various receiver channels preceding the common adder have a common AGC system.

Again the simplest performance criterion to consider first is the mean value of the normalized local S/N power ratio y. Here, if we assume that the local mean squares of the noise components are equal and each is denoted by N_{rms}^2, and if we set $a_1 = a_2 = \ldots = a_K = 1$, then Eq. (39) becomes

$$r(t) = \left[\sum_{k=1}^{K} (V_k/\sqrt{2})\right]^2 \Big/ (KN_{\text{rms}}^2) \tag{57}$$

whence

$$2N_{\text{rms}}^2\, r(t) = \frac{1}{K}\sum_{k=1}^{K} V_k^2 + \frac{1}{K}\sum_{\substack{k,j=1\\ k\neq j}}^{K} V_k V_j\,. \tag{57a}$$

If we take the statistical average of each side, noting that $E[V_k^2] = v^2 = 2\sigma_e^2$, that $E[V_k V_j] = E[V_k]E[V_j] = (\pi/4)\,v^2$ for independent Rayleigh-distributed envelopes, and that the second sum on the right-hand side contains $K^2 - K$ terms, we obtain

$$E_K[y] = E[r(t)/(v^2/2N_{\text{rms}}^2)]$$

$$= 1 + (\pi/4)(K-1) \tag{58}$$

This expression should be compared with (33) for optimal selection, and with (45) for maximal-ratio combining.

The amplitude of the resultant signal component out of an equal-gain combiner is simply the sum of the amplitudes of the component signals in the combined channels. Thus, with the choice of unity weighting factors made in this discussion, we have

$$V = \sum_{k=1}^{K} V_k \tag{59}$$

for an equal-gain combiner. Similarly, if the mean-square noise is the same for all channels, the total mean-square noise out of an equal-gain combiner is given by KN^2_{rms}. If the output signal-plus-noise level is rescaled so that the output mean-square noise is given by N^2_{rms}, the corresponding expression for the square of the signal amplitude is given by the right-hand side of Eq. (57a) which evidently is not easily compared with Eq. (47) for the maximal-ratio combiner.

If a threshold V_{th} exists for message extractability, then

$$P(V \leqslant V_{\mathrm{th}}) = P\left(\sum_{k=1}^{K} V_k \leqslant V_{\mathrm{th}}\right). \tag{60}$$

This is the probability distribution function of the sum of K random variables, evaluated at $V = V_{\mathrm{th}}$. If the V_k's are assumed to be independent, the probability density function of their sum is again expressible as the K-fold convolution of their individual density function. Unfortunately, this is much more easily said than done for more than two Rayleigh density functions. Consequently, the probability distribution function for the sum of only two Rayleigh-distributed variables is available in terms of defined and known mathematical functions.[18] Using this, we have for the outage probability with a dual equal-gain combiner

$$P_2(V \leqslant V_{\mathrm{th}}) = 1 - e^{-V^2_{\mathrm{th}}/v^2} - \sqrt{\pi/2}\left(\frac{V_{\mathrm{th}}}{v}\right) e^{-V^2_{\mathrm{th}}/2v^2}\; erf\left(\frac{V_{\mathrm{th}}/\sqrt{2}}{v}\right) \tag{61}$$

where $erf(x)$ is the error function

$$\frac{2}{\sqrt{\pi}} \int_0^x e^{-t^2}\, dt$$

which is tabulated. For $K \leqslant 8$, tables of $P_K(V \leqslant V')$ have been computed by Mason, Ginsburg, and Brennan,[21] and curves based on these have been published.[2]

The probability distribution function for the normalized local S/N power ratio y is expressible in terms of the preceding results as follows. First, note that Eq. (57) can be rewritten as

$$u \equiv \left[K \frac{r(t)}{v^2/(2N^2_{\mathrm{rms}})}\right]^{1/2} = \sum_{k=1}^{K} (V_k/v). \tag{62}$$

Therefore

$$P(u \leqslant u') = P_K\left(\sum_{k=1}^{K} V_k \leqslant vu'\right) \tag{63}$$

and

$$P_K\ (y \leqslant Y) = P\,(u \leqslant \sqrt{KY}\,). \tag{64}$$

VI. UTILIZATION OF THE PRECEDING RESULTS

The advantages of diversity reception over single-channel reception may be viewed in at least two important ways. First, all other important considerations (such as transmitter power, antenna costs, etc.) being equal, the reliability of a communication system is increased (or outage time is decreased) by using diversity. Second, for a given tolerable outage time, less transmitter power would be needed with diversity than without it. (For a specified reliability, the ratio of the transmitter power required without to power required with is often termed the "diversity gain"; but the significance of diversity gain is hampered by the strong dependence of this "gain" upon the specified value of reliability.) Diversity makes it possible also to relax other system design requirements, such as quality of receivers, sizes of antennas, circuit and component reliability, maintenance or attendance considerations, etc.

The results of the preceding section can be utilized in order to determine

(a) for fixed transmitter power, whether the amount of reduction in the outage time (or the increase in system reliability) justifies the added cost and complexity of going from single-channel reception to K-fold diversity;

(b) how much reduction in transmitter power and/or antenna size, receiver sensitivity, etc., is permissible without any corresponding increase in outage time (or decrease in system reliability);

(c) the simplest way to achieve either, or a combination of both, of the objectives (a) and (b) without incurring new problems in circuit maintenance, reliability, adjustment, or adequate instrumentation.

In the overall planning of a communication system, the use of an appropriate diversity technique can be an important aid toward a more desirable distribution of the costs among the important parts of the system than is sometimes possible in single-channel reception.

Graphical presentations based on the results of the preceding section are given in Figs. 10, 11, and 12. In Fig 10, plots are given of $10\log_{10}(E_K[y])$ as a function of K, for the expressions of $E_K[y]$ that are given in Eqs. (33), (45), and (58). These plots give the increase (in db) in the average value of the local S/N power ratio achieved in going from single-channel to K-fold diversity reception.[2] It is of interest to note that the increase for equal-gain combining is less than one db below that for maximal-ratio combining for all $K \leqslant 24$, and as $K \to \infty$ the difference goes to 1.05 db! However, the

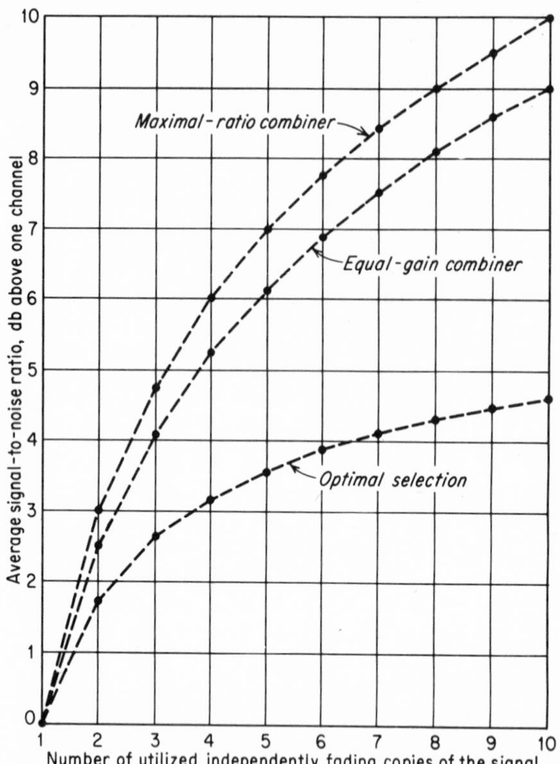

Fig. 10. Improvement in average received signal-to-noise power ratio resulting from diversity operation with a number of independently fading (Rayleigh-distributed) copies of the signal all having the same value of median amplitude. Noise in each channel is assumed to be independent of the signal and also of the noise in the other channels, and to have a zero mean and a constant mean-square value over time intervals in which the median signal level is substantially constant. (After D. G. Brennan, Ref. 2.)

curve for optimal selection falls below the other two and its departure from them widens appreciably with increasing K.

The curves presented in Figs. 11 and 12 play a dual role. The ordinate designation pertains to the ratio Y/y_M expressed in db where y_M is the median value of the normalized local S/N power ratio for one channel. The same curves also give the per-cent-of-time distributions of V'/V_M (expressed in db) if the numbers marked on the vertical scale are multiplied by 2. Note that $y_M = 0.693$ if y_k has the probability distribution function given in Eq. (30), and that $y/y_M = r/R_M$, where R_M is the median value of the S/N power ratio for one

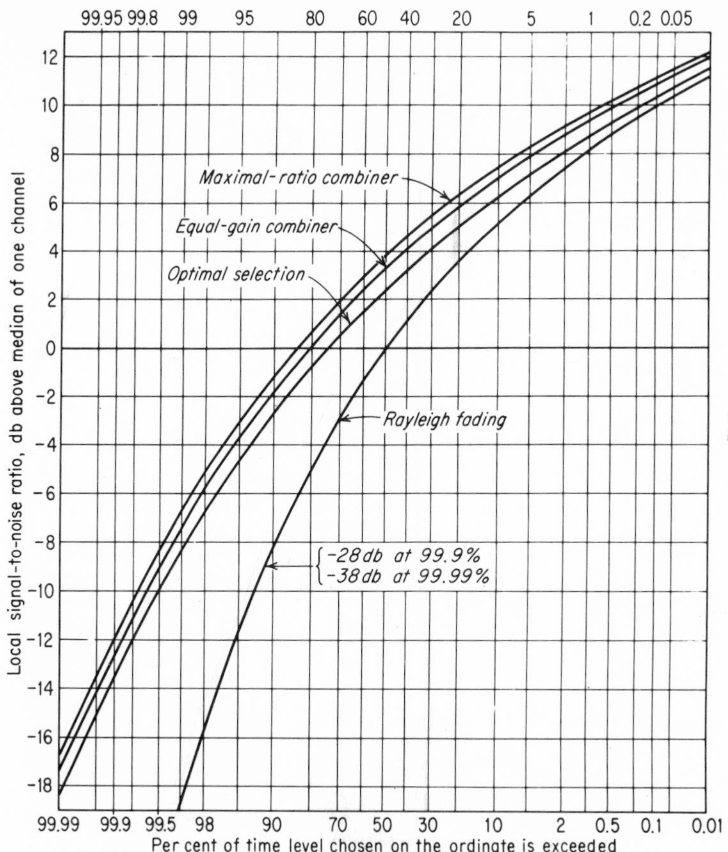

Fig. 11. Per-cent-of-time distributions of received signal-to-noise power ratio (and of received signal envelope if the numbers on the vertical scale are multiplied by 2) for a single channel and for *two-channel diversity* with each of the three signal utilization techniques discussed in the text. Signals are assumed to have independent Rayleigh-fading patterns with equal median amplitudes. Noise in each channel is assumed to be independent of the signal and also of the noise in the other channels, and to have a zero mean and a constant mean-square value over time intervals in which the median signal level is substantially constant. For optimal selection, the only necessary restriction on the noise is that its mean-square value be constant. (After D. G. Brennan, Ref. 2.)

channel. The abscissa values are computed from $100\,[1 - P_K(y \leqslant Y)]$, where $P_K(y \leqslant Y)$ is given by the expressions of the preceding section.

It is important to remember that the analyses of the preceding section, which led to the plots of Figs. 10, 11, and 12, were based

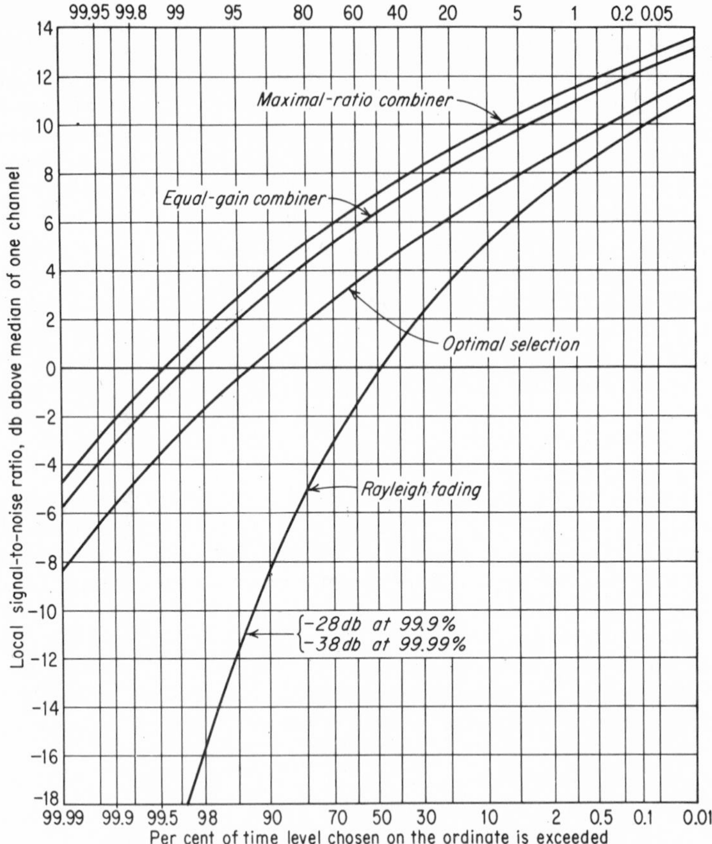

Fig. 12. Per-cent-of-time distributions of received signal-to-noise power ratio (and of received signal envelope if the numbers on the vertical scale are multiplied by 2) for a single channel and for *four-channel diversity* with each of the three signal utilization techniques discussed in the text. Signals are assumed to have independent Rayleigh-fading patterns with equal median amplitudes. Noise in each channel is assumed to be independent of the signal and also of the noise in the other channels, and to have a zero mean and a constant mean-square value over time intervals in which the median signal level is substantially constant. For optimal selection, the only necessary restriction on the noise is that its mean-square value be constant. (After D. G. Brennan, Ref. 2.)

on a statistical model of the fading envelope that characterized the distribution of the instantaneous values of V during time intervals of duration T_{int}. During such time intervals, the median value of V is by hypothesis essentially a constant, and one speaks of the associated statistical properties of V as describing the probability distribution of V "about a specified median." The plots of Figs. 11 and 12 also describe the probability distribution (for intervals of duration T_{int}) of the amplitude or of the normalized S/N power ratio of the output from a K-fold diversity system. In this description, V and $r(t)$ are normalized with respect to (or measured in units of) their constant single-channel median values in intervals of duration T_{int}.

Thus, the system performance characteristics during intervals of duration T_{int} can be estimated from curves such as those in Figs. 10, 11, and 12 if the important parameters, such as V_{th} and V_M, are known for each interval. For example, the outage time is determined from a knowledge of the ratio V_{th}/V_M for each interval. In general, this ratio changes from interval to interval as a result of fluctuations in V_M (and possibly V_{th}). The estimated outage time will therefore fluctuate from interval to interval, in synchronism with the variations in V_{th}/V_M. These fluctuations are not affected by the application of diversity techniques.

In the study of the long-term variability of system performance, it is sometimes convenient to visualize or to portray the per-cent-of-time distributions during some T_{int} interval with the values of $r(t)$ and $V(t)$ referred to their single-channel medians in some other T_{int} interval or expressed in units of some arbitrary reference values. Thus one may seek the effect upon the ordinate scales in Figs. 11 and 12 of a change in the reference values of $r(t)$ and $V(t)$ from some values R_{M2} and V_{M2} to some other values R_{M1} and V_{M1}. In order to determine this effect we first observe that

$$\frac{r(t)}{R_{M2}} = \frac{r(t)}{V_{M2}^2/(2N_{rms}^2)} = \left(\frac{V_{M1}}{V_{M2}}\right)^2 \cdot \frac{r(t)}{R_{M1}}$$

whence

$$10 \log_{10}\left(\frac{r(t)}{R_{M1}}\right) = 20 \log_{10}(V_{M2}/V_{M1}) + 10 \log_{10}\left(\frac{r(t)}{R_{M2}}\right) \tag{65}$$

where we have assumed that N_{rms}^2 is the same for the different T_{int} intervals under consideration. Remember that the $r(t)$ under consideration is supposed to have a median R_{M2}. Consequently, a change in the value of the reference median from V_{M2} to V_{M1} can be taken into account by shifting the position of the zero-db line on the vertical scale in Figs. 11 and 12 a distance that equals $20 \log_{10}(V_{M2}/V_{M1})$ db. The resulting curves will also describe the per-cent-of-time distributions for $20 \log_{10}(V/V_{M1})$ when the median of V is V_{M2}. It must be emphasized, however, that such translations of the zero-db line of the vertical scale are necessary only when the reference values of $r(t)$ and $V(t)$ are chosen to be different from their single-channel median values in each particular T_{int} interval for the purpose of using a "common datum" for all intervals. The curves of Figs. 11 and 12 apply in any given time interval T_{int} as long as the medians that are chosen as reference quantities for $r(t)$ and $V(t)$ are those of the single-channel $r(t)$ and $V(t)$ during that *same* interval.

In the design of high-reliability systems, curves such as those in Figs. 11 and 12, can be considered to give the distributions of $r(t)$ or $V(t)$ during the interval of duration T_{int} when R_M is least or V_{th}/V_M is highest, and the design can proceed accordingly. During other time intervals when the conditions for reception are more favorable, the reliability of the system can be estimated either on the basis of the highest value of V_{th}/V_M after an appropriate translation of the zero-db line, or by entering the original curves at the level of the new value of V_{th}/V_M that is appropriate to the interval under consideration.

VII. COMPARISON OF THE SIGNAL-UTILIZATION TECHNIQUES

For the narrow-band gaussian model of independently fading signals, and with assumptions of uncorrelated random noise that is independent of signals and has zero means and equal mean squares in the various channels, the results achieved with optimal selection, equal-gain combining and maximal-ratio combining can be easily compared with single-channel reception on the basis of the considerations discussed in section VI and the graphical presentations in Figs. 10, 11, and 12. Yet it is very illuminating to consider another approach to the comparison of the potentialities of the various techniques, especially against non-Rayleigh fading, which is based on an analytical aid originally presented by Altman and Sichak.[18]

The discussion is best carried out in terms of dual diversity because of the simplicity with which we can portray and visualize two-dimensional presentations. We can start by asking the question: For what pairs of values for the rms S/N ratios in the two available channels will the resultant output ratio be equal to some specified value γ, if each of the signal-utilization techniques is applied? The answer to this question for each technique can be expressed in terms of some contour, or locus, in a two-dimensional presentation whose coordinates are specified by the rms S/N ratios in the two channels.

In optimal selection, the output rms S/N ratio will equal γ only when the S/N ratio in one of the channels is equal to γ while the ratio in the other has any value between zero and γ. The input S/N ratios must therefore locate some point on the locus sketched in Fig. 13.

In a maximal-ratio combiner, an output rms S/N ratio γ will result only when (by Brennan's theorem)

$$(S_1/N_{rms})^2 + (S_2/N_{rms})^2 = \gamma^2$$

which defines the appropriate locus as being the first-quadrant portion of a circle of radius γ centered at the origin (Fig. 13).

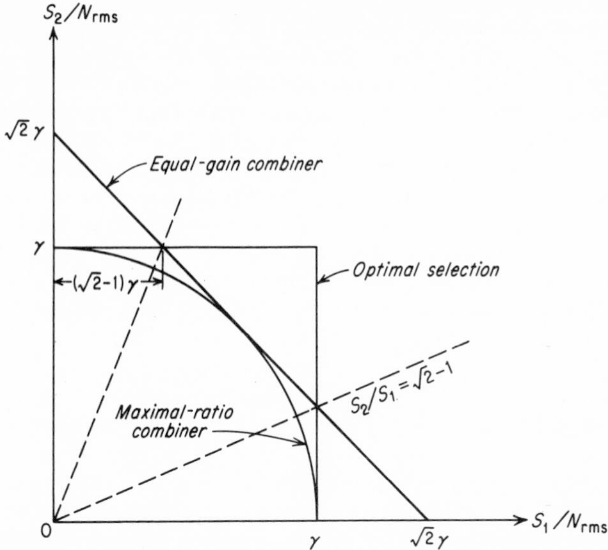

Fig. 13. Loci of pairs of values of rms S/N ratios in the two channels which will result in a specified output rms S/N ratio γ.

With an equal-gain combiner, the locus is defined by

$$\frac{S_1 + S_2}{\sqrt{N_{\text{rms}}^2 + N_{\text{rms}}^2}} = \gamma,$$

whence

$$(S_1/N_{\text{rms}}) + (S_2/N_{\text{rms}}) = \sqrt{2}\ \gamma.$$

This defines the straight line drawn in Fig. 13.

The locus for the maximal-ratio combiner is enclosed completely between the other two loci and the coordinate axes. This signifies that a maximal-ratio combiner requires lower values of input S/N ratios in order to yield a specified output ratio than the other two techniques. This is consistent with the fact that a maximal-ratio combiner always realizes the maximum achievable S/N power ratio from a number of noisy signals. For input signal amplitude ratios in the range $0.414 < S_1/S_2 < 1/0.414$, an equal-gain combiner performs better than an optimal-selection system, but the converse is true outside of this range. This observation defines the circumstances (under the assumptions of this discussion) under which an equal-weight superposition of the noisy signals will result in a net enhancement of the signal over the noise. It is intuitively clear that when one of the channels becomes much poorer than the other, the noise contribution of the poorer channel to the resultant output will outweigh its relative signal contribution.

Note that the locus for the equal-gain combiner approximates the locus for the maximal ratio combiner quite closely whenever $0.414 \leqslant S_1/S_2 \leqslant 1/0.414$, whereas the optimal-selection curve lies closer to the maximal-ratio combiner curve whenever S_1/S_2 falls outside of this range. This immediately suggests* that the performance of a maximal-ratio combiner can be approached closely by a system that performs as an equal-gain combiner whenever $0.414 \leqslant S_1/S_2 \leqslant 1/0.414$ and as an optimal selector whenever S_1/S_2 falls outside of this range. Such a system exemplifies the alternate-switching-and-combining technique mentioned in section II.

It is clear from the preceding observations that whether or not the performance of an equal-gain combiner will be superior to that of an optimal-selection system depends entirely upon the joint probability density function $p(S_1/N_{\text{rms}}, S_2/N_{\text{rms}})$. This density function can be visualized as a surface over the plane of Fig. 13, whose elevation over the plane at every point $(S_1'/N_{\text{rms}}, S_2'/N_{\text{rms}})$ is given by $p(S_1'/N_{\text{rms}}, S_2'/N_{\text{rms}})$. The volume enclosed between any portion of this surface and the orthogonal projection of this portion on the plane equals the fraction of time in any interval of duration T_{int} that S_1/N_{rms} and S_2/N_{rms} will fall simultaneously within the projection on the plane. The total volume between the surface and the plane is the probability of an event that must occur, and hence is unity (by definition). If the surface is so shaped that its elevation over the region defined by $0.414 \leqslant S_1/S_2 \leqslant 1/0.414$ on the plane generally exceeds its elevation over the remainder of the plane, then the use of an equal-gain combiner will lead to a better overall system performance than is possible with optimal selection. This is most frequently the case in practice, and is certainly true for Rayleigh fading. However, an optimal-selection system will perform better than an equal-gain combiner if the converse is true.

In deriving the loci of Fig. 13 we have assumed that each channel contributes the same amount of incoherent noise power. The variables of Fig. 13 can therefore be considered to be signal amplitudes, or signal rms values, with an appropriate scale factor. Let the scaling in Fig. 13 be adjusted to read values of V_1, V_2, and V, and let $V' = \sqrt{2N_{\text{rms}}}\,\gamma$. Consider the surface defined by $p(V_1, V_2)$. Integration of $p(V_1, V_2)$ over the area that is enclosed within each locus yields $P_2(V \leqslant V')$ for the technique associated with the locus. For two independent Rayleigh-distributed envelopes of equal medians,

$$p(V_1, V_2) = \frac{4}{v^4} V_1 V_2 e^{-(V_1^2 + V_2^2)/v^2} \qquad \text{for } V_1, V_2 \geqslant 0$$

$$= 0 \qquad \text{otherwise.}$$

The exponential decays quickly with radial distance from the origin. An examination of the areas that are not shared by the enclosures within the optimal-selection locus and the equal-gain locus shows

*This observation was made by F. J. Altman, and later by G. L. Mellen independently. It is sometimes referred to as the Altman-Mellen combining technique (see Ref. 21).

that the presence of the radially decaying exponential factor in $p(V_1, V_2)$ will not cause any preferential weighting in favor of either of these two techniques. But the factor $V_1 V_2$ has a peak value along the line $V_1 = V_2$ and is zero along $V_1 = 0$ and $V_2 = 0$. Therefore $P_2(V \leqslant V')$ will be greater for optimal selection than for equal-gain combining because even though the total areas of the unshared regions are equal, the values of $V_1 V_2$ are greater over the optimal-selection region than they are over the equal-gain region.

Before a final choice of technique can be made, the available techniques must be compared from the practical viewpoint also. Experience with operational maximal-ratio combiners over the last few years has indicated that this type of approach may be quickly becoming of academic interest only. The main reasons for this are:

(a) the instrumentation of post-detection maximal-ratio combiners requires more numerous components and more involved circuitry than either pre-detection or post-detection equal-gain combiners;[23]

(b) the adjustments are also more critical and the maintenance problem more acute, so that as a result of maladjustments a maximal-ratio combiner may actually perform worse than an equal-gain combiner operating under the same conditions;

(c) no practically satisfactory pre-detection maximal-ratio combiner has yet been developed although one has been proposed, and serious attempts in that direction have so far not been fruitful.

These difficulties naturally stem from the elaborate operations that are usually required for the realization of the optimum combination of the available signals.

Pre-detection equal-gain combining has significant advantages over post-detection combining (whether equal-gain or maximal-ratio) with respect to threshold of satisfactory reception in the presence of random noise unless the demodulation process amounts to a distortionless translation of the desired spectrum. This is to be expected at least on the basis of one important consideration: Pre-detection combining provides an opportunity to improve the signal relative to the noise *before* passing the signal plus noise through the final detection stages where irreversible S/N ratio degradations may be encountered.

The other signal-utilization techniques have practical problems too. Notable examples:

1. Post-detection switching causes transients that may be intolerable. But switching transients can be minimized by going into pre-detection switching; however, pre-detection switching brings in another type of transient that can also be intolerable in FM or phase-modulation systems: The instantaneous phases of the incoming carriers are not the same and switching from one to the other will cause a phase step and a consequent frequency pulse. This difficulty can be abated by adding phase-control circuitry before the switching stage.

2. Equal-gain combining requires careful control of the gains in the receiver channels in order to ensure that the gains are truly *equal*, and hence to ensure equal weighting of the superimposed signals. Thus, the signal-processing circuits whose outputs are superimposed must have identical transfer characteristics. A common AGC system must be used.
3. Pre-detection combining requires the addition of phase control circuitry in order to ensure that the signals are always superimposed *in phase*. With frequency diversity, the two signal frequencies must be controlled by the same oscillator at the transmitter: The signals must be frequency translates of the *same* modulated signal. At the receiver, the frequency-diversity signals must be heterodyned down to the same i-f frequency before combining.

VIII. EFFECT OF NON-INDEPENDENCE OF FADING SIGNALS

The performance characteristics of the techniques described in the preceding sections are adversely affected if the various channels do not fade independently. For example, in optimal-selection (and other switching) systems no signal improvements can be derived under conditions of 100% correlation (but the same is not true for the other combining systems). The correlation between the available signals is often easily made negligible by appropriate design. But there are circumstances in which practical considerations limit the freedom with which choices can be made, and substantial correlation must be expected among the available signals. In such circumstances, it is important to be able to estimate the effect of correlation among the signals upon the achieved results.

The simplest case to consider is that of a dual optimal-selection system with correlated Rayleigh fading. For this situation, we show in section AIII of the Appendix that the outage probability (or the probability that the envelope of the stronger of the two available signals is less than the threshold value V_{th}) is given by

$$[P(V_1 \leqslant V_{\text{th}},\, V_2 \leqslant V_{\text{th}})]_{\xi \neq 0} = \sum_{n=0}^{\infty} \alpha_n \xi^n \tag{66}$$

where

$$\xi = (\mu_c^2 + \mu_{cs}^2)/\sigma_e^4,$$

$$\alpha_0 = [P(V_1 \leqslant V_{\text{th}},\, V_2 \leqslant V_{\text{th}})]_{\xi = 0}$$

= the value of $P(V_1 \leqslant V_{\text{th}},\, V_2 \leqslant V_{\text{th}})$ in the case of *independent* Rayleigh fading,

$$\alpha_1 = [(V_{\text{th}}/v)^2 e^{-(V_{\text{th}}/v)^2}]^2$$

$$\alpha_2 = [1 - \tfrac{1}{2}(V_{\text{th}}/v)^2]^2 \alpha_1$$

$$\alpha_3 = [1 - (V_{\text{th}}/v)^2 + \tfrac{1}{12}(V_{\text{th}}/v)^4]\, \alpha_2 + \frac{(V_{\text{th}}/v)^8}{144}\, \alpha_1$$

and so on. In terms of the correlation coefficient $\rho_{V_1V_2}$ between the fading envelopes V_1 and V_2 we also show in section AIII of the Appendix that

$$[P(V_1 \leqslant V_{\text{th}},\ V_2 \leqslant V_{\text{th}})]_{\rho_{V_1V_2} \neq 0} \cong [P(V_1 \leqslant V_{\text{th}},\ V_2 \leqslant V_{\text{th}})]_{\rho_{V_1V_2} = 0} + \frac{\pi/4}{4-\pi}[(V_{\text{th}}/v)^2 e^{-(V_{\text{th}}/v)^2}]^2 \rho_{V_1V_2} \quad (67)$$

with an error that is less than

$$[1-(V_{\text{th}}/v)^2]^2/15 \quad (68)$$

for $0 \leqslant \rho_{V_1V_2} \leqslant 1/2$ and $(V_{\text{th}}/v)^2 \geqslant 0$, with the exception of $1.46 \leqslant (V_{\text{th}}/v)^2 \leqslant 2.54$ in which case the error is less than 5×10^{-3}. The error will evidently be negligible for $0 \leqslant (V_{\text{th}}/v)^2 \leqslant 4$. Under these conditions, the outage probability is increased an amount approximately given by

$$\frac{\pi/4}{4-\pi}[(V_{\text{th}}/v)^2 e^{-(V_{\text{th}}/v)^2}]^2 \rho_{V_1V_2} \leqslant 0.916\, \rho_{V_1V_2}/e^2 \quad (69)$$

which is less than 0.062 (since $\rho_{V_1V_2}$ is assumed $\leqslant 1/2$).

Under conditions of 100% correlated Rayleigh fading,

$$[P(V_1 \leqslant V_{\text{th}},\ V_2 \leqslant V_{\text{th}})]_{\rho_{V_1V_2} = 1} = 1 - e^{-(V_{\text{th}}/v)^2}$$
$$= [P(V_1 \leqslant V_{\text{th}},\ V_2 \leqslant V_{\text{th}})]_{\rho_{V_1V_2} = 0} + e^{-(V_{\text{th}}/v)^2}[1 - e^{-(V_{\text{th}}/v)^2}] \quad (70)$$

This shows that optimal-selection diversity with independent Rayleigh-fading signals decreases the outage probability an amount given by

$$e^{-(V_{\text{th}}/v)^2}[1 - e^{-(V_{\text{th}}/v)^2}]. \quad (71)$$

A convenient measure of the deterioration caused by nonzero $\rho_{V_1V_2}$ is the ratio of the attendant increase in outage probability to the quantity given by (71). This ratio gives the fractional reduction in the ultimate reliability improvement (which is achieved only when $\rho_{V_1V_2} = 0$) that is caused by nonzero $\rho_{V_1V_2}$. For $0 \leqslant \rho_{V_1V_2} \leqslant 1/2$ and $0 \leqslant (V_{\text{th}}/v)^2 \leqslant 4$, the fractional reduction in reliability improvement is given with good approximation by

$$0.916\, \frac{(V_{\text{th}}/v)^4}{e^{(V_{\text{th}}/v)^2} - 1}\, \rho_{V_1V_2}. \quad (72)$$

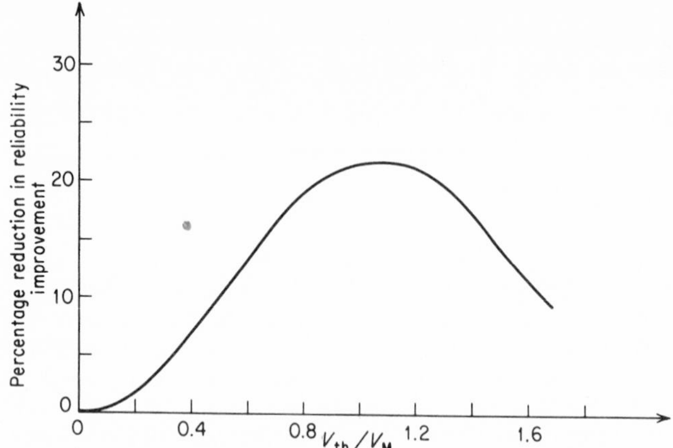

Fig. 14. Percentage reduction in the reliability improvement of dual optimal-selection diversity caused by nonzero correlation between the fading envelopes. Ordinate scale marked for $\rho_{V_1V_2} = 1/e \cong 0.37$. For other values of $\rho_{V_1V_2} \leq 1/2$ multiply ordinate scale by 2.718 $\rho_{V_1V_2}$.

Figure 14 shows a plot of this function for $\rho_{V_1V_2} = 1/e = 0.37$. The peak percentage reduction in reliability improvement is 21.6% for $\rho_{V_1V_2} = 1/e$ and 29.6% for $\rho_{V_1V_2} = 1/2$, and this peak occurs for $V_{\text{th}}/V_M \cong 1.1$.

The effect of non-independent fading upon the performance of K-fold optimal-selection diversity ($K \geqslant 3$) and of K-fold equal-gain combining ($K \geqslant 2$) has not yet been determined analytically because the analysis (even for jointly gaussian fading signals) does not show any signs of manageability. Pierce and Stein[8] have solved the problem for K-fold diversity using maximal-ratio combining for the case of jointly gaussian fading signals. Their analysis makes very interesting use of the well-developed theory of the gaussian process, but its coverage requires more details than can be justified here.

It is instructive to go back to Fig. 13 for a comparison of the effect of nonindependent fading upon the performance of dual-diversity systems that use each of the three signal utilization techniques. First we note that the less independent the fading patterns of the signals the greater the fraction of time in which the S/N ratios of the diversity channels will be nearly equal. Consequently, the performance of optimal-selection systems should deteriorate more quickly than that of equal-gain combiners and we can immediately conclude that the increase of outage probability with $\rho_{V_1V_2}$ for equal-gain systems will always be less than the corresponding increase computed above for optimal selection. Moreover, the theoretical performance of equal-gain systems will approach that of maximal ratio systems. As $\rho_{V_1V_2} \to 1$, the performance of equal-gain systems becomes identical with that of maximal-ratio systems (because the latter begin to weight the signals equally). In the limit of $\rho_{V_1V_2} = 1$, the outage probability for equal-gain and maximal-ratio dual combiners with Rayleigh fading is

$$P_{\rho_{V_1V_2}=1} = 1 - e^{-V_{\text{th}}^2/2v^2} \tag{73}$$

in contrast with $1 - e^{-V_{\text{th}}^2/v^2}$ for a single channel. A simple argument in support of (73) is as follows: Let the voltage-weighting factor in the addition of the two available noisy fading signals be a. With synchronous Rayleigh fading patterns for the two signal components and fully uncorrelated noises in the two channels, the combiner output consists of a Rayleigh fading resultant signal component whose instantaneous amplitude equals $2a$ times the instantaneous amplitude of the channel signal component, plus a resultant noise component whose mean-square value equals $2a^2$ times the mean-square value of the component-channel noise. Raising the mean-square value of the noise by a factor of $2a^2$ raises the threshold of message extractability from V_{th} for the individual channels to $\sqrt{2}\, a\, V_{\text{th}}$ for the combiner output. But the signal amplitude is raised simultaneously by a factor of $2a$. Therefore the ratio

$$\frac{\text{(square of amplitude threshold)}}{\text{(mean square signal amplitude)}}$$

for the output of the combiner is $V_{\text{th}}^2/2v^2$ in contrast with V_{th}^2/v^2 for the individual channels. Accordingly, the Rayleigh distribution formula gives the outage probability specified in Eq. (73) for the signal at the output of the equal-gain or maximal-ratio combiner.

IX. CONCLUDING REMARKS

The reliability of a communication system is basically determined by the properties of the signal at the receiving site and by the operating condition of the equipment. In this volume, our major concern is the received-signal reliability. Accordingly, we have concentrated in the present chapter on the effect of diversity upon the signal reliability, and have ignored the equally important topic of equipment reliability. It is however important to point out that the judicious use of diversity can lead to important advantages in system operational reliability even in the absence of any opportunities for improved signal reliability (but this represents an extension of the meaning of "diversity"). Thus even though some of the possible avenues for signal diversification (described in section IV) may be dismissed on the basis of their being unpromising for improving the signal reliability, they cannot generally be discounted for real achievements in operational system reliability. Likewise, certain types of diversity operations that promise good signal reliability improvements are sometimes dismissed in favor of other less effective operations because of the equipment reliability problem. This is particularly true in multihop microwave systems, where outages caused by equipment failures sometimes exceed the most pessimistic estimates of signal outages.

APPENDIX

AI. Correlation Coefficient of Envelopes of Two Narrow-Band Gaussian Processes

From Eq. (16) we have

$$E[V_1V_2] = \int_0^\infty\int_0^\infty \frac{V_1^2V_2^2}{B} I_0\left(\frac{V_1V_2}{B}\sqrt{\mu_c^2+\mu_{cs}^2}\right) e^{-\frac{\sigma_e^2}{2B}(V_1^2+V_2^2)} \ . \qquad \text{(A-1)}$$

Now

$$I_0(x) = \sum_{n=0}^{\infty} \frac{(x/2)^{2n}}{(n!)^2}$$

with an infinite radius of uniform and absolute convergence. If we substitute in Eq. (A-1) and interchange the integration and summation signs (subject to the convergence of the result), we have

$$E[V_1V_2] = \sum_{n=0}^{\infty} \frac{(\mu_c^2+\mu_{cs}^2)^n}{2^{2n}(n!)^2} \cdot \frac{1}{B^{2n+1}}$$

$$\int_0^\infty\int_0^\infty V_1^{2(n+1)}\, V_2^{2(n+1)}\, e^{-\frac{\sigma_e^2}{2B}(V_1^2+V_2^2)}\, dV_1 dV_2 \qquad \text{(A-2)}$$

We now observe that the double integral is the square of

$$I = \int_0^\infty y^{2(n+1)} e^{-y^2/2(B/\sigma_e^2)}\, dy$$

whose relation to the $2(n+1)^{\text{th}}$ central moment of a gaussian random variable of variance $\sigma_y^2 = B/\sigma_e^2$ is obvious. Thus

$$I = \frac{(2n+2)!}{2^{n+1}\cdot(n+1)!} \cdot \sqrt{\frac{\pi}{2}} \cdot \left(\frac{\sqrt{B}}{\sigma_e}\right)^{2n+3} .$$

If we substitute the expressions for I^2 and for B into Eq. (A-2), the result is

$$E[V_1V_2] = \frac{\pi\sigma_e^2}{8}(1-\xi)^2\sum_{n=0}^{\infty} A_n\xi^n \qquad \text{(A-3)}$$

where $\xi = (\mu_c^2 + \mu_{cs}^2)/\sigma_e^4$, and

$$A_n^{1/2} = \frac{(2n+2)!}{2^{2n}(n+1)!\,n!} \tag{A-4}$$

$$= \frac{4}{\sqrt{\pi}} \cdot \frac{\Gamma(n+3/2)}{n!}$$

$$\cong \frac{2}{\sqrt{\pi}} \cdot \frac{2n+1}{\sqrt{n}} \text{ for large } n.$$

The series in Eq. (A-3) converges for all $|\xi| < 1$. If $(1-\xi)^2$ is expanded and entered under the summation sign, collection of terms in like powers of ξ leads to

$$E[V_1V_2] = \frac{\pi\sigma_e^2}{8}\left[4 + \sum_{n=1}^{\infty} C_n \xi^n\right] \tag{A-5}$$

where

$$C_n = A_n - 2A_{n-1} + A_{n-2}$$

$$= [(1/2)(3/2)(5/2)\ldots(n-5/2)(n-3/2)]^2/(n!)^2$$

$$= \frac{1}{\pi}\left[\frac{\Gamma(n-1/2)}{n!}\right]^2, \quad n = 1, 2, 3, \ldots \tag{A-6}$$

It is important to note that C_n is a positive real number. The earlier values of C_n are $C_1 = 1$, $C_2 = 1/16$, $C_3 = 1/64$, $C_4 = (5/64)^2$.

Finally, we substitute from Eq. (A-5) into Eq. (13), noting that $m_{V1} = m_{V2} = \sigma_e\sqrt{\pi/2}$ and that $\sigma_{V1}^2 = \sigma_{V2}^2 = \sigma_e^2(4-\pi)/2$, to obtain

$$\rho_{V_1V_2} = \frac{\pi/4}{4-\pi}\sum_{n=1}^{\infty} C_n \xi^n. \tag{A-7}$$

This result shows that if the narrow-band gaussian model (*i.e.*, Rayleigh envelope fading and uniformly distributed phase) holds, $\rho_{V_1V_2}$ must be non-negative. The value $\rho_{V_1V_2} = 0$ necessarily means that $\xi = 0$, and hence that $\mu_c = \mu_{cs} = 0$.

AII. Expression for the Incomplete Γ Function

Starting from

$$\gamma_n(u) = \frac{1}{n!}\int_0^u x^n e^{-x}\,dx \tag{A-8}$$

we find by integrating by parts that

$$\gamma_n = \gamma_{n-1} - \frac{1}{n!}u^n e^{-u}. \tag{A-9}$$

Therefore, if we start from $\gamma_0 = 1 - e^{-u}$ and apply the recursion formula, we finally obtain

$$\gamma_n = 1 - e^{-u} \sum_{k=0}^{n} \frac{u^k}{k!} \tag{A-10}$$

$$= e^{-u} \sum_{k=n+1}^{\infty} \frac{u^k}{k!} . \tag{A-11}$$

Alternatively, if we write

$$f(\alpha) = \int_0^u e^{-\alpha x}\, dx = \frac{1}{\alpha}\,(1 - e^{-\alpha u}) \tag{A-12}$$

then

$$(-1)^n \gamma_n(u) = \frac{1}{n!}\left[\frac{\partial^n}{\partial \alpha^n} f(\alpha)\right]_{\alpha=1} . \tag{A-13}$$

The differentiation can be avoided by noting that the quantity on the right-hand side in Eq. (A-13) is the coefficient of $(\alpha - 1)^n$ in the Taylor expansion

$$f(\alpha) = \sum_{k=0}^{\infty} b_k (\alpha - 1)^k$$

The easiest way to arrive at this expansion is to write

$$f(\alpha) = \frac{1}{1 + (\alpha - 1)}\,[1 - e^{-u}\, e^{-(\alpha-1)u}]$$

$$= \left\{\sum_{l=0}^{\infty} (-1)^l (\alpha - 1)^l\right\} \left\{1 - e^{-u} \sum_{m=0}^{\infty} \frac{u^m}{m!} (-1)^m (\alpha - 1)^m\right\}$$

$$= \sum_{l=0}^{\infty} (-1)^l (\alpha - 1)^l - e^{-u} \sum_{l=0}^{\infty} \sum_{m=0}^{\infty} (-1)^{l+m} \frac{u^m}{m!} (\alpha - 1)^{l+m}$$

$$= \sum_{k=0}^{\infty} (-1)^k \left[1 - e^{-u} \sum_{m=0}^{k} \frac{u^m}{m!}\right] (\alpha - 1)^k$$

whence

$$\gamma_K(u) = 1 - e^{-u} \sum_{m=0}^{K} \frac{u^m}{m!} .$$

AIII. The Outage Probability of a Dual Optimal-Selection System with Correlated Rayleigh-Fading Signals

The joint probability density function of the envelopes of two correlated jointly gaussian narrow-band fading signals is given in Eq. (16) of the text. In the notation of section AI

$$p(V_1, V_2) = \frac{V_1 V_2}{B} I_0 \left(\frac{V_1 V_2}{B} \sigma_e^2 \sqrt{\xi} \right) e^{-\frac{\sigma_e^2}{2B}(V_1^2 + V_2^2)} \, .$$

In an optimal-selection system, the probability that the envelope of the stronger of the two available signals is less than the threshold value V_{th} is

$$P(V_1 \leqslant V_{\text{th}}, V_2 \leqslant V_{\text{th}}) = \int_0^{V_{\text{th}}} \int_0^{V_{\text{th}}} p(V_1, V_2) \, dV_1 dV_2$$

$$= \frac{1}{B} \sum_{n=0}^{\infty} \left(\frac{\sigma_e^2}{2B} \right)^{2n} \xi^n \left[\frac{1}{n!} \int_0^{V_{\text{th}}} V^{2n+1} e^{-V^2/(2B/\sigma_e^2)} \, dV \right]^2$$

where we have used the power-series expansion of $I_0(x)$. The appearance of this expression is simplified by the change of variables

$$x = V^2/(2B/\sigma_e^2) \tag{A-14}$$

to the form

$$P(V_1 \leqslant V_{\text{th}}, V_2 \leqslant V_{\text{th}}) = \frac{B}{\sigma_e^4} \sum_{n=0}^{\infty} \left[\frac{1}{n!} \int_0^{x_{\text{th}}} x^n e^{-x} dx \right]^2 \xi^n . \tag{A-15}$$

The coefficient of ξ^n is recognized as being the square of the incomplete Γ function defined in Eq. (A-8). Thus

$$P(V_1 \leqslant V_{\text{th}}, V_2 \leqslant V_{\text{th}}) = \frac{B}{\sigma_e^4} \sum_{n=0}^{\infty} \gamma_n^2 (x_{\text{th}}) \, \xi^n . \tag{A-16}$$

This expression was first derived by Staras.[24] The fact that the incomplete Γ function is tabulated makes this expression a useful end result for numerical computations. But this expression does not bring out the powers of ξ explicitly because B/σ_e^4 and x_{th} are themselves functions of ξ.

An explicit power-series expansion of P as a function of ξ is most expeditiously obtained by applying the standard formula for the mth coefficient to Staras's expression, (A-16). We first note that

$$B/\sigma_e^4 = 1 - \xi \tag{A-17}$$

and

$$x_{\text{th}} = \frac{V_{\text{th}}^2/2\sigma_e^2}{1 - \xi} = \frac{(V_{\text{th}}/v)^2}{1 - \xi} \tag{A-18}$$

where v is the rms value of V. Thus

$$P(V_1 \leqslant V_{th},\ V_2 \leqslant V_{th}) = (1-\xi)\sum_{n=0}^{\infty} \gamma_n^2(x_{th})\ \xi^n$$

$$= \gamma_0^2 - \sum_{n=1}^{\infty} (\gamma_{n-1}^2 - \gamma_n^2)\ \xi^n \quad . \tag{A-19}$$

Now let

$$P(V_1 \leqslant V_{th},\ V_2 \leqslant V_{th}) = \sum_{m=0}^{\infty} \alpha_m\ \xi^m \tag{A-20}$$

where

$$\alpha_m = \frac{1}{m!}\ \frac{d^m P}{d\xi^m}\bigg]_{\xi=0} \quad . \tag{A-21}$$

If the differentiations are applied to the right-hand side of Eq. (A-16), we find that

$$\alpha_0 = \gamma_0^2\,(V_{th}^2/v^2) = [1 - e^{-(V_{th}/v)^2}]^2$$

= the value of $P(V_1 \leqslant V_{th},\ V_2 \leqslant V_{th})$ in the case of *independent* Rayleigh fading,

$$\alpha_1 = [(V_{th}/v)^2\, e^{-(V_{th}/v)^2}]^2$$

$$\alpha_2 = \{[1 - \tfrac{1}{2}\,(V_{th}/v)^2]\,(V_{th}/v)^2\, e^{-(V_{th}/v)^2}\}^2$$

$$= \alpha_1[1 - \tfrac{1}{2}\,(V_{th}/v)^2]^2$$

$$\alpha_3 = [1 - (V_{th}/v)^2 + \tfrac{1}{12}\,(V_{th}/v)^4]\,\alpha_2 + \frac{(V_{th}/v)^8}{144}\,\alpha_1$$

and so on. We can therefore write.

$$[P(V_1 \leqslant V_{th},\ V_2 \leqslant V_{th})]_{\xi\neq 0} = [P(V_1 \leqslant V_{th},\ V_2 \leqslant V_{th})]_{\xi=0} + [(V_{th}/v)^2\, e^{-(V_{th}/v)^2}]^2 \times \xi\{1 + [1 - \tfrac{1}{2}(V_{th}/v)^2]^2\,\xi + \cdots\} \tag{A-22}$$

If we let P_ξ and P_0 denote the values of P for $\xi \neq 0$ and for $\xi = 0$, we can also write

$$P_\xi = P_0 + [(V_{th}/v)^2\, e^{-(V_{th}/v)^2}]^2\,\{\xi + [1 - \tfrac{1}{2}\,(V_{th}/v)^2]^2\,\xi^2\} + R_3(\xi)$$

where

$$|R_3(\xi)| \leqslant \{(V_{th}/v)^2\, e^{-(V_{th}/v)^2}\,[1 - \tfrac{1}{2}\,(V_{th}/v)^2]\}^2\,\frac{\xi^3}{1-\xi}$$

$$\leqslant \frac{1}{e^2}\,[1 - \tfrac{1}{2}\,(V_{th}/v)^2]^2\,\frac{\xi^3}{1-\xi}$$

for $(V_{th}/v)^2 \geqslant 0$ with the exception of $(V_{th}/v)^2$ values between $2 \pm 0.385\sqrt{(1-\xi)/\xi^3}$ for which $|R_3(\xi)| < 5 \times 10^{-3}$. For example, if $0 \leqslant \xi \leqslant 0.64$, then $|R_3(\xi)| < [1 - \frac{1}{2}(V_{th}/v)^2]^2/10$ for all $(V_{th}/v)^2 \geqslant 0$ with the exception of $1.55 \leqslant (V_{th}/v)^2 \leqslant 2.45$, in which case $|R_3(\xi)| < 5 \times 10^{-3}$.

A similar argument shows that

$$P_\xi \cong P_0 + [(V_{th}/v)^2 e^{-(V_{th}/v)^2}]^2 \xi \tag{A-23}$$

with an error less than $[1 - \frac{1}{2}(V_{th}/v)^2]^2/15$ for $0 \leqslant \xi < 1/2$, and $(V_{th}/v)^2 \geqslant 0$ with the exception of $1.46 \leqslant (V_{th}/v)^2 \leqslant 2.54$, in which case the error $< 5 \times 10^{-3}$.

Before we can express $P(V_1 \leqslant V_{th}, V_2 \leqslant V_{th})$ in terms of the envelope correlation coefficient $\rho_{V_1V_2}$, we first need an expression for ξ in terms of $\rho_{V_1V_2}$. Such an expression is not yet known, but reasonable approximations can be derived with the help of Eq. (A-7). For example, we can write

$$\rho_{V_1V_2} = \frac{\pi/4}{4-\pi}[\xi + \frac{1}{16}\xi^2 + \frac{1}{64}\xi^3 + R_4(\xi)]$$

where

$$R_4(\xi) = \sum_{n=4}^{\infty} C_n\xi^n < \frac{8}{50}\sum_{n=4}^{\infty}(\xi/2)^n = \frac{8}{50}\cdot\frac{(\xi/2)^4}{1-(\xi/2)} < \frac{1}{50}\cdot\frac{\xi^4}{(2-\xi)}$$

Since $\xi < 1$, the maximum value of the bound on the relative error is 1/50 (or 2%). This means that for $0 \leqslant \xi < 1$,

$$\rho_{V_1V_2} \cong \frac{\pi/4}{4-\pi}[\xi + \frac{1}{16}\xi^2 + \frac{1}{64}\xi^3] \tag{A-24}$$

to within an error that is less than 2%. Similar arguments show that for all $0 \leqslant \xi < 1$,

$$\rho_{V_1V_2} \cong \frac{\pi/4}{4-\pi}[\xi + \frac{1}{16}\xi^2] \text{ with error} < 4\% \tag{A-25}$$

and

$$\rho_{V_1V_2} \cong \frac{\pi/4}{4-\pi}\xi \tag{A-26}$$

with an error < 10%. For $0 \leqslant \xi \leqslant 1/2$, the approximate expression (A-26) gives $\rho_{V_1V_2}$ with an error that is less than 2%.

Finally, note that if we let $b = (\pi/4)/(4-\pi)$, then the slope of ρ/b as a function of ξ is always greater than unity. Therefore, values of ξ determined from either of the approximate expressions (A-24), (A-25), or (A-26) for specified values of ρ/b will be accurate to within less than the error bound associated with the expression used.

REFERENCES

1. D. G. Brennan, "A New Approach to Certain Types of Random Functions," presented at the Physical Society Symposium on Fluctuation Phenomena and Stochastic Processes, University of London, March, 1959.
2. D. G. Brennan, "Linear Diversity Combining Techniques," *Proc. IRE,* vol. 47, pp. 1075-1102, June, 1959.
3. D. G. Brennan and M. L. Phillips, "Phase and Amplitude Variability in Medium Frequency Ionospheric Transmission," Technical Report No. 93 (ASTIA No. 110016), Lincoln Laboratory, Massachusetts Institute of Technology, Sept. 16, 1957.
4. R. W. E. McNicol, "The Fading of Radio Waves of Medium and High Frequencies," *Proc. IRE,* vol. 96, pp. 517-524, October, 1949.
5. W. B. Davenport, Jr., and W. L. Root, *Introduction to Random Signals and Noise,* McGraw-Hill Book Company, Inc., New York, 1958.
6. H. Cramer, *Mathematical Methods of Statistics,* Princeton University Press, Princeton, N.J., 1946.
7. K. S. Packard, "Effect of Correlation on Combiner Diversity," *Proc. IRE,* vol. 46, pp. 362-363, January, 1958.
8. J. N. Pierce and S. Stein, "Multiple Diversity with Nonindependent Fading," *Proc. IRE,* vol. 48, pp. 89-104, January, 1960.
9. J. L. Glaser and L. P. Faber, "Evaluation of Polarization Diversity Performance," *Proc. IRE,* vol. 41, pp. 1774-1778, December, 1953.
10. G. L. Grisdale, J. G. Morris, and D. S. Palmer, "Fading of Long-Distance Radio Signals and a Comparison of Space- and Polarization-Diversity Reception in the 6-18 MC Range," *Proc. IEE,* Pt. B, vol. 104, pp. 39-51, January, 1957.
11. J. H. Chisholm, P. A. Portmann, J. T. deBettencourt, and J. F. Roche, "Investigations of the Angular Scattering and Multipath Properties of Tropospheric Propagation of Short Radio Waves Beyond the Horizon," *Proc. IRE,* vol. 43, pp. 1317-1335, October, 1955.
12. R. Bolgiano, Jr., N. H. Bryant, and W. E. Gordon, "Diversity Reception in Scatter Communication with Emphasis on Angle Diversity," Cornell University Elec. Eng. Res. Report No. 359, Ithaca, N.Y., January, 1958.
13. J. H. Chisholm, L. P. Rainville, J. F. Roche, and H. G. Root, "Angular Diversity Reception at 2290 MC Over a 188-Mile Path," *Trans. IRE, PGCS,* vol. CS-7, pp. 195-201, September, 1959.
14. H. T. Friis and C. B. Feldman, "A Multiple Unit Steerable Antenna for Short Wave Reception," *Proc. IRE,* vol. 25, p. 841, July, 1937.
15. L. R. Kahn, "Ratio Squarer," *Proc. IRE,* vol. 42, p. 1704, November, 1954.

16. C. L. Mack, "Diversity Reception in UHF Long-Range Communications," *Proc. IRE,* vol. 43, pp. 1281-1289, October, 1955.
17. D. G. Brennan, "On the Maximum Signal-to-Noise Ratio Realizable from Several Noisy Signals," *Proc. IRE,* vol. 43, p. 1530, October, 1955.
18. F. J. Altman and W. Sichak, "A Simplified Diversity Communication System for Beyond-the-Horizon Links," *Trans. IRE, PGCS* vol. CS-4, pp. 50-55, March, 1956.
19. K. Pearson (ed.), *Tables of the Incomplete* Γ *Function,* Cambridge University Press, London, 1946.
20. "Tables of the Error Function and Its Derivative," Natl. Bur. Standards, Appl. Math. Ser. No. 41, Washington, D.C., 1954.
21. W. C. Mason, M. Ginsburg, and D. G. Brennan, "Tables of the Distribution Functions of Sums of Rayleigh Variables," to be published.
22. D. G. Brennan and R. V. Locke, Jr., "The Altman-Mellen Diversity Combiner," to be published.
23. R. T. Adams and B. M. Mindes, "Evaluation of IF and Baseband Diversity Combining Receivers," *Trans. IRE, PGCS,* vol. CS-6, pp. 8-13, June, 1958.
24. H. Staras, "Diversity Reception with Correlated Signals," *J. Appl. Phy.,* vol. 27, pp. 93-94, January, 1956.

CHAPTER **8**

Statistical Decision Theory and Communications: The Simple Binary Decision Problem

William M. Siebert

I. INTRODUCTION

The topic of this chapter is described by different authors with a variety of different words—signal detection, extraction, filtering, estimation, decision, discrimination, separation, resolution, and smoothing, to mention a few. Unfortunately, including both connotations and annotations, these words have a hopelessly confusing, overlapping, and ambiguous set of meanings. In particular, it is necessary to distinguish two quite different meanings for the phrase "signal detection:"

(a) "Signal detection" in the sense of separating a desired signal from the background of noise and other interfering signals in which it is buried; and

(b) "Signal detection" in the sense of operating on the desired signal in such a way as to derive the modulation waveform in a form appropriate to the ultimate observer.

In the analysis of the behavior of a specific system these two aspects of the detection problem almost inevitably become mixed. But in this chapter we shall take a synthetic point of view and concentrate on the first aspect—at least in part on the grounds that once the desired (transmitted) signal has been ascertained as well as possible, the demodulation of this signal is, mathematically at least, a trivial problem. Specifically, we shall study what are usually called "optimum"* methods for extracting or detecting signals in noise.

II. FILTERING THEORY VERSUS DECISION THEORY

The theory of the separation of signals from noise can be divided roughly into two parts which we shall call *filtering theory* and *decision theory*. The distinction between filtering and decision is perhaps best illustrated by several examples.

(a) A filtering theory example—Suppose that we are looking for a signal in a background of additive noise. Let $f(t)$ be the received signal, $s(t)$ be the desired signal, and $n(t)$ be the noise so that

*"Optimum" has become one of those words that are almost impossible to use without apologetic quotation marks.

$$f(t) = s(t) + n(t) . \tag{1}$$

We propose to separate $s(t)$ from $n(t)$ by means of a linear filter described by its impulse response $h(t)$. We seek that $h(t)$ which, with $f(t)$ as an input, will minimize on the average the square of the difference between the desired signal $s(t)$ and the actual signal present at the output of the filter. Mathematically we seek an $h(t)$ that will minimize

$$\begin{aligned} \epsilon &= E\left[\left\{s(t) - \int_{-\infty}^{\infty} f(\tau)h(t-\tau)d\tau\right\}^2\right] \\ &= R_s(0) - 2\int_{-\infty}^{\infty} R_s(\tau)h(\tau)d\tau \\ &+ \int_{-\infty}^{\infty}\int_{-\infty}^{\infty} [R_s(\tau-\rho) + R_n(\tau-\rho)]\, h(t-\tau)h(t-\rho)d\tau d\rho \end{aligned} \tag{2}$$

where we have assumed that $s(t)$ and $n(t)$ are sample functions from independent stationary random processes with autocorrelation functions $R_s(\tau)$ and $R_n(\tau)$ respectively and that either $s(t)$ or $n(t)$ has zero mean. Writing $R_s(\tau)$ and $R_n(\tau)$ in terms of the corresponding power spectral densities, $S_s(\omega)$ and $S_n(\omega)$, we obtain

$$\epsilon = \frac{1}{2\pi}\int_{-\infty}^{\infty} \left\{S_s(\omega)\left|1 - H(\omega)\right|^2 + S_n(\omega)\left|H(\omega)\right|^2\right\} d\omega, \tag{3}$$

which is to be minimized by an appropriate choice of $H(\omega)$. To do this, we must evidently know, *i.e.*, be given, $S_s(\omega)$ and $S_n(\omega)$. If there are no constraints on $H(\omega)$ (such as physical realizability), then, since the integrand is always positive, the integral is minimized by minimizing the integrand for each ω separately. Clearly $H(\omega)$ should be real and positive. Differentiating the integrand with respect to $H(\omega)$ and setting the result equal to zero yields

$$\frac{d}{dH(\omega)}\left\{S_s(\omega)(1 - H(\omega))^2 + S_n(\omega)H^2(\omega)\right\} = -2(1 - H(\omega))S_s(\omega) + 2H(\omega)S_n(\omega) = 0$$

or

$$H(\omega) = \frac{S_s(\omega)}{S_s(\omega) + S_n(\omega)} \tag{4}$$

which is the desired solution. Equation (4) describes the (generally unrealizable) linear filter that minimizes the mean square difference between the actual output and the desired output (in this case simply the signal component of the input).

(b) A decision theory example—Suppose that in each of a succession of time intervals of duration T we know that the received signal consists of either one *known* signal $s_1(t)$ or another *known* signal $s_2(t)$, and in either case additive noise $n(t)$. ($s_1(t)$ and $s_2(t)$ might, for example, represent MARK and SPACE and be pulses of sinusoids of different known frequencies as in FSK.) We seek a device that will *decide* on the basis of the received waveform in each interval which of the two possible signals was transmitted in that interval. We might, for example, proceed in the following manner (reminiscent of our preceding example). Let $f(t)$ be the received signal in the interval $0 < t < T$. We will announce $s_1(t)$ as present if the mean square difference between $f(t)$ and $s_1(t)$ is *less* than the mean square difference between $f(t)$ and $s_2(t)$; otherwise, we will announce $s_2(t)$ present. In symbols, announce $s_1(t)$ present if

$$\frac{1}{T}\int_0^T [f(t) - s_1(t)]^2 dt < \frac{1}{T}\int_0^T [f(t) - s_2(t)]^2 dt . \tag{5}$$

Assuming $s_1(t)$ and $s_2(t)$ have equal energy, *i.e.*, that

$$\int_0^T s_1^2(t)dt = \int_0^T s_2^2(t)dt \tag{6}$$

we may expand the integrands and cancel common terms to obtain the equivalent rule: Announce $s_1(t)$ present if

$$\int_0^T f(t)s_1(t)dt > \int_0^T f(t)s_2(t)dt . \tag{7}$$

Now if $h(t)$ is the impulse response of a linear filter and if $f(t)$ is the input, then the output at $t = T$ can be written as

$$\int_0^T f(t)h(T-t)dt. \tag{8}$$

Comparing this expression with the integrals above we can realize our decision rule in the following form (Fig. 1). Construct two linear filters *(matched filters)* having impulse responses $s_1(T-t)$ and $s_2(T-t)$ respectively. Let $f(t)$ (the received signal) be the input to both filters. Sample the output of these filters at $t = T$ and compare the sample amplitudes. If the first exceeds the second report that $s_1(t)$ was present; otherwise report $s_2(t)$. Alternatively, the comparison circuit could be designed to have as an output a positive video pulse if $s_1(t)$ is selected and a negative pulse if $s_2(t)$ is selected, or indeed whatever form of output is appropriate.

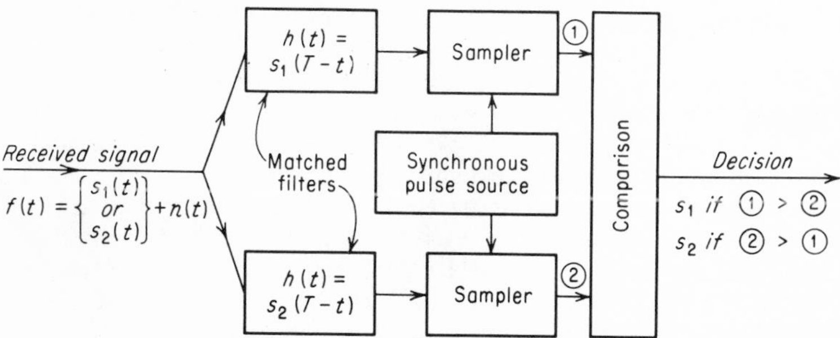

Fig. 1. Decision circuit using matched filters.

(c) Comparison of filtering theory and decision theory—The two examples we have discussed are similar in that in both an average square error was minimized. But there the similarity ends. Perhaps the most striking difference is that in the filtering approach we selected the form of the *processing device* (a linear time-invariant filter) and let the output take such form as it would, whereas in the decision approach, we selected the form of the *output* (*e.g.*, a binary waveform) and let the system be whatever turned out—in this case, a non-linear time-variant device. This distinction has a marked effect on the type of errors that occur in the two systems. Filtering theory methods—particularly those based on mean square error—tend to discriminate against large errors at the expense of a continual small error. Often this seems reasonable; for example, in many communication systems employing conventional types of modulation. But it is also often unreasonable—in fire-control systems "a miss is as good as a mile," and in a binary data system no meaning can be attached to an output "somewhere between 0 and 1." In such cases, decision theory methods may be more appropriate—when a decision system makes an error, it is a large one; most of the time (hopefully) it is exactly correct. The choice clearly depends in large part on the character of the desired signal. If the signal can be described in each interval by a selection of one from a number of discrete states or by the values of a discrete set of parameters, then deciding which state the desired signal is in on the basis of the received waveform is often the most appropriate way to proceed. But if the states of the desired signal are ill-defined and blend smoothly into one another (*e.g.*, a speech waveform or filtered noise) then filtering methods are probably better suited. On the other hand, decision methods in general require that much more detailed information be available at the receiver about the character of both signals and noise than do filtering methods. In the examples above, for instance, we required complete knowledge of $s_1(t)$ and $s_2(t)$ as well as synchronism between receiver and transmitter in order to carry out the decision theory example, whereas the filtering theory example required only knowledge of power spectra. Often this matter of what type of knowledge might reasonably be available at the receiver is the dominant force in selecting the method of analysis to be employed, but it must be kept in mind that many times the information available at the receiver is also under our control—depending, for example, on whether we choose to control certain quantities and make certain measurements or not.

The methods of filtering theory have, of course, been carried far beyond the trivial example outlined above. The classic work of Wiener included a realizability condition and permitted prediction of the signal and other operations as well as filtering. Extensions have been made by numerous workers to include a variety of non-linear and time-variant problems, as well as error criteria other than least mean squares. But this material has been well-covered in various papers and books; we shall have little more to say about it here. On the other hand, decision theory as applied to signal detection is a

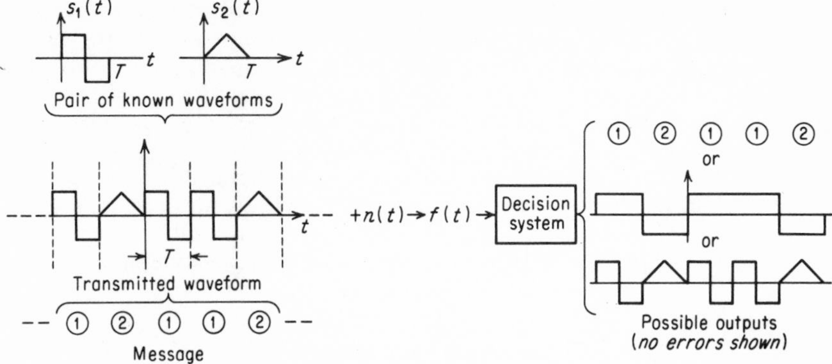

Fig. 2. Canonic decision problem.

much more recent topic. The remainder of this chapter will constitute an introduction to the type of problems and methods of thinking appropriate to the application of decision theory to signal detection. In the succeeding chapter, a more formal, but still heuristic, discussion of the same material is presented to suggest the range and scope of the method.

III. THE CANONIC DECISION PROBLEM

The decision problem discussed in the preceding section might with some justice be called the *canonic decision problem*. In the next few sections we shall apply various methods other than least mean squares to obtain solutions to this same problem. It is therefore worth while to state the problem again with some care.

We assume that the time scale is broken up into intervals of duration T seconds and that the time scales at receiver and transmitter are synchronous, (Fig. 2). We assume further that the received waveform, $f(t)$, consists of one or the other of a pair of known waveforms, $s_1(t)$ or $s_2(t)$, together with an independent stationary additive noise which, when necessary, we shall assume to be a gaussian process with a flat spectrum (white) over all frequencies and with a zero mean. It should be emphasized that $s_1(t)$ and $s_2(t)$ are assumed to be *known in all detail* (including, for example, amplitude and carrier phase) but are otherwise completely arbitrary. Later on, we shall permit the signal to have certain unknown parameters, but for the moment we shall assume, unrealistically perhaps, that the only uncertainty about the signal waveform is the question of which of the two waveforms, $s_1(t)$ or $s_2(t)$, is present in each interval. We shall further assume that the probability of $s_1(t)$ or $s_2(t)$ is *a priori* equally-likely in each interval and that choices are not correlated from interval to interval. Together with the assumption that the noise is a white gaussian process, this implies that there is no information in the received waveform $f(t)$ *outside* the interval $0 < t < T$ that is relevant to the decision about $s_1(t)$ or $s_2(t)$ *inside* the interval $0 < t < T$, and similarly for successive intervals. We may thus choose the interval $0 < t < T$ as typical. We assume that our problem is to decide at the end of each interval (*e.g.*, at $t = T$) which waveform, $s_1(t)$ or $s_2(t)$, was present during that interval. How this decision is to be presented is irrelevant—some possible choices are shown in Fig. 2.

In the preceding section, we found a possible solution to this problem by selecting that waveform, $s_1(t)$ or $s_2(t)$, whose mean square difference from $f(t)$ was smallest. As we argued there, this is equivalent (assuming $s_1(t)$ and $s_2(t)$ have equal energy) to announcing $s_1(t)$ if

$$\int_0^T f(t)s_1(t)dt > \int_0^T f(t)s_2(t)dt \tag{7}$$

and $s_2(t)$ otherwise. Equation (7) can be interpreted either as "choose that waveform whose cross-correlation with $f(t)$ is largest"—which leads to the name *correlation detection*—or as "pass $f(t)$ through filters matched to $s_1(t)$ and $s_2(t)$, and choose the signal corresponding to the filter whose output at $t = T$ is largest"—which leads to the name *matched-filter detection.* There are a variety of ways in which the operation indicated in (7) can be carried out physically, some of which might more reasonably be thought of as correlators and others as filters, but mathematically, correlation detection and matched-filter detection are identical.

The difficulty with this least-mean-squares approach to a decision is that it is entirely *ad hoc*. There is nothing implied in the method that suggests that the solution obtained is "better" or "worse" than any other solution. However, as we shall see, the solution we have obtained (correlation or matched-filter detection) *is* in a very general sense an "optimum" or "best-possible" solution to the canonic detection problem. But to understand this, we shall have to explore various other approaches to the problem.

IV. A SIGNAL-TO-NOISE RATIO APPROACH

To any communications engineer, the most familiar measure of quality is surely the signal-to-noise ratio. Let us try to "optimize" the performance of our decision system by maximizing a signal-to-noise ratio. We postulate a decision system that begins with a single linear filter, with input $f(t)$ and with impulse response $h(t)$. This impulse response is to be chosen such that if $s_1(t)$ alone were the input to the filter then the output at $t = T$ would be large and *positive*, whereas if $s_2(t)$ alone were the input to the filter, the output at $t = T$ would be large and *negative*. Finally, if noise alone were the input to the filter, the magnitude of the output at $t = T$ should be *small* on the average. With $f(t)$ as the input, we shall then announce $s_1(t)$ present if the output at $t = T$ is greater than zero, and shall announce $s_2(t)$ present otherwise. To find a "best" filter we shall seek that $h(t)$ which maximizes the *signal-to-noise ratio* defined as the square of the difference of the responses of the filter at $t = T$ to $s_1(t)$ and $s_2(t)$

divided by the mean square noise response at $t = T$; namely,

$$\text{Signal / Noise} = \alpha = \frac{\left(\int_0^T s_1(t)h(T-t)dt - \int_0^T s_2(t)h(T-t)dt\right)^2}{E\left[\left(\int_0^T n(t)h(T-t)dt\right)^2\right]} \quad . \tag{9}$$

Recalling that $n(t)$ is white gaussian noise with correlation function

$$R_n(\tau) = N_0\delta(\tau),$$

where $\delta(t)$ is the unit impulse function and N_0 is the noise power density in watts/cps (double-sided spectrum), we may write

$$\alpha = \frac{\left(\int_0^T [s_1(t) - s_2(t)]h(T-t)dt\right)^2}{N_0 \int_0^T h^2(T-t)dt} \tag{10}$$

Multiplying both sides by

$$\frac{N_0}{\int_0^T [s_1(t) - s_2(t)]^2 dt}$$

[since $s_1(t)$ and $s_2(t)$ are known, and presumably not identical, this is merely multiplication by a constant and does not influence the maximization with respect to $h(t)$], we obtain

$$\frac{N_0\alpha}{\int_0^T [s_1(t) - s_2(t)]^2 dt} = \frac{\left(\int_0^T [s_1(t) - s_2(t)]\, h(T-t)dt\right)^2}{\int_0^T h^2(T-t)dt \int_0^T [s_1(t) - s_2(t)]^2 dt} . \tag{11}$$

This is now in a form to which we can apply a very useful relation known as the Schwarz Inequality, which states that for any two functions, $[s_1(t) - s_2(t)]$ and $h(T-t)$, the right-hand side of (11) is ≤ 1. The equality to *one* holds if and only if

$$h(T-t) = s_1(t) - s_2(t)$$

or

$$h(t) = s_1(T-t) - s_2(T-t), \quad 0 < t < T . \tag{12}$$

The filter giving the maximum value of α is thus characterized by (12) and the maximum possible signal-to-noise ratio is

$$\alpha = \frac{\int_0^T [s_1(t) - s_2(t)]^2 dt}{N_0} \quad . \tag{13}$$

To interpret this result, we observe that, with $f(t)$ as an input, the filter of (12) has, at $t = T$, the response

$$\int_0^T f(t)\, h(T-t)dt = \int_0^T f(t)s_1(t)dt - \int_0^T f(t)s_2(t)dt \tag{14}$$

and our decision rule takes the form: Announce $s_1(t)$ if

$$\int_0^T f(t)s_1(t)dt > \int_0^T f(t)s_2(t)dt \tag{15}$$

and $s_2(t)$ otherwise, which is exactly the same result as we previously obtained by the least-mean-squares approach. The filter $h(t)$ can then be realized by subtracting the outputs of a pair of matched filters (or the decision rule can be implemented by comparing these outputs). We thus have an interpretation of a matched filter as one that *maximizes a signal-to-noise ratio.*

The maximum value that this signal-to-noise ratio can have—as given by (13)—is extremely interesting. Expanding the numerator yields

$$\alpha = \frac{\int_0^T s_1^2(t)dt - 2\int_0^T s_1(t)s_2(t)dt + \int_0^T s_2^2(t)dt}{N_0} . \tag{16}$$

The first and last terms in the numerator are simply the energies E_1 and E_2, in the two signals, and the middle term is the cross-correlation between the two signals. There are two cases of special interest. The first corresponds to the situation in which the cross-correlation between the two signals is zero—*i.e.*, the signals are *orthogonal.* Such a situation might result, for example, if $s_1(t)$ and $s_2(t)$ were sinusoids at different frequencies as in FSK. In this case

$$\alpha = \frac{E_1 + E_2}{N_0}$$

and if $E_1 = E_2 = E$,

$$\alpha = \frac{2E}{N_0} . \tag{17}$$

The second case corresponds to the situation in which $s_1(t)$ is (except for a scale factor) the *negative* of $s_2(t)$. This gives the largest possible value of α but is sometimes hard to achieve in practice. An example would be a synchronous system in which a complete phase reversal is used to differentiate MARK and SPACE. In this case

$$\alpha = \frac{(\sqrt{E_1} + \sqrt{E_2})^2}{N_0}$$

and if $E_1 = E_2 = E$,

$$\alpha = \frac{4E}{N_0} . \tag{18}$$

In either case, the output signal-to-noise ratio (and also the error probabilities, as we shall see) *depends only on the signal energy and the noise power density*. In particular, α does *not* depend on the signal *bandwidth,* despite the fact that the *input* signal-to-noise (power) ratio is inversely proportional to bandwidth. There is thus nothing particularly remarkable about reliable detection of a signal that is arbitrarily far down in the noise provided only that its *energy* is large enough.

Despite the apparent reasonableness, however, of maximizing a signal-to-noise ratio, this approach to an optimum solution of the decision problem is philosophically almost as indefensible as the least-mean-squares procedure. We arbitrarily specified, for example, that the system be *linear* (except for the comparison). And there is no guarantee that improving α necessarily reduces the probability of *error*—which presumably should, in a decision system, be our ultimate test of quality. There are indeed cases in which *increasing* a signal-to-noise ratio by certain methods actually *increases* probabilities of error. We therefore pass on in the next section to decision theory proper and attempt to minimize the error probabilities directly.

V. A POSTERIORI PROBABILITY AND BAYES' SOLUTION

The most general possible decision system (constrained only by the requirement that it be consistent) amounts to a list assigning to each possible input (received waveform in the interval $0 < t < T$) one of the two outputs—$s_1(t)$ or $s_2(t)$, MARK or SPACE, or the equivalent. Often times it is useful to visualize this list in the following way. Each received waveform, $f(t)$, $0 < t < T$, can be represented by its values or samples at a succession of times in the interval $0 < t < T$. These samples in turn may be considered as the coordinates of a point in a multi-dimensional space; each point in this space represents a different received waveform. A decision system, or decision rule, is then defined by assigning one or the other of the outputs to each point in the space. This amounts to dividing the signal space into two mutually exclusive and exhaustive volumes labeled "announce $s_1(t)$" and "announce $s_2(t)$".

Let us suppose that, on some basis, we have divided the multidimensional space into two volumes, V_1 and V_2, and let us suppose that we have received a particular waveform $f(t)$ that happens to lie in the volume V_1. This means that we are supposed to *announce* that $s_1(t)$ was transmitted. But of course it is entirely possible that this is wrong, that even though $f(t)$ in some sense "looks more like" $s_1(t)$, still $s_2(t)$ was actually transmitted and the noise just happened to have a confusing effect. In the course of a long series of decisions we can expect the particular waveform $f(t)$ (or a close approximation to it) to show up a number of times. In only a fraction of these occurences will $s_1(t)$ actually have been transmitted; in the remainder $s_2(t)$ will have been transmitted. But since $f(t)$ is the only information we have there is no way in which we can distinguish these cases. Clearly, in order to minimize the average number of errors that we will make, we should for each $f(t)$ compute the probability of receiving this $f(t)$ under the assumption that $s_1(t)$ was transmitted and separately compute the probability of receiving this $f(t)$ under the assumption that $s_2(t)$ was transmitted. Then we should assign $f(t)$ to V_1 or V_2 (*i.e.*, announce $s_1(t)$ or $s_2(t)$ as present) depending on which probability is larger. In symbols, let

$p[f(t) \mid s_i(t)]$ = (conditional) probability* of receiving $f(t)$ when $s_i(t)$ is known to have been transmitted.

Then our decision rule amounts to: Compute the *likelihood ratio*

$$\Lambda = \frac{p[f(t) \mid s_1(t)]}{p[f(t) \mid s_2(t)]}$$

and announce $s_1(t)$ if $\Lambda > 1$, $s_2(t)$ if $\Lambda < 1$. This decision rule is a particular case of what is called *Bayes' solution* to the canonic decision problem.

There is a wide variety of decision rules which, like Bayes' solution, depend on the likelihood ratio. That this is reasonable can be seen from the following argument. After we have received a particular $f(t)$ the most that we can know about the state of the transmitter are the probabilities that $s_1(t)$ or $s_2(t)$ were sent—i.e., $p[s_1(t) \mid f(t)]$ and $p[s_2(t) \mid f(t)]$. Since, however, either $s_1(t)$ or $s_2(t)$ must have been transmitted, the sum of these two probabilities must be unity, and either one is sufficient by itself to describe our state of knowledge.

Now according to the theorem of inverse probability

$$p[s_1(t) \mid f(t)] = \frac{p[f(t) \mid s_1(t)]\, p[s_1(t)]}{p[f(t) \mid s_1(t)]\, p[s_1(t)] + p[f(t) \mid s_2(t)]\, p[s_2(t)]} = \frac{\Lambda \dfrac{p[s_1(t)]}{p[s_2(t)]}}{1 + \Lambda \dfrac{p[s_1(t)]}{p[s_2(t)]}} \qquad (20)$$

The quantities $p[s_1(t)]$ and $p[s_2(t)]$ are called the *a priori* probabilities because they describe our expectations about the possible presence of the signals *before* receiving $f(t)$; similarly $p[s_1(t) \mid f(t)]$ and $p[s_2(t) \mid f(t)]$ are called the *a posteriori* probabilities because they describe our state of knowledge *after* receiving $f(t)$. It is clear from (20) that the only way in which the received waveform, $f(t)$, influences the *a posteriori* probability is through the value of Λ. Thus Λ can be thought of as a "sufficient statistic"—*it condenses in one number all the data in* f(t) *relevant to a decision* between $s_1(t)$ and $s_2(t)$. Hence if a receiver or data-processing device computes Λ for each $f(t)$, it has reduced the data in an optimum fashion, throwing away nothing that could later be of value. What should be done with Λ to obtain a decision will depend on value judgements and circumstances, but the computation of Λ cannot be wrong. Specifically, from (20), if $s_1(t)$ and $s_2(t)$ are *a priori* equally-likely (as we have assumed all along), then the corresponding particular case of Bayes' solution—compare Λ with unity, announcing $s_1(t)$ if greater, $s_2(t)$ if less—is seen to be

*By the "probability of $f(t)$" we of course mean the joint probability of the corresponding samples at a succession of times in the interval, $0 < t < T$.

equivalent to choosing that transmitted signal which is most probable *a posteriori.*

Although it is far from obvious, the decision system that implements "compare Λ with unity" is operationally identical (for white gaussian noise) with a correlation or matched-filter detector. To show this we must investigate the probabilities $p[f(t) \mid s_1(t)]$ and $p[f(t) \mid s_2(t)]$ more closely. In particular $p[f(t) \mid s_1(t)]$ is merely the probability that a white gaussian noise will have the waveshape

$$n(t) = f(t) - s_1(t)\,, \qquad 0 < t < T\,.$$

However from Chapter 3, IX, a band-limited white gaussian noise of bandwidth W can be represented by

$$n(t) = \sum_{k=1}^{2TW} n(t_k) \frac{\sin 2\pi W\left(t - \frac{k}{2W}\right)}{2\pi W\left(t - \frac{k}{2W}\right)}$$

where $t_k = \frac{k}{2W}$ and the $n(t_k)$ are statistically-independent gaussian random variables with zero mean and variance equal to $2WN_0$. The probability that $n(t)$ equals $[f(t) - s_1(t)]$ is then simply the joint probability of having each $n(t_k)$ equal to the corresponding $[f(t_k) - s_1(t_k)]$; *i.e.*,

$$p[f(t) \mid s_1(t)] = \frac{1}{(4\pi WN_0)^{TW}} e^{-\frac{1}{4WN_0}\sum_{k=1}^{2TW}[f(t_k)-s_1(t_k)]^2} \tag{21}$$

and

$$\Lambda = e^{-\frac{1}{4WN_0}\sum_{k=1}^{2TW}\{[f(t_k)-s_1(t_k)]^2-[f(t_k)-s_2(t_k)]^2\}}\,.$$

Letting $\frac{1}{2W} = \Delta t$, the time separation between samples, and passing to the limit as $W \to \infty$, we obtain

$$\Lambda = e^{-\frac{1}{2N_0}\int_0^T\{[f(t)-s_1(t)]^2-[f(t)-s_2(t)]^2\}\,dt}\,. \tag{22}$$

If $\int_0^T s_1^2(t)dt = \int_0^T s_2^2(t)dt$, and if one observes that comparing Λ with unity is equivalent to comparing $\ln\Lambda$ with 0, the Bayes' solution to the decision problem becomes: Compare

$$\int_0^T f(t)s_1(t)dt - \int_0^T f(t)s_2(t)dt$$

with zero, announcing $s_1(t)$ if positive, $s_2(t)$ if negative—which is identical with the decision rules we have obtained previously, *i.e.*, matched-filter or correlation detection.

VI. PROBABILITY OF ERROR

In order to evaluate the probabilities of error for the canonic decision problem it is most convenient to take the matched filter form of the detector—*i.e.*, consider $f(t)$ as the input to a filter with impulse response

$$h(t) = s_1(T-t) - s_2(T-t) .$$

If the output at $t = T$ exceeds zero announce $s_1(t)$; otherwise $s_2(t)$. We shall assume orthogonal signals with equal energy, *i.e.*,

$$\int_0^T s_1(t)s_2(t)dt = 0$$

$$\int_0^T s_1^2(t)dt = \int_0^T s_2^2(t)dt = E .$$

The signal component of the output is E if $s_1(t)$ is present and $-E$ if $s_2(t)$ is present. The noise at time T has mean square value

$$\sigma^2 = N_0 \frac{1}{2\pi} \int_{-\infty}^{\infty} | H(\omega) |^2 d\omega$$
$$= N_0 \int_0^T h^2(t)dt = 2EN_0 .$$

Since the filter is linear and the input noise is gaussian, the sample of the output is gaussian with mean square equal to $2EN_0$ and mean E or $-E$ depending on whether $s_1(t)$ or $s_2(t)$ is present (see Fig. 3). If $s_1(t)$ and $s_2(t)$ are equally likely and if the comparison threshold is zero, then the probability of error is simply

$$P_e = \int_0^{\infty} \frac{1}{2\pi\sqrt{2EN_0}} e^{-\frac{(x+E)^2}{4EN_0}} dx$$

$$= \int_{\sqrt{E/2N_0}}^{\infty} \frac{1}{\sqrt{2\pi}} e^{-y^2/2} dy$$

which is the familiar error integral. A plot of P_e is shown in Fig. 4. This result also applies to the case of non-orthogonal signals, *i.e.* when

$$\int_0^T s_1(t)s_2(t)dt = \gamma_{12} \neq 0,$$

if E is replaced throughout by $E - \gamma_{12}$.

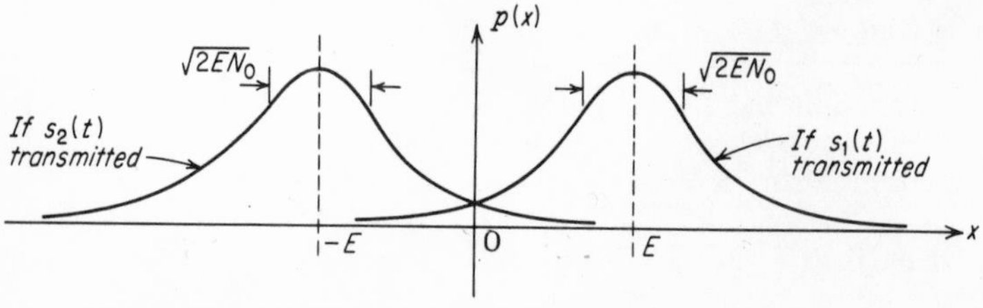

Fig. 3. Output probability densities—matched filter.

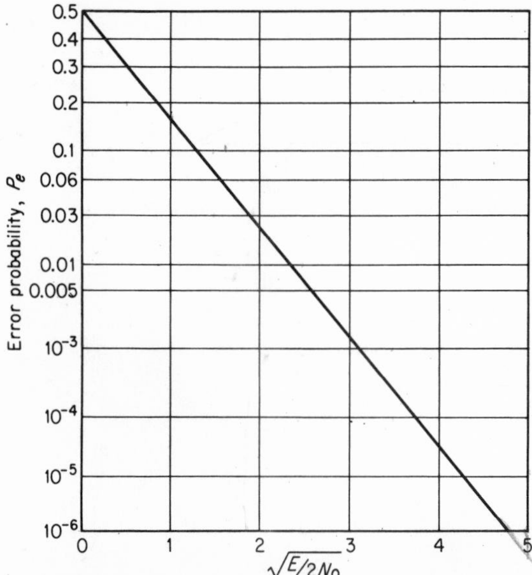

Fig. 4. Probability of error, canonic decision problem (equal-energy, orthogonal signals).

VII. CONCLUDING REMARKS

The cumulative effect of the three or four different ways in which we have looked at the canonic decision problem is impressive. At least for the canonic decision problem in the presence of white gaussian noise, correlation detection is an optimum method—and we need put no qualifications on "optimum." But this is rather an exceptional result for a decision problem; in a more general case it is impossible to avoid a strong influence of *a priori* knowledge and value judgements on the form of the resulting decision system. Some examples of this will appear in the next chapter.

CHAPTER 9

Statistical Decision Theory and Communications: A More General Formulation

William L. Root

I. INTRODUCTION

The discussion of the preceding chapter has been devoted to the canonic decision problem in order to illustrate the type of communication problem that can be tackled profitably by decision-theoretic analysis. It is now appropriate to extend the ideas somewhat and consider statistical decision procedures more generally in connection with communication. A first question to be asked is: When does a statistical decision problem arise in radio communication? The answer is, evidently, whenever the received signals are distorted by the channel in a way that is not known precisely but which follows some regular pattern *on the average;* or, in other words, whenever some of the statistical properties of the channel are known. In the canonical signal extraction problem treated in the previous chapter, the signals are distorted by the addition of white noise. The noise waveforms are not known—if they were, suitable signal processing could cancel their effect—but they are governed by certain probability relations, the knowledge of which, as was shown, can be exploited in specifying a receiver. In general, random signal corruption may occur because of additive noise, such as antenna noise or thermal noise in the front end of a receiver, or atmospherics, or because of changes in the structure of the signal resulting from the mode of propagation, such as multipath or scattering. In any such case, if something is known or can be found out about the statistics of the distortion, then the problem of how best to interpret the received signal is within the domain of statistical decision theory. It should be emphasized that the purpose of statistical decision theory is to show how to treat imperfect data rationally; if the data are very good, there is little need for decision theory, and if the data are very bad, the best one can do may still not be good enough.

In order to tie together different specific problems, let us now introduce an abstract formulation of a class of statistical problems of interest here. Three basic elements of the class of problems in question are *observations, parameters* (or "states of nature"), and *decisions*. The intuitive meaning of observations and decisions should be clear; by a "parameter" we mean some kind of quantity that serves to index the state of nature which actually exists and which the observation is intended to shed light on. Let us consider a set Y of observations y, a set Ω of parameters ω, and a set D of decisions d. We suppose that each parameter value ω determines a probability law $P(y|\omega)$ governing the appearance of possible observations y in Y. We also suppose that each decision d determines a subset of Ω; for, since the states of nature are indexed by an abstract set of points ω, any attribute of the states of nature is determined by specifying which points ω possess it, or, equivalently, by specifying a subset of Ω.

The problem confronting the observer, or the "statistician," is to answer some question about the state of nature (which is unknown to him) from his observation y. He does this by choosing a *decision rule* $d(y)$ that assigns to each possible observation y in Y a decision $d = d(y)$ in D. Then he plays a game with Nature: Nature chooses a probability law $P(y|\omega)$, unknown to the observer, which governs the chances of occurrence of any particular observation y. To the observation y which is made, the observer applies his decision rule; that is, he finds $d(y)$. The decision, $d = d(y)$, is a judgement that the state of nature actually in effect has some particular attribute, or, abstractly, that ω belongs to some particular subset of Ω. All this is based, of course, on the assumption that the observer wants to make his decision according to a pre-established rational principle. One can conceive situations in which he might not; for example, he might want to examine by eye a photographic record of received waveforms and judge subjectively what signals were present and when.

In the canonic decision problem, the space of observations Y could be taken to be the space of all possible received waveforms, the parameter set Ω to be a set of two points, ω_0 (signifying MARK) and ω_1 (signifying SPACE). The admissible decisions are: MARK, or SPACE. The kind of decision rule developed consisted of reducing the observation y, the received waveform, to a pair of numbers by passing it through two special matched filters and comparing these numbers.

II. LOSS AND RISK FUNCTIONS, A PRIORI PROBABILITIES

In order to single out good decision rules—or a "best" decision rule, if there is such a thing—we must have criteria for comparing decision rules. Examples of such criteria are the expected loss resulting from incorrect decisions, and the *a posteriori* probability of a correct decision. We shall now formalize the idea of loss somewhat, in the framework of the rather general statistical problem described in the introduction of this chapter.

By a *loss function*, $L(d, \omega)$, we mean a nonnegative function of decisions and parameter values. It is specified by the observer (or the "statistician") with the intent of assigning a reasonable penalty to the observer for each possible incorrect decision, given a state of nature as indexed by ω. We may as well always require that if d' is a correct decision for a given ω' then $L(d', \omega') = 0$. Now, given a particular ω, different and independent observations will in general yield different results because ω determines only a probability distribution for y. With different observations, there will result in general different decisions and different losses. It is natural to ask what the average loss would be. The average loss is called the risk, $r_d(\omega)$; it depends on ω and on the decision rule used and it is given by

$$r_d(\omega) = \int_Y L(d(y), \omega)\, dP(y|\omega) \tag{1}$$

Thus, the loss is computed for each possible observation y and is then averaged according to the frequency of occurrence of the different observations. Evidently, the observer wants to minimize his risk by choosing the best decision function. The trouble is, if no more information is given to the observer than we have thus far assumed, a decision rule $d(y)$ that reduces $r_d(\omega)$ for one value of ω may increase it for another. Since the observer does not know ω—indeed, he is essentially trying to find ω—this is not a very satisfactory situation. However, one can certainly say that if $r_{d1}(\omega) \leq r_{d2}(\omega)$ for all values of the parameter ω and if for at least one value of ω, $r_{d1}(\omega) < r_{d2}(\omega)$, then d_1 is clearly a better decision rule than d_2. A decision rule is commonly called *admissible* if there are none better in the sense just specified. One major problem in statistics is to find classes of admissible decision rules.

The observer may, however, know more. He may know that Nature chooses the parameter ω, that is the distribution $P(y|\omega)$, according to a probability law. Such a probability distribution governing the existence of the states of nature (as indexed by ω) is called an *a priori* probability, and we shall denote it by $d\pi(\omega)$. If it is reasonable to assume the existence of an *a priori* probability, and if the observer knows what it is, then he can average the risk with respect to this probability to get

$$\text{Expected risk} = r_d = \int_\Omega \int_Y L(d(y), \omega)\, dP(y|\omega)\, d\pi(\omega) \tag{2}$$

A natural definition of an optimum decision rule (for a given loss function and *a priori* probability law) is that it is one that minimizes the expected risk. Such a decision rule is called the *Bayes solution* to the decision problem. When the observer has sufficient knowledge to introduce a loss function and an *a priori* probability law, the Bayes solution usually appears to be a satisfactory solution to the decision problem, particulary if the statistical experiment is to be performed again and again and a decision is to be made each time.

A relatively simple special case is the problem of testing between two simple hypotheses. For this problem only two possible states of nature can exist, which we index by ω_0 and ω_1. One hypothesis, H_0, is that the state ω_0 obtains, the other, H_1, is that the state ω_1 obtains. The allowed possible decisions are that either H_0 or H_1 is the true hypothesis. Thus there are decisions corresponding to the single-element subsets $[\omega_0]$ and $[\omega_1]$ of Ω. The *a priori* probability law is specified by the two probabilities $\pi_0 = \text{Prob}(\omega_0)$ and $\pi_1 = \text{Prob}(\omega_1)$. The expression (2) for the expected risk is then

$$r_d = \int_Y L(d(y), \omega_0)\, dP(y|\omega_0) \cdot \pi_0 + \int_Y L(d(y), \omega_1)\, dP(y|\omega_1) \cdot \pi_1 \tag{3}$$

Since there are only two possible decisions, any decision rule amounts to dividing the space of observations into two disjoint sets, Y_0 and Y_1, with the convention that if the observation falls in Y_0, H_0 is chosen, if the observation falls in Y_1, H_1 is chosen. Hence, writing $L_{0,1}$ for $L(d(y), \omega_1)$ when y is in Y_0 and $L_{1,0}$ for $L(d(y), \omega_0)$ when y is in Y_1 and setting the loss equal to zero for both possible correct decisions, we have from (3)

$$\begin{aligned} r_d &= \pi_0 \int_{Y_1} L_{1,0}\, dP(y|\omega_0) + \pi_1 \int_{Y_0} L_{0,1}\, dP(y|\omega_1) \\ &= \pi_0 \int_Y L_{1,0}\, dP(y|\omega_0) + \int_{Y_0} [\pi_1 L_{0,1}\, dP(y|\omega_1) - \pi_0 L_{1,0}\, dP(y|\omega_0)) \\ &= \pi_0 L_{1,0} + \int_{Y_0} [\pi_1 L_{0,1}\, dP(y|\omega_1) - \pi_0 L_{1,0}\, dP(y|\omega_0)] \end{aligned} \tag{4}$$

since $\text{Prob}(Y_1) = 1 - \text{Prob}(Y_0)$. Now, letting $p(y|\omega_0)$ and $p(y|\omega_1)$ be the probability density functions for the distributions $dP(y|\omega_0)$ and $dP(y|\omega_1)$, we have

$$r_d = \pi_0 L_{1,0} + \int_{Y_0} \{\pi_1 L_{0,1} p(y|\omega_1) - \pi_0 L_{1,0} p(y|\omega_0)\}\, dy \tag{5}$$

Clearly, then, the average risk r_d is minimized by choosing the set Y_0 (which, of course, is equivalent to specifying a decision rule) so that it contains exactly those points y for which

$$\pi_0 L_{1,0}\, p(y|\omega_0) > \pi_1 L_{0,1}\, p(y|\omega_1)$$

or,

$$\frac{p(y|\omega_0)}{p(y|\omega_1)} > \frac{\pi_1 L_{0,1}}{\pi_0 L_{1,0}} \tag{6}$$

The ratio $p(y|\omega_0)/p(y|\omega_1) = l(y)$ is the *likelihood* ratio. Thus the minimum-expected-risk (or Bayes) hypothesis test procedure is to compare the likelihood ratio $l(y)$ with a fixed threshold, accept H_0 if $l(y)$ exceeds the threshold, and accept H_1 if $l(y)$ is less than the threshold. It will be noticed from the expression for r_d that it does not matter, as far as average risk is concerned, which decision is made when $l(y)$ equals the threshold.

One will notice that the immediately preceding discussion fits exactly the canonical decision problem of Chapter 8 if one identifies ω_0 with transmission of MARK and ω_1 with transmission of

SPACE. Indeed, we have essentially repeated an argument that was given in Chapter 8 to justify a likelihood-ratio test.

As the mathematical model is made more realistic, it usually becomes more complicated; and even in binary-alphabet communication the statistical reception problem involves testing between *composite* hypotheses. In this situation there are again two hypotheses, to be denoted by H_0 and H_1, but either one or both of the hypotheses refer to a whole class of possible states of nature. That is, the parameter set Ω contains many points ω, but we are interested in finding out only whether the true ω belongs to a particular subset Ω_0 or to its complement Ω_1. Again the decision rule is specified completely by dividing Y into two disjoint sets Y_0 and Y_1, to be used in the same way as above. The expected risk can now be written from (2), with the same meaning attached to $L_{0,1}$ and $L_{1,0}$ as before, as

$$r_d = L_{1,0} \int_{\Omega_0} \int_{Y_1} dP(y\,|\,\omega)\, d\pi(\omega) + L_{0,1} \int_{\Omega_1} \int_{Y_0} dP(y\,|\,\omega)\, d\pi(\omega) \qquad (7)$$

Letting $p(y\,|\,\omega)$ be the probability density function for y given ω [so that $p(y\,|\,\omega)\,dy = dP(y\,|\,\omega)$] and using again the fact Prob $(Y_1) = 1$ $-$ Prob (Y_0), we have

$$r_d = L_{1,0} + \int_{Y_0} dy\, \left\{ L_{0,1} \int_{\Omega_1} p(y\,|\,\omega)\, d\pi(\omega) - L_{1,0} \int_{\Omega_0} p(y\,|\,\omega)\, d\pi(\omega) \right\} \qquad (8)$$

This formula is analogous to (5). Obviously r_d is minimized by choosing for Y_0 the set of points y for which

$$L_{1,0} \int_{\Omega_0} p(y\,|\,\omega)\, d\pi(\omega) > L_{0,1} \int_{\Omega_1} p(y\,|\,\omega)\, d\pi(\omega) \qquad (9)$$

Consequently, for a given observation y, we shall conclude that H_0 is true if the inequality above is satisfied, and that H_1 is true if it is not. This is again a kind of likelihood-ratio test, for the test inequality may be written

$$\frac{\text{Prob }(y < \eta \leq y + dy,\, \Omega_0)}{\text{Prob }(y < \eta \leq y + dy,\, \Omega_1)} > \frac{L_{0,1}}{L_{1,0}}\,.$$

This formulation is sufficiently general to cover most cases of binary communication channels. The generality is built into the parameter set Ω, which in such an application may take care of any parametrizable randomness in the received signal, as for example, random phase and amplitude of an *rf* carrier, in addition to the essential randomness in what is transmitted. The chief difficulty with this minimum-expected-risk test is that it is sometimes unrealistic to assign *a priori* probability laws to all the random quantities that influence the observation because of a lack of knowledge of their behavior.

If one is unwilling to introduce *a priori* probabilities for the parameter set in the problem of testing between two hypotheses, an alternative to the above is to use the *generalized maximum-likelihood test*, which is a first cousin to maximum-likelihood parameter estimation. The idea is to find $\omega = \omega'$ in Ω which, if correct, maximizes the probability of occurrence of the observation y; then if ω' is unique and lies in the subset Ω_0, one chooses H_0, and if ω' lies in Ω_1, one chooses H_1. This can be written

$$\text{choose } H_0 \text{ if: } \max_{\omega \text{ in } \Omega_0} p(y|\omega) > \max_{\omega \text{ in } \Omega_1} p(y|\omega)$$

$$\text{choose } H_1 \text{ if: } \max_{\omega \text{ in } \Omega_0} p(y|\omega) < \max_{\omega \text{ in } \Omega_1} p(y|\omega)$$

In the case of testing between simple hypotheses this test reduces to the maximum-likelihood test which yields minimum average risk when

$$\pi_0 = \pi_1 = \frac{1}{2} \text{ and } L_{0,1} = L_{1,0}.$$

III. EXAMPLES

The canonical signal-reception problem, which has already been discussed, provides one example in which it is required to test between two simple hypotheses. We shall now consider two more examples that involve communication using a binary alphabet (so that a test between two hypotheses is required) but in these examples the hypotheses are composite so that the statistical decision problem is more sophisticated.

A. Constant-Amplitude, Random-Phase FSK (Frequency-Shift Keying) in White Gaussian Noise

We assume that the MARK and SPACE symbols are represented respectively by the time functions

$$\left.\begin{aligned} s_0(t) &= A \cos \omega_0 t \\ s_1(t) &= A \cos \omega_1 t \end{aligned}\right\} \quad 0 \leqslant t \leqslant T$$

We further assume that the signals arrive at the receiver with constant amplitude A but random rf phase and that the received signals are imbedded in white noise. Thus the received waveform is either

$$y(t) = A \cos (\omega_0 t + \theta) + n(t), \; 0 \leqslant t < T$$

or

$$y(t) = A \cos (\omega_1 t + \theta) + n(t), \; 0 \leqslant t < T$$

We shall suppose that the random phase θ takes on any value between 0 and 2π with equal probability, that MARK and SPACE are equally likely, and that the losses ($L_{0,1}$ and $L_{1,0}$) assigned to the two kinds of error are equal. We want to specify a receiver that is optimum in the sense of providing a minimum-expected-risk solution (Bayes solution) to the hypothesis test problem.

From (9) it follows that the test is to announce MARK at the receiver if

$$\frac{\int_{\Omega_0} p(y|\omega)\,d\pi(\omega)}{\int_{\Omega_1} p(y|\omega)\,d\pi(\omega)} > 1$$

and announce SPACE otherwise. The parameters ω must determine MARK or SPACE and the value of θ. Thus each ω is of the form (i, θ), $i = 0, 1;\ 0 \leqslant \theta < 2\pi$, where i and θ are independent, Prob $(i = 0)$ = Prob $(i = 1) = 1/2$, and Prob $(a < \theta \leqslant a + da) = da/2\pi$. For noise bandwidth W and power density N_0, we have from Eq. (21) of Chapter 8, with $l = 2TW$,

$$\int_{\Omega_0} p(y|\omega)d\pi(\omega) = \frac{1}{4\pi}\left(\frac{1}{\sqrt{2\pi 2WN_0}}\right)^l$$

$$\times \int_0^{2\pi} \exp\left\{-\frac{1}{4WN_0}\sum_{k=1}^{l}\left[y_k - A\cos(\omega_0\frac{kT}{l} + \theta)\right]^2 d\theta = \frac{1}{4\pi}\left(\frac{1}{\sqrt{4\pi WN_0}}\right)^l\right.$$

$$\times \exp\left[-\frac{1}{4WN_0}\sum_{k=1}^{l} y_k^2\right]\int_0^{2\pi}\exp\left\{\frac{2A}{4WN_0}\sum_{k=1}^{l} y_k\cos(\omega_0\frac{kT}{l} + \theta)\right\}$$

$$\times \exp\left\{-\frac{A^2}{4WN_0}\sum_{k=1}^{l}\cos^2(\omega_0\frac{kT}{l} + \theta)\right\} d\theta \qquad (10)$$

The second exponential under the integral sign becomes essentially independent of θ as W and l become large, and hence θ can be set equal to zero in it. If we write

$$\sum_{k=1}^{l} y_k\cos(\omega_0\frac{kT}{l} + \theta) = \cos\theta\sum_{k=1}^{l} y_k\cos\omega_0\frac{kT}{l}$$

$$-\sin\theta\sum_{k=1}^{l} y_k\sin\omega_0\frac{kT}{l}$$

and use the formula

$$\frac{1}{2\pi}\int_0^{2\pi} e^{c\cos\theta + d\sin\theta}\,d\theta = I_0\left(\sqrt{c^2 + d^2}\right)$$

where $I_0(x) = J_0(jx)$ is a Bessel function of the first kind of zero order, we obtain

$$\int_{\Omega_0} p(y\,|\,\omega)\,d\pi(\omega) = \frac{1}{2}\left(\frac{1}{\sqrt{4\pi W N_0}}\right)^l \exp\left[\frac{-1}{4WN_0}\sum_{k=1}^{l} y_k^2\right]$$

$$\exp\left[\frac{-A^2}{4WN_0}\sum_{k=1}^{l}\cos^2\omega_0\frac{kT}{l}\right] \tag{11}$$

$$\times\, I_0\left(\sqrt{\frac{A^2}{4W^2N_0^{\,2}}\left[\sum_{k=1}^{l} y_k\cos\omega_0\frac{kT}{l}\right]^2 + \left[\sum_{k=1}^{l} y_k\sin\omega_0\frac{kT}{l}\right]^2}\right)$$

The expression for $\int_{\Omega_1} p(y\,|\,\omega)\,d\pi(\omega)$ is the same except that ω_0 is replaced throughout by ω_1. For large W and l the ratio

$$\left[\sum_{k=1}^{l}\cos^2\omega_0\frac{kT}{l}\right]/(l/2)$$

is approximately one and it is almost independent of ω_0 for large ω_0. Moreover, as W and $l \to \infty$,

$$\frac{1}{2W}\sum_{k=1}^{l} y_k\cos\omega_0\frac{kT}{l} \to \int_0^T y(t)\cos\omega_0 t\,dt$$

$$\frac{1}{2W}\sum_{k=1}^{l} y_k\sin\omega_0\frac{kT}{l} \to \int_0^T y(t)\sin\omega_0 t\,dt$$

Thus the natural logarithm of the likelihood ratio becomes

$$\ln\frac{\int_{\Omega_0} p(y\,|\,\omega)\,d\pi(\omega)}{\int_{\Omega_1} p(y\,|\,\omega)\,d\pi(\omega)} = \ln I_0\left(\left|\frac{A}{N}\int_0^T y(t)e^{j\omega_0 t}\,dt\right|\right) - \ln I_0\left(\left|\frac{A}{N}\int_0^T y(t)e^{j\omega_1 t}\,dt\right|\right) \tag{12}$$

and the criterion for choosing H_0, or MARK, is that this quantity be greater than zero. Since $I_0(x)$ is a monotone function and the log is also monotone, the test reduces to comparing the arguments of the Bessel functions. That is, one announces MARK if

$$\left|\int_0^T y(t)e^{j\omega_0 t}dt\right| > \left|\int_0^T y(t)e^{j\omega_1 t}dt\right| \tag{13}$$

and SPACE otherwise. Physically this may be interpreted as passing the received waveform through two $\frac{\sin \omega}{\omega}$ filters in parallel, one centered at ω_0 and one at ω_1, and comparing the envelopes of their outputs at the end of the symbol interval. This is an intuitively satisfying result because the $\frac{\sin \omega}{\omega}$ filters are matched filters for the two signals, and taking the envelope removes the useless phase information. Notice that the specification of the receiver does not depend on the signal-to-noise ratio.

B. Random-Amplitude, Known-Phase, Arbitrary Signals in Colored Gaussian Noise.

We assume that the form of the signals at the receiver is arbitrary but known to within an amplitude factor (plus or minus); and we denote the normalized signals at the receiver by $s_0(t)$, $s_1(t)$, $0 \leq t < T$. This implies that phase information is known to within phase reversals. However, we assume that the amplitude of the signals is not only unknown, but may vary from symbol to symbol and might, at a given instant, even take on different values depending on whether MARK or SPACE was sent. One may assume an *a priori* distribution of amplitudes and determine a minimum-average-risk decision rule, somewhat as in the previous sample. In order to illustrate a different technique, however, we shall assume that the distribution of amplitudes is unknown and use the generalized maximum likelihood test. Again let the period of observation be of length T, and let the received waveform be sampled at N regular intervals during this period. Later we formally let $N \to \infty$. The received waveform is either

$$y(t) = \beta s_0(t) + n(t), \quad 0 \leq t < T$$

or

$$y(t) = \beta s_1(t) + n(t), \quad 0 \leq t < T$$

and since the noise is colored, the waveforms at the different sampling times will no longer in general be independent.

Let us denote the covariance matrix of the noise at the N equally spaced sample points by

$$\Lambda = [\lambda_{ij}], \; i, j = 1, \ldots, N$$

$$\lambda_{ij} = E[n_i n_j] = E[n_{i+k} n_{j+k}] \text{ for any } k \text{ since the noise is stationary.}$$

Let the inverse of the matrix Λ be $\Gamma = [\gamma_{ij}]$, and denote the determinant of Λ by $|\Lambda|$. Then the joint probability density function for the noise-alone waveform is

$$p(y) = \frac{1}{(2\pi)^{n/2} |\Lambda|^{1/2}} \exp\left\{-\frac{1}{2|\Lambda|} \sum_{m,n=1}^{N} \gamma_{nm} y_n y_m\right\}.$$

Let

$$\left.\begin{aligned} a_k &= s_0(t_k) \\ b_k &= s_1(t_k) \end{aligned}\right\} \; t_k = k\text{'th sample point}$$

The joint probability densities of the received waveform on the hypothesis MARK was sent and on the hypothesis SPACE was sent are then, respectively,

$$p(\beta; y \mid \omega_0) = p(\beta; y_1, \ldots, y_N \mid \omega_0) = \frac{1}{(2\pi)^{N/2} |\Lambda|^{1/2}}$$

$$\times \exp\left\{ -\frac{1}{2|\Lambda|} \sum_{m,n=1}^{N} \gamma_{nm}(y_n - \beta a_n)(y_m - \beta a_m) \right\} \tag{14}$$

and,

$$p(\beta; y \mid \omega_1) = p(\beta; y_1, \ldots, y_N \mid \omega_1) = \frac{1}{(2\pi)^{N/2} |\Lambda|^{1/2}}$$

$$\times \exp\left\{ -\frac{1}{2|\Lambda|} \sum_{m,n=1}^{N} \gamma_{nm}(y_n - \beta b_n)(y_m - \beta b_m) \right\} \tag{15}$$

According to the maximum-likelihood principle we maximize each of these separately with respect to β and compare the results. In the notation used for the discussion of the abstract hypothesis test problem, each $\omega = (i, \beta)$, $i = 0$ or 1, β a real number, and ω is in Ω_0 if $i = 0$ and in Ω_1 if $i = 1$. The value of β which maximizes $p(\beta; y \mid \omega_0)$ is easily found (for example by taking logarithms and differentiating) to be

$$\beta_0 = \frac{\sum_{m,n=1}^{N} \gamma_{nm} a_n y_m}{\sum_{m,n=1}^{N} \gamma_{nm} a_n a_m} \equiv \frac{1}{C_0} \sum_{m,n=1}^{N} \gamma_{nm} a_n y_m \tag{16}$$

and similarly the value of β which maximizes $p(\beta; y \mid \omega_1)$ is

$$\beta_1 = \frac{\sum_{m,n=1}^{N} \gamma_{nm} b_n y_m}{\sum_{m,n=1}^{N} \gamma_{nm} b_n b_m} \equiv \frac{1}{C_1} \sum_{m,n,=1}^{N} \gamma_{nm} b_n y_m \tag{17}$$

where C_0 and C_1 are defined implicitly. The natural logarithm of the resulting likelihood ratio is

$$\ln \frac{p(\beta_0; y \mid \omega_0)}{p(\beta_1; y \mid \omega_1)}$$

$$= \frac{1}{2|\Lambda|} \left\{ \sum_{m,n=1}^{N} \gamma_{nm}(\beta_1{}^2 b_n b_m - \beta_0{}^2 a_n a_m) + 2 \sum_{m,n,=1}^{N} \gamma_{nm}(\beta_0 a_n - \beta_1 b_n) y_m \right\}$$

$$= \frac{1}{2|\Lambda|}\left\{\frac{1}{C_0}\left(\sum_{m,n=1}^{N} \gamma_{nm} a_n y_m\right)^2 - \frac{1}{C_1}\left(\sum_{m,n=1}^{N} \gamma_{nm} b_n y_m\right)^2\right\} \tag{18}$$

Thus the generalized maximum-likelihood test is to choose H_0 (announce MARK is received) if

$$\frac{1}{C_0}\left(\sum_{m,n=1}^{N} \gamma_{nm} a_n y_m\right)^2 > \frac{1}{C_1}\left(\sum_{m,n,=1}^{N} \gamma_{nm} b_n y_m\right)^2$$

and choose H_1 otherwise. Before letting $N \to \infty$, let us rewrite this inequality by introducing

$$f_m = \sum_{n=1}^{N} \gamma_{mn} a_n$$

$$g_m = \sum_{n=1}^{N} \gamma_{mn} b_n$$

The test inequality becomes

$$\frac{1}{C_0}\left(\sum_{m=1}^{N} f_m y_m\right)^2 > \frac{1}{C_1}\left(\sum_{m=1}^{N} g_m y_m\right)^2$$

and we observe that

$$\sum_{m=1}^{N} \lambda_{nm} f_m = \sum_{m=1}^{N} \lambda_{nm} \sum_{k=1}^{N} a_k \gamma_{mk}$$

$$= \sum_{k=1}^{N} a_k \sum_{m=1}^{N} \lambda_{nm} \gamma_{mk} = a_n$$

and similarly $\sum_{m=1}^{N} \lambda_{nm} g_m = b_n$ since each of the matrices $[\lambda_{ij}]$ and $[\gamma_{ij}]$ is the inverse of the other. Now let $\delta = T/N$ be the time interval between sample points, then formally as $N \to \infty$ the equations

$$\sum_{m=1}^{N} \lambda_{nm}\left(\frac{f_m}{\delta}\right)\delta = a_n, \quad \sum_{m=1}^{N} \lambda_{nm}\left(\frac{g_m}{\delta}\right)\delta = b_n$$

become $\int_0^T R(t,\tau)\, f(\tau) d\tau = s_0(t),\ 0 < t < T,$ (19)

$$\int_0^T R(t,\tau)\, g(\tau)\, d\tau = s_1(t),\ 0 < t < T, \tag{20}$$

respectively. The test inequality becomes

$$\frac{\left(\int_0^T f(t)y(t)dt\right)^2}{\int_0^T f(t)s_0(t)dt} > \frac{\left(\int_0^T g(t)y(t)dt\right)^2}{\int_0^T g(t)s_1(t)dt} \tag{21}$$

where the "test functions" $f(t)$ and $g(t)$ are solutions to the integral equations (19) and (20).

If we let

$$h_0(t) = f(T-t),\ 0 \leqslant t \leqslant T$$

$$h_1(t) = g(T-t),\quad 0 \leqslant t \leqslant T$$

the test inequality can be written

$$\frac{\left(\int_0^T h_0(T-t)\,y(t)dt\right)^2}{\int_0^T h_0(T-t)s_0(t)dt} > \frac{\left(\int_0^T h_1(T-t)\,y(t)dt\right)^2}{\int_0^T h_1(T-t)s_1(t)dt} \tag{22}$$

where

$$\int_0^T R(t,\tau)\,h_0(\tau)d\tau = s_0(T-t),\ 0 < t < T \tag{23}$$

$$\int_0^T R(t,\tau)\,h_1(\tau)d\tau = s_1(T-t),\ 0 < t < T \tag{24}$$

The integrals in the numerators of the test inequality (22) can be realized by linear filters with impulse responses $h_0(t)$ and $h_1(t)$ respectively; so the decision rule can be implemented by passing the input waveforms to the receiver through two parallel filters, taking the magnitudes of the outputs, weighting these magnitudes and comparing. In the special case of white noise $h_0(t) = s_0(T-t)$, $h_1(t) = s_1(T-t)$ and the filters become the conventional matched filters. Also, the integrals in the denominators of (22) become just the values of energy of the two signals.

CHAPTER 10

Representation of Signals

Robert M. Lerner

I. INTRODUCTION

As the communication art becomes more sophisticated, engineers are being called on to deal more and more with complicated signals. This trend is typified by the use of noise-like signals to combat multipath (as in RAKE[1]), various suggestions for improving the range and velocity resolution of radars,[2] and the desire to evolve ways of reducing the complication of a signal (as in the case of narrowband coding schemes for speech[3]). As yet, however, no set of analytical tools has been developed which make the behavior of such complicated signals both easy to compute and simple to understand. In this chapter, we review some of the earlier techniques for dealing with signals, and the difficulties that arise in using them; we then generalize a unit-function procedure (first suggested by Gabor[4]) into a flexible procedure for picturing and computing the behavior of complicated signals.

One cannot go very far with the problem of representing a general signal in any other manner than by an abstract symbol, such as S, without some preconceptions as to the precise properties of S that one wishes to represent. Consider, for instance, a speech signal. One may be interested in this signal as a waveform; or in mechanistically identifying the words that make it up; or in its intelligibility to a listener; or in its semantic content. Here are four aspects of a speech signal S. Surely, they are related in some general way; but it is by no means clear that a "good" representation of one of these aspects, say, waveform, is related in a one-to-one manner to another, say identification.†

Therefore, it is necessary to set down some restrictions. The first of these is that we are interested in characterizing that aspect of S that is usually called "waveform" and is usually given as a function of time. The second restriction is that we require the representation to be useful, in the sense that it facilitates computation, analysis, or "seeing what goes on" in the generation and processing of signal waveforms.

Now, if S is given as a function of time, $s(t)$, then clearly no further representation is needed unless some problem is too difficult, not sufficiently clear, or not easy enough to solve with S as given. Some other representation of S will be useful if it permits one to

†As a matter of fact, one of the basic difficulties in mechanizing the recognition of speech is that this one-to-one correspondence does not exist.

break up the problem at hand into component pieces which *can* be solved, or *are* clear, or *are* easy; then one must be able to put the pieces back together to indicate the solution of the general problem. This procedure might well be called "logical superposition."

In order to get anywhere in a majority of practical problems, involving complicated signals being processed by complicated systems, one must not only have the possibility of logical superposition; one must have physical superposition as well.

That is to say, the signal processing to be described must be at least approximately linear or piecewise linear. For instance, a standard method of treating such non-linear systems as modulators or "parametric" amplifiers is to replace the non-linear problem by a linear one with time-varying coefficients.[5]

In a linear problem, the logical procedure outlined above reduces to representing $s(t)$ as a weighted sum of a set of preselected waveforms, $y_n(t)$:

$$s(t) = \sum_n a_n y_n(t) \tag{1}$$

The $y_n(t)$ are so chosen that for any one of them the analysis, computation, or visualization of the particular problem at hand is easy. To find out what happens to $s(t)$, one determines what happens to individual y_n's and adds up the results with the appropriate weightings, a_n.

Clearly, (1) is not the only way of representing a signal, even for processing signals by linear systems. Nevertheless, a third restriction to the scope of this paper is that we will discuss only representations of S in the form of a sum such as (1), or an equivalent integral.

In particular, we seek preselected waveforms, $y_n(t)$ with some or all of the following properties:

(a) The $y_n(t)$ must be such that any signal that is likely to be encountered can be expressed as a convergent weighted sum of the $y_n(t)$ as in (1).

(b) The $y_n(t)$ ought to be easy to compute with. For use in describing physical systems, it may also be required that the $y_n(t)$ correspond to the outputs of arrays of simple filters.

(c) Inasmuch as signals usually "occur" at some time and are roughly "limited" to some bandwidth, each of the $y_n(t)$ should have a well-defined "time of occurrence" (and corresponding duration) and a well-defined "frequency" at which it occurs (and a corresponding bandwidth).

(d) The $y_n(t)$ should be in some sense simple.

In what follows, we first discuss the merits and indicate the limitations of representing signals by a Fourier spectrum. Next we take up the use of orthogonal functions and the question of completeness. Following a short discussion of Gabor's problem, we introduce the generalized unit functions and use them to characterize several illustrative problems.

II. STANDARD SIGNAL REPRESENTATIONS

The technique for signal analysis best known to communication engineers is spectral analysis, in which a function of time $f(t)$ is in effect represented by a sum of sine waves by the Fourier integral†

$$f(t) = \frac{1}{2\pi}\int_{-\infty}^{\infty} F(\omega)e^{j\omega t}\,d\omega \tag{2}$$

in which

$$F(\omega) = \int_{-\infty}^{\infty} f(t)e^{-j\omega t}\,dt. \tag{3}$$

The outstanding advantage of the Fourier representation (2) is that if a signal function whose spectrum is $S(\omega)$ is passed through a (stationary) linear filter whose system function is $H(\omega)$, the spectrum of the output signal, $G(\omega)$ is given by the product

$$G(\omega) = H(\omega)S(\omega) \tag{4}$$

whereas if one must work with the signal function $s(t)$ and the filter impulse response $h(t)$ one must evaluate the convolution integral

$$g(t) = \int_{-\infty}^{\infty} h(\xi)s(t-\xi)\,d\xi \tag{5}$$

to obtain the filter output $g(t)$. Basically, constant-parameter linear system analysis consists of extablishing, manipulating, and evaluating the expressions and integrals (2) through (5).

If we try to apply Fourier analysis methods to "random" signals, we encounter difficulties. One may make a Fourier analysis of any finite sample of speech, $x(t)$—but as the speaker goes on talking, the communication of the new material will radically alter the corresponding $X(\omega)$, so that $X(\omega)$ does not converge to any limiting form as the interval of analysis is extended indefinitely. What holds true for speech holds also for any function of time which is random in the sense that its entire future is not predictable from a complete knowledge of its past. In particular, for any process that continuously generates new information, the amplitude spectrum $X(\omega)$ fails to exist. The basic difficulty is that all waveforms of which the signal is to be built extend over the same infinite (or semi-infinite) time interval. Accordingly, to accommodate new material with the passage of time the coefficients of the entire array of constituent waveforms must be re-arranged.

Now it is true that in the case of the kinds of signals described

†For solving linear-system problems the (single-sided) Laplace transform, which is basically a sum of damped sinusoids, is more commonly used. (M. F. Gardner and J. L. Barnes, *Transients in Linear Systems*, John Wiley and Sons, New York, 1942.) The special advantages and less restricted generality of the "double-ended" Laplace transform in the treatment and classification of linear fixed-parameter systems have been illustrated in Chapter 3 of the present volume.

above, a power spectral density can be defined which, in the limit, does exist.† This power spectral density is related to the statistical parameters of the signal, in particular its autocorrelation function. As a result of these properties, the power spectral density (and the sinusoidal analysis that goes with it) is for many design problems as useful as a knowledge of the signal itself. But it does not represent the signal, since the signal cannot, in general, be uniquely reconstructed from it. Some other means of representation for the signal itself must be found.

Accordingly, we return to our original representation of the signal, Eq. (1), with the expectation that to do a satisfactory job of representing continuously information-bearing signals, some (or all) of the $y_n(t)$ must "occur" at different times. If such is the case, the inclusion of new material will affect the coefficients mainly of those $y_n(t)$ which "occur" during the time epoch of that material and leave the coefficients of the $y_n(t)$ which "occur" in other epochs of the signal substantially unaltered.

If we restrict ourselves to signals whose frequency components include nothing in excess of a low-pass bandwidth W cps, one such representation is indeed very well known, viz. the sampling theorem[4,6] presented in section VIII of Chapter 3. Here,

$$y_n(t) = \frac{\sin \pi(2Wt - n)}{\pi(2Wt - n)} \tag{6}$$

$$s(t) = \sum_{n=-\infty}^{\infty} a_n \frac{\sin \pi(2Wt - n)}{\pi(2Wt - n)} . \tag{7}$$

With this choice of $y_n(t)$ the computation of the coefficients a_n is indeed simple; one merely samples the signal $s(t)$ at regular intervals of time, $\tau = 1/2W$. Of course, the class of signals that are limited to a low-pass bandwidth of W cps scarcely includes all possible $s(t)$. But we can consider the entire frequency spectrum (negative as well as positive frequencies) to be divided into a set of bands, each of width $2W$ and proceed with an analysis of the same type (although not precisely the same form)[7] as in Eq. (7).

Basically such an analysis expresses the signal $s(t)$ in terms of a set of $\sin x/x$ functions whose spectra are displaced by units of $2W$ in frequency and which "occur" at regular intervals $1/2W$ in time. Indeed, the basic concern of this chapter is to generalize an analysis

†Most of the applications of Fourier analysis to engineering problems in the description and processing of random waveforms stem from the work of Norbert Wiener and his students. Regrettably, from the point of view of the average practicing engineer most of the original and/or comprehensive sources in this area range from the incomprehensible to the unavailable. A discussion of the power spectrum of a random waveform appears in Wiener's book, *The Extrapolation, Interpolation, and Smoothing of Stationary Time Series*, John Wiley and Sons, New York, 1949, p. 37 ff. The application of these ideas is discussed in engineering language in Y. W. Lee, T. P. Cheatham, Jr., and J. B. Wiesner, "Application of Correlation Analysis to the Detection of Periodic Signals in Noise," *Proc. IRE*, vol. 38, pp. 1165-1171; October, 1950.

of this type by expressing $s(t)$ in terms of the time and frequency translates of an "elementary signal" having finite energy. The choice of $\sin x/x$ as an elementary signal is, however, not a particularly happy one. True, the coefficients a_n are easy to find but $\sin x/x$ suffers from at least two serious computational difficulties: first, it does not fall to zero fast enough with increasing x for infinite sums of the form of Eq. (7) to converge absolutely; second, neither the elementary signal nor its spectrum lend themselves particularly well to analysis problems in which one would like to carry out integrals by contour integration.

The advantages of basing the $y_n(t)$ on a judicious choice of elementary signal $v(t)$ can be best shown by an illustrative example. Suppose that one wishes to transmit a sequence of numbers—sampled data—which are generated at the rate ν per second. Let the set of these numbers be $\{b_n\}$; then clearly they can be transmitted by assigning them as the coefficients of a set of waveforms $v[t - (n/\nu)]$. When a restricted bandwidth is available for the transmission, an "obvious" choice for $v(t)$ is a $\sin x/x$ function:

$$s(t) = \sum_n b_n \frac{\sin \pi(\nu t - n)}{\pi(\nu t - n)} \tag{8}$$

This choice of $v(t)$ has the advantage that the b_n may be recovered by sampling the signal at the appropriate times. But what if the sampling time is in error by a fraction, ε, of a sample interval $1/\nu$? We then obtain

$$s[(k + \varepsilon)/\nu] = b_k \frac{\sin \pi\varepsilon}{\pi\varepsilon} + \frac{\sin \pi\varepsilon}{\pi}\left[\frac{b_{k-1}}{1 - \varepsilon} - \frac{b_{k+1}}{1 + \varepsilon} - \frac{b_{k-2}}{2 - \varepsilon} + \frac{b_{k+2}}{2 + \varepsilon} + \frac{b_{k-3}}{3 - \varepsilon} - \frac{b_{k+3}}{3 + \varepsilon} + \cdots \right] \tag{9}$$

The expression in the brackets involves substantial fractions of b's other than the one which we are seeking; in fact, it is not even summable† in the case of an arbitrary infinite sequence of bounded b_k. Suppose now instead of using $\sin x/x$ functions, we choose as $v(t)$ the form

$$v(t) = \frac{\sin \pi t}{\sinh \pi t}. \tag{10}$$

This function decreases to zero exponentially with large t, and is plotted in Fig. 1. If we generate a signal from $\sin x/\sinh x$ elementary signals,

$$s(t) = \sum_n b_n \frac{\sin \pi(\nu t - n)}{\sinh \pi(\nu t - n)}, \tag{11}$$

the b's may be recovered by sampling at the proper time, just as in the case of $\sin x/x$ functions. However, owing to the exponential de-

†With a proper choice of b_n, the sum in the bracket may converge conditionally, but not absolutely.

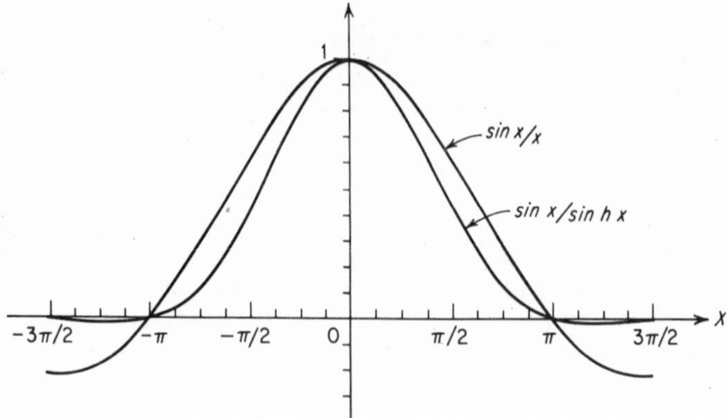

Fig. 1. Elementary signals.

cay of the sin $x/\sinh x$ functions the expression for samples taken at the "wrong" time converges rapidly:

$$
\begin{aligned}
s[(k+\varepsilon)/\nu] &= b_k \frac{\sin \pi\varepsilon}{\sinh \pi\varepsilon} + \sin \pi\varepsilon \left[\frac{b_{k-1}}{\sinh \pi(1-\varepsilon)} - \frac{b_{k+1}}{\sinh \pi(1+\varepsilon)} - \cdots\right] \\
&= b_k \frac{\sin \pi\varepsilon}{\sinh \pi\varepsilon} + \sin \pi\varepsilon\,[0.086\, b_{k-1} - 0.0036\, b_{k-2} + \cdots]e^{\pi\varepsilon} \\
&\quad - \sin \pi\varepsilon\,[0.086\, b_{k+1} - 0.0036\, b_{k+2} + \cdots]e^{-\pi\varepsilon} \\
&\quad + \cdots, \qquad |\varepsilon| < 0.5.
\end{aligned} \tag{12}
$$

Thus the "crosstalk" between samples is small if the sampling is accidentally (or deliberately) carried out at the wrong times; generally, only the next adjacent samples will make contributions of any consequence. Moreover, the spectrum of the sin $x/\sinh x$ signal, although slightly wider than that of the corresponding sin x/x, goes exponentially to zero outside the passband.

The foregoing illustration is a problem in signal synthesis. It was introduced to show the advantages that might be gained from an *ad hoc* choice of an elementary signal. It was not the intent of the discussion to suggest that sin $x/\sinh x$ *should* be used to synthesize sampled data signals; but, clearly, it *could* be so used to some advantage.

As we proceed we shall develop a kind of generalized sampling procedure by which a general signal can be represented as a weighted sum of the time and frequency translates of an elementary signal $v(t)$. This $v(t)$ can be any convenient waveform; it need not be restricted to either of the sampling functions just discussed. However, before we can introduce and apply this general representation of a signal, it is necessary to go through a few mathematical preliminaries. This is done in the next three sections.

III. COMPLEX FUNCTIONS

The waveforms that occur in nature are real functions of time. In many problems, however, it is convenient to express a signal, $s(t)$, as the sum of a set of elementary signals that are complex functions of time, or to regard the signal $s(t)$, as being a complex function of time. Both these uses of functions of a complex variable are in a sense artificial, in that the logical construct, the complex number, has no counterpart in the physical world. Nevertheless, we draw a distinction between the use of the sum of a set of complex signals to represent a *real* waveform, $s(t)$, and regarding a real signal as being derived from a *complex* $s(t)$.

The first case presents few difficulties. If in the expression for $s(t)$

$$s(t) = \sum_n a_n y_n(t) \tag{13}$$

some of the $y_n(t)$ are complex (and linearly independent), then $s(t)$ can be real only if for every complex term in the sum, $a_k y_k(t)$, there is another term in the sum, $a_k^* y_k^*(t)$, which is its complex conjugate.† Once this fact has been recognized, there are no further formal difficulties with complex $y_n(t)$ in Eq. (13). There are, however, certain useful conventions that we shall adopt throughout. By definition, we label the conjugate of an a_k or a y_k with the negative subscript:

$$a_{-k} = a_k^*$$
$$y_{-k}(t) = y_k^*(t). \tag{14}$$

If a given $y_k(t)$ is real, then $y_{-k}(t)$ and $y_k(t)$ are equal, and we assign to each one-half the total contribution of that $y_k(t)$ to the sum. (The sole exception to this last convention is $y_0(t)$, which by Eq. (14) is necessarily real, and occurs only once.)

Once the set of conjugate conditions, Eq. (14), has been set down, we appreciate that all the information necessary to specify $s(t)$ is contained in terms of positive index only. There is accordingly a strong motive for examining the *complex signal*, $\sigma(t)$, that results from summing Eq. (13) over the positive index only:

$$\sigma(t) = \frac{1}{2} a_0 y_0(t) + \sum_{n=1}^{\infty} a_n y_n(t). \tag{15}$$

From the index conventions we have

$$s(t) = \sigma(t) + \sigma^*(t)$$

or

$$s(t) = 2 \operatorname{Re} \sigma(t). \tag{16}$$

†The asterisk over a symbol or function indicates the complex conjugate.

Thus the physical signal is twice the real part of the signal that is obtained by neglecting the y's having negative index. Of course, if $s(t)$ is to be expressed in terms of each of two quite different sets of functions, say $\{x_n(t)\}$ and $\{y_n(t)\}$, there is no a priori reason why the two corresponding $\sigma(t)$ should be the same. (Clearly, the real parts will be the same, but that is all.)

It is reasonable to ask whether there is any "natural" way of deriving a complex $\sigma(t)$ from an $s(t)$, without any reference to a particular set of $y_n(t)$. Clearly, in the absence of any restrictions any imaginary part, $\mathscr{s}(t)$, will do. One obvious restriction is to insist that $\sigma = s + j\mathscr{s}$ be an analytic function of the complex variable $\theta = t + j\tau$ in a finite strip of the θ-plane that includes the real t-axis. This turns out to be a rather weak restriction, unless we assume that σ is analytic everywhere within one half of the complex θ-plane, including the t-axis. In such circumstances, the real and imaginary parts of σ are related by the Hilbert Tranform:[4, 8]

$$\mathscr{s}(t) = \frac{1}{\pi}\int_{-\infty}^{\infty} \frac{s(\xi)}{t-\xi}\, d\xi \tag{17}$$

Strictly speaking, Eq. (17) can be applied only if $s(t)$ is analytic and vanishes sufficiently fast at infinity. As a matter of fact, it can be applied to any reasonable $s(t)$ through the use of convergence factors:

$$\mathscr{s}(t) = \lim_{a \to 0} \frac{1}{\pi} \int_{-\infty}^{\infty} \frac{s(\xi) \cosh a\xi}{t - \xi}\, d\xi \tag{18}$$

in which the integral is to be taken as the Cauchy principle value near $\xi = t$.

Form (17) is also the one that results if we insist that the operation that produces the imaginary part be a linear operation that transforms $\sin \omega t$ into $\cos \omega t$ for all real ω. The complex signal function whose imaginary part is given by (17) also results when we drop the negative frequencies from a Fourier representation of $s(t)$. This complex signal function is often referred to as the *analytic signal*. Further discussion of Hilbert transforms and analytic signals is presented in section II of Chapter 12.

IV. ORTHOGONALITY

It is all very well to find a specific set of functions for which a problem solution is easy. It is another matter to express any general function as a sum of these. One general way of turning the trick is through the device of orthogonalization. A set of functions $\{u_m\}$ is said to be orthogonal in some interval A if

$$\int \cdots \int_A F(x_1, x_2, \ldots) u_m(x_1, x_2, \ldots) u_n^*(x_1, x_2, \ldots) dx_1 dx_2 \ldots \begin{cases} = 0, & m \neq n \\ \neq 0, & m = n \end{cases} \tag{19}$$

They are called orthogonal and normalized (or orthonormal) if for $m = n$

$$\int_A \cdots \int F(x_1, x_2, \ldots) u_m(x_1, x_2, \ldots) u_m^*(x_1, x_2, \ldots)\, dx_1\, dx_2 \ldots = 1 \tag{20}$$

In these two expressions, the $x_1, x_2, \ldots$ represent all the independent variables, and F is a fixed, real, positive function of them. (Generally, in representing signals, F is taken equal to unity.) The integral is taken over some convenient interval, which is the same for all the u_m.

If, then, we can represent a general function of a single variable as

$$s(x) = \sum_m a_m u_m(x) \tag{21}$$

where the u_m are orthogonal and normalized, we find by multiplication and integration that

$$\int_A F(x)\, s(x) u_n^*(x)\, dx = a_n \tag{22}$$

and the job of expressing S in terms of u's is all done.

Suppose $\{v_n(x)\}$ is a set of N functions that we wish to orthogonalize, where N is as large as convenient, but finite.† That is to say, we wish to find an orthonormal set of functions which are linear combinations of the v_n:

$$u_1 = c_{11}v_1 + c_{12}v_2 + c_{13}v_3 + \ldots + c_{1N}v_N$$

$$u_2 = c_{21}v_1 + c_{22}v_2 + c_{33}v_3 + \ldots + c_{2N}v_N$$

$$\cdots\cdots\cdots\cdots\cdots\cdots\cdots\cdots$$

$$u_N = c_{N1}v_1 + c_{N2}v_2 + c_{N3}v_3 + \ldots + c_{NN}v_N \tag{23}$$

in which the constants c_k are to be determined so that

$$\int_A F(x) u_m(x) u_n^*(x)\, dx = 0, \quad m \neq n$$
$$= 1, \quad m = n \tag{24}$$

in some interval, A.

Now, Eqs. (23) contain N^2 unknowns, which means that N^2 independent equations or conditions must be set down before the unknowns can be found. Equation (24) apparently provides N^2 equations, one for every combination of m and n. However, interchanging m and n in (24) makes no difference, so that instead of N^2 conditions, (24) only provides $N(N + 1)/2$ independent equations.

Thus, the requirement that the u_m be orthonormal is not sufficient to specify the c_{kl}. Another set of conditions, implying $N(N - 1)/2$ equations consistent with (24), is at our disposal. In order to discuss

†If N is allowed to be infinite, most of the results that follow continue to be valid, but certain mathematical difficulties arise which would needlessly complicate the present discussion.

precisely the nature of several alternatives for these additional conditions, it is desirable to assume that $F(x) = 1$ and that the $v_n(x)$ are linearly independent. The results obtained under the first assumption can be easily extended to any positive real $F(x)$. The second assumption is necessary to ensure that the $v_n(x)$ are really different, and it signifies that there exists no set of constants $\{q_n\}$ for which

$$q_1 v_1(x) + q_2 v_2(x) + \cdots + q_N v_N(x) = 0 \tag{25}$$

everywhere inside the interval, A.

If the expressions (23) are actually used to substitute for the u's in the integral of (24) there result the set of equations

$$\begin{aligned} \sum_{l,k} c_{ml} \varphi_{lk} c^*_{nk} &= 0, \quad m \neq n \\ &= 1, \quad m = 0 \end{aligned} \tag{26}$$

in which

$$\varphi_{lk} = \int_A v_l(x) v^*_k(x) dx. \tag{27}$$

To proceed further, it is well to recognize that there exists a powerful tool for representing and manipulating expressions such as (23) and (26), known as matrix algebra. We represent the collection of numbers c_{ml} by the matrix $\mathbf{C}$, and the collection c_{lm} by the "transposed" matrix $\mathbf{C}_t$. We also define an identity matrix $\mathbf{I}$ of numbers I_{mn} such that

$$\begin{aligned} I_{mn} &= 0, \quad m \neq n \\ &= 1, \quad m = n. \end{aligned} \tag{28}$$

Further, we define the rule for multiplying matrices:

If

$$\mathbf{A} = \mathbf{BC}$$

then

$$a_{mn} = \sum_k b_{mk} c_{kn}. \tag{29}$$

In this notation, the totality of Eqs. (26) can be written

$$\mathbf{C \Phi C}^*_t = \mathbf{I}. \tag{30}$$

Equations (23) in this notation are written

$$\begin{bmatrix} u_1(x) \\ u_2(x) \\ \cdot \\ \cdot \\ \cdot \\ u_N(x) \end{bmatrix} = \begin{bmatrix} c_{11} & c_{12} & \cdots & c_{1N} \\ c_{12} & c_{22} & \cdots & c_{2N} \\ \cdot & \cdot & \cdots & \cdot \\ \cdot & \cdot & \cdots & \cdot \\ \cdot & \cdot & \cdots & \cdot \\ c_{1N} & c_{2N} & \cdots & c_{NN} \end{bmatrix} \begin{bmatrix} v_1(x) \\ v_2(x) \\ \cdot \\ \cdot \\ \cdot \\ v_N(x) \end{bmatrix} \tag{31}$$

or

$$\mathbf{U}(x) = \mathbf{C}\,\mathbf{V}(x). \tag{32}$$

These expressions bear such a close resemblance to those that are used to describe linear operations on vectors,† that it is customary to speak of the collections $\mathbf{U}(x)$ and $\mathbf{V}(x)$ as "vectors" whose components are the individual u's and v's. This analogy is carried further to characterize the equation

$$s(t) = \sum_n a_n u_n(t) \tag{33}$$

as expressing the signal vector, $s(t)$, as a sum of the component vectors $u_n(t)$. Proceeding by direct analogy with vector algebra, one defines the "dot-product" of two waveforms by the integral of their product:

$$s_1(t) \cdot s_2(t) = \int_A s_1(t) s_2^*(t)\,dt. \tag{34}$$

The squared "length" of such a vector is the integral square

$$(\text{squared length of } S) = \int_A |s(t)|^2\,dt = \int_A s(t) s^*(t)\,dt \tag{35}$$

and the "distance" between two signals is measured by the "length" of their difference:

$$\begin{aligned}(\text{squared distance from } S_1 \text{ to } S_2) &= \int_A |s_1(t) - s_2(t)|^2\,dt \\ &= \int_A [s_1(t) - s_2(t)]\,[s_1^*(t) \\ &\qquad - s_2^*(t)]\,dt. \end{aligned} \tag{36}$$

In vector algebra, two vectors are at right angles to each other, or orthogonal, if their dot-product is zero. Quite clearly, (34) has been so contrived that the "vectors" $\{u_m(x)\}$ that satisfy the orthogonality integral (24) [with $F = 1$]‡ are "unit vectors" of an "orthogonal coordinate system."

Neither the matrix notation of Eq. (30) nor the vector terminology are essential to discussions of the solution of Eq. (26); they are nevertheless useful in providing a notation and language in terms of which to manipulate and discuss the expressions that are encountered.

The standard procedure** for finding the weighting coefficients, **C**, proceeds in a straightforward manner from the original equations. First, all the constants above the main diagonal in (29) are set equal to zero, that is

$$c_{mn} = 0 \text{ for } n > m. \tag{37}$$

†See E. A. Guillemin, *The Mathematics of Circuit Analysis*, John Wiley & Sons, Inc., New York, 1949, Chapter III.

‡If F is a function of x, it should appear as a factor in the integrands of (34), (35), and (36).

**This is the so-called Gramm-Schmidt procedure.

Under these circumstances $u_1(x)$ is directly proportional to $v_1(x)$ only:

$$u_1(x) = d_{11}v_1(x); \tag{38}$$

$u_2(x)$ is a linear combination of v_1 and v_2; $u_3(x)$ a linear combination of v_1, v_2, and v_3, and so on.

Assumption (37) has a great deal to recommend it. Although we do not discuss the details here,† it is clear from (37) and (38) that the $u_n(x)$ can be built up by a direct constructive method in which the coefficients are explicitly determined one at a time. Furthermore, it turns out that with this assumption one can augment a collection of N u_n's to $N + 1$ u_n's by introducing a new $v_{N+1}(x)$ without having to recompute the $u_1, u_2, \ldots, u_N$.

As a matter of fact, however, most of these advantages are more apparent than real when N is at all large. The detail work in determining the $\{u_n\}$ is so laborious that the actual use of the methods resulting from assumption (37) has been limited primarily to existence proofs and homework problems for students. The effect of this computational difficulty has been to strongly limit the use of orthogonal functions to those $v_n(x)$ that are known from analysis to be orthogonal in the first place.

Setting $N(N - 1)/2$ surplus coefficients equal to zero is not, however, the only way of disposing of them. We now explore another possibility that leads to a very powerful matrix method for solving orthogonalization problems. It will be recalled that the linear relation between the $u_n(x)$ and the $v_n(x)$ could be written in matrix notation

$$\mathbf{U} = \mathbf{C}\,\mathbf{V}. \tag{39}$$

It will also be recalled that the condition that the $u_n(x)$ be orthonormal could be written

$$\mathbf{C}\,\mathbf{\Phi}\,\mathbf{C}_t^* = \mathbf{I} \tag{40}$$

in which $\mathbf{\Phi}$ is the matrix of dot products, φ_{mn}:

$$\varphi_{mn} = \int_A v_m(x)v_n^*(x)\,dx \tag{41}$$

A natural way of reducing the surplus variables in the matrix expression (40) is to set $\mathbf{C}_t^*$ equal to $\mathbf{C}$, which means that $c_{mn} = c_{nm}^*$. Thus (40) becomes

$$\mathbf{C}\,\mathbf{\Phi}\,\mathbf{C} = \mathbf{I}. \tag{42}$$

We need only introduce the notation of an inverse matrix $\mathbf{C}^{-1}$, defined by

$$\mathbf{C}^{-1}\mathbf{C} = \mathbf{C}\,\mathbf{C}^{-1} = \mathbf{I} \tag{43}$$

†See Wiener, *op. cit.*, pp. 31-32; also B. Friedman, *Principles and Techniques of Applied Mathematics*, John Wiley & Sons, New York, 1956, pp. 16-17.

to obtain

$$\begin{aligned}\mathbf{\Phi} &= \mathbf{C}^{-1}\mathbf{C}^{-1}\\ &= \mathbf{C}^{-2} \text{ (by definition)}.\end{aligned} \tag{44}$$

Now, if it were possible to treat the matrices in (44) as ordinary symbols of algebra we would "solve" (44) for $\mathbf{C}$ by writing

$$\mathbf{C} = \mathbf{\Phi}^{-1/2} . \tag{45}$$

This is in fact possible!†

Now, (45) suggests that we should compute the negative square root of a matrix. This is in general a more involved computational problem than the step-by-step method of Eqs. (37) and (38) above. However, in most cases of practical interest another formal analogy with ordinary algebra can be put to use, which makes the computation of (45) particularly easy. In ordinary algebra, the binomial expansion

$$(1 + x)^n = 1 + nx + \frac{n(n-1)}{2!}x^2 + \ldots \tag{46}$$

converges for all x whose magnitude is less than one. In matrix algebra, a similar formal expansion‡

$$(\mathbf{I} + \mathbf{X})^n = \mathbf{I} + n\mathbf{X} + \frac{n(n-1)}{2!}\mathbf{X}^2 + \ldots \tag{47}$$

converges for sufficiently small values of the elements of the matrix $\mathbf{X}$ (specifically if all the latent roots of the matrix $\mathbf{X}$ have magnitudes less than unity). A necessary condition that the series converge is that the sum of the squares of the terms in any row or column of $\mathbf{X}$ be less than one. In order to make use of (47) it is desirable to assume that the $\{v_n(x)\}$ have been normalized to start with, which makes the main diagonal of the $\mathbf{\Phi}$ matrix a string of ones. In (47) the matrix $\mathbf{I}$ is then the main diagonal of $\mathbf{\Phi}$ and $\mathbf{X}$ is everything else. The usefulness of (47) is then in the fact that it is usually possible to choose the $\{v_n(x)\}$ so that they are *nearly* orthogonal. In such cases (47) converges rapidly, and only the first two or three terms of (47) are necessary (the first two terms can be written down by inspection).

Thus in the case at hand, it will be usually possible to use (47) to solve Eq. (45) for the $\mathbf{C}$ matrix:

$$\begin{aligned}\mathbf{C} &= \mathbf{\Phi}^{-1/2}\\ &= \mathbf{I} - \frac{1}{2}(\mathbf{\Phi} - \mathbf{I}) + \frac{3}{8}(\mathbf{\Phi} - \mathbf{I})^2 - \ldots .\end{aligned} \tag{48}$$

†For a proof and fuller discussion of this and also the binomial expansion (47) see R. M. Lerner, "Representation of Signals," Trans. of International Symposium on Circuit and Information Theory, *Trans. IRE CT-6* and also *IT-5*, pp. 214-216, May 1959.

‡See Friedman, *op. cit.*, p. 34 ff. Another discussion of functions of matrices appears in R. A. Frazer, W. J. Duncan, and A. R. Collar, *Elementary Matrices*, Cambridge University Press, 1955; Chapter 2.

In this manner, the coefficients in the linear combinations of $\{v_n(x)\}$ that yield an orthonormal set of functions $\{u_n(x)\}$ can be found with a minimum of computational labor, even when the number of members of the set, N, is very large.

The entire emphasis of this section has been on representing a signal in terms of a set of orthogonal $\{u_n(t)\}$. The original $\{v_n(t)\}$ have been regarded as poor relations, whose sole duty is to support the $\{u_n(t)\}$ in the days of their youth. Generally, this attitude is justified, inasmuch as it is possible to make much sharper statements about an orthogonal representation than a non-orthogonal one. In any given problem, however, it may not be necessary to actually know the form of the $\{u_n(t)\}$ and it may even be that in some practical problem we actually require the coefficients $\{b_n\}$ in an expansion in terms of $\{v_n(t)\}$,

$$s(t) = \sum_n b_n v_n(t). \tag{49}$$

If we multiply both sides of (49) by $F(t)\, v_m^*(t)$ and integrate, we obtain

$$\int_A F(t) s(t)\, v_m^*(t)\, dt = J_m = \sum_n b_n \varphi_{nm} \tag{50}$$

or

$$\mathbf{J}_m = \mathbf{\Phi}_{mn}^* \mathbf{b}_n. \tag{51}$$

Hence, we have for the coefficients $\mathbf{b}_n$

$$\mathbf{b} = \mathbf{\Phi}^{*\,-1}\, \mathbf{J}\,. \tag{52}$$

V. COMPLETENESS

We must now consider the question: In what sense and under what circumstances is it possible to express an arbitrary signal $s(x)$ as an infinite sum of weighted members of a sequence of $v_n(x)$ elementary functions; namely,

$$s(x) = \sum_{n=-\infty}^{\infty} a_n v_n(x)\ ? \tag{53}$$

One case in which (53) surely holds is that in which the $\{v_n(x)\}$ form an orthogonal set $\{u_n(x)\}$ that evolves from the solution of a boundary value problem starting with the differential equation of a particular physical system, and $s(x)$ is a possible configuration of that system. The set of functions for which (53) in some sense holds is not, of course, necessarily restricted to the possible configurations of the physical system associated with the set $\{u_n(x)\}$. Sinusoids, for instance, may be used to represent a far wider variety of functions than the configurations of a stretched string [a physical system for which the differential equations lead to sinusoidal $u_n(x)$ in (53)] would suggest. There is, however, no governing differential equation, the "signal equation," of which signals are the solutions, so that the question of the validity of the infinite expansion (53) for a general signal cannot be settled in this simple manner.

A related case arises every time some engineer decides he will confine his discussion to the case in which the spectral energy of the signal outside of some finite band is zero—or what is the same thing, uses $\sin x/x$ functions. He has, in effect, picked a set of $\{u_n(x)\}$. But if he thinks that

$$s(x) - \sum_{n=-\infty}^{\infty} a_n u_n(x) \tag{54}$$

is going to vanish identically in this instance, where $s(x)$ is any function whose entire history is not predictable from a section of finite duration, he is sadly mistaken, for he has in effect assumed that $s(x)$ is everywhere analytic. On the other hand, if the same engineer says that in his judgment the difference is negligible for his particular case, and that his choice of $\{u_n(x)\}$ leads to the desired answers most easily, then he is acting wholly in accord with the philosophy behind this discussion.

Thus, in order to use a representation such as (53), we must either restrict $s(x)$ and/or settle for something less than exact identity in the representation. In practice, one does both. In the absence of an overwhelming physical argument, just how far one proceeds with restricting the class of $s(x)$ is a matter of taste and convenience. The vast majority of mathematically possible $s(x)$ that have, for instance, finite energy are violently discontinuous for nearly every value of $s(x)$; clearly these are pathological and need not be considered. One must not assume that $s(x)$ is too well behaved, however, lest he run afoul of the difficulty mentioned earlier in connection with the finite bandwidth assumption, viz., analyticity. For if $s(x)$ is sufficiently well behaved so that all derivatives exist† at every point, the entirety of $s(x)$ can be constructed by analytic continuation from a knowledge of $s(x)$ in any finite interval of x, no matter how small. It is also possible to assume the existence of all derivatives up to the *mth*. But why stop with the *mth*? Physically, the *mth* derivative of $s(x)$ is *a priori* as legitimate a signal as $s(x)$; so that the question of what is a reasonable assumption about the nature of $s(x)$ has been only put off, not answered.

In relaxing the condition that (53) be satisfied identically, one could require only that‡

$$|s(x) - \sum_n a_n v_n(x)| < \varepsilon \text{ for all } x \tag{55}$$

†Strictly speaking, the derivative must be suitably bounded so that a Taylor series expansion of $s(x)$ can be made around any point x. To this end, the bound $|s^{(n)}(x)| < n! M(x)$ for all finite x where $M(x)$ is bounded, is sufficient.

‡In Eq. (55) and throughout the rest of this section we do not require that the sums which we discuss be infinite sums.

where ε is a preassigned small positive number.† This kind of condition runs into difficulty unless the infinite sum converges uniformly; further, one cannot let $\varepsilon \to 0$ without returning to the identity, (53). A better way of specifying the almost-equality of $s(x)$ and the sum is through an integral of the magnitude of the difference. Thus, we may choose $\{a_n\}$ so as to minimize the integral of the square of the magnitude of the difference:

$$\int_A F(x) \left| s(x) - \sum_n a_n v_n(x) \right|^2 dx = \min = \varepsilon' \tag{56}$$

in which $F(x)$ is a convenient positive real weighting function, usually one. If the $\{v_n(x)\}$ are in fact an orthogonal set $\{u_n(x)\}$ and the a_n can be so chosen that the integral (56) vanishes for a given class of $s(x)$, then the $\{u_n(x)\}$ are said to be "complete" with respect to that class of $s(x)$. It will be noted in this connection that $s(x)$ and the sum can differ by finite amounts at a countable number of points (say all rational or all algebraic points), yet the integral may vanish.

A discussion of the generality with which the $\{v_n(x)\}$ may represent an $s(x)$ in the sense that the integral in (56) vanishes is beyond the scope of this treatment. We shall be content to consider only those functions, $s(x)$, that are uniformly continuous.

In order to find the values of the coefficients which minimize ε', one sets the derivatives of (56) with respect to the coefficients, a_n, equal to zero:

$$\frac{\partial}{\partial a_1} \int_A F(x) \left| s(x) - \sum_n a_n v_n(x) \right|^2 dx = 0 \tag{57}$$

$$\frac{\partial}{\partial a_2} \int_A F(x) \left| s(x) - \sum_n a_n v_n(x) \right|^2 dx = 0$$

$$\vdots$$

Performing the indicated differentiation with respect to a_k leads to the equations

$$2 \int_A F(x)\left[s(x) - \sum_n a_n v_n(x)\right] v_k^*(x)\, dx = 0,\; k = 0, \pm 1, \pm 2, \ldots\, . \tag{58}$$

If the $\{v_n\}$ are an orthonormal set $\{u_n(x)\}$, then, for the *nth* coefficient a_n, this leads immediately to the equation

$$a_n = \int_A F(x) s(x) u_n^*(x)\, dx. \tag{59}$$

It will be recognized that this is precisely the formula that was obtained for the case of a finite collection of orthogonal $\{u_n(x)\}$ when it was known that $s(x)$ could be expressed exactly as a weighted sum of $\{u_n(x)\}$. When the equality is not exact, (59) suggests that the or-

†This assumption has been explored by R. E. Wernikoff, "A Theory of Signals," Sc.D. Thesis in the Dept. of Electrical Engineering, M.I.T., January, 1958; also published as Tech. Rep. No. 331, Research Lab. of Electronics, M.I.T., January 31, 1958.

thogonal-function method of finding the coefficients leads to the minimum value for the integral of the square of the discrepancy.

More generally, if the $\{v_n(x)\}$ are not an orthogonal set, then (58) can be written in matrix notation

$$\mathbf{J} = \mathbf{\Phi}^*\mathbf{A} \tag{60}$$

in which $\mathbf{A}$ is a column matrix† of the $\{a_n\}$, and $\mathbf{J}$ is a column matrix of the integrals on the righthand side of (59). For present purposes, we assume that $\mathbf{\Phi}$ has an inverse. (A collection of $\{v_n(x)\}$ for which the correlation matrix, $\mathbf{\Phi}$, has an inverse will be *called* linearly independent. This definition includes, with slight modifications, the previous definition of linear independence for a finite collection of functions.) Thus we write

$$\mathbf{A} = \mathbf{\Phi}^{-1}\mathbf{J} \tag{61}$$

which formally specifies the a_n coefficients. As was done in the previous section, the formal solution, (61) can often be implemented by a binomial expansion

$$\mathbf{\Phi}^{-1} = \mathbf{I} - [\mathbf{\Phi} - \mathbf{I}] + [\mathbf{\Phi} - \mathbf{I}]^2 - [\mathbf{\Phi} - \mathbf{I}]^3 + \ldots \tag{62}$$

which converges if all the latent roots of the matrix $(\mathbf{\Phi} - \mathbf{I})$ have magnitudes less than unity. The conditions under which the algebra and properties of finite matrices can be extended to infinite matrices are beyond the scope of this paper. It can be stated here, however, that the extension can be made if the rows and columns of the infinite matrix are vectors of finite length.

There is an additional useful property of a representation of $s(x)$ that is complete in the mean-square sense, namely the Parseval theorem for the orthogonal set $\{u_n(x)\}$. This property is best stated for orthonormal $\{u_n(x)\}$, in which case it takes the form

$$\int_A F(x)\, |s(x)|^2 dx = \sum_n |a_n|^2 . \tag{63}$$

This expression follows directly from an expansion of Eq. (56). This theorem is familiar in connection with Fourier expansions, in which case $F(x)$ is unity, and one draws the conclusion that the integral of the squared magnitude of the signal is equal to the integral of the squared magnitude of the spectrum. This kind of formula can also be used to establish completeness; *i.e.*, a necessary and sufficient condition that a set of orthonormal functions be complete with respect to some class of signals, $s(x)$, is that a Parseval theorem, (63), hold true.

At this point in the discussion, we have amassed a considerable array of mathematical techniques for representing signals other than as a sum of sine waves. How can we use them? The first step towards a really useful and flexible tool for signal analysis was taken by Gabor, who—from the point of view of the preceding discussion—extended an analysis valid in the interval to successive intervals in

†Not to be confused with the interval of integration, A.

time. The point of view of the preceding discussion, however, was not at all the point of view taken by Gabor. In the next section, some of the questions that Gabor treated are discussed. A junction is then effected between some qualitative principles suggested by Gabor's work and the mathematical technique discussed above to generate sets of $\{u_n(x)\}$ having substantial conceptual, computational, and analytical usefulness in the representation and design of signals.

VI. THE TIME-BANDWIDTH PROBLEM

In 1946 D. Gabor published a paper[4] on signal theory, under the title, "Theory of Information," setting forth a number of ideas that have received far less critical attention than they deserve. The problem to which Gabor addressed himself was to find a way of describing speech signals, which have structure both in time and frequency, produced by changes of the shape and excitation of the vocal mechanism.

Gabor's starting point was the "sampling theorem," which states that a signal that in some sense lasts for a length of time T and in some sense occupies a bandwidth W can be characterized by a collection of $2TW$ numbers. He then pictured a complicated signal as being built up out of a collection of elementary signals to which one, and only one, of these numbers could be assigned. He therefore sought to select as an elementary signal a waveform that would have a minimum duration-bandwidth product, hopefully unity. This elementary signal turned out to have an envelope of the form e^{-x^2}, to within a scale factor that determines the "duration," τ, of the signal; under the envelope is a "carrier" that determines the frequency, f_m, around which the spectrum of the signal is distributed. Within any interval of length τ, the signal is pictured as being the sum of elementary signals "occupying" the interval, whose "frequencies," f_m, are separated by distances equal to $1/\tau$. The next succeeding time interval of the signal is constructed of elementary signals "occupying" that interval, and so on. Thus Gabor obtained a set of functions suitable for characterizing signals such as speech, in which the addition of new material with the passage of time neither affects the analysis already made nor alters the values of coefficients already obtained.

In what follows, we shall depart from both the order and to some extent, the philosophy of Gabor's paper, for several reasons. First, Gabor found it convenient to introduce a complex-valued time signal, the "analytic signal," an extremely useful concept[4,8] which will be introduced and utilized in Chapter 12, but which would nevertheless needlessly complicate the present discussion. Second, he employed a formal analogy to quantum mechanics which, although analytically sound, is loaded with conceptual dangers. Third, although we shall keep the broad outlines of Gabor's pattern of elementary signals, the use of e^{-x^2} functions is unnecessarily restrictive. In this section we shall consider the time-bandwidth problem; in the next section, the selection, orthogonalization, completeness, and use of a generalized set of elementary signals.

If one is to discuss signals that, in some sense, have a duration T and a bandwidth W, it is clearly desirable to *define* T and W in such a way that they can be computed for any given waveform $s(t)$. Gabor identified the duration of a waveform $y = y(x)$ with the radius of gyration of the area under the curve $|y(x)|^2$ about a y axis passing through its centroid:

$$(\text{duration})^2 = 4 \frac{\int_{-\infty}^{\infty} |y|^2 (x - x_0)^2 \, dx}{\int_{-\infty}^{\infty} |y|^2 \, dx} \tag{64}$$

where x_0 is so chosen that

$$\int_{-\infty}^{\infty} (x - x_0) |y|^2 \, dx = 0.$$

This definition has the advantage of leading to a nonzero lower bound on the duration-bandwidth product (TW product) for a signal. That is to say, if such an expression is used to calculate the duration and corresponding bandwidth of a signal, the Schwarz inequality† can be manipulated to give the result

$$TW \geqslant \pi. \tag{65}$$

The definition of duration used by Gabor is inconvenient from several points of view. First, in order to achieve a reasonable definition of bandwidth in the case of band-pass signals, it is necessary to use a single-sided spectrum [and consequently a complex signal $\sigma(t)$]. Second, there are important applications (notably time-sharing schemes) in which a total waveform is broken up into pieces that can be transmitted at different times. In this connection, an expression for the integrated duration of the dismembered waveform ought to be independent of the order and time intervals in which the individual pieces are transmitted. Gabor's definition causes the calculated duration to depend critically on both of these factors. Third, if one wishes to fix the effective duration or bandwidth of a signal in a variational problem, one discovers that the constraint is often satisfied in a trivial way by a pair of impulses separated by the given duration.

A number of other definitions of duration can be constructed, however, which lead to a duration-bandwidth product having a lower bound different from zero. Recent discussions in information theory[9] have produced the result that if the squared magnitude of a signal and its spectrum are both regarded as probability densities, the sum of

†See Gabor's paper[4] for details.

the entropies has a lower bound. This fact suggests the definition of duration Δx:

$$\Delta x = \exp\left[-\int_{-\infty}^{\infty} \frac{|s(x)|^2}{E} \ln \frac{|s(x)|^2}{E}\, dx\right] \tag{66}$$

where $E = \int_{-\infty}^{\infty} |s(x)|^2 dx$ = signal energy. With this definition, the lower bound on the entropy sum becomes a lower bound on the TW product of the signal.

A somewhat more tractable definition of duration, which meets all three of the objections to Gabor's definition listed above, is

$$\Delta x = \frac{\left[\int_{-\infty}^{\infty} |s(x)|dx\right]^2}{\int_{-\infty}^{\infty} |s(x)|^2 dx} \,. \tag{67}$$

This definition also leads to a duration-bandwidth (TW) product with a lower bound of the order of magnitude of unity.† The revised definition also has the property that its value is independent of the kind of operation on a signal $s(t)$ in which different parts of $s(t)$ are sent at different times, pursuant to some time sharing scheme.

The existence of definitions of duration that result in inequalities of the form

$TW \geqslant l^2$, l^2 of the order of magnitude of unity

has tempted some individuals to draw unwarranted parallels to the uncertainty relationship in quantum mechanics. Indeed Gabor's definition of duration, (64), is taken by analogy with quantum mechanics. But the analogy is formal only. In particular, one cannot conclude from (65) that one can measure the frequency of a sinewave only to within one cycle/second in the course of π seconds; anyone who has ever used a frequency multiplier to increase the *convenience* of a more accurate measurement will testify otherwise. The ultimate accuracy of macroscopic measurements is limited by random fluctuations (*i.e.*, noise) not by *a priori* considerations, as in the case of the microscopic formulae of quantum mechanics. In order for (65) to imply a true uncertainty principle such as occurs in quantum mechanics, it would have to be *a priori* impossible, in some sense, to make simultaneous observations on the same signal through two different filters!

With the adoption of a definition for duration such as (67), the analogy to quantum mechanics evaporates, and one realizes more fully that all definitions of bandwidth or duration are arbitrary, and, in the last analysis, a matter of convenience. It is satisfying to find

†This kind of definition for a duration of an object follows naturally from a counting rule presented in reference 10 which states that if all of a set of N objects have the same size $|a|$ then $(\sum_{n=1}^{N} |a_n|)^2 = N\sum_{n=1}^{N} |a_n|^2$. This is shown in reference 10.

definitions such as (67), (66), and (64) that lead to minimum TW products of the order of magnitude of one; but a reasonable definition of duration need not lead to a minimum TW product other than zero. For example, a definition of duration fully as reasonable as (67) is[10]

$$\Delta x = \frac{\left[\int_{-\infty}^{\infty} |s(x)|^2 dx\right]^2}{\int_{-\infty}^{\infty} |s(x)|^4 dx}. \tag{68}$$

For all of the usual simple signals (e^{-t^2}, $e^{-|t|}$, $\sin t/t$, etc.) this formula gives TW products near unity. But the signal whose spectrum is

$$\begin{aligned} S(\omega) &= \omega^{-1/4}, \quad 0 < |\omega| < 1 \\ &= \omega^{-2}, \quad 1 < |\omega| < \infty \end{aligned} \tag{69}$$

has, according to (68), zero TW product.

The precise meaning of a duration-bandwidth product remains unclear in the case of complicated signals for which TW is much greater than one. Thus the statement that a signal which lasts for time T and occupies bandwidth W can be characterized by $2TW$ numbers can be only approximately true except under rather special assumptions concerning the definition of T and W. For instance, a function cannot be limited to a duration T and bandwidth W in the sense that $s(t)$ and the corresponding spectrum both vanish outside of intervals of width T and W, respectively.

One special way of giving exact meaning to the characterization in terms of $2TW$ numbers is through the assumption that the signal is band-limited, *i.e.*, its (double-sided) spectrum, $S(\omega)$, vanishes outside the interval of frequencies up to W:

$$S(\omega) = 0 \text{ for } |\omega/2\pi| > W. \tag{70}$$

Recall from section VIII of Chapter 3 that such a signal can be represented by a sum of $\sin x/x$ functions

$$s(t) = \sum_{n=-\infty}^{\infty} a_n \frac{\sin \pi(2Wt - n)}{\pi(2Wt - n)} \tag{71}$$

in which the a_n's are determined by examining the signal at times t_n separated by intervals of $1/2W$ sec; namely,

$$a_n = s(t_n) = s(n/2W). \tag{72}$$

From a segment of the signal of length T, $2TW$ of the a_n can be determined by this sampling procedure. Of course, these $2TW$ numbers do not characterize the band-limited $s(t)$ for all time, nor do they completely characterize $s(t)$ during the interval T—unless all those a_n's that are not included in the set of $2TW$ numbers are zero. As a matter of fact, the $\sin x/x$ function falls off so slowly, that a_n's that would be determined at sample points well outside the interval T may profoundly affect the signal inside the interval, T.

An extreme example is the signal for which a_n is given by

$$a_n = 1, \text{ if } n \text{ is divisible by 4}$$
$$= 0, \text{ otherwise.} \tag{73}$$

Between a pair of consecutive sample zeros, this signal reaches a maximum value of about one-fifth; if one considers only those a_n's that are measured during a long time interval of length T, however, the reconstructed signal rises in the neighborhood of the ends of the interval to a value near 0.1 ln $(2TW)$. Thus, while it is true that, in a sense, a band-limited signal is characterized completely by $2W$ samples per second, it is also true that in general the samples taken during any finite period of time, T, may only poorly approximate the signal, except at the sample points.

The general conclusion to be drawn from this discussion is that the idea of duration-bandwidth product has considerable merit in estimating the number of coefficients (degrees of freedom) that may be required to specify a signal. The value of TW product as a quantitative measure, will, however, depend on whatever more or less arbitrary definition of duration is employed, and on the particular signal being analyzed. A second conclusion can also be argued, viz., that Gabor's desire to build complicated waveforms out of elementary signals having unity duration-bandwidth product attached too much emphasis to obtaining a minimum TW product. Gabor failed to emphasize that what was important about a collection of elementary signals was not the precise values of their individual TW products—which, after all, depend on whatever definition of duration is used—but the arrangement of the array of elementary signals at intervals of time and frequency.

VII. GENERALIZED ELEMENTARY SIGNALS

Gabor chose to represent signals as a sum of elementary signals derived from an arbitrary definition of duration-bandwidth products. We shall here extend this kind of representation to more general elementary signals. Suppose we start with any elementary signal, $v(t)$. We initially place no restrictions on $v(t)$ other than that it be convenient and have finite energy. (Presumably, "convenience" implies that $v(t)$ is appropriately continuous and has a low TW product.) Suppose we define the collection of elementary signals $\{v_n(t)\}$ as the successive time translates of $v(t)$ by a time interval, θ:

$$v_n(t) = v(t - n\theta). \tag{74}$$

We may well inquire into the usefulness of the set of functions $\{v\ (t)\}$ in representing an arbitrary signal $s(t)$ in the form

$$s(t) = \sum_n a_n v_n(t). \tag{75}$$

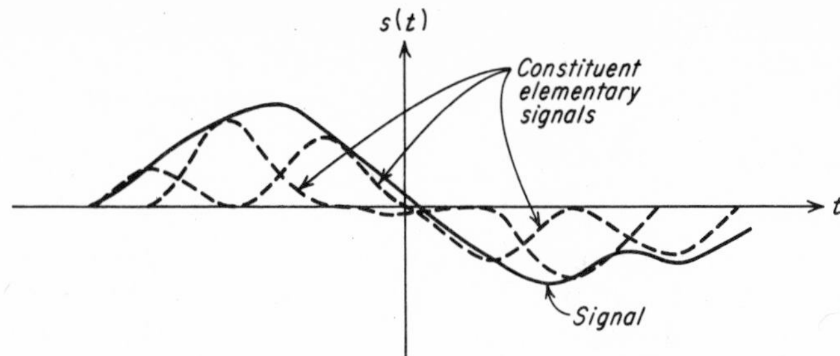

Fig. 2. Synthesis of a slowly varying signal.

It is clear that if the signals $v_n(t)$ "last" for a time that is nearly equal to their spacing, θ, they can be considered as being "samples" of the signal $s(t)$ taken at regular intervals of θ seconds. If $s(t)$ is such that it can be represented by $1/\theta$, or fewer, samples per second, then it is clear that a least-squares determination of the kth coefficient a_k will yield roughly the value of $s(t)$ at $t = k\theta$. An illustrative example is shown in Fig. 2. In general, the a_n's cannot be chosen so that the distance (as defined in Eq. 36) between the two sides of (75) is zero. Nevertheless, the approximation may be good enough for engineering purposes, especially if $v(t)$ changes only slowly in the interval θ.

Of course, one cannot express an arbitrary waveform in terms of just these building blocks. To remedy this situation, consider now not only $v(t)$, but the products of $v(t)$ with the periodic exponential factors $e^{j2\pi mt/\theta}$, to generate the set of frequency and time translates of $v(t)$, $\{v_{mn}(t)\}$, where

$$v_{mn}(t) = v(t - n\theta)\, e^{j2\pi mt/\theta} \,. \tag{76}$$

The effect of a unit change in index n is to shift the function $v(t)$ one unit of θ in time; the effect of a unit change in index m is to shift the spectrum of $u(t)$ by a unit of $1/\theta$ in frequency.

With appropriate restrictions on $v(t)$, this set of functions is complete in the sense that we can write any "well-behaved" signal $s(t)$ as

$$s(t) = \sum_{m,n} a_{mn} v_{mn}(t). \tag{77}$$

The proof is given in the appendix at the end of this chapter.

In order to picture a representation such as (77), we may assume that the energy of $v(t)$ is concentrated "near" $t = 0$ and the energy of its spectrum, $V(\omega)$, is concentrated "near" $\omega = 0$, so that there is a sense in which we can say that $v(t)$ occurs "at" zero time and "at" zero frequency. One then covers an (x, y) plane with a gridwork whose lines cross the x-axis at intervals equal to θ, and cross the y-axis at intervals of $1/\theta$. (See Fig. 3.) With each rectangle of the resulting checkerboard, we associate one of the a_{mn}. Now, the x-axis of the checkerboard is a time axis, in the sense that it specifies the inter-

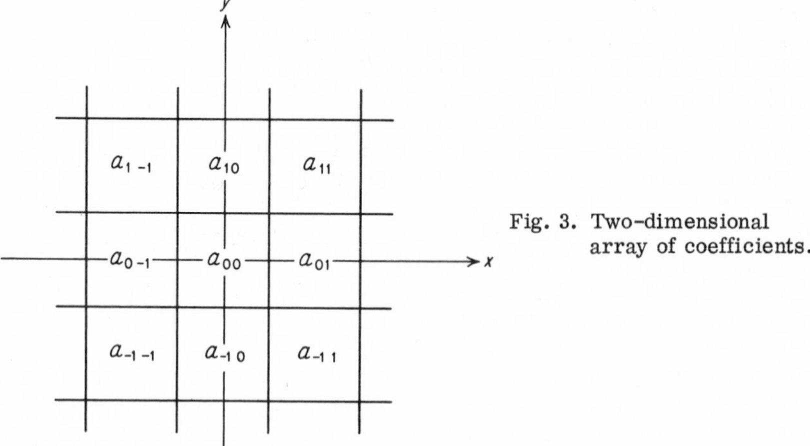

Fig. 3. Two-dimensional array of coefficients.

val of time "at" or "in" which a given elementary function "occurs." The y-axis is a frequency axis, in the sense that it specifies the interval of frequency occupied by a given elementary signal. For these reasons, this checkerboard picture is called a (t, w) plane representation.

If a signal $s(t)$ has little energy that occurs outside a time interval of duration T, and has little energy that lies outside a (single-sided) frequency range of W, then the a_{mn} in parts of the (t, w) plane outside of the interval (T, W) will be small. Such a signal will require no more than about $2TW$ numbers to specify it.

Gabor required of his elementary signals that they should in some sense be restricted in duration and bandwidth to the confines of the appropriate rectangle in Fig. 3. That restriction is here discarded as being artificial; the basic pattern of this representation is set not by the choice of $v(t)$, but by the choice of the translation interval θ. Each different choice of θ will lead to a different way of breaking up a region of time and frequency. For instance, in Fig. 4(a), a (T, W) region of specified area is divided equally in time and frequency. We might have chosen θ so as to give no division of W in frequency (which

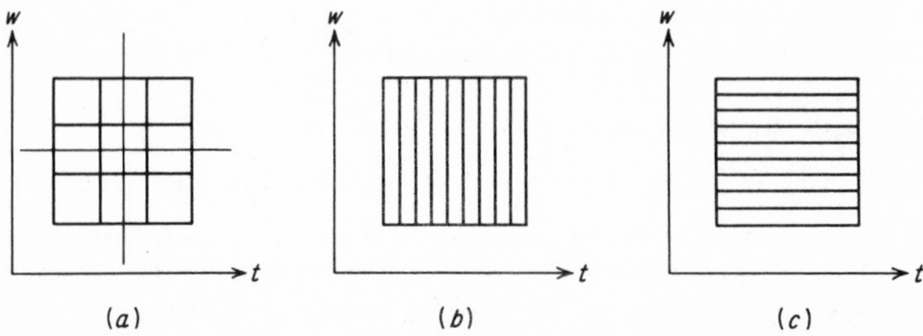

Fig. 4. Some of the possible divisions of a region of the (t, w) plane.

corresponds to specifying a signal by successive samples in time), as in Fig. 4(b). We might have chosen strips parallel to the time axis as in Fig. 4(c). (This corresponds to specifying a signal by its spectrum). Or we might have chosen some other ratio of sides for the rectangle. In every case, the rectangles have the same area, and it requires roughly the same number of a's to specify the signal.

The values of the a_{mn} will depend on the choice of $v(t)$ as well as θ. But if we only take the precaution that we choose the duration of $v(t)$ about equal to θ (and its bandwidth about equal to $1/\theta$), then for any given choice of the grid constant, θ, the values of the a_{mn} vary surprisingly little with the choice of $v(t)$. Accordingly, $v(t)$ may be chosen for reasons foreign to the diagram—because of its analytic properties, or because of the possibility of building a network having a transient response, $v(t)$.

To reduce these qualitative ideas to quantitative practice, $v(t)$ must be such that the $v_{mn}(t)$ are linearly independent.† An immediate consequence of this assumption is that the $v_{mn}(t)$ can be orthogonalized by the matrix method to a set $\{u_{mn}(t)\}$.

In order to use the matrix methods, it is necessary to enumerate the two-dimensional array of functions in some order. An alternative, adopted here, is to regard the correlation matrix $\mathbf{\Phi}$ as a four-dimensional array of numbers $\varphi_{mn,\,kl}$. Generally speaking, the set of equations represented by a relationship between non-singular matrices has the same solution regardless of the order in which the equations or their individual terms are written. Accordingly, the order in which the v-functions are enumerated is not important; in fact, it is not necessary to enumerate them at all, if one can construct a four-dimensional matrix algebra that yields the same results as if the v's had been enumerated. An extension of the rules of two-dimensional matrix algebra suggests the rule for multiplying 4-d matrices:
If

$$\mathbf{A}_4 = \mathbf{B}_4 \mathbf{C}_4$$

then

$$A_{pq,\,rs} = \sum_{m,\,n} B_{pq,mn} C_{mn,\,rs} \quad . \tag{78}$$

The unit matrix, $\mathbf{I}_4$, is then given by

$$I_{pq,\,mn} = \begin{cases} 1, \text{ if } p = m \text{ and } q = n \\ 0, \text{ otherwise} \end{cases} \tag{79}$$

The inverse matrix to $\mathbf{A}_4$, $\mathbf{A}_4^{-1}$, is defined so that the product of the

†In the appendix it is shown, in effect, that this will be the case if $v(t)$ has only isolated zeros in some time interval at least θ seconds long and if its spectrum has only isolated zeros in a frequency interval at least $1/\theta$ cps wide, and further if the sum $\sum_{r=-\infty}^{\infty} e^{j2\pi r\nu_0} v(x - r\theta)$ is non-zero in any finite interval of x for almost all ν_0. This last condition is satisfied if $v(x)$ is linearly independent of its time translates in any finite interval of x.

two is $\mathbf{I}_4$. Since $\mathbf{I}$ commutes with any matrix, the right- and left-hand inverses of $\mathbf{A}$ are the same.† Finally we define the transpose of $\mathbf{A}$, $\mathbf{A}_t$, by

$$[A_{pq,\,rs}]_t = [A_{rs,\,pq}]. \tag{80}$$

With these definitions, the algebra of the four-dimensional $\mathbf{\Phi}$ matrix is fully equivalent to that of the two-dimensional $\mathbf{\Phi}$ matrices previously employed.

In any event, if $\mathbf{\Phi}$ is the correlation matrix of the v's, then

$$\mathbf{u}(t) = \mathbf{\Phi}^{-1/2}\,\mathbf{v}(t) \tag{81}$$

where $\mathbf{v}(t)$ is the matrix of the $v_{mn}(t)$, $-\infty < m, n < +\infty$. Now the labelling of the various orthonormal u-functions obtained in (81) is arbitrary. It is easy to show (by permutation of indices) that if $u(t)$ is one of these u-functions, then the θ-time and $1/\theta$ frequency translates of $u(t)$,

$$u_{mn}(t) = u(t - n\theta)e^{j2\pi mt/\theta}, \tag{82}$$

are also u-functions, and that these $u_{mn}(t)$ are an exhaustive listing of the functions $u(t)$ obtained in (81).

In fact, *this is one of the major advantages of the* $\mathbf{\Phi}^{-1/2}$ *method of orthogonalization.* No simple relationship as (82) exists for $u_{mn}(t)$ as found from the time and frequency translates of $v(t)$ if the usual Gramm-Schmidt procedure is used.

A set of orthonormal signals $u_{mn}(t)$ derived from a $u(t)$ as in (82) will be called a set of *unit functions*, abbreviated u-functions or u.f. The elementary signal, $v(t)$, from which the $u_{mn}(t)$ are derived by orthogonalization will be called a *basis signal.*

As a specific illustration of these ideas, consider the use of a hyperbolic secant function as a basis function:

$$v(t) = \sqrt{\frac{\pi}{\theta}}\,\operatorname{sech} \pi t/\theta. \tag{83}$$

The set of functions $v_{mn}(t)$ are

$$v_{mn}(t) = \sqrt{\frac{\pi}{\theta}}\,\operatorname{sech} \pi(t/\theta - n)\, e^{j2\pi mt/\theta} \tag{84}$$

The terms of the correlation matrix are given by

$$\begin{aligned}\varphi_{mn,\,kl} &= \int_{-\infty}^{\infty} v_{mn}(t)\, v_{kl}^{*}(t)\, dt \\ &= \frac{\pi \sin \pi(m-k)(n-l)}{\sinh \pi(m-k) \sinh \pi(n-l)}\, e^{j\pi(m-k)(n-l)} \quad .\end{aligned} \tag{85}$$

It is to be noted that this collection of coefficients is a function only of the differences $(m - k) = p$ and $(n - l) = q$. This property is gen-

†Assume that the right- and left-hand inverses are different, say C and D. Then $CA = AD = I$. Hence $CAD = C$. But $CA = I$. Hence $D = C$. QED.

eral for the correlation of v_{mn}-functions and u-functions. Thus we write

$$\varphi_{mn,\,kl} = \varphi_{p,\,q} = \frac{\pi \sin \pi pq}{\sinh \pi p \sinh \pi q}\, e^{j\pi pq} \quad . \tag{86}$$

In this case all the φ's are zero except those for which either p or q or both are zero. Further, the non-zero φ's go exponentially to zero with increasing value of the non-zero index. The $v_{mn}(t)$ are thus almost orthogonal, and the binomial expansion of the square-root of a matrix is valid.

$$\begin{aligned} u_{0,0}(t) = v_{0,0}(t) &- \frac{1}{2}\sum_{p,\,q} \varphi'_{p,\,q}\, v_{p,\,q}(t) \\ &+ \frac{3}{8}\sum_{p,\,q,\,r,\,s} \varphi'_{r,\,s}\,\varphi'_{p-r,\,q-s}\, v_{pq}(t) \\ &- \frac{5}{16}\sum_{p,\,q,\,r,\,s,\,\rho,\,\sigma} \varphi'_{r,\,s}\,\varphi'_{\rho-r,\,\sigma-s}\,\varphi'_{p-\rho,\,q-\sigma}\, v_{pq}(t) + \cdots \; . \end{aligned} \tag{87}$$

It will be remembered that the coefficients φ' are in general equal to the φ's, except that $\varphi'_{0,0}$ is zero.

Numberical evaluation of (87) gives for $u(t)$

$$\begin{aligned} \sqrt{\frac{\theta}{\pi}}\, u(t) = {} & \operatorname{sech}(\pi t/\theta)\,[1.09 - 0.27 \cos \pi t/\theta + 0.02 \cos 2\pi t/\theta + \ldots] \\ & - [\operatorname{sech} \pi(t/\theta - 1) + \operatorname{sech} \pi(t/\theta + 1)][0.133 - 0.01 \cos \pi t/\theta + \ldots] \\ & - [\operatorname{sech} \pi(t/\theta - 2) + \operatorname{sech} \pi(t/\theta + 2)][0.045 - \ldots] \\ & - \ldots \; . \end{aligned} \tag{88}$$

The two functions $u(t)$ and $v(t)$ are compared in Fig. 5.

Actually, such detailed calculations as these are rarely necessary for purposes of analysis.

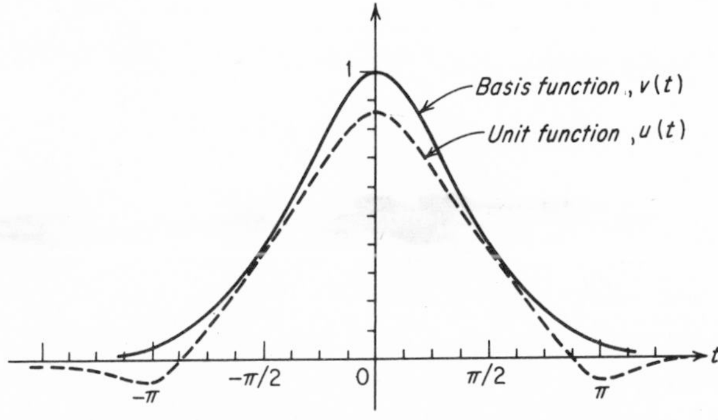

Fig. 5. Comparison of elementary signals.

VIII. APPLICATIONS TO SIGNAL ANALYSIS AND SYNTHESIS

Having obtained a method for breaking up signals into single pieces, we wish to illustrate its usefulness. Consider, first, the case of a sinusoid whose frequency is swept linearly (a so-called linear-FM signal). The spectrum of such a signal is quite complicated, and there is little in it to correspond to the notion of a frequency that varies linearly with time. However, if the frequency varies through W cps in T seconds, the analysis in terms of u-functions becomes very simple indeed provided θ is so chosen that the (m,n) grid divides T and W into equal numbers of intervals. Such a representation is shown in Fig. 6 (the u-function chosen is a rectangular pulse of duration θ). Note that the only a_{mn} of any consequence are those lying on the main diagonal of the checkerboard; thus the u-function representation corresponds to the intuitive notion of the signal as a "frequency" that varies linearly with "time." Note that although it apparently requires $2TW$ numbers to describe a waveform, with the proper choice of θ nearly all of the energy is associated with only $2\sqrt{TW}$ of them in the case of an FM wave.

This example illustrates an important point: A waveform may be

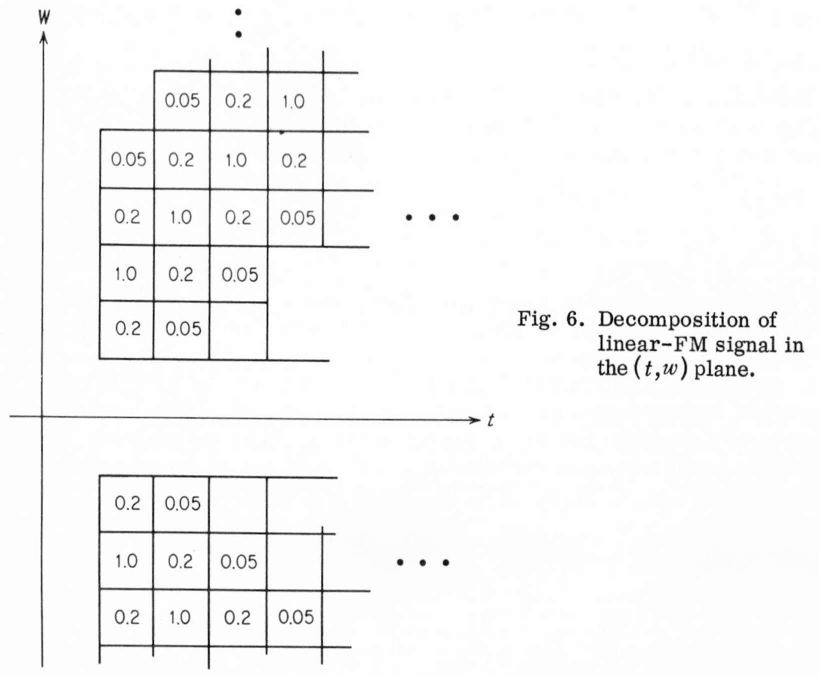

Fig. 6. Decomposition of linear-FM signal in the (t,w) plane.

much less complicated than the product of its duration and bandwidth might indicate—but it may require some manipulation to find the choice of θ that makes this fact obvious.

An important application of the (t, w) plane is to the representation of signals such as speech. Up to this point, the (t, w) plane has been divided into rectangles corresponding to the $u_{mn}(t)$, and a single number, a_{mn}, associated with each rectangle. This is all that is necessary; but if we so desire we can produce a continuum of numbers defined over the (t, w) plane. If $s(t)$ is a signal, then we can define $S(t, w)$ by the transformation

$$S(t, w) = \int_{-\infty}^{\infty} s(\xi)\, u^*(\xi - t) e^{-j2\pi w\xi} d\xi. \tag{89}$$

This S is related to the a_{mn} by

$$a_{mn} = S(n\theta, m/\theta). \tag{90}$$

Thus, given the orthogonality of $u_{mn}(t)$ with respect to the translation interval θ, we can write

$$s(t) = \sum_{m,n} S(n\theta, m/\theta)\, u_{mn}(t). \tag{91}$$

Inasmuch as the orthogonality of a system of unit functions based on $u(t)$ implies the orthogonality of such a system based on $u_{xy}(t)$, where x and y are arbitrary translations of $u(t)$ in time and frequency, and

$$u_{xy}(t) = u(t - x) e^{j2\pi yt}, \tag{92}$$

it follows that the values of $S(t, w)$ at the crosspoints of any grid laid on the (t, w) plane, for which the separation of the cross lines is θ in time and $1/\theta$ in frequency, yield a valid representation of $s(t)$:

$$s(t) = \sum_{m,n} S[n\theta + x, m/\theta + y]\, u(t - n\theta - x) e^{j2\pi(y + m/\theta)t} \tag{93}$$

$$\equiv \sum_{m,n}{}' S_{(xy)mn}\, u_{(xy)mn}(t)$$

A standard means of analyzing signals such as speech is by taking a "short-time spectrum" known as a sonagram. A sample of speech of duration T is recorded. A piece of paper is wrapped around a drum that rotates and is marked by a stylus that advances slightly along the axis of the drum with each rotation. (See Fig. 7.) With each revolution of the drum, the recorded signal is played through once. This signal is effectively passed through a narrow-band filter whose center frequency is varied slowly with the axial position of the stylus. The

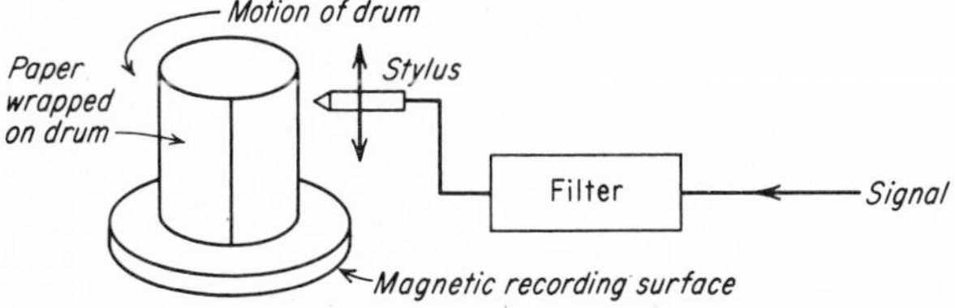

Fig. 7. Mechanism of sonagraph.

stylus marks the paper with a degree of blackness proportional to the intensity of the filter output.

If the system behaved precisely as described, it is clear that the density of markings on the paper would be proportional to the function $S(t, w)$ defined above, in which $u(-t)$ is the filter impulse response—were it centered at zero frequency— and w is the actual center frequency of the filter. Actually, the filtering is carried on at a high frequency by heterodyning the signal into a band well above the audio range. Thus all phase information is lost in the marking process, and the sonogram becomes a plot of the magnitude, $|S(t, w)|$, of $S(t, w)$. Were the phase also recorded, the values of the sonagraph plot at the points of a latices $(\theta, 1/\theta)$ would suffice to completely specify the original signal. Since the phase information is not retained, one can only conjecture that enough information is contained in the plot of $|S(t, w)|$ to permit the accurate reconstruction of the original signal.

A quite different (and much more powerful) application of the matrix methods of signal representation is to establish techniques for actually carrying out the complicated signal-processing procedures that are indicated by some applications of modern communication theory.† This is clearly a broad topic whose implications extend far beyond the scope of the present volume.

The major difficulty to be faced in effecting a junction between the signal theory and the design of circuits to produce and process signals is that signal analysis must be carried out in terms of functions that have convenient analytic properties, whereas—until the advent of the tapped delay line,‡ at least—network synthesis must be carried out in terms of the response of finite, lumped-parameter networks. Clearly, there are two attacks that can be made on such a problem. We might take a waveform that has proved useful in signal analysis and show how to construct it from a collection of exponentially damped transients; or, we might exhibit signals that are easily approximated by the response of a lumped linear system and suggest its usefulness in analysis. We shall restrict the discussion here to the first possibility. In particular, we shall discuss the use of waveforms that are frequency translates of a simple damped RC-type response.

Consider the collection of functions $\{v_m(t)\}$ in which

$$\begin{aligned} v_m(t) &= e^{-at} e^{jmt/\theta}, \qquad t > 0 \\ &= 0, \qquad\qquad\qquad t < 0. \end{aligned} \tag{94}$$

It is immediately apparent that any signal that can be constructed from these is, except for the damping factor e^{-at}, periodic with period θ. Hence, anything that occurs within the first such period must

†See, for instance, the discussion in the next chapter of "smearing filters" for use in an impulse noise environment. See also references 1, 2, and 3 at the end of this chapter.

‡For an application of the tapped delay line to signal synthesis, see R. M. Lerner, "A Matched-Filter Detection System for Complicated Doppler-Shifted Signals," *Trans. IRE, PGIT*, Matched-Filter Issue, pp. 373-385, June, 1960.

occur in the next period, reduced by a factor $e^{-a\theta}$. As a consequence, it will be possible to come close to a function that is zero outside of the interval θ—although at the expense of a large damping factor, a, and possibly at the expense of building a signal, $s(t)$, out of the differences between large quantities. On the other hand, inasmuch as $1/x$ and e^{-x} behaviors are vastly different, the $v_m(t)$ in (94) can be used to approximate to a bandlimited signal or a sin t/t function only if the period θ is taken long compared to the reciprocal of the desired bandwidth and a great number of the $v_m(t)$ enter with roughly equal weighting into the approximation.

The general way of producing approximations to a given signal, $s(t)$, from the $v_m(t)$ of (94) would be to orthogonalize them to $u_m(t)$ by the matrix procedure of section IV, and then find by integration the coefficients β_m in

$$s(t) = \sum_m \beta_m u_m(t), \tag{95}$$

or to find by integration and matrix inversion the coefficients α_m in

$$s(t) = \sum_m \alpha_m v_m(t), \tag{96}$$

as described in the last paragraph of section IV.

If we take the normalizing factor $F(t)$ in the definition of orthogonality to be unity and the interval, A, to be the entire time axis (or considering the nature of the $v_m(t)$, $0 < t < \infty$) then we must either invert or take the negative square root of the correlation matrix, $\mathbf{\Phi}$, in which

$$\varphi_{mn} = \frac{a\theta}{a\theta - j(m-n)\pi} \; . \tag{97}$$

It must be emphasized that these are not necessarily the best choices of weighting factors and interval of orthogonality, but we shall postpone the introduction of a more convenient choice. If we assume that the $v_m(t)$ reach their $e^{-\pi}$ point in one period θ (or, what is the same thing, if the spectra of adjoining $v_m(t)$ overlap at their half-power points) then $a\theta = \pi$ and we have for mn^{th} element of $\mathbf{\Phi}$

$$\varphi_{mn} = \frac{1}{1 + j(m-n)} = \frac{1}{1 + jp}\,, \text{ where } p = m - n. \tag{98}$$

These elements for the matrix $\mathbf{\Phi}$ decrease too slowly with p for $\mathbf{\Phi}^{-1}$ to be computable by the binomial expansion of Eq. (62).

What can one do at this point?

One possibility is that there are several simple linear combinations of the $v_m(t)$ which have much more rapidly converging matrices. If a set of functions $v_m(t)$ is defined by the relationship

$$\mathbf{V}'(t) = \mathbf{Q}\,\mathbf{V}(t), \tag{99}$$

then we have for the new correlation matrix

$$\mathbf{\Phi}' = \mathbf{Q}\,\mathbf{\Phi}\,\mathbf{Q}_t \; . \tag{100}$$

In particular, if $v'_m(t) = v_m(t) - v_{m-1}(t)$, then the correlation matrix for the new functions becomes

$$\varphi'_{mn} = \frac{2}{[1 + j(p - 1)][1 + jp][1 + j(p + 1)]} \,. \tag{101}$$

It turns out that the binomial expansion for the inverse of this matrix actually does converge, but slowly.

As was remarked above, the choice of unity for the normalizing factor and the half line for the interval of orthogonality is not necessarily the best choice when dealing with the frequency translates of an exponentially damped waveform. We may as well recognize that except for the damping factor, the $v_m(t)$ are periodic with period θ, and choose for the interval of orthogonality the period θ. The most convenient weighting factor is then the square of the inverse of e^{-at}. Under these conditions, the $v_m(t)$ are orthogonal as they stand!

$$\int_0^\theta e^{2at} v_k(t)\, v_m^*(t)\, dt = \int_0^\theta e^{j2\pi kt/\theta} e^{-j2\pi mt/\theta} d\theta = \begin{cases} \theta, \text{if } k = m \\ 0, \text{if } k \neq m \end{cases} \tag{102}$$

Furthermore, the integrals for the coefficients take relatively elementary forms. If $s(t)$ is given by (95), we have for the coefficients β_k

$$\begin{aligned} \beta_k &= \frac{1}{\theta} \int_0^\theta e^{2at} s(t) \overline{v_k(t)}\, dt \\ &= \frac{1}{\theta} \int_0^\theta (e^{at} s(t))\, e^{-j2mkt/\theta} dt. \end{aligned} \tag{103}$$

At least this is a familiar integral—the Fourier transform of a function that is equal to $e^{at}s(t)$ in the interval $(0,\theta)$ and then repeats in succeeding and preceding intervals of length θ.

By way of a specific illustration of the procedure just outlined, consider the truncation procedure† in designing a signal, $s(t)$, whose autocorrelation function

$$\varphi_{ss}(\tau) = \int_{-\infty}^{\infty} s(t)\, s^*(t - \tau)\, dt \tag{104}$$

drops rapidly to zero in a delay interval short compared with the total duration of the signal. It is well known that if a sample of random noise of length T and bandwidth W is used as $s(t)$, the autocorrelation function drops to an rms value of about $1/\sqrt{2TW}$ of its value at the origin after a few units of $1/W$ in t. However, several classes

†This is a procedure whereby a periodic waveform having known desirable signal-processing properties is converted into a non-periodic finite-energy waveform which has similar properties. See the illustration of an L-sequence smeared-signal waveform in Fig. 21 of Chapter 11 and the corresponding footnote on p. 275. See also R. M. Lerner "Signals Having Uniform Ambiguity Functions," *IRE Convention Record*, 1958, pt. 4, pp. 27-36.

of *periodic* signals[11, 12] are known whose autocorrelation functions drop to $1/TW$ or less (even zero) of their value at the (periodic) origin in τ.

A description of the method by which these signals are constructed is beyond the scope of this paper (see Lerner,[11] Zierler,[12] for details, and also see Siebert[13] for a related discussion). It suffices to say here that the spectrum is also periodic in the absence of bandwidth-restricting filtering, and consists of components of equal magnitude:

$$s_p(t) = \sum_m \alpha_m e^{j2\pi mt/\theta}, \quad |\alpha_m| = \text{constant}.$$

The signal design problem is to derive from the periodic $s_p(t)$ a signal having finite duration that will continue to have a low autocorrelation function at all points away from the origin.[11] It can be shown that the desired signal can be obtained by multiplying $s_p(t)$ by a slowly varying "truncating function" which should be zero outside of one period of $s_p(t)$; *i.e.*,

$$s(t) = \sum_m \alpha_m T(t) e^{j2\pi mt/\theta}, \quad T(t) = 0 \text{ outside of } 0 < t < \theta, \tag{105}$$

in which $T(t)$ is the truncation function. A requirement on $T(t)$ is that its spectrum be narrow and drop rapidly to zero at high frequencies. This requirement is happily consistent with the desire to construct each of the functions $W_m(t)$

$$W_m(t) = T(t) e^{j2\pi mt/\theta} \tag{106}$$

out of as few of the $v(t)$ as possible.

In order that the spectrum of $T(t)$ drop to zero sufficiently fast at infinity, we set not only $T(t)$ but one or two of its derivatives equal to zero at the ends of the interval, θ. One such function whose first derivative vanishes at the end points is

$$\begin{aligned} T(t) &= 1 - \cos 2\pi t/\theta, \quad 0 < t < \theta \\ &= 0, \qquad \text{otherwise}. \end{aligned} \tag{107}$$

The spectrum of this function goes to zero as $1/f^2$ at infinity. A function of slightly wider bandwidth whose second derivative also vanishes at the end points is

$$\begin{aligned} T(t) &= \sin \pi t/\theta - \frac{1}{3} \sin 3\pi t/\theta, \quad 0 < t < \theta \\ &= 0, \qquad \text{otherwise}. \end{aligned} \tag{108}$$

For the purpose of numerical illustration, we select (107). For this choice of $T(t)$, we can compute the selection of $v_k(t)$ required to approximate each of the $W_m(t)$. We might just as well compute the weighting factors, β_k, for $W_0(t)$, since the β_k for all the other W's

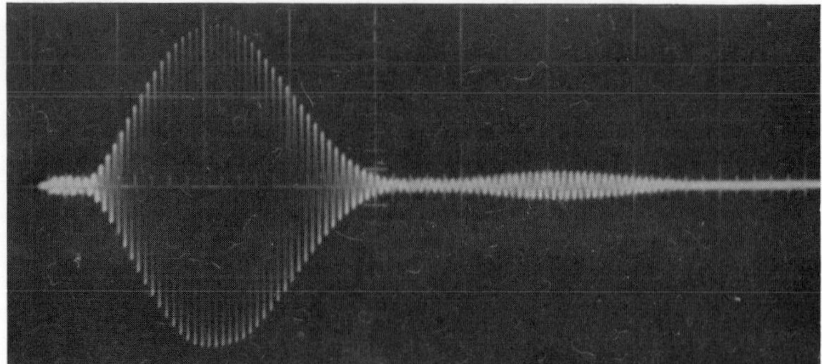

Fig. 8. Oscillogram of elementary signal with 1-cos x envelope.

can be obtained from these by corresponding changes in the indices.

$$\beta_k = \frac{1}{\theta}\int_0^\theta e^{+at}[1 - \cos 2\pi t/\theta]\, e^{-j2\pi kt/\theta}\, dt$$

$$= \frac{4\pi^2(e^{a\theta} - 1)}{[a\theta - j2\pi(k-1)][a\theta - j2\pi k][a\theta - j2\pi(k+1)]} \cdot \qquad (109)$$

In constructing the $W(t)$ shown in Fig. 8, $a\theta$ was chosen equal to $5\pi/4$. Under these circumstances, the numerical values of the various β's are:

$\beta_0 = 5.50$ $\qquad$ $\beta_3 = 0.181 \angle 128.0°$

$\beta_1 = 3.45 \angle -130.6°$ $\qquad$ $\beta_4 = 0.043 \angle 117.8°$

$\beta_2 = 2.00 \angle 151.2°$ $\qquad$ and so on.

The coefficients of negative index are, of course, the complex conjugates of these. Coefficients through $\beta_{\pm 2}$ were deemed sufficient for constructing the $W(t)$ pictured above. The result of combining a group of these $W(t)$ to form a signal is shown in Fig. 9; the experimental

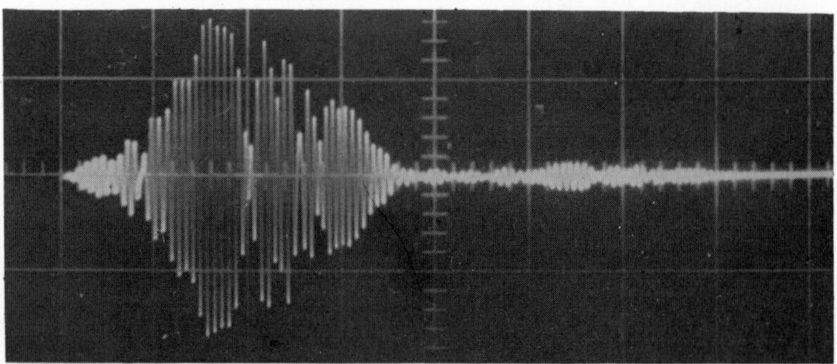

Fig. 9. Superposition of frequency translates of elementary signal of Fig. 8 to synthesize a complicated waveform.

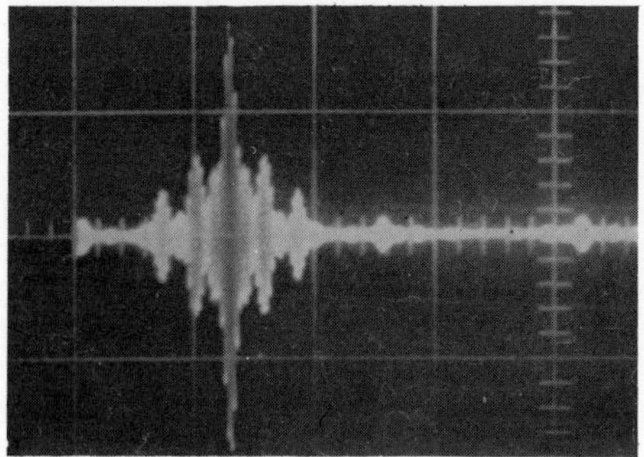

Fig. 10. Experimental autocorrelation function of the impulse response of the overall filter used in the synthesis of Fig. 9.

autocorrelation function (obtained by running a tape recording of the impulse response of the overall filter backwards and passing the reversed signal through the same filter) is shown in Fig. 10.

The process that yielded an $s(t)$ that satisfies certain requirements on its autocorrelation function is typical of the possibilities inherent in the step-by-step synthesis of complicated signals. We start with a conveniently "realizable" set of basis functions, $v_m(t)$. From these, we build a second set of basis functions, $w_n(t)$, which are appropriate to a particular step in solving a given problem, and express the signal or network function, $s(t)$, in terms of the $w_n(t)$. There may in fact be a number of these $s(t)$, say the set $\{s_k(t)\}$. These, in turn, can be used in the next step of the problem:

$$\mathbf{w}(t) = \boldsymbol{\alpha}\,\mathbf{v}(t)$$
$$\mathbf{s}(t) = \boldsymbol{\beta}\,\mathbf{w}(t)$$
$$\cdots\cdots\cdots$$
$$\mathbf{z}(t) = \boldsymbol{\Delta}\,\mathbf{y}(t) \tag{110}$$

At the end of the entire process, we can combine all the individual steps into one:

$$\mathbf{z}(t) = \boldsymbol{\Delta} \ldots \boldsymbol{\beta}\boldsymbol{\alpha}\,\mathbf{v}(t). \tag{111}$$

Thus one obtains a matrix of coefficients which specify the desired end result, $z(t)$, in terms of the physically constructable $v_m(t)$, in situations in which the matrix of coefficients would be difficult or impossible to set down directly:

$$\mathbf{z}(t) = \mathbf{Q}\,\mathbf{v}(t), \text{ where } \mathbf{Q} = \boldsymbol{\Delta} \ldots \boldsymbol{\beta}\boldsymbol{\alpha}\,. \tag{112}$$

Once a desired set of functions $\{z(t)\}$ has been expressed in terms of $v(t)$'s that can be constructed from finite lumped-parameter linear passive networks, only half the job is done—but it is the more difficult half. The second half of the job may be to assemble a collection of circuit components that will exhibit the response described by the mathematics. There are almost as many ways of effecting this reduction to practice as there are circuit configurations. However, two extreme possibilities stand out. In the first instance, one may use any one of a host of realization techniques to construct separated, self-contained filters to represent or process each of the members of the set $\{z(t)\}$. At the other extreme, one may use a single bank of very simple filters (say single- or double-tuned circuits), and construct the $\{z(t)\}$ according to $\mathbf{Q}$ by the use of resistive, inductive, or capacative adding matrices.

The latter procedure will generally be the most economical in terms of components. It has the further advantage that it requires very little arithmetical work beyond the computation of the $\mathbf{Q}$ matrix. Indeed, the operations corresponding to the $\boldsymbol{\alpha}$, $\boldsymbol{\beta}$, ... matrices may be implemented individually if it is so desired, but often at the expense of added complexity in the interconnecting equipment.

IX. CONCLUSION

A basic tool for signal analysis and synthesis has been set forth in the present chapter. It is important to point out that no "optimum" unit function has emerged from the discussion; consequently, a certain amount of judgement, suitable to the problem at hand, must be exercised in selecting the unit functions. Second, it is necessary to realize that with the exception of speech (or other vibrations) and FM signals, there are few signals that have been used in the communication art which are most conveniently described in terms of a two-dimensional array of coefficients. Nevertheless, there is much that can be accomplished with the techniques introduced in this chapter. Perhaps the most important single contribution is to bridge a gap that has existed between the techniques available to the signal analyst, who must keep his expressions tractable, and the network designer, who is limited to what he can build with tuned circuits and, more recently, tapped delay lines. A limit of what can be accomplished along these lines appeared in section VIII of this chapter. Many important applications will undoubtedly be found for the (t, w) plane matrix method of representing signals as the requirement for dealing with complicated signals increases.

APPENDIX

We prove here the completeness of a set of functions $u_{mn}(t)$ or $v_{mn}(t)$ that are the time and frequency translates of a single function $u(t)$ or $v(t)$, as stated in connection with Eq. (77) in the text. The terminology used here is that of the mathematician, but no claim is made for the rigor that would satisfy the mathematician. However, the author believes all the statements to be reasonable, in that whatever rough places exist could be clarified by a competent mathematician without essentially changing the course and intent of the argument.

. We intend to show that if a function, say $v(t)$, and its Fourier transform† $\hat{v}(\nu)$ are both in L_1 and L_2 (absolutely integrable and of integrable absolute square) and if, further, $v(t)$ is A.E. (almost everywhere) non-zero in an interval of length θ and $\hat{v}(\nu)$ A.E. non-zero in an interval of width $1/\theta$, then any function, $s(t)$, in $L_2(A)$ may be expressed in terms of the $v_{mn}(t)$ in the sense that there exists a set of a_{mn} such that the integral

$$\int_A | s(t) - \sum_{m,n} a_{mn} v_{mn}(t) |^2 \, dt, \quad \sum_{m,n} | a_{mn} |^2 \text{ finite,} \tag{A1}$$

vanishes, where A is any preassigned finite interval of t.

Let $\overline{V}$ be the L_2 closure of the space which includes all finite linear combinations of the $v_{mn}(t)$. Since the $v_{mn}(t)$ are all of finite (and equal) length, the set $\{v_{mn}(t)\}$ contains a basis for $\overline{V}$. Now, either $s(t)$ lies in $\overline{V}$, or there exists a vector $w(t)$ in $\overline{V}$, called the projection of $s(t)$ on $\overline{V}$, such that the difference, $z(t) = s(t) - w(t)$, is normal to every vector in $\overline{V}$. Now, if the magnitude of $z(t)$ in the interval A is zero, (A1) vanishes and the functions $s(t)$ and $w(t)$ are equivalent. We wish to show that a non-zero $| z(t) |$ in A contradicts the hypothesis that $s(t)$ is in L_2. In particular, we will construct from the $v_{mn}(t)$ a function that differs from almost any desired sine wave, $\exp j2\pi\nu t$, by an arbitrarily small amount in the interval A. But no function in L_2 not equivalent to zero in the interval A can be orthogonal in that interval to $\exp j2\pi\nu t$ for almost every finite ν. Accordingly, the assumption that $z(t)$ has non-zero magnitude in A is untenable, and the set of functions $v_{mn}(t)$ is complete.

We now proceed to construct $\exp j2\pi\nu_0 t$ in the interval A. Without any loss of generality we can take the origin as the center of the interval. Consider the sum of v-functions

$$S_m(t) = \sum_n (\exp j2\pi n\nu_0) \left(\frac{\sin n\pi b}{n\pi b} \right)^2 v_{mn}(t) \tag{A2}$$

where

$$v_{mn}(t) = v(t - n\theta)\, e^{j2\pi mt/\theta}.$$

This function has a spectrum, $\hat{S}_m(\nu)$, which is the product of the spectrum of $v_{m0}(t)$, viz. $\hat{v}_m(\nu)$, and a periodic spectrum. As illustrated in Fig. A1, this periodic spectrum is zero, except for a sequence of isoceles triangles having height $1/b$, base $2b$, and apexes located at the points ν_k defined by

$$\nu_k = \nu_0 + k/\theta, \; k = 0, \pm 1, \pm 2, \ldots \; . \tag{A3}$$

For large b, this spectrum is very close to a sequence of triangular

†In contrast with the notation of Chapters 6 and 12, the symbol ^ over a letter is used here to denote the Fourier transform (rather than the Hilbert transform) of the corresponding time function. Also ν here represents frequency in cps.

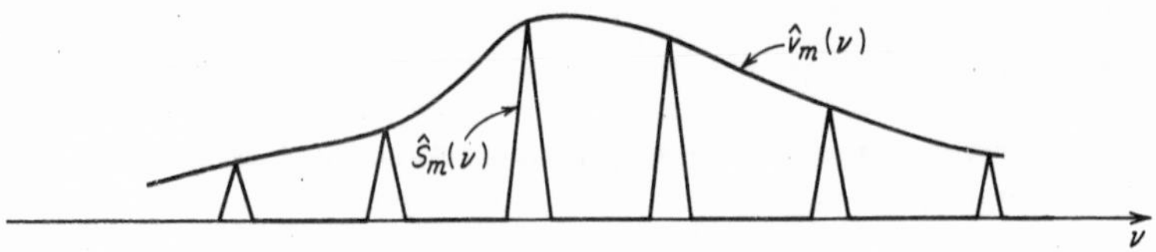

Fig. A1. Spectra of $S_m(t)$ and $v_{m0}(t)$.

spectra whose amplitudes are $\hat{v}_m(\nu_k)$, viz. the spectrum of the function

$$Q_m(t) = \sum_k \hat{v}_m(\nu_k)\left(\frac{\sin b\pi t/\theta}{b\pi t/\theta}\right)^2 \exp j2\pi\nu_k t\ . \tag{A4}$$

As a matter of fact, since $\hat{v}$ and v are in L_1, $\hat{v}_m(\nu)$ is uniformly continuous, and

$$\lim_{b\to 0}\,[\hat{S}_m(\nu) - \hat{Q}_m(\nu)] = 0 \tag{A5}$$

and the integral

$$\int_A |\,S_m(t) - Q_m(t)\,|^2\, dt \tag{A6}$$

can be made arbitrarily small by taking b sufficiently small. Now, we have in (A4) a sum of exponentials. Can we write a linear combination of the $Q_m(t)$ functions that is, in the limit of $b\to 0$, equal to $\exp j2\pi\nu t$? That is, does there exist a set of α_p such that

$$R(\nu_0,\,t) = \sum_p \alpha_p Q_p(t) = \left(\frac{\sin b\pi t/\theta}{b\pi t/\theta}\right)^2 \exp j2\pi\nu_0 t,\ \sum_p |\,\alpha_p\,|^2 \text{ finite.} \tag{A7}$$

We recognize that from (A2)

$$\hat{v}_m(\nu_k) = \hat{v}_0(\nu_{k-m}). \tag{A8}$$

Consequently, from (A3) and (A4) we ask that

$$\sum_p \alpha_p \hat{v}_0(\nu_{k-p}) = \begin{cases} 0,\text{for all } k \neq 0 \\ 1,\text{for } k = 0\ . \end{cases} \tag{A9}$$

This problem is that of asking for a vector $\boldsymbol{\alpha}$, whose components are α_p, which is perpendicular to all except $\boldsymbol{\mu}_0$ of the set of vectors $\boldsymbol{\mu}_k$ whose components are $\hat{v}_0(\nu_{k-p})$.

It will be possible to find such an $\boldsymbol{\alpha}$ if there does not exist a relationship of linear dependence among the $\boldsymbol{\mu}_k$, that is, if there exist no set of numbers β_k different from zero such that

$$\sum_k \beta_k \boldsymbol{\mu}_k = 0,\ 0 < \sum_k |\beta_k|^2 \text{ finite.} \tag{A10}$$

Writing (A10) out, we have

$$\sum_p |\sum_k \beta_k \hat{v}_0(\nu_0 + \{k - p\}/\theta)|^2 \neq 0. \tag{A11}$$

If we take the Fourier transform of the expression within the absolute value signs considering p as the independent variable, we obtain an expression $g(x)$ which is periodic with period θ, multiplied by exp $2\pi j \nu_0 x$. Hence we have by Parseval's theorem

$$\int_\theta |g(x)|^2 \, dx \neq 0 \text{ implies } \sum_p |\sum_k \beta_k \hat{v}_0(\nu_0 + [k - p]/\theta)|^2 \neq 0 \,. \tag{A12}$$

But this $g(x)$ is given by

$$g(x) = \left[\sum_k \beta_k e^{-j2\pi kx/\theta}\right] \left[\sum_s e^{j2\pi\nu_0 s\theta} \, v(x - s\theta)\right]. \tag{A13}$$

Now β_k not all equal to zero cannot be so chosen as to make the integral in (A12) vanish unless the second bracket in the expression for $g(x)$ vanishes in some finite interval of x. But it is known *a priori* that $v(x)$ does not vanish A.E. in an interval at least equal to θ. In these circumstances, it is possible to construct $v(x)$ such that the sum in the right-hand bracket will vanish for some fixed value of ν_0—but it seems highly unlikely that a $v(x)$ can be found such that the bracket will vanish in an interval of x *over a finite range of* ν_0 (or θ). If such $v(x)$'s can be found, then they are none of the common functions that might be chosen for $v(x)$, and are clearly such a peculiar subset of the $v(x)$ which fulfill the conditions of lying both in L_1 and L_2 that they can without loss of engineering generality be excluded from consideration as possible $v(x)$. Given this exclusion, the integral (A12) cannot be zero except for a set of ν_0 of zero measure; (A10) cannot hold for almost all ν_0; the vector α can be found that satisfies (A9) for almost all ν_0; and we can generate $R(\nu_0, t)$ in (A7) for almost all ν_0. If we consider $T(\nu_0, t)$ to be defined by

$$T(\nu_0, t) = \sum_m a_m S_m(t), \tag{A14}$$

then $T(\nu_0, t)$, which is a linear combination of the $v_{mn}(t)$, approximates $e^{j2\pi\nu_0 t}$ in the interval A arbitrarily closely if b is taken sufficiently small. Thus

$$\lim_{b \to 0} \int_A |T(\nu_0, t) - R(\nu_0, t)|^2 \, dt$$

$$= \lim_{b \to 0} \int_A |T(\nu_0, t) - \exp j2\pi\nu_0 t + (\exp j2\pi\nu_0 t - R(\nu_0, t))|^2 dt$$

$$= \lim_{b \to 0} \int_A |T(\nu_0, t) - \exp j2\pi\nu_0 t|^2 \, dt$$

$$= 0 \,. \tag{A15}$$

Hence we can construct $\exp j2\pi\nu_0 t$ in the interval A out of the $v_{mn}(t)$ for almost all ν_0. Accordingly, by the argument following Eq. (A1) the set of functions $\{v_{mn}(t)\}$ is complete in L_2 over any preassigned finite interval A.

REFERENCES

1. R. Price and P. E. Green, Jr., "A Communication Technique for Multipath Channels," *Proc. IRE,* vol. 46, pp. 555-570, March, 1958.
   S. M. Sussman, "A matched-Filter Communication System for Multipath Channels," *Trans, IRE, PGIT,* Matched-Filter Issue, pp. 367-373, June, 1960.
2. P. M. Woodward, *Probability and Information Theory with Applications to Radar,* Pergamon Press, London, 1953.
   W. M. Siebert, "A Radar Detection Philosophy," *Trans. IRE, PGIT,* vol. IT-2, pp. 204-221, September, 1956.
3. E. E. David, Jr., "Signal Theory in Speech Transmission," *Trans. IRE, PGCT,* vol. CT-3, pp. 232-244, December, 1956.
4. D. Gabor, "Theory of Information," *J. Inst. Elec. Engrs.,* pt. III, vol. 93, pp. 429-457, November, 1946.
5. J. M. Manley and H. E. Rowe, "General Properties of Nonlinear Elements," *Proc. IRE,* vol. 44, pp. 904-913, July, 1956.
6. C. E. Shannon, "Communication in the Presence of Noise," *Proc. IRE,* vol. 37, pp. 10-21, January, 1949.
7. D. A. Linden, "A Discussion of Sampling Theorems," *Proc. IRE,* vol. 47, pp. 1219-1226, July, 1959.
8. J. Dugundji, "Envelopes and Pre-envelopes of Real Waveforms," *Trans, IRE, PGIT,* vol. IT-4, pp. 53-57, March, 1958.
9. R. Bourret, "A Note on an Information Theoretic Form of the Uncertainty Principle," *Inform. and Control,* vol. 1, pp. 398-401, December, 1958.
10. R. M. Lerner, "Means for Counting 'Effective' Numbers of Objects or Durations of Signals," *Proc. IRE,* vol. 47, p. 1653, September, 1959.
11. R. M. Lerner, "*Use of L Sequences in Signal Design*" (to be published).
12. N. Zierler, "Linear Recurring Sequences," *J. Soc. Ind. App. Math.,* vol. 7, p. 31, 1959.
13. W. M. Siebert, "Studies of Woodward's Uncertainty Function," Mass. Inst. Tech., Research Lab. Electronics, Quart. Progr. Rept., Apr. 15, 1958.

CHAPTER 11

Design of Signals

Robert M. Lerner

I. INTRODUCTION

The synthesis of signals is a relatively new art. This fact is somewhat surprising, inasmuch as the communication systems for which signal synthesis is appropriate—namely those which transmit symbols, as in telegraphy—were the first land-line and radio systems to be used. However, before one can make a systematic approach to most *synthesis* problems, it is necessary to have available a thorough, meaningful *analysis* of the relevant parts of the system under study. So long as communication systems were more or less satisfactory without it, analytic understanding was slow in coming. It has required the pressure of the demands of modern military weapons design (in particular, the performance requirements on radars and fire-control systems) in the past two decades to bring this analytic knowledge (for example the statistical filtering and decision theory described briefly in Chapters 8 and 9) to the point where it is the kind of engineering tool that one may use in a systematic study of the synthesis of signals.

In this chapter, we shall develop the foundations of the art of designing signals for use in communication channels having additive disturbances. The discussion covers four topics. First, we shall investigate briefly the place of signal synthesis in system engineering; second, we shall discuss the principles of signal design for additive gaussian noise; third, we shall take up the question of "colored" gaussian noise and discuss the appropriateness of the gaussian-noise model with respect to actual communication circuits; and finally, we shall consider signals appropriate for channels disturbed by additive impulse noise.

While we shall make full use of the results of analysis, we shall try not to obscure the basic philosophy with mathematics. Accordingly, many results will be stated, rather than proved; and we shall feel fully justified in stating the results of experience where analysis has proved too complicated or difficult to be useful.

II. SYSTEM ENGINEERING

Although the material in this chapter can be discussed as a separate discipline, it is worthwhile to begin with a clear idea of the situations in which signal synthesis can be useful. With such insight, it is then possible to judge the results to be expected from efforts to design better signals relative to the value of efforts expended on improving a communication system in other ways.

As suggested in the introductory chapter, it is often convenient to divide models of communication systems into two categories—"analog" systems and "digital" systems. The model which is appropriate in a given situation depends in part on the character of the message and especially on the standard of system performance. Signal design as considered in this chapter has meaning only in those communication situations that are best characterized by the second or "digital" model.

One model for a "digital" communication system is shown in Fig. 1. The messages to be transmitted are discrete, so that it is possible to say that the message delivered by the receiver is either correct or incorrect. This model is thus particularly appropriate to those communication systems in which digital data or coded texts are being transmitted. We may think of the operation of this system in the following way. An information source chooses for transmission one out of a finite set of possible messages. The receiver does not know in advance precisely which one of these possible alternatives will be selected by the transmitter. (If the receiver had this knowledge *a priori*, there would be no need for the communication system.) Hence the receiver must deduce the message selected for transmission from an observation of the received signal. To this end the transmitter associates with each possible transmitted message a distinct signal waveform that may be transmitted over the available transmission channel. The channel unfortunately effects changes in these signals, some of them random changes, so that it is usually necessary for the receiver to make a guess as to which signal was in fact transmitted. This operation is called "detection" or "decoding," depending on the context.

The model used in Fig. 1 is too general to be of much practical use. In most communication systems, the set of all likely transmittable messages is too large to be dealt with as such. Accordingly, we break down the messages into a sequence of simpler parts called symbols. What we wish to transmit is then a sequence of these symbols. To this end, transmittable signal waveforms are associated with the symbols rather than the messages themselves, and the receiver makes its guesses on a per-symbol rather than a per-message basis. A further refinement in the model is to break the process of association of waveforms with symbols into two steps, a digital one

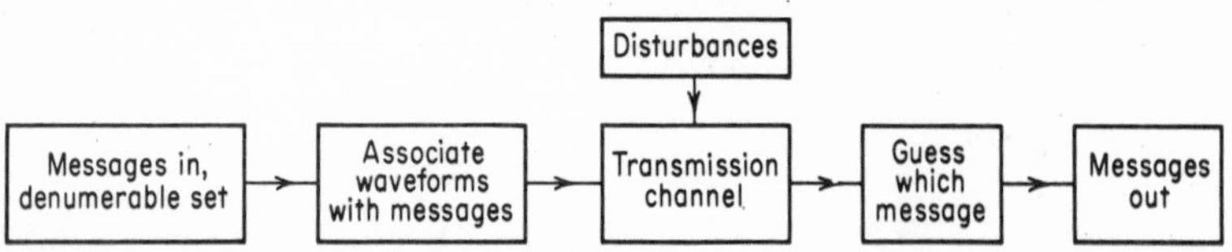

Fig. 1. Model for "digital" communication system.

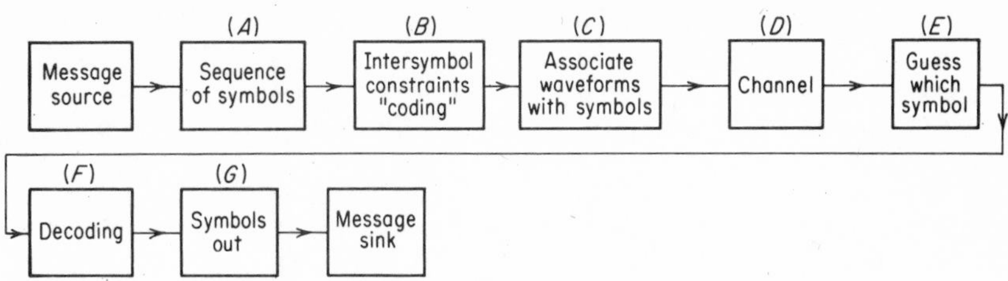

Fig. 2. Detailed block diagram of a digital transmission system.

and an analog one. In the first, intersymbol constraints are introduced, usually to permit the receiver to detect or correct possible errors in the transmission of the individual symbols. This operation is called "coding." In the second step, analog waveforms are associated with each of the constrained symbols without considering the symbols that precede it or succeed it. Correspondingly, the receiver first guesses the symbols independently, and then examines them in accordance with the constraints in a decoding operation. These two sets of operations are shown in the system model of Fig. 2 as blocks (B), (C) and (E), (F). They are analog and digital implementations of the same basic kind of operation. By proper design in either or both of these system blocks, it is possible to reduce the percentages of mistakes that occur in the transmission system. Indeed, information theory (see Chapter 23) suggests that, provided the source is delivering information at a rate that is less than the channel capacity C of the transmission channel, the probability of errors can be made arbitrarily low (in principle, and at the expense of sufficiently complicated signal processing). The theory further states that it is not possible to transmit more than an average of C correct digits per second over the channel.

Now, in actual systems the rate of signaling always falls somewhat short of the channel capacity, C, since this rate presumes (and thus far in the art, necessitates) an exceedingly complicated signaling system. But that most actual voice-bandwidth channels in point of fact seem to be capable of only a few hundred bits per second appears to be an excessive disparity. The reason is not hard to find—the signaling systems in use make almost no use of the statistical properties of the transmission medium other than to attempt to operate in a region of the band in which the magnitude of the frequency response is reasonable. As a result, these systems are extremely sensitive to impulse noise, which is a major form of noise in many radio systems and all telephone systems. They are also badly upset by delay distortion, which causes different frequency components of the signal to be delayed by different times, up to a differential of 0.005 to 0.01 seconds on many long voice circuits.

There are a number of possible means of attacking the problems thus created. Suppose a point-to-point communication system of the type shown in Fig. 2 is unsatisfactory. With generally available devices and components in each of the blocks, the message sources are generating symbols too rapidly to get to the message destinations with a sufficiently small probability of error. Evidently, if matters are to be improved, any and all blocks of the system must be open to examination. Let us examine them.

1. *Message Destination or "Sink."* The end use of the message is, after all, what determines whether the message should be transmitted at all, and what reliability is required of the transmission. Eliminating the need for the data carried by the message, or the need for reliable data, eliminates the problem. In a less trivial sense, it may be that an operation of data reduction at the sink can be transferred to the source with a subsequent decrease in the demands on the interconnecting channel.

2. *Message Source.* It may be possible to reduce the rate at which data is generated by the source:

(a) As mentioned above, a data reduction step performed in the sink may be transferred to the source.

(b) The data to be transmitted may come in bursts, i.e., at very high rates when there is significant data but with long "dead time" between significant transmissions. If the time delay is tolerable, the data may be stored and transmitted at the average rate rather than the burst rate.*

(c) The message symbols, although generated continuously, may be subject to such severe constraints ("redundancy") that in point of fact the message is representable by many fewer symbols. This possibility differs from (a) in that the reduced form of the message may not be acceptable to the sink, in which case it is necessary to recreate the original message before delivery to the sink.

In this connection two additional comments are in order. First, what is suggested here is obviously a coding-decoding operation—not to overcome channel disturbances or to transmit the signal, but to reduce the number of symbols necessary to specify it. Second, this coding-decoding operation may be very difficult to implement, even when the redundancy is known to be very high. A case in point is speech. It has long been known that the speech signal that occupies a 3 kc bandwidth *ought* to be representable by a signal that occupies less than a hundred cps of bandwidth.† As suggested above, it is clear that if this latter signal is intended for the human ear as a sink, speech must be resynthesized from it (the coded signal must be decoded). But, no really acceptable speech coding-decoding system has yet been demonstrated.

3. *The Transmission Path.* By all means, use a better transmis-

*The converse situation exists in UHF meteor ionization-trail communication. See the discussion of the "Janet" system in *Proc. IRE*, vol. 45, December, 1957, *e.g.*, Forsyth *et al.*, "The Principles of JANET – A Meteor-Burst Communication System," pp. 1642-1657.

†R. M. Fano, "Information Theory and Speech Analysis," *J. Acoustical Soc. Am.*, vol. 22, p. 695, 1950. The first device to achieve successfully such a representation was constructed by Homer Dudley about 1937. (See Dudley, *J. Acoustical Soc. Am.*, vol. 11, p. 169, October, 1939).

sion medium if one is available. Two approaches are available here:

(a) Select the best of the available paths and then fix these up as best one can to provide the desired service. This is what has been done with present commercial "Data Grade" telephone lines. This is what diversity techniques can do for fading radio paths. However, there is a limit to which this sort of thing can be carried. No amount of fixing will produce reliable communication through a deep fade in HF ionospheric transmission.

(b) If possible, select a better transmission medium. As was pointed out in the introductory chapter, it is a rare communication system design problem in which one does not have some choice in the type of transmission medium that may be exploited.

4. *The Detector.* The results of detection theory are well known, but not as well known as they ought to be, particularly in connection with digital-data transmission. A major source of confusion here is that information theory has talked about discrete symbols (in particular, binary symbols) that are transformed into one another with certain probabilities of error. As a matter of fact, however, physical channels are not discrete binary channels; one selects waveforms to represent the symbols in transmission, and makes decisions at the receiver as to which waveforms were in fact transmitted. If the reliability with which these decisions are made can be increased, the probability of error between the discrete terminals of the channel goes down—a situation that is rarely made clear in the discussion of discrete information theory.

In point of fact, the reliability of a statistical decision is known to increase with the amount of signal energy that can be integrated at the receiver, provided the exact form of the expected *received* signal waveforms is known. Thus several possibilities for improvement of the detection process exist.

(a) Use "optimum" detectors, (*e.g.* matched filters* when the channel disturbance is additive gaussian noise) if these or their near equivalents are not already in use.

(b) Since for a given binary data rate and system power limitation the energy per binary symbol is fixed, integrate over as many bits of received signal as possible.

(c) Introduce at the detector a means for measuring slow changes in the characteristics of the transmission path so that the set of possible *received* waveforms will be sufficiently well known to allow full use of the received energy.

5. *The Coder or Waveform Selector.* The remarks made above concerning the selection of waveforms for use in a physical transmission channel apply with even greater emphasis to the coding operation. Thermal or "white" gaussian noise will at some time resemble any arbitrary waveform, but for non-gaussian disturbances this is not necessarily true. Thus there are the following possibilities:

*A survey of matched filter techniques is contained in *Trans. IRE, PGIT*, vol. IT-6, Matched Filter Issue, June, 1960.

(a) At the transmitter, use as symbols only those waveforms that are least likely to be confused with one another by the addition of noise.
(b) At the receiver, integrate as much signal energy as possible by effectively using a large alphabet of symbols.
(c) Introduce constraints between the symbols at the transmitter so that the receiver may detect and correct errors.

The engineering question now is by which combination of these techniques does one get the most return for his money. In particular, what is the relative value and importance of a sufficiently sophisticated choice of the signal waveforms in block (C) of the communication system model of Fig. 2? In general these questions cannot be answered without further details about the particular environment for which the communication system is to be designed. If the message source, sink, and transmission medium are specified, and if further it is assumed that a detector is used in block (E) which comes reasonably close to making a "best guess" in some appropriate statistical sense, then the discussion narrows down to a comparison of the last three alternatives mentioned above. In this connection we note that if the system error rate is "low" to start with, then a comparatively simple error-detecting-and-correcting scheme [technique (c)] can make it entirely negligible at the expense of a slight increase in the number of transmitted symbols. On the other hand, when the initial error rate is high, either on the average or because of a temporary fade in the system performance, error-correction coding becomes complicated. Unfortunately, it is precisely during performance fades that substantial improvement is required. Whereas technique (c) becomes expensive when the error rate is high, techniques (a) and (b), which attempt to lower the symbol error by improving the guessing technique, may still be applicable.

III. DESIGN OF SIGNALS FOR CHANNELS DISTURBED BY ADDITIVE WHITE GAUSSIAN NOISE

The optimum procedures for detecting (*i.e.*, guessing) signals in the presence of additive white gaussian noise have been illustrated in Chapters 8 and 9. The decision as to which signal was actually transmitted is based on a comparison (at a given time) of the outputs of a set of filters matched to each noise-free signal that can possibly be received, or upon some equivalent set of operations on the received signal. Here, we make use of the results of decision theory to guide the design of signals for use in channels in which additive white gaussian noise is the primary disturbance. We shall discuss only a few special cases of signal selection for this kind of noise environment.

Consider first the simplest case. The choice is to be made between two symbols uniquely specified at the receiver by $s_1(t)$ and $s_2(t)$. We assume that the symbols are equally likely and that the cost of an incorrect guess is independent of the symbol transmitted. We further assume that the waveforms $s_1(t)$ and $s_2(t)$ have equal energy, E:

$$\int_{-\infty}^{\infty} s_1^2(t)dt = \int_{-\infty}^{\infty} s_2^2(t)dt = E \quad . \tag{1}$$

(Equality of waveform energy is, indeed, optimum under the previous assumptions.) The cost of making mistakes with this set of assumptions depends monotonically on the probability of confusing one symbol with the other. When the gaussian noise energy is N_0 watts/cps (in this chapter we shall use a single-sided spectrum) the probability of making such a confusion is shown in section VI of Chapter 8 to be

$$P_c = \text{prob. of confusion} = \Phi\left(\sqrt{(E/N_0)(1-\rho_{12})}\right) \tag{2}$$

in which $\Phi(x)$ is the normal error integral

$$\Phi(x) = \frac{1}{\sqrt{2\pi}} \int_{x}^{\infty} \exp\,(-\xi^2/2)d\xi \tag{3}$$

and

$$\rho_{12} = (1/E) \int_{-\infty}^{\infty} s_1(t)\,s_2(t)\,dt = \gamma_{12}/E \tag{4}$$

$$= \text{correlation coefficient between } s_1(t) \text{ and } s_2(t).$$

P_c decreases monotonically to zero as $(E/N_0)(1 - \rho_{12})$ increases to infinity. As stressed in Chapter 8, the details of the waveforms $s_1(t)$ and $s_2(t)$ do not enter directly into the expression (2) for the probability of a confusion. Neglecting for the moment the factor $(1 - \rho_{12})$, which can vary only between 0 and 2, the probability of confusion depends only on the ratio of signal energy E to the noise power per cps. An intuitive interpretation of this fact is that there is no signal waveform that looks "least" like gaussian noise; for any value of ρ_{12}, gaussian noise will turn any one waveform into any other waveform of the same energy with equal probability.

If one is transmitting signals at a fixed rate, n per second, and with a fixed amount of available average power, then the energy per symbol, E, is fixed also. In this case the only remaining design parameter is ρ_{12}. Clearly ρ_{12} should be as negative as possible so that the argument of the error function in Eq. (2) can be as large as possible. One chooses $s_1(t)$ and $s_2(t)$ accordingly.

The results so far obtained can be used to indicate the answer to an often-asked question, "which is the best system for digital-data transmission, frequency shift keying, phase reversal, or AM?" Actually, none of these is best in the sense of being an "ultimate" data communication system, but we can compare them with respect to the gaussian noise environment. The use of FSK at a given power level corresponds to choosing ρ_{12} equal to zero. (The average product of two functions is zero if their spectra occupy different frequency bands.) In this circumstance, the probability of confusion is

$$P_c = \Phi\left((E/N_0)^{1/2}\right) = \Phi\left((S/nN_0)^{1/2}\right) \tag{5}$$

where S is the average power of the transmission. But the orthogonal-signal value, $\rho_{12} = 0$, is not the smallest value to which we can design ρ_{12}. By taking

$$s_2(t) = -s_1(t) \tag{6}$$

we have

$$\rho_{12} = -1\,, \tag{7}$$

in which case the system is 3 db better off than it was in the case of FSK or other orthogonal signals, and

$$P_c = \Phi\left((2E/N_0)^{1/2}\right) = \Phi\left((2S/nN_0)^{1/2}\right). \tag{8}$$

(The decision between alternative signals in this case is 6 db better off with respect to signal energy than is the corresponding decision between the presence and absence of signal in the radar detection case.) It should be emphasized that this 3 db improvement over orthogonal signals is a potential property of *any* waveform-reversal* system, of which the carrier-phase-reversal system is but a special case. It should be further emphasized that this full 3 db improvement over FSK (or other orthogonal signals) is available only with a receiver design that provides a "clean" (*i.e.*, substantially noise-free) reference, by means of which the sign of the received signal waveform may be assigned. Otherwise, comparing the presently received waveform with a previously received (noisy) waveform as a standard degrades the performance by one decibel in a 180° phase reversal system, and by up to 3 db in a multiphase system.** The AM system is also at least 3 db worse off than a waveform-reversal system. The quickest way to demonstrate this is to point out that an amplitude modulation data-transmission system is at best no different than a phase-reversal scheme, except for the presence of a carrier that takes at least half the available power without carrying any information. (A suppressed-carrier double-sideband or single-sideband system, can of course, be made equivalent to the phase-reversal system.)

So far we have considered a decision between only two alternative symbols. Suppose now we try to extend the method to the design of signals when there are M symbols whose corresponding waveforms are $s_1(t)$, $s_2(t)$, ..., $s_M(t)$ and which have equal energy. Unfortunately, for $M > 2$, no simple formula for the probability of confusion exists, and indeed, for $M > 3$ integrals appear that have not been tabulated. Accordingly, we fall back on the practice of making the probabilities of pair-wise confusions as low as possible. The probability of con-

*We are using the word "reversal" here in the sense of a change in polarity.

**This has been shown by C. R. Cahn in "Performance of Digital Phase-Modulation Communication Systems," *Trans. IRE, PGCS*, vol. C5-7, pp. 3-6, May, 1959.

fusing any pair of signals, say $s_m(t)$ and $s_k(t)$, depends on the correlation coefficient, ρ_{mk}. With $M > 2$ it is clearly impossible to take all the $\rho_{mk} = -1$; for if $\rho_{12} = -1$ and $\rho_{23} = -1$, then ρ_{13} is necessarily +1, which is to say that the signals $s_1(t)$ and $s_3(t)$ can differ only by a scale factor. By considering the properties of a regular polyhedron having M vertices in $M-1$ space (*i.e.*, a regular simplex), it is possible to show* that the most negative value that can be simultaneously taken by the correlation coefficients between members of an M-waveform alphabet is

$$\rho_{mk} = -\frac{1}{M-1} \ . \tag{9}$$

Suppose symbols are being transmitted at regular intervals of T in time. Then unless all the $\rho_{mk}(nT)$ are nearly zero (n any non-zero positive or negative integer), the decision at any one time will be interfered with by the effects of "tails" of signals transmitted at other times. One way to prevent this intersymbol crosstalk is to
For moderately large values of M, this minimum value of ρ_{mk} is not too different from zero. Hence, for cases in which the alphabet of symbols to be transmitted is large, we seek to associate with those symbols a set of orthogonal or nearly orthogonal waveforms, in the knowledge that the set of mutual-confusion probabilities cannot be made uniformly much lower by the most sophisticated choice of signal waveforms. (Furthermore, in the case of orthogonal signals, the probability of confusion can be calculated, as we shall show.)

So far we have discussed only a decision made at one fixed time, between the symbols that were possibly transmitted at some other fixed time. In practice, a succession of symbols is transmitted and it is necessary to make a succession of decisions at the receiver. It is in this connection that details about the waveform of $s_1(t)$, ..., $s_M(t)$ are important—in particular, details about the effective bandwidth. In principle, the waveforms due to all likely sequences of symbols should be treated as "symbols" in making a statistical decision about the transmission. The difficulty with doing this is that the amount of equipment needed at the receiver grows exponentially with the number of symbols in a sequence. In order to avoid the need for this kind of complexity in the receiver, it is necessary that the signal produced in the output of any matched filter by the transmission of a symbol be zero or nearly zero at all times at which decisions are made, except for the one time at which the transmission of that particular symbol is at issue.

Thus, in considering a sequence of symbols, the design parameters are the set of normalized cross-correlation functions $\rho_{mk}(\tau)$

$$\rho_{mk}(\tau) = (1/E) \int_{-\infty}^{\infty} s_m(t) s_k(t+\tau)\, dt \ . \tag{10}$$

*This is a suggestion by P. E. Green, Jr. (private communication). He has also suggested that this choice of ρ_{mk} results in minimum total probability of confusion (as well as minimum pairwise confusion probabilities), although no supporting calculation is yet available.

choose waveforms $s_1(t)$, $s_2(t)$, ..., $s_M(t)$ whose duration is T or less. The general restriction, however, is not that the duration of the signal be short, but that its bandwidth be sufficiently large. (Indeed, in choosing signals for a channel of strictly limited bandwidth, it is impossible to avoid signals that overlap in time.)

To illustrate the point that it is the bandwidth rather than the duration of a signal that is important in obtaining $\rho_{mk}(\tau)$ with suitably low intersymbol crosstalk, let us consider the transmission of a sequence of binary digits by a waveform-reversal system. In particular, we wish to use a waveform that lasts much longer than the time interval between symbols, but that nevertheless does not give rise to intersymbol crosstalk in an optimum receiver. The signal waveform, $s(t)$, can be obtained by pulsing a linear filter whose impulse response is $s(t)$. The succession of waveforms that represent the message can therefore be obtained by feeding to this linear filter a succession of impulses that are positive or negative according as the digits to be transmitted are ones or zeros. Now let the signal digits arrive at the rate of 2500 per second, so that $T = 0.4$ milliseconds. Let them be represented initially by a train of simple pulses whose bandwidth is sufficiently great so that the individual pulse waveforms do not overlap in time. Also let the linear filter that generates $s(t)$ be one whose *amplitude* response is flat over this bandwidth, but whose *phase* response contains so much delay distortion that each individual input pulse is smeared out over 10 milliseconds of time in the output. The on-line signal that is transmitted by this filter thus contains at any one time the superposition of waveforms due to 25 successive symbols, inasmuch as $s(t)$ lasts 25 times as long as the interval between symbols. At the receiver, however, another filter having flat amplitude response in a wide bandwidth can be used to equalize the delay distortion introduced by the first filter, with the result that the original non-overlapping pulses are approximately reconstituted in its output! The design of one such $s(t)$ has been described by Darlington[1] in a somewhat different context, viz., reducing the peak power requirements of certain pulse transmission systems. The particular $s(t)$ which he proposed is a sinusoid whose frequency is swept linearly with time; it may be obtained as the impulse response from a filter whose phase shift varies quadratically with frequency.

As a final topic in this section, we consider the problem of designing signals for the lowest possible error rate. Let us suppose that the average power and number of symbols to be delivered per second to the receiver are given, and that ρ_{12} has been properly selected. With all these selections, the error rate is still too high. What can be done to improve it further? Clearly, one must in some sense raise the energy integrated for each decision.

In order to have more energy per decision, one must in effect transmit fewer "symbols" per second. This fact is the basis for the statement commonly made, that "when you have a channel that is too noisy, you can trade data-transmission rate for lower error rate."

Often, a method of making the trade is added, ".... by using sufficiently narrow-bandwidth signals." Statements of this kind are at their best misleading, especially when cast in the form of an error-rate for signal-waveform-bandwidth trade. The fundamental fallacy of these statements is that information theory points out that no such trades are necessary. According to that theory, it is possible to achieve error-free transmission at rates up to

$$C = W \log_2 (1 + S/WN_0) \tag{11}$$

binary digits per second (where W is the channel bandwidth, S the average signal power, and N_0 is the gaussian noise power per cps of bandwidth);* this error-free capability is available provided one is willing to invest in sufficiently sophisticated signaling systems. A more correct statement of the error reduction trade is that one trades complexity in the design of the signaling system for freedom from errors upon reception.

To be sure, to increase the reliability of each decision, one must have more energy and therefore transmit fewer waveforms per second. Nevertheless, the same data rate can be maintained if the information carried by each waveform decision is correspondingly increased. The information carried by such a decision increases directly as the logarithm of the number of alternatives amongst which the choice is made. One therefore increases the size of the signal alphabet so as to be able to transmit the same information with fewer symbols per second. Narrow-banding necessarily increases the energy integrated in an "optimum" decision—but it also severely limits the possibility of increasing the alphabet of usable waveforms.

If the symbol waveforms are orthogonal (all $\rho_{mk} = 0$), all intersymbol confusions are equally likely. If the probability of a single confusion is P_c, then the probability of making a mistake in the case of an M-symbol alphabet is given by

$$P_{eM} = 1 - (1 - P_c)^{M-1} \quad . \tag{12}$$

If P_c is small to start with, this expression becomes

$$P_{eM} \cong (M - 1)P_c \, . \tag{13}$$

As a matter of fact, (13) is an upper bound for the probability of confusion, regardless of the value of the correlation coefficients, ρ_{mk}. For let the probability of confusion between the mth symbol and the kth be P_{mk}. If we regard each of the $M - 1$ possible confusions as mutually exclusive events (*i.e.*, for a given transmitted signal and noise, at most one of them is permitted to occur), then we have immediately

$$P_{eM} = \sum_k P_{mk} \, , \; k \neq m. \tag{14}$$

In fact, the ensemble of possible confusions are not all mutually ex-

*Note that this capacity is maximum not when the bandwidth W is made small but rather as W becomes very large so that $C \to S/N_0$ bits per second. See ref. 2.

clusive; this fact can, however, only operate to reduce the total probability of confusion as given by (14). Hence (14) is an upper bound on the probability of incorrectly indicating the mth symbol of an alphabet and (13) is an upper bound on the probability of confusion when all pair-wise confusions are equally likely.

In particular, in the case of a decision between M symbols for which the ρ_{mk} are all equal to $-1/(M-1)$, the probability of confusion is

$$P_{eM} \cong (M-1)\,\Phi\left(\sqrt{\frac{M}{M-1}\cdot\frac{E}{N_0}\cdot\ln M}\right) \tag{15}$$

for values of the argument greater than about five. It can be seen from Eq. (15) that the effectiveness of using a large number of symbols in the alphabet grows at best logarithmically with the size of the alphabet. In going from a binary alphabet to one with 32 symbols, one gains about 3 db if E/N_0 is greater than about +5 db. (The factor $1/(M-1)$ in the argument of Φ implies the use of optimum signal design in all cases. If orthogonal signals are used in all cases, the gain is about 6 db.) Since the gain in effective signal energy increases so slowly with the number of symbols in the alphabet, the use of alphabets whose size ranges from a dozen to a hundred-odd symbols seems to be the practical limit of exploiting this particular avenue to increasing the reliability of the channel without affecting the rate at which data is delivered. In case further reductions in error rate are necessary, a digital coding scheme probably offers the best promise for success.

IV. "COLORED" NOISE AND "I-F" FILTERS

Generally, at those energy levels at which a signal is likely to be disturbed by additive gaussian noise, communication systems operate with a relatively narrow bandwidth. Although such noise may in some cases exhibit a gross dependence of the noise power density on the frequency, it may be considered to be "white" or to have uniform spectrum in the frequency region actually occupied by the signal.* However, it is convenient to consider many types of signal interference and cross talk as "almost gaussian" noise; in these cases the noise may well have a highly non-uniform spectrum.

The problem of signaling through non-white noise has been dealt with by a number of authors.† The detection problem has a relatively simple solution for the case of additive colored gaussian noise, if we

*A possible exception to this general rule would be celestial noise at the microwave hydrogen-line frequency.

†See, for instance, W. B. Davenport, Jr., and W. L. Root, *Introduction to the Theory of Random Signals and Noise*, McGraw-Hill Book Company, Inc., New York, 1958, Chapter 11, section 7, and Chapter 14. For a discussion of the equivalent problem in the case of *analog* model of a communication system, see H. W. Bode and C. E. Shannon, "A Simplified Derivation of Linear Least-Square Smoothing and Prediction Theory," *Proc. IRE*, vol. 38, pp. 417-426; April, 1950.

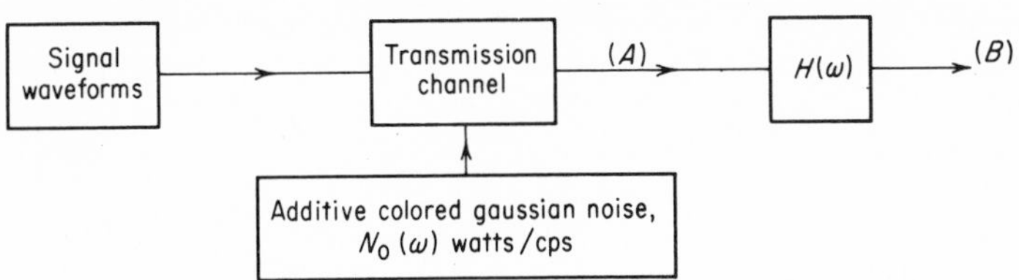

Fig. 3. Modification of transmission channel by filter $H(\omega)$ to produce "white" noise in the output.

make the same assumptions about the signal as we did in the previous section. Suppose the noise power spectral density to be given by $N_0(\omega)$ watts per cps of bandwidth. Let us interpose between the received signal plus noise at (A) in Fig. 3 and a signal-guessing device at (B) a linear filter whose frequency response is the reciprocal of $N_0(\omega)$ over the total frequency range for which signal and interference have significant components:

$$|H(\omega)|^2 = [N_0(\omega)]^{-1} \tag{16}$$

This filter, essentially, makes the noise at point (B) white. Since, however, we could presumably operate on the signal at point (B) to recover the original signal at point (A) (*e.g.*, by passing the signal at (B) through a filter $[H(\omega)]^{-1}$), the signal at point (B) contains all the information that was in the original signal at point (A). Nothing is lost, then, by pretending that we have received the signal at (B) rather than the original signal, and proceeding from there. The expected signals at point (B), however, are no longer the transmitted waveforms $s_1(t)$, $s_2(t)$, ..., $s_M(t)$, but these waveforms as filtered by $H(\omega)$. If $n(t)$ is the impulse response of the filter, then the expected waveforms at (B) are the signals $r_1(t)$, ..., etc., where the $r_k(t)$ are given by the convolution

$$r_k(t) = \int_{-\infty}^{\infty} s_k(\xi) h(t - \xi)\, d\xi. \tag{17}$$

Since the noise at point (B) is white, a best guessing procedure there is to connect to that point filters matched to the $r_k(t)$ and to compare their outputs. Thus the results of detection theory suggest the use of a filter in the receiver which suppresses interfering signals in those frequency regions in which they can be expected. This is scarcely news to the designers of i-f strips for communications receivers!

Two things are worth noting about the form of this preliminary "i-f response", $H(\omega)$. First, only its magnitude is specified by the defining equation (16). Second, the magnitude of $H(\omega)$ does not at all depend on the distribution of the signal energy. In connection with the first point, a reasonable further constraint on $H(\omega)$ is to choose its phase characteristic to satisfy certain conditions of physical realizability; this kind of constraint is not of major importance in the present discussion, primarily because the question of time delay in signal processing is assumed not to be an issue here. What does matter

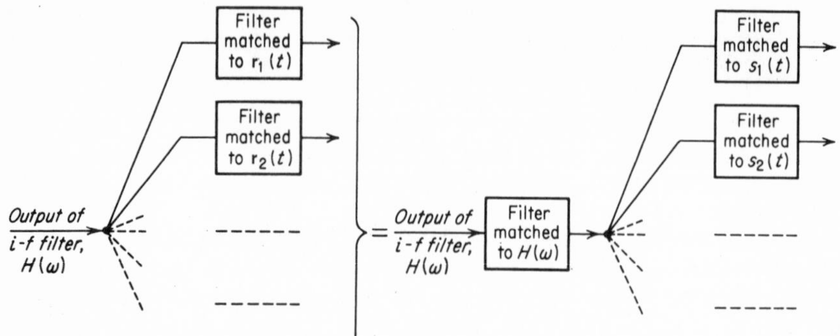

Fig. 4. Decomposition of matched-filter system.

from the present point of view is that we eventually have some signal processing which is equivalent to building a set of filters matched to the outputs of $H(\omega)$ when the inputs are the original signal waveforms $\{s_k(t)\}$. If the filters are actually constructed, then, as illustrated in Fig. 4, they are equivalent to a cascade of a filter matched to $H(\omega)$ and a set matched to the $\{s_k(t)\}$.

Now the output of that part of the filtering system which is "matched" to the i-f strip in principle corrects all the phase distortion introduced there. If this phase correction is going to be necessary in the long run, one might as well take it into account at the start of the i-f filter design. One therefore should design the filter $H(\omega)$ with a linear phase shift* or, what is the same thing, an impulse response that is nearly symmetric with respect to some point in time. The filter matched to the i-f response $H(\omega)$ can then be an identical filter. Note that the transmission system is assumed to be linear up to the points at which the decisions are made. Hence this second filter can be placed anywhere in this transmission chain between the source of noise and the decision circuits. In particular, it may be made part of the i-f strip so that the i-f strip becomes ideally $|H(\omega)|^2$ and the decision filters are ideally matched to the $\{s_k(t)\}$ as in the right hand side of Fig. 4—except for the finite delay demanded by physical realizability. If the revised i-f strip, $|H(\omega)|^2$, introduces appreciable* uncorrected phase distortion, then the filters matched to the $\{s_k(t)\}$ will not integrate all of the available signal energy and this degrades the system performance. In such a case, if one is unwilling or unable to equalize the phase distortion, one will be restricted to signaling in only that portion of the available bandwidth which is phase-distortion free.

*Since the addition of small components 90° out of phase with a signal does not much affect the total amplitude, a good rule of thumb for phase distortion is that the difference between the actual phase shift and a constant delay (linear phase) with frequency remain substantially less than 90° over the useful signal passband. If a cascade of two identical filters is to be used, then the phase distortion in each should remain below 45°.

We return now to our second comment, namely, that the optimum spectral magnitude of $H(\omega)$ depended only on the distribution of the expected noise interference, not on the location of the signal spectrum. It immediately follows that with regard to a signal design we should like to put the signal in a passband of $H(\omega)$ where the noise is low. One might be tempted to go further and think that the most reliable communication would be obtained if the signal energy were to be concentrated in a single narrow region of $H(\omega)$ where the transmission of the signal energy is greatest and the noise least. Such a conclusion is essentially a restatment of the "bandwidth for reliability exchange" fallacy; it is not correct. In all such cases, it is necessary to remember that the ultimate reliability of a channel depends upon whether the actual signaling rate is less than the channel capacity. In general, the higher the channel capacity for a given signaling rate, the easier it is in terms of equipment to realize a negligible error rate.

In the case of a channel disturbed by white gaussian noise, the channel capacity is given by

$$C = W \ln (1 + S/N) \text{ nats/sec.} \tag{18}$$

Let the signal power spectral density be $\mathcal{S}(\omega)$ and the noise power spectral density be $N_0(\omega)$. Consider a channel whose bandwidth $\Delta\omega$ is so narrow that $\mathcal{S}(\omega)$ and $N_0(\omega)$ are substantially constants. The capacity of this channel is given by

$$\Delta C = \frac{\Delta\omega}{2\pi} \ln \left[1 + \frac{\mathcal{S}(\omega)\Delta\omega}{N_0(\omega)\Delta\omega}\right]. \tag{19}$$

Channel capacity is defined in such a way that the capacities of independent channels add when they are used together. Hence, to get the capacity of the colored-gaussian-noise channel with a given noise power spectrum and signal power spectrum, we can integrate (19) over the total bandwidth, W, into which we can put the signal energy.*

$$C_{\mathcal{S}} = \int_W \frac{d\omega}{2\pi} \ln \left[1 + \frac{\mathcal{S}(\omega)}{N_0(\omega)}\right] \tag{20}$$

Now, "the" channel capacity C is defined as the largest value of $C_{\mathcal{S}}$ that can be obtained from (20) by varying the form of $\mathcal{S}(\omega)$, subject always to the constraint that the total signal power is S. In order to be able to obtain vanishing error rates with the least complication in coding equipment we also desire to pick a signal spectrum $\mathcal{S}(\omega)$ so as to produce the largest value of $C_{\mathcal{S}}$. In this connection *it is generally true that the largest values of utilized channel capacity,* $C_{\mathcal{S}}$, *are obtained not when the signal bandwidth is chosen to be narrow, but rather when the signal is chosen to spread out over the entire available*† *transmission bandwidth.*

To obtain the largest value of $C_{\mathcal{S}}$ for a colored noise distribution

*The discussion here and in the remainder of this section follows closely that given by Shannon, Ref. 2, p. 13.

†Within the restrictions imposed by $H(\omega)$ (*i.e.*, $N_0(\omega)$) (see Eq. 22 and ff.)

subject to a given total power S, we can apply the calculus of variations to (20) to obtain

$$\delta C = \int_W \frac{d\omega}{2\pi}\left\{\delta \ln\left[1 + \frac{\mathcal{S}(\omega)}{N_0(\omega)}\right] - \frac{\delta\mathcal{S}(\omega)}{\lambda}\right\}$$

$$= \int_W \frac{d\omega}{2\pi}\left\{\frac{\delta\mathcal{S}(\omega)}{N_0(\omega) + \mathcal{S}(\omega)} - \frac{\delta\mathcal{S}(\omega)}{\lambda}\right\}$$

$$= 0 \ . \tag{21}$$

To satisfy this equation for all variations, $\delta\mathcal{S}(\omega)$, we must have

$$N_0(\omega) + \mathcal{S}(\omega) = \text{const} = \lambda \tag{22}$$

except for regions of W in which $\mathcal{S}(\omega)$ may vanish identically. The constant λ is so chosen as to make the total amount of signal power in the bandwidth W equal to S. If there are no regions in W in which $\mathcal{S}(\omega)$ vanishes identically, then

$$\lambda = (S + N)/W \tag{23}$$

where N is the total noise power in the bandwidth W. Under these circumstances, the expression for the maximum value of $C_{\mathcal{S}}$ is

$$\mathcal{C} = \int_W \frac{d\omega}{2\pi} \ln\left[\frac{S + N}{W N_0(\omega)}\right] \tag{24}$$

and the optimum power spectral density for the set of transmitted signals is

$$\mathcal{S}(\omega) = \frac{S + N}{W} - N_0(\omega) \ . \tag{25}$$

The manner in which sets of signals $\{s_k(t)\}$ which exhibit this power spectral density are to be designed is a degree of freedom that remains to be settled by the requirements and preferences of the signal design engineer.

There is an important practical consequence of the fact that $\mathcal{S}(\omega)$ in Eq. (25) is the difference of two spectra, one of which is a constant. If the noise is concentrated in a narrow bandwidth, it is possible for the $\mathcal{S}(\omega)$ required by Eq. (25) to be negative, whereas actually $\mathcal{S}(\omega)$ must always be non-negative. For such regions, we must take $\mathcal{S}(\omega) = 0$ as the smallest realizable value, and recompute the optimum $\mathcal{S}(\omega)$ outside such a region. The result of these calculations is that the total passband W is broken up by stop bands. In each separate passband the optimum $\mathcal{S}(\omega)$ obeys a difference relationship such as Eq. (25), but there is a question of distributing the energy between passbands and properly picking the edges of the passbands. The details of this ultimate optimization, subject to the boundary conditions implied by a given practical problem, are beyond the scope of the present discussion. It suffices to point out here that the relationship (25) leads to

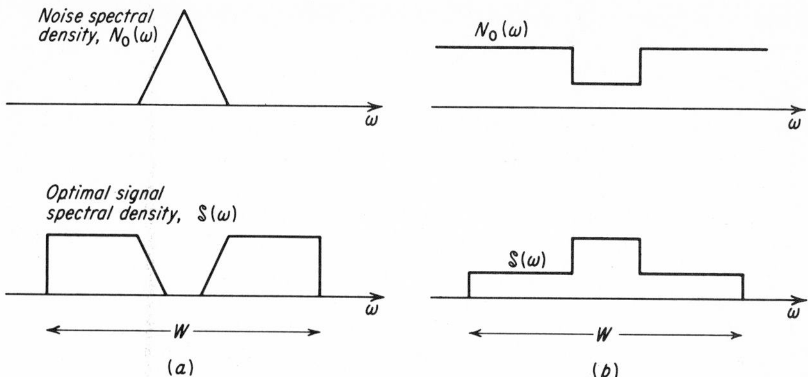

Fig. 5. Examples of optimum signal power spectral densities corresponding to: (a) narrow-band triangular noise power spectral density; and (b) uniform noise power spectral density with a narrow-band slot.

the result that the transmitted signal power should be kept out of regions in which there is relatively strong interference; if the narrow-band interference is strong enough, no signal energy at all should lie within that band.

Two possible results of the preceding discussion are illustrated in Figs. 5a and 5b. In both cases it is assumed that the bandwidth available for signaling is a region W of the frequency spectrum. In the case assumed in Fig. 5a, there lies within W a narrow-band source of interference of sufficient magnitude to split the optimum signal spectrum $\mathcal{S}(\omega)$ into two separate bands. In the case assumed in Fig. 5b, there is a "window" in the interference spectrum having sufficient depth so that consequently most (but not all) of the optimum distribution of signal energy lies within the window passband.

V. NON-GAUSSIAN NOISE

In all of the preceding discussion, we have assumed a gaussian noise distribution. It is relevant at this point to ask to what extent this distribution is typical of those that actually disturb communication systems; it is even more relevant to ask to what extent the conclusions reached above may be successfully applied to the design and operation of physical communication links when the perturbing noise is not in fact gaussian. A full discussion of these questions is beyond the scope of this chapter, but we can say that some characteristics of the gaussian noise distribution are shared by certain other "almost-gaussian" distributions. It is a matter of experience that such noise may be successfully treated as if it were gaussian. On the other hand, other noise distributions (including much unintentional man-made noise) tend to be "impulse noise" distributions; in such cases conclusions reached on the basis of experience with, or analysis of, gaussian noise may be misleading or mistaken.

The essential characteristics of a gaussian noise process are that it exhibits no particular preferred waveform and that it tends to deliver energy at a uniform rate. It is generally true that a noise process tends to deliver energy at a constant rate if large excursions from the mean are exceedingly unlikely. Experience suggests that it is this second feature that also characterizes "almost-gaussian" processes.

The classical gaussian noise sources are emission-limited shot noise,* such as occurs in the emission current of vacuum photocells, and thermal agitation noise such as is developed by all lossy impedances. In general, barring interference from coherent signals, it is reasonable to assume that the random noise disturbing a radio system is gaussian only if it is operating above about 150 mc. Below this frequency, the major sources of circuit noise are terrestrial in

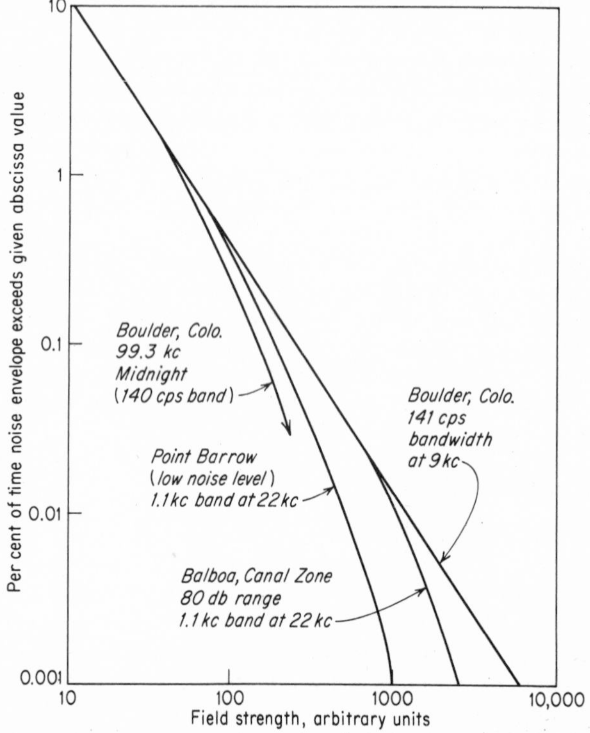

Fig. 6. Amplitude distribution of low-frequency radio noise envelopes. (After Watt and Maxwell, ref. 3.)

*The so-called "1/f" shot noise of semiconductor diodes is also gaussian so long as avalanche breakdown is not involved. See J. Hilibrand, "Characterization of Probability Distributions for Excess Physical Noises," Sc.D. Thesis, Dept. of Electrical Engineering, Mass. Inst. Tech. (August 1956). Also published as Technical Report No. 276, Research Laboratory of Electronics, M.I.T., Cambridge, Mass.

origin and may include such violently non-gaussian components as ignition noise and atmospherics (lightning). However, almost any interference for which excursions far beyond the rms value are (except for slow fading) extremely unlikely can be considered "gaussian." A sine wave is a good example; in most calculations a narrow-band gaussian process can be replaced by an appropriate sinusoid, and vice versa, with little (if any) error. Speech and most standard automatic data-transmission systems produce output signals that are "almost-gaussian." Indeed, the Central Limit Theorem (Chapter 2, section 2.5) states that if several independent processes of this type are superimposed, the sum tends rapidly to a gaussian process as the number of components (of roughly equal power) is increased.

On the other hand, the noise processes encountered at the lower frequencies may be so violently non-gaussian as to effectively preclude the application of the Central Limit Theorem. In Fig. 6 we replot data obtained by Watt and Maxwell[3] for some common atmospheric noise distributions in the frequency range 9-100 kc.

On the logarithmic horizontal scale, a change in level merely moves a curve parallel to itself. We have taken advantage of this fact to normalize the curves so that they coincide in the high probability

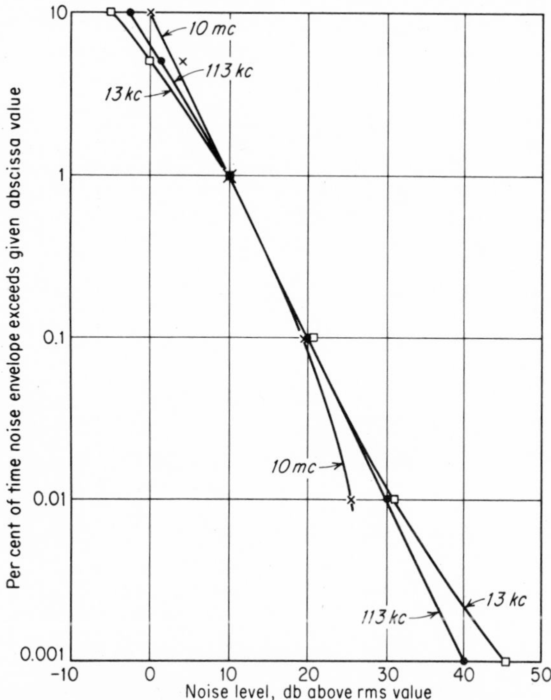

Fig. 7. Atmospheric noise distributions (13 kc-10 mc). (Data from Crichlow, Roubique, Spaulding, and Beery, ref. 4.)

region. These distributions tend to obey the law that the probability of exceeding a value x varies as $x^{-3/2}$ except when the probability is very low. Later data[4] (reproduced in Fig. 7) show that atmospheric noise at higher frequencies is also non-gaussian.

Generally, the details of such a distribution will depend on the time for which the noise is integrated before the variations in its envelope are measured. The distribution (according to the Central Limit Theorem) becomes approximately gaussian* when the integration time is sufficiently large so that energy is delivered smoothly rather than impulsively at the integration output. With these distributions, however, the required integration time may be very large indeed, as is illustrated by Fig. 8 (also taken from Ref. 4). Here the noise distribution is measured as a function of bandwidth. The vertical scale in Fig. 8 is a log-log scale, so that a gaussian (or a Rayleigh) distribution is nearly a straight line with a slope of −2. In these plots, decreasing the bandwidth through which the noise is observed corresponds to increasing the length of time for which it is integrated. Note that the bandwidth of the 22 kc atmospheric noise measured here has to be decreased from about 1 kc to less than 1 cps before the low probability region of the curve begins to pull in towards a −2 slope.

Not very many measurements have been carried out on the distribution of noise to be found in radio and wire circuits. It seems to

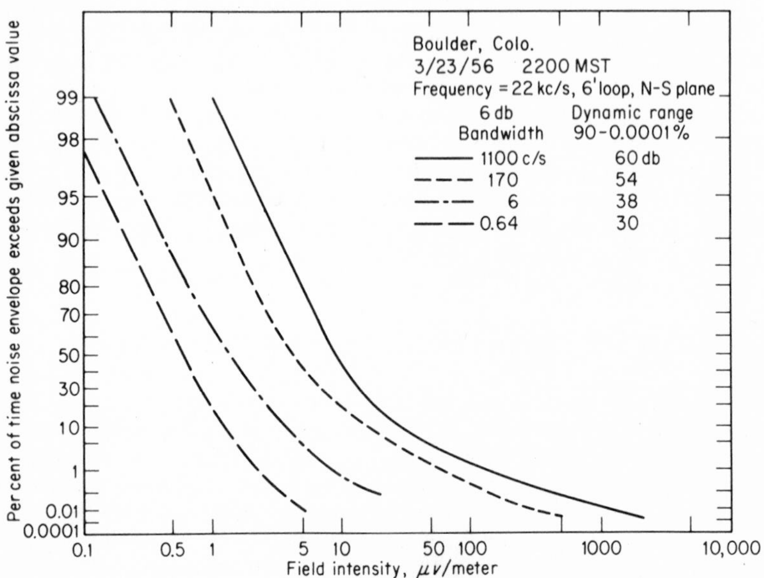

Fig. 8. Amplitude distributions of atmospheric noise envelopes as functions of receiver bandwidth.

*We are considering here that a Rayleigh distribution of an envelope belongs to the class of "gaussian" distributions.

be generally true, however, that where such noise can be originally ascribed to such impulsive sources as lightning, ignition, contact noise, gas discharges, and switching, the probability that the signal exceeds a value x approaches a function of the form x^{-k} where the exponent k lies between about one and three. Another possible law, favored by the investigators at the National Bureau of Standards,[3,4] is that the probability of exceeding a value x varies for large x as e^{-x^n}, where n is a number less than one. A plot of log-log of probability versus log x produces a straight-line curve for the exponential law, whereas a plot of log of probability versus log x gives a straight line if the hyperbolic law (x^{-k}) is true. The experimental data seems to fit either assumption. Data for much lower envelope probabilities would be necessary to determine which kind of law (if either) is closest to nature. In Figs. 9a and 9b we have plotted the distribution of noise* in a one-half-hour sample on a particularly noisy telephone circuit, in which the cumulative noise distribution varies either as $1/x^{2.7}$ or as $e^{-\sqrt{x}}$ over several decades in probability.

An even greater dearth of information exists with respect to situations in which impulse noise tends to occur in "bursts" of many distinct pulses. Some analysis has been carried out on the impulse noise that gives rise to errors in the transmission of data over telephone-cable circuits. At the time of this writing, there is evidence from a limited amount of data that the distribution of arrival times of such noise pulses does not fit the classical Poisson distribution.†

Clearly, much more data needs to be taken on the detailed characteristics of impulsive-noise distributions. Then only can one construct the realistic kind of mathematical model of impulse noise that is required for a rigorous analytic treatment of the problems of signaling in the presence of such noise. In the absence of such data and such a treatment, it is still possible to set forth some general procedures for combating impulse noise, procedures that differ in some major features from those appropriate to combating gaussian noise. This is the aim of the next section.

VI. SIGNALING IN THE PRESENCE OF IMPULSE NOISE

In spite of the lack of precise knowledge about the details of impulsive-noise distributions, this type of noise does exhibit known characteristics that can be exploited in signal design and detection:

First, the mechanism by which such noise is produced can usually be traced back through a simple physical system to a source which (for all practical purposes) produces true mathematical impulses. Accordingly, the observed noise waveform resembles the impulse

*Data for this curve were obtained by D. H. Hamilton, Jr., of Lincoln Laboratory, from a tape recorded by Dr. Emil Hopner of IBM Research Laboratories, Palo Alto, California.

†Private communications from R. Enticknap and P. Mertz. The data of Watt and Maxwell (ref. 3, Jan. 1957) also fail to fit the Poisson distribution.

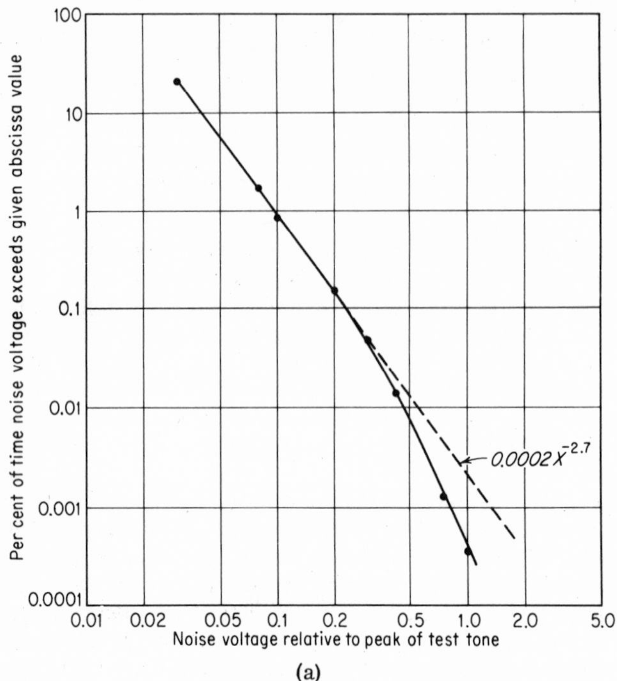

(a)

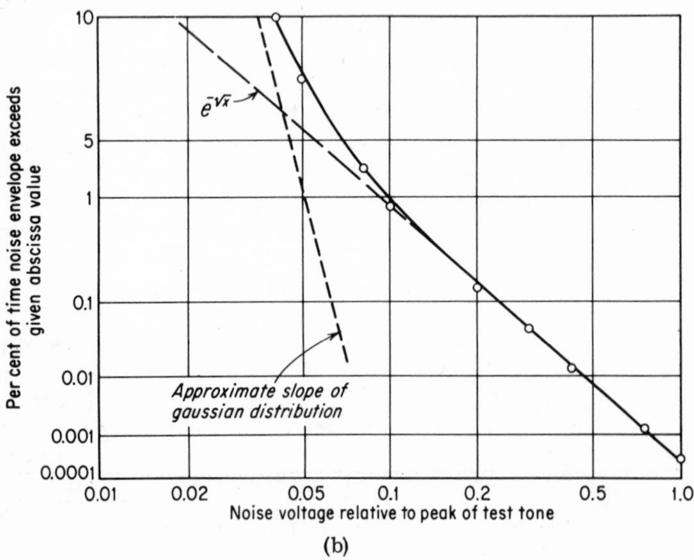

(b)

Fig. 9. Telephone-line noise distribution,
(a) Logarithmic ordinate.
(b) Log log ordinate.

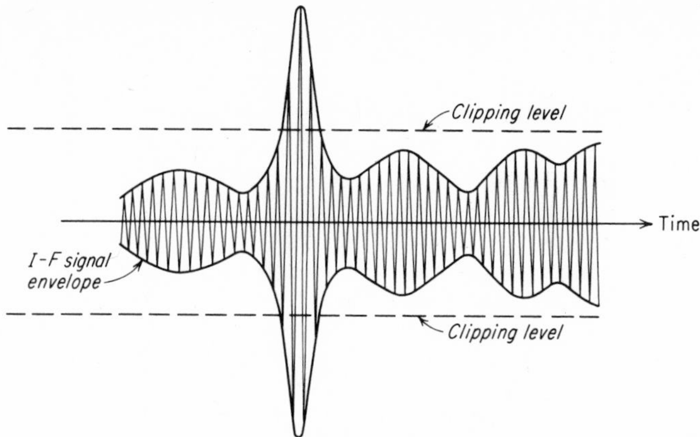

Fig. 10. I-F impulse-noise clipper.

response of a simple physical system, viz. that between the pulse source and the observer.

Second, the noise source delivers energy in bursts rather than smoothly in time.

With respect to the first characteristic, one strives to protect the transmission by choosing signal waveforms that bear little resemblance to the expected noise waveforms; in this connection it may even prove possible to identify the noise whenever it occurs and substantially eliminate its effect.

With respect to the second characteristic, we shall in this section generally deal with systems in which the average noise power which might be delivered in the output of a matched filter is so low that it would be inconsequential as gaussian noise. One then tries to design signals so that the noise energy appearing at the point where decisions must be made is delivered at the low average rate instead of in bursts. The two types of waveform design just suggested are indeed supplementary, so that under some circumstances a combination of the two can virtually eliminate the effect of impulse noise.

Indeed, one of the oldest noise-suppression circuits for radio receivers makes use of both techniques (although it is conceived in terms of the first). The method is aimed at noise—such as that due to ignition and nearby lightning strokes—which resembles ideal impulses having a much broader bandwidth than that of the signal itself. The basic idea of the scheme is illustrated in Fig. 10. Here, an amplifier that has much more bandwidth than that needed for the signal alone is used to obtain enough signal-plus-noise level to saturate non-linear circuits. A clip-level is established just above the maximum expected value of the signal envelope, so that the peaks of the noise spikes are removed. The duration of the noise spike is short compared to the rate at which the signal envelope changes; hence, most of the remaining disturbance to the signal is made up of frequency components lying outside the band of the signal and may be removed by subsequent narrow-band filtering. Variants on the method perform the clipping operation on the detected signal and/or use nonlinear feedback from the clipper to further minimize the effect of the noise.

From the point of view of the present discussion, the function of the clipper is twofold: To recognize the presence of the noise in the first place and to counteract its effect in signal reception. The recognition is possible because we have tacitly assumed a signal process that delivers energy at a substantially uniform rate; thus, when clipping occurs one can say with some certainty* that impulsive noise is responsible. The narrow-banding operation is in a sense a way of smoothing out the rate of delivery of the remaining noise energy (although it is not as effective in this particular regard as some of the schemes to be discussed later on).

The clipping circuit is scarcely the only way of recognizing the presence of impulse noise. Clearly, if the noise is limited to one of a small set of possible waveforms, it will be generally possible to recognize it whenever it occurs, so long as one chooses a set of signal waveforms that differ substantially from these. Presumably, such detailed recognition is tantamount to eliminating the effect of the noise. For instance, in the example cited above, an obvious refinement is to separate the noise spike from the signal by a band-elimination filter which gets rid of most of the signal. The clip level can then be set so low that any noise spike of significance will be "recognized" instead of just the ones that are about equal to, or greater than, the average signal envelope. Tne original impulse can then be regenerated and subtracted from the signal-plus-noise to give signal only.

Such direct elimination of the effects of impulse noise is usually not practicable. Sufficient interference-free surplus bandwidth to permit absolute separation of signal and noise is generally not available. Moreover, the set of possible "impulsive" waveforms is generally too large to permit the kind of waveform identification necessary to guarantee the success of the subtractive elimination process. (In this connection it is worth noting that the propagation medium may introduce substantial waveform distortion, as is the case with atmos-

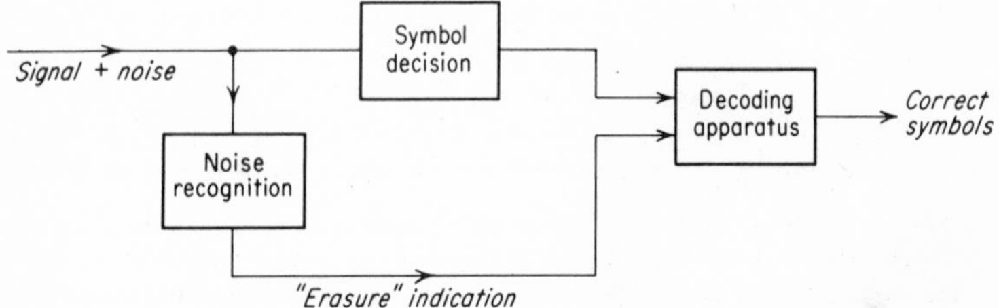

Fig. 11. Use of noise recognition in error correction.

*The degree of certainty depends, of course, on the actual signal distribution.

pherics propagating through (or in) the ionosphere and as is the case with respect to the delay distortion introducted by repeater amplifiers in a multilink communication system.)

Even when the *identification* of impulsive noise is not good enough to permit its elimination from the point of view of signal design, the fact of *recognition* may be useful if error-correcting coding is used. With reference to Fig. 11, suppose that in the signal-plus-noise distribution we can always recognize the occurrence of a noise burst that is sufficiently large to cause an error in the symbol-decision process. Although such a recognition does not label errors when they occur, it does single out the restricted set of symbol decisions whose veracity is subject to doubt. Now there are two basic problems in constructing an error-correcting coding scheme: *Discovering* which symbols are in error and *correcting* the errors. Of the two, the problem of labeling the mistakes is by far the more difficult and produces most of the complexity in implementation. Generally, the coding problem is greatly simplified if those symbols which are likely to be in error are labeled as worthless decisions. Such labeling is called "erasure" and a channel in which such labeling accounts for all the errors is called an "erasure channel." The decoding equipment required to achieve nearly error-free performance in the erasure channel is at least an order of magnitude less complicated* than that required when the errors must be located by means of intersymbol constraints.

From an engineering point of view, it is sensible to label as worthless a relatively large number of correct decisions if it can thereby be guaranteed that one will also erase all the errors. (We assume here that the function of the error-correcting code is to convert a moderate error rate of one in 10^3 to 10^5 to a very low one, so that erasing 10 valid symbols to every genuine error has only slight effect on the channel capacity.) The question, whether the noise bursts in a given communication channel can be recognized with sufficient certainty to guarantee catching all the errors, is one that must be answered by as yet unavailable statistical information about the channel noise. Indeed, one of the strong motivations for obtaining more extensive data on the statistics of impulsive noise distributions is to determine whether channels so disturbed can be treated as erasure channels for the purpose of error-correction coding.

Even when it is not possible to recognize impulse noise with sufficient certainty to remove its effect, it may still be possible to take advantage of the statistics of the noise in designing "noise-proof" signals. Consider Fig. 12 in which we plot the probability that the noise in a given bandwidth exceeds a given level x. Except in the case

*At the present state of knowledge, the minimum computation required per decoded symbol when the errors are initially unidentified increases as some power of the number of symbols between which constraints are operative ("code length"). In the case of an erasure channel the amount of computation required (on the average) per decoded symbol is bounded rather than increasing indefinitely with "code length." See M. Epstein, "Algebraic Decoding for a Binary Erasure Channel," 1958, *IRE Convention Record*, Part IV, pp. 56-69.

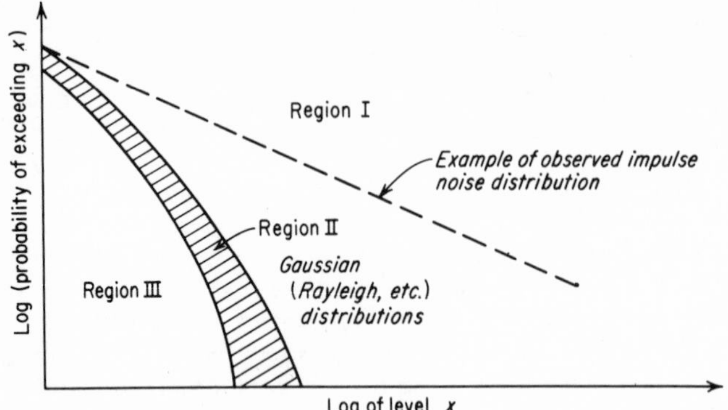

Fig. 12. Noise probability distributions.

of gaussian noise, it is not possible to relate such a diagram directly to the ultimate probability of making errors. The Central Limit Theorem basically asserts that, given sufficient integration time, it is always possible to convert a process that naturally lies in Region I of the diagram to a gaussian process, Region II, at the point at which decisions are made. We shall now examine in some detail the methods by which such an integration can be performed.

Let us assume a noise distribution that is, in point of fact, due to the transient response of the transmission path to substantially instantaneous changes in the state of the path or neighboring devices (switching transients, ignition and contact noise, etc.). It may to the first approximation be represented as a succession of more or less widely spaced simple transients whose approximate duration T_P is the reciprocal of the system bandwidth.* Let us now assume the avail-

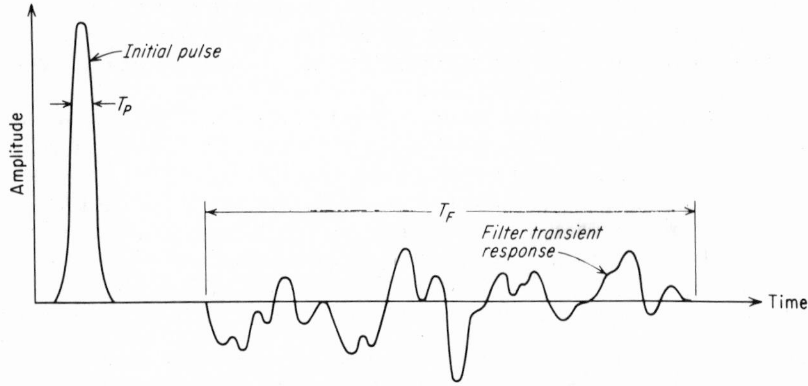

Fig. 13. A complicated impulse response.

*We presume here that the FCC or the channel itself places a restriction on the available system bandwidth.

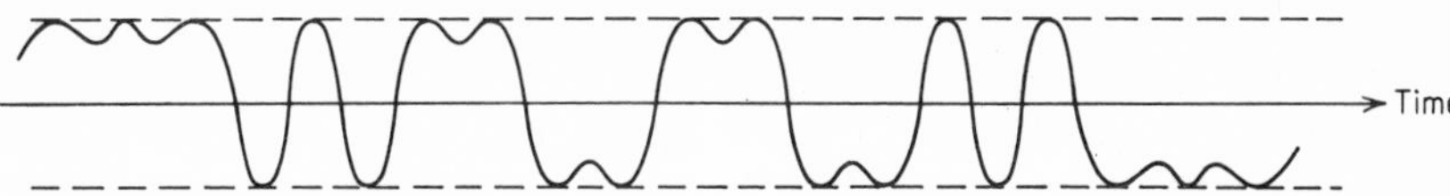

Fig. 14. Portion of pseudo-random waveform having constant-amplitude envelope.

ability of a linear filter whose impulse response has a very large duration-bandwidth product, for example, an output that resembles a long sample of gaussian noise. Let us further suppose that this filter has the same effective bandwidth as the channel, but that its transient response (being not simple but very complicated) lasts for a much longer time T_F. (See Fig. 13.) It is evident that as the noise pulse passes through this filter, the energy that was delivered in time T_p is now smeared out over the longer time T_F. Correspondingly, the amplitude of this noise is decreased by a factor of

$$\text{(Amplitude out/Amplitude in)} = \sqrt{T_P/T_F}\,, \quad T_F \gg T_P \tag{26}$$

if it is assumed that the filter gain is such that the output power is equal to the input power. Evidently, this smoothing out of the noise may be continued to the point at which the length of the smearing, T_F, becomes comparable with the average time interval between pulses, at which point the smoothing can go little further.

What has happened to the distribution function of the noise in this process? The special case in which the time between pulses is independent of pulse amplitude is especially enlightening in this regard. Although a sample of gaussian noise was given as an example of a suitable smearing waveform, other waveforms are available which smoothly occupy a bandwidth W and last for a very long time T_F, and which have constant-amplitude envelopes. A portion of such a waveform is shown in Fig. 14. Evidently, when the duration of the smearing is about equal to the time between pulses, the amplitude of the noise has been reduced by approximately the square root of the ratio of the pulse duration to the average interval between pulses. At this point the energy flow is somewhat as illustrated in Fig. 15. It is smooth in blocks of length T_F. Occasionally there are gaps between blocks as at "A" or interference regions where blocks overlap, as at "B".

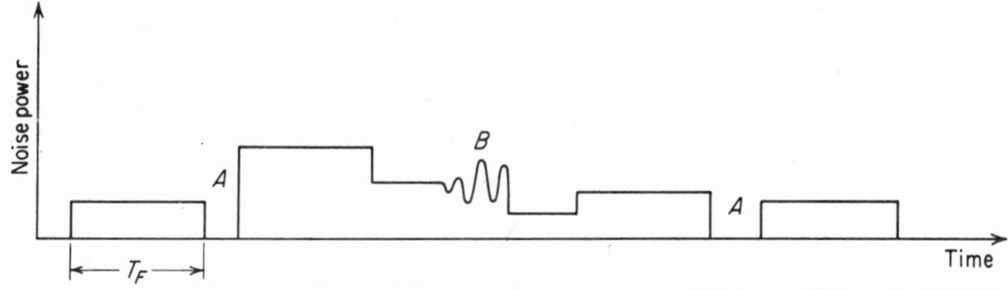

Fig. 15. Effect of smearing on the delivery of impulse noise energy.

The heights of the blocks vary in proportion to the energies of the noise pulses that initiate them. As the length of the smearing out is increased to extend over time intervals long compared with the time between pulses,

(a) the local average rate of noise energy flow approaches the long-time average power; and

(b) the regions of overlap, B, extend to cover the entire time axis.

Now the regions B are the places where the smearing functions due to two or more pulses add up. The maximum amplitude in such a region cannot exceed the sum of the amplitudes of the constituent blocks. If the individual pulses are independent and if the smearing function is well chosen, it is evident that this maximum amplitude will be reached relatively often when only a few blocks are interfering, and relatively rarely when the effects of many pulses of approximately the same energy overlap. When the duration of the smearing, T_F, is very long compared with the interval between the largest pulses, many independent constituents of approximately equal size will add up in producing the observed waveform. The Central Limit Theorem may then be invoked to conclude that the limiting form of the filtered noise distribution is gaussian, as T_F becomes indefinitely large.

We thus have two limiting conditions for the distribution of the filtered noise. The first, ($T_F = 0$), is the original distribution of the impulse noise; the second (T_F indefinitely large) is the distribution of gaussian noise. Between these two extremes, the probability that the noise amplitude exceeds a given level may vary with smearing time in the manner illustrated in Fig. 16. The peak amplitude of any given noise impulse always drops as the T_F is increased, but the probability (averaged over all pulses and all time) that the noise exceeds any given value may actually *increase* because the duration of any pulse increases with T_F faster than its amplitude drops.* With

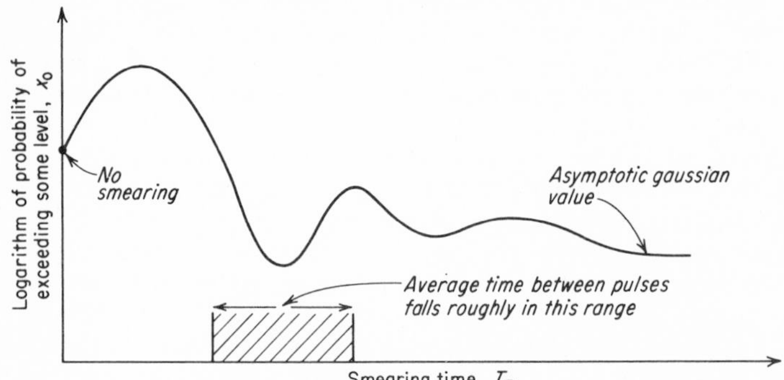

Fig. 16. Possible variation of the value of noise probability with smearing time.

*Indeed, it can be shown that if the initial probability distribution function $P(x)$ is proportional to x^{-k} for large x, then the modified probability distribution function $P_s(x_0)$, where x_0 is some specified level, initially rises or falls with T_F accordingly as k is less than or greater than two.

sufficient T_F, however, the effects due to peak impulses are lowered below the level x and the probability of exceeding x begins to drop with T_F. When T_F becomes comparable with the time between pulses, the probability may pass through one or more minima and maxima with increasing T_F before reaching its ultimate gaussian value. Such maxima are due to the effects of overlapping only a few energy-flow blocks, as described in the preceding paragraph. Although Fig. 16 is not taken from actual experimental data,* it does illustrate effects that can reasonably be expected to occur† in the integration of impulse noise distributions.

The existence and location of the initial maximum and/or the subsequent maxima may vary with x as well as with the distribution, but it is evident that the very possibility of their existence raises design questions if the smearing technique is to be really useful. The remedy for the first maximum (or failure of the probability to drop very rapidly with T_F) is the clipper already discussed in connection with Fig. 10. If such a clipper precedes the smearing filter, the peak noise level is at most equal to the signal level, so that subsequent smearing can only lower the probability that it exceeds the signal level. The secondary maxima can be avoided if one avoids T_F of the same order of magnitude as the average time between pulses. In particular, if the pulses tend to occur in pairs as in the case of lightning (recurrence time = 10 msec.) or telephone dialing (recurrence time = 0.1 sec) the use of a T_F substantially different from the time of separation is indicated.

Thus far we have been speaking only of the distribution of the noise itself and have said nothing about the signal. Once it has been decided to smear the noise out over a given time, one must do this in such a way that the signal itself is not badly degraded. The effect of smearing out is essentially an integration in time; it does not depend in its over-all behavior on the bandwidth of the smearing filter. The condition that the filter output have bandwidth W was inserted in the previous discussion for the sake of simplicity. One could perfectly well use for the smearing filter a "simple" filter (*e.g.* a single tuned circuit) whose bandwidth varies inversely as T_F. It is then necessary to distribute the input data among $2T_F W$ channels, each containing such a narrow-band filter, in order to maintain the maximum signaling rate implied by a total bandwidth of W.

It is not necessary, however, to resort to multiple channels to achieve the desired protection against impulse noise. It is only necessary to select waveforms to represent the transmitted symbols that will bear as little resemblance to impulses as possible. In particular, we choose as signals wideband pseudorandom waveforms, such as

*Some preliminary measurements on the noise data of the kind described in Fig. 9 tend to confirm the tendencies described in Fig. 16.

†A simple example (chosen primarily because the calculations are easy) of a distribution in which the effects of Fig. 16 are in fact pronounced is the following: A noise which consists of pulses of equal amplitude spaced at equal intervals of time, the only random feature being that the successive pulse amplitudes are independently plus or minus with equal probability.

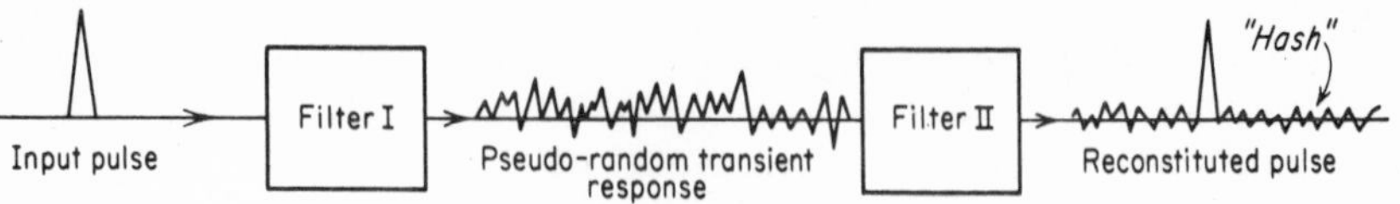

Fig. 17. Smearing-desmearing filter system.

that of Fig. 14, that last for the time T_F. At the receiver, the process for guessing which symbols were transmitted then also involves an integration over time T_F and thus automatically performs the smearing-out process on the noise!

A detailed discussion of the techniques for selecting the waveforms is beyond the scope of the present treatment; indeed the art of designing such waveforms is still incompletely understood. As for designing suitable smearing filter characteristics, three basic techniques have been suggested. They are:

(a) The matched filter designed around all-pass (or band-pass) sections in the frequency domain.

(b) The matched filter designed on the basis of a tapped delay line in the time domain.

(c) The use of mismatched filters with pseudo-random responses.

The basic problem to be faced in all of these procedures is illustrated in Fig. 17. Here an ideal impulse passing through Filter I produces an on-line signal of duration T_F. Filter II must collect this smeared-out signal into a short pulse. In order to do so, its transient response must also last for at least the length of time T_F; consequently, the output pulse is in general also accompanied by an undesired "side-lobe" or "hash level" response that lasts for a length of time at least equal to $2T_F$. If filters I and II are "matched" filters (optimum for gaussian noise) and if, in addition, the smeared waveform is pseudorandom,* then in general there is on the average as much total energy in the "hash" as there is in the desired pulse. Another way of saying the same thing is that if the signal delivered by Filter I has a duration-bandwidth product of TW, the rms level of the hash in the output of a matched Filter II is in general down by only $\sqrt{2TW}$ from the amplitude of the main output pulse. Now, if we are dealing with a collection of isolated signal pulses, the presence of the hash is of no consequence. But if the signal impulses occur at a rate comparable with the bandwidth of the output pulse, then the hash due to successive pulses adds up to produce a "self-jamming" noise equal in power to that of the desired output signal. To avoid this disastrous level of self-jamming noise, a way must be found to reduce the hash level in the output of the desmearing filter to 20 db or more below the value obtained with random smearing waveforms and matched filters.

The first of the matched filter techniques mentioned above makes use of a filter in which the smearing action is due only to phase dis-

*In the sense that the (large number of) parameters required to specify it are chosen from some random distribution.

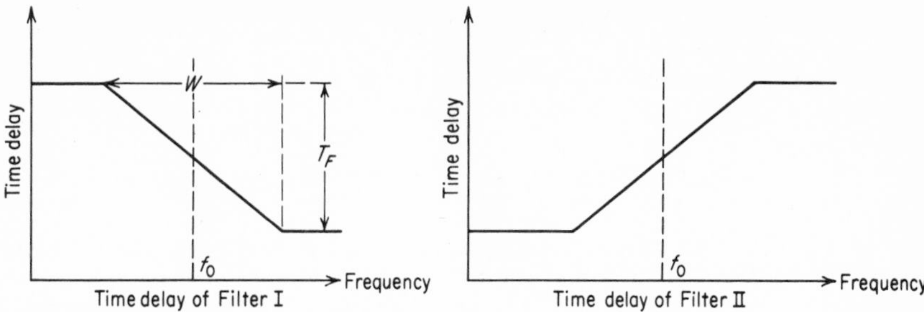

Fig. 18. Linear "FM" matched filters.

tortion in the filter. Both filters I and II are designed to have a flat amplitude response in the signal passband (for example, through the use of "all-pass" sections). The time delay* characteristics of the two filters are made to be complementary, so as to add to a constant time delay. A simple illustration of such a design is the linearly varying time delay shown in Fig. 18.

Key, Fowle, and Haggarty have generalized the design of such delay curves to permit simultaneous control of the passband spectrum shape and the envelope of the transient response when $TW \gg 1$.† In particular, they find that if the magnitude of the spectral response of each filter is that of a single-tuned circuit, namely,

$$|F(\omega)| = \frac{\alpha}{\sqrt{\alpha^2 + (\omega - \omega_0)^2}}, \qquad \begin{aligned} \omega_0 &= \text{band center frequency}, \\ 2\alpha &= 2\pi W = \text{bandwidth} \end{aligned}$$

then a rectangular envelope will result for the on-line signal if

$$\text{Time delay} \propto \tan^{-1}\left(\frac{\omega - \omega_0}{\alpha}\right).$$

A somewhat different approach has been reported by Sussman.[5] A number of all-pass sections are designed, each of which has a delay of T over a narrow part of the total bandwidth. (See Fig. 19.)

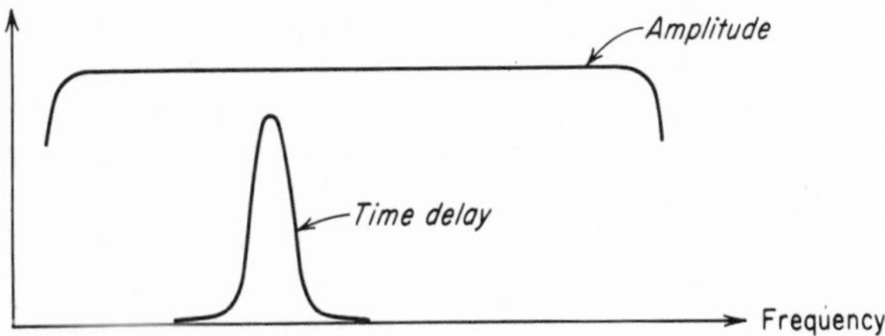

Fig. 19. All-pass response.

*Time delay is defined as the derivative of network phase shift with respect to (radian) frequency.

†The results of Key, Fowle, and Haggarty are not yet generally available (see L. Smullin (ed.), *High-Power Radar*, McGraw-Hill Book Company, Inc., to be published. The result given here is mentioned with permission of the authors.

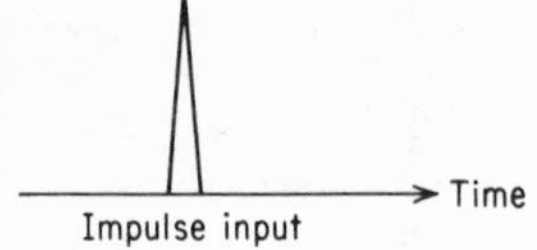

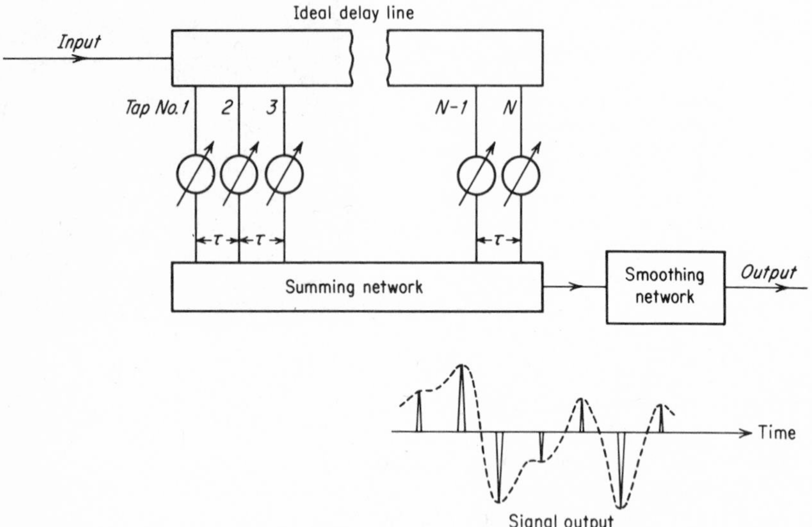

Fig. 20. Delay-line model of signal generation.

A number of such sections each having a delay T in adjoining narrow bandwidths of the order of magnitude $1/T$ are cascaded to produce a composite response having a time delay T over a bandwidth W, $TW \gg 1$. Half of the component sections are assigned "at random" to filter I, the remainder to filter II. Thus filter I exhibits violent delay distortion which smears out an input pulse into a signal of duration T, while filter II corrects this delay distortion, recreating the narrow pulse.

A tapped delay line is convenient for the generation of transient responses directly in the time domain.* (See Fig. 20.) At the outputs of such a delay line, the input pulse is (ideally) available delayed by equal increments in time. These outputs are then weighted and summed so as to produce a sampled-data approximation to a given waveform such as that shown by the dotted envelope in Fig. 20. Generally, the delay line system will have only limited bandwidth so that with sufficiently close spacing of the taps, the filter output will tend to be smoothly varying (as in the dotted curve) instead of spikey. If the filter I characteristic is obtained by a given array of amplitude adjustments on the delay-line taps, a matched filter II characteristic

*For a detailed discussion of the design of such a system, see ref. 6.

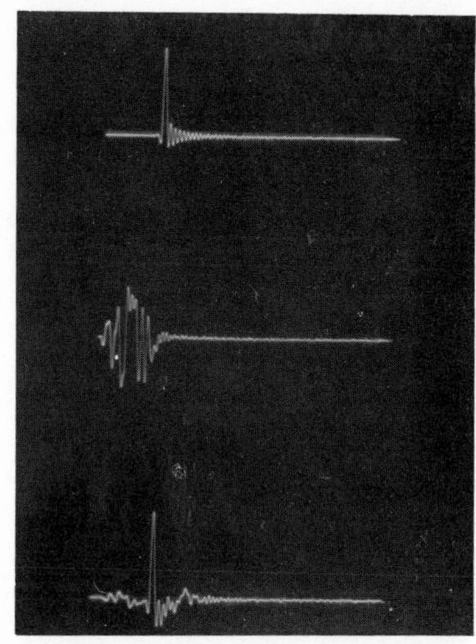

Fig. 21. Smearing-filter system response:
Top trace: Exciting pulse
Middle trace: Filter I output
Bottom trace: Filter II output
Ideally, bottom waveform should be symmetric but trailing ringing in the original pulse (top trace) together with transient response of amplifier combine to bring about the noticeable trailing overshoots.

may be obtained by setting up the same amplitudes on the delay line but in the reverse order as for filter I. By properly choosing the tap weights, the matched filter cascades I and II can be designed to have a hash level of the order of magnitude $1/N$ of the main spike instead of $1/\sqrt{N}$, where N is the number of independent sample points (taps) in each filter. Figure 21 shows in the middle trace of an oscillograph the output of such an experimental delay-line filter I with an effective N of about 15; the bottom trace represents the output of a cascade delay-line filter II.*

The mismatched filter technique is the only one available for reducing the hash level inherent in the matched-filter detection of an arbitrary signal. Here the filter II characteristic is not matched to filter I but rather it is taken to be as close to the frequency-domain *inverse* of the characteristic of filter I as is consistent with the resulting enhancement of the additive noise level. In particular, the *inverse* is attempted only in the passband of the filter I signal. If the characteristic of filter I, $F_1(\omega)$, is written as the product of a magnitude function and a phase function,

$$F_{\mathrm{I}}(\omega) = |F_{\mathrm{I}}(\omega)|\, e^{j\rho(\omega)},$$

then a *matched* filter characteristic $F_{\mathrm{II}}(\omega)$ will differ from $F_{\mathrm{I}}(\omega)$ in that it has the inverse (*i.e.* negative) phase characteristic,

$$F_{\mathrm{II}}(\omega) = |F_{\mathrm{I}}(\omega)|\, e^{-j\rho(\omega)}.$$

*The signal used here is one of a general class that can be obtained by making the kth tap output plus or minus (except for a slowly varying envelope) according as k is a quadratic residue modulo P, a prime number. The hash in the correlation function of such signals is of the order of magnitude $1/P$ in amplitude. Further discussion of this class of signals is presented in ref. 7.

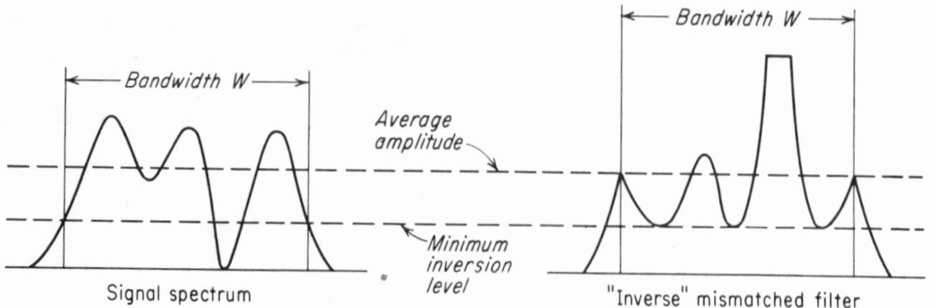

Fig. 22. Mismatched filter amplitude characteristic.

Thus the cascade of the two filters is

$$F_{\mathrm{I}}(\omega)F_{\mathrm{II}}(\omega) = |F_{\mathrm{I}}(\omega)|^2$$

It is the variation in $|F_{\mathrm{I}}(\omega)|^2$ across the passband that produces the "hash" level in the matched filter output. If the cascade of filters I and II has no amplitude variation as well as no phase distortion, then the hash is effectively eliminated. This can be done by taking

$$|F_{\mathrm{II}}(\omega)| = \frac{1}{|F_{\mathrm{I}}(\omega)|} \quad \text{except where } |F_{\mathrm{I}}(\omega)| \text{ is small.}$$

Such a mismatched filter chatacteristic is shown in Fig. 22.

VII. STATUS OF SIGNAL DESIGN TECHNIQUES

We have seen in this chapter that when a communication system is disturbed by additive gaussian noise, a reasonably complete theoretical treatment of the problems of signal design is available. The conclusions and techniques based on this treatment may be extended to other additive noise distributions for which substantial excursions from the average rate of noise energy delivery are extremely unlikely. A number of sophisticated communication systems have been successfully tested which make use of the results of this theory.[5,6]

However, when the noise distribution is impulsive, (as is likely to be the case in communication circuits operating below 150 Mc), then much less is known either about the actual statistics of the noise or about the theory of optimum signal design. Two important features of signaling and detection in the presence of impulse noise seem to be (a) the use of signals that have a long duration compared with that of a given impulsive disturbance and (b) the use of a clipping circuit preceding the signal recognition filters. The combination of these two techniques in the form of a cascade of a smearing filter, transmission channel, a clipping circuit, and a desmearing filter, is a recent development. The practical application of such an arrangement to high-reliability digital transmission systems is being tried at the time of this writing. The initial results are quite encouraging.

As the demand for reliable communication systems increases, it can be reasonably expected that the gaps in our statistical knowledge of non-gaussian noise will be filled and a more satisfactory theoretical understanding will become available for designing signal waveforms least likely to be confused by the presence of such noise.

REFERENCES

1. S. Darlington, U.S. Patent 2,678,997, issued May 18, 1954.
2. C. E. Shannon, "Communication in the Presence of Noise," *Proc. IRE*, vol. 37, pp. 10-21, January, 1949.
3. A. D. Watt and E. L. Maxwell, "Measured Statistical Characteristics of VLF Atmospheric Radio Noise," *Proc. IRE*, vol. 45, pp. 55-62, January, 1957.
   Also, "Characteristics of Atmospheric Noise from 1 to 100 KC," *Proc. IRE*, vol. 45, pp. 787-794, June, 1957.
4. W. Q. Crichlow, C. J. Roubique, A. D. Spaulding, and W. M. Beery, "Determination of the Amplitude-Probability Distribution of Atmospheric Radio Noise from Statistical Moments," *J. Research Nat. Bur. Standards*, vol. 64D, no. 1, pp. 49-56, January-February, 1960.
5. S. M. Sussman, "A Matched Filter Communication System for Multipath Channels," *Trans. IRE, PGIT*, Matched-Filter Issue, pp. 367-373, June, 1960.
6. R. M. Lerner, "A Matched Filter Detection System for Complicated Doppler Shifted Signals," *Trans. IRE, PGIT*, Matched-Filter Issue, pp. 373-385, June, 1960
7. R. M. Lerner, *Use of L Sequences in Signal Design* (to be published)

CHAPTER 12

Sequential Reception of Time-Variant Dispersive Transmissions

John M. Wozencraft

I. INTRODUCTION

The actual design of receivers for digitalized communication systems is not a problem of formalized synthesis. In practice, models amenable to mathematical analysis are not usually representative enough of physical reality, and the additional factors of cost and complexity are always present. As an adjunct to engineering experience, however, formal mathematical synthesis based on idealized models can and does provide valuable insight. Sometimes it points the way to new, different, and interesting engineering approaches; sometimes it leads to a better understanding of approaches already successful in the art.

This chapter is primarily concerned with the mathematical problem of functional receiver design for digitalized communication over linear, randomly time-variant, dispersive propagation media that are perturbed by additive white gaussian noise, and have a single output and input. This problem has been considered in detail by Price,[1,2] Green,[2] Turin,[3,4] Fano,[5] and Kailath.[6,7] It is a good example of mathematical and physical insight jointly spurring the development of a novel and successful system, known as "Rake." In addition, we consider briefly another independent approach to this same problem by Doelz, *et al.*,[8] known as "Kineplex."

The formulation and presentation of the material differs here in detail from that of the original authors, partly in an attempt to generalize and partly in an attempt to unify. But the essence of the present treatment is completely embedded in the philosophical approach of the original workers, and the main argument depends particularly upon the channel models (Chapter 6) and receiver formulation of Kailath.[6,7,9,10]

II. HILBERT TRANSFORMS

In dealing with band-pass signals, it is convenient to make use of complex notation and Hilbert transforms.[11] These transforms are defined by the Cauchy principal value of the following integrals.

$$\hat{x}(t) = \frac{1}{\pi}\int_{-\infty}^{\infty} \frac{x(\tau)\,d\tau}{t-\tau}; \qquad x(t) = -\frac{1}{\pi}\int_{-\infty}^{\infty} \frac{\hat{x}(\tau)}{t-\tau}\,d\tau \tag{1}$$

Given any integrable-square, real time function $x(t)$, and its Fourier transform $X(f)$,* we can easily find the Fourier transform $\hat{X}(f)$ of $\hat{x}(t)$.

$$\hat{X}(f) = \int_{-\infty}^{\infty} \hat{x}(t) e^{-j2\pi ft} \, dt = \frac{1}{\pi} \int_{-\infty}^{\infty} \int_{-\infty}^{\infty} \frac{x(\tau)}{t-\tau} e^{-j2\pi ft} \, d\tau \, dt$$

Let $\nu = t - \tau$, $d\nu = dt$

$$\hat{X}(f) = \int_{-\infty}^{\infty} x(\tau) e^{-j2\pi f\tau} \, d\tau \int_{-\infty}^{\infty} \frac{\cos 2\pi f\nu - j \sin 2\pi f\nu}{\pi \nu} \, d\nu$$

The integration on ν is equal to $-j$ for $f > 0$, and $+j$ for $f < 0$. Accordingly,

$$\hat{X}(f) = \begin{cases} -jX(f) & (\text{for } f > 0) \\ +jX(f) & (\text{for } f < 0) \end{cases} \tag{2}$$

It follows that we may define the "Hilbert transforming" filter

$$\hat{H}_1(f) = \begin{cases} -j & (\text{for } f > 0) \\ +j & (\text{for } f < 0) \end{cases} \tag{3}$$

such that

$$\hat{H}_1(f) X(f) = \hat{X}(f) . \tag{4}$$

It also follows that iterated application of the operator $\hat{H}_1(f)$ yields

$$\hat{H}_1(f) \hat{H}_1(f) X(f) = -X(f)$$

and hence

$$\hat{\hat{x}}(t) = -x(t) . \tag{5}$$

Next let us consider a complex time function†

$$\chi(t) = x(t) + j\hat{x}(t) \tag{6}$$

and inquire about its Fourier transform $\mathrm{X}(f)$.

$$\mathrm{X}(f) = X(f) + j\hat{X}(f)$$

$$\mathrm{X}(f) = \begin{cases} X(f) + X(f) = 2X(f) & (\text{for } f > 0) \\ X(f) - X(f) = 0 & (\text{for } f < 0) \end{cases} \tag{7}$$

Conversely, it is also true that, for any integrable-square complex time function $\chi(t)$ whose Fourier transform is identically equal to

*The Fourier transform of a function will consistently be denoted by the appropriate capital letter.

†Greek letters will be used throughout to denote complex time-functions, and Roman letters to denote real time-functions.

zero for $f < 0$, the imaginary part of $\chi(t)$ is the Hilbert transform of the real part. We write this

$$\text{Im}\,[\chi(t)] = \hat{\text{Re}}\,[\chi(t)] \quad \text{if } X(f) = 0 \text{ for } f < 0. \tag{8}$$

In order to lend physical significance to the Hilbert transform, it is interesting to consider single-sideband modulation. Let us take a real low-pass waveform $g(t)$, whose spectrum $G(f) = 0$ for $|f| > W$, multiply it by the high-frequency $(f_1 > W)$ sinusoid $2 \cos 2\pi f_1 t$ to obtain $y(t)$, and filter out the upper sideband to obtain $x(t)$. Using the symbol $*$ to denote convolution, we have

$$y(t) = 2g(t) \cos 2\pi f_1 t$$

and

$$Y(f) = G(f) * [\delta(f - f_1) + \delta(f + f_1)]$$

where $\delta(f)$ is a unit-impulse function at $f = 0$. Therefore

$$Y(f) = G(f - f_1) + G(f + f_1)$$

$$x(t) = \int_{-f_1 - W}^{-f_1} G(f + f_1)\, e^{j2\pi ft}\, dt + \int_{f_1}^{f_1 + W} G(f - f_1)\, e^{j2\pi ft}\, df \;.$$

Now let $\mu = f + f_1$ in the first integral, and $\nu = f - f_1$ in the second.

$$x(t) = e^{-j2\pi f_1 t} \int_{-W}^{0} G(\mu)\, e^{j2\pi\mu t}\, d\mu + e^{+j2\pi f_1 t} \int_{0}^{W} G(\nu)\, e^{j2\pi\nu t}\, d\nu$$

Finally, let

$$\Gamma(f) = \begin{cases} 2G(f) & \text{for } f > 0 \\ 0 & \text{for } f < 0 \end{cases}$$

Since $g(t)$ is real, $G(f) = G^*(-f)$, and

$$G(f) = \begin{cases} \frac{1}{2}\Gamma(f) & \text{for } f > 0 \\ \frac{1}{2}\Gamma^*(-f) & \text{for } f < 0 \end{cases}$$

where the asterisk as a superscript denotes "complex conjugate." Substituting Γ for G in the integrals, and extending the limits of integration to infinity, we have

$$x(t) = e^{-j2\pi f_1 t} \int_{-\infty}^{\infty} \frac{1}{2}\Gamma^*(-\mu)\, e^{j2\pi\mu t}\, d\mu$$

$$+\, e^{+j2\pi f_1 t} \int_{-\infty}^{\infty} \frac{1}{2}\Gamma(\nu)\, e^{j2\pi\nu t}\, d\nu$$

$$x(t) = \frac{1}{2}\gamma^*(t)\, e^{-j2\pi f_1 t} + \frac{1}{2}\gamma(t)\, e^{+j2\pi f_1 t}$$

where, from Eqs. (6) and (7), $\gamma(t) = g(t) + j\hat{g}(t)$.

Accordingly, letting

$$x(t) = \text{Re } \chi(t), \qquad \chi(t) = \gamma(t)\, e^{j2\pi f_1 t} \tag{9}$$

we have

$$x(t) = g(t) \cos 2\pi f_1 t - \hat{g}(t) \sin 2\pi f_1 t \quad . \tag{10}$$

In order to regain $g(t)$, we need only to multiply $x(t)$ by 2 cos $2\pi f_1 t$, and select the low-pass components with a filter of width W. Similarly, $\hat{g}(t)$ results from multiplying $x(t)$ by 2 sin $2\pi f_1 t$, and low-pass filtering the product. One can obtain $\hat{g}(t)$ from $g(t)$ very simply by SSB modulation and quadrature demodulation. We note that this procedure is entirely consistent with the phase-shift definition of the Hilbert transforming filter $\hat{H}_1(f)$.

Since SSB modulation and Hilbert transformation are reversible operations, we conclude that any real band-limited time function, whether low-pass or band-pass, is completely defined by a corresponding complex time function having an identically-zero spectrum for $f < 0$. Such a time-function is called an *analytic signal.*

III. SAMPLING OF ANALYTIC SIGNALS

By virtue of the constraints imposed by ideal band-pass filters, a band-limited signal of spectrum width W can be completely determined by means of $2W$ appropriately chosen samples per second. In principle, such an ideal filter is not physically realizable, and its impulse response extends from $-\infty$ to $+\infty$ in time. In practice, however, filters as nearly ideal as may be desired can be realized if sufficient time delay (and money) is allowed. The rms error in the sampling representation of the output of such a filter can be reduced arbitrarily toward zero by taking sufficiently more than $2W$ samples per second over a sufficiently long (but finite) period of time.

In calculating probabilities involving time functions, it is convenient to deal with the equivalent sample values rather than the functions themselves. Accordingly, we include here a brief derivation (following Shannon[12] and Woodward[11]) of a sampling theorem for analytic band-limited time functions.

Let $\gamma(t) = g(t) + j\hat{g}(t)$ be a complex low-pass time function, and $\Gamma(f)$ be its Fourier transform, where

$$\Gamma(f) = 0 \text{ for all } f \text{ outside the range } 0 < f < W\,. \tag{11}$$

We introduce the useful Fourier transform pairs*

$$\frac{1}{W} \sum_{i=-\infty}^{\infty} \delta\left(t - \frac{i}{W}\right) \longleftrightarrow \sum_{i=-\infty}^{\infty} \delta(f - iW) \tag{12}$$

*In the interest of brevity, the proofs of statements following directly from Fourier transformation are omitted here and in the sequel.

and

$$\frac{\sin \pi t}{\pi t} \equiv \operatorname{sinc} t \longleftrightarrow \operatorname{rect}(f) \equiv \begin{cases} 1 \text{ (for } |f| < \frac{1}{2}) \\ 0 \text{ (elsewhere)} \end{cases} \tag{13}$$

It follows from the definition of the Fourier transform that

$$We^{+j\pi Wt} \operatorname{sinc} Wt \longleftrightarrow \operatorname{rect}\left(\frac{f}{W} - \frac{1}{2}\right) . \tag{14}$$

On account of Eq. (11), we may write

$$\Gamma(f) = \left[\Gamma(f) * \sum_{i=-\infty}^{\infty} \delta(f - iW)\right] \operatorname{rect}\left(\frac{f}{W} - \frac{1}{2}\right)$$

and

$$\gamma(t) = \left[\gamma(t) \frac{1}{W} \sum_{i=-\infty}^{\infty} \delta\left(t - \frac{i}{W}\right)\right] * We^{j\pi Wt} \operatorname{sinc} Wt .$$

Interchanging the order of summation and integration, we obtain the result

$$\gamma(t) = \sum_{i=-\infty}^{\infty} \gamma_i \operatorname{sinc}(Wt - i)\, e^{j\pi(Wt - i)} \tag{15}$$

where $\gamma_i = \gamma(i/W)$ is a notational convention which we shall follow throughout. The complex low-pass function $\gamma(t)$ is completely determined by complex samples taken every $1/W$ seconds.

If we equate the real and imaginary parts of the functions on each side of Eq. (15), we obtain

$$\operatorname{Re} \gamma(t) = g(t) = \sum_{i=-\infty}^{\infty} \operatorname{sinc}(Wt - i)\,[g_i \cos \pi(Wt - i) - \hat{g}_i \sin \pi(Wt - i)] \tag{16}$$

and

$$\operatorname{Im} \gamma(t) = \hat{g}(t) = \sum_{i=-\infty}^{\infty} \operatorname{sinc}(Wt - i)\,[g_i \cos \pi(Wt - i) + \hat{g}_i \sin \pi(Wt - i)] . \tag{17}$$

If we wish to consider a band-pass time function instead, then according to Eq. (9) we set

$$x(t) = \gamma(t)\, e^{j2\pi f_1 t}$$

and obtain

$$x(t) = \sum_{i=-\infty}^{\infty} \gamma_i \operatorname{sinc}(Wt - i)\, e^{j\pi[(2f_1 + W)t - i]} \tag{18}$$

This result is easily converted to a more standard form by defining the center frequency $f_0 = f_1 + W/2$, and letting $\gamma_i = \chi_i e^{+j2\pi f_1 i/W}$. Then

$$\chi(t) = \sum_{i=-\infty}^{\infty} \chi_i \operatorname{sinc}(Wt - i)\, e^{j2\pi f_0 (t - i/W)} \tag{19}$$

and

$$x(t) = \operatorname{Re} \chi(t); \qquad \hat{x}(t) = \operatorname{Im} \chi(t) \; . \tag{20}$$

In section V of this chapter, we shall have occasion not only to represent time functions as samples, but also to reconvert from sums of samples to time integrals. Consider a complex integral of the form $\int_{-\infty}^{\infty} \zeta(t)\, \chi^*(t)\, dt$, where both $\zeta(t)$ and $\chi(t)$ have non-zero spectra only for $f_0 - W/2 < f < f_0 + W/2$. Invoking the sampling theorem of Eq. (19), we have

$$\begin{aligned} \int_{-\infty}^{\infty} \zeta(t)\, \chi^*(t)\, dt &= \int_{-\infty}^{\infty} \left[\sum_{i=-\infty}^{\infty} \zeta_i \operatorname{sinc}(Wt - i)\, e^{j2\pi f_0 (t - i/W)} \right] \\ &\qquad \cdot \left[\sum_{\ell=-\infty}^{\infty} \chi_\ell^* \operatorname{sinc}(Wt - \ell)\, e^{-j2\pi f_0 (t - \ell/W)} \right] dt \\ &= \sum_{i,\ell=-\infty}^{\infty} \zeta_i \chi_\ell^* e^{j2\pi f_0 \left(\frac{\ell - i}{W}\right)} \\ &\qquad \times \int_{-\infty}^{\infty} \operatorname{sinc}(Wt - i) \operatorname{sinc}(Wt - \ell)\, dt \; . \end{aligned}$$

The sinc functions form an orthogonal set, and the integral on the right-hand side equals zero for $i \neq \ell$, and $1/W$ for $i = \ell$. Therefore,

$$\int_{-\infty}^{\infty} \zeta(t)\, \chi^*(t)\, dt = \frac{1}{W} \sum_{i=-\infty}^{\infty} \zeta_i \chi_i^* \; . \tag{21}$$

If we let $\zeta(t) = z(t) + j\hat{z}(t)$ and $\chi(t) = x(t) + j\hat{x}(t)$, and equate the real and imaginary parts of the quantities in Eq. (13), we obtain

$$\int_{-\infty}^{\infty} [z(t)\, x(t) + \hat{z}(t)\, \hat{x}(t)]\, dt = \frac{1}{W} \sum_{i=-\infty}^{\infty} (z_i x_i + \hat{z}_i \hat{x}_i) \tag{22}$$

and

$$\int_{-\infty}^{\infty} [\hat{z}(t)\, x(t) - z(t)\, \hat{x}(t)]\, dt = \frac{1}{W} \sum_{i=-\infty}^{\infty} (\hat{z}_i x_i - z_i \hat{x}_i) \; . \tag{23}$$

In the particular case in which $\zeta(t) = \chi(t)$, we have

$$\int_{-\infty}^{\infty} |\chi(t)|^2 \, dt = \int_{-\infty}^{\infty} [x^2(t) + \hat{x}^2(t)] \, dt$$

$$= \frac{1}{W} \sum_{i=-\infty}^{\infty} |\chi_i|^2 = \frac{1}{W} \sum_{i=-\infty}^{\infty} (x_i^2 + \hat{x}_i^2) \tag{24}$$

The convolution theorem for complex time functions is given by

$$\int_{-\infty}^{\infty} \chi(t) \, \zeta^*(t + \tau) \, dt = \int_{-\infty}^{\infty} \chi(f) \, \zeta^*(f) \, e^{-j2\pi f\tau} \, df \tag{25}$$

where $\chi(f)$ and $\zeta(f)$ are the Fourier transforms of $\chi(t)$ and $\zeta(t)$.
If we set $\tau = 0$ and let $\chi(t) = x(t)$ and $\zeta(t) = z(t)$, we obtain the familiar result

$$\int_{-\infty}^{\infty} x(t) \, z(t) \, dt = \int_{-\infty}^{\infty} X(f) \, Z^*(f) \, df \, . \tag{26}$$

Similarly, letting $\chi(t) = \hat{x}(t)$, $\zeta(t) = \hat{z}(t)$, and using Eq. (2), we have

$$\int_{-\infty}^{\infty} \hat{x}(t) \, \hat{z}(t) \, dt = \int_{0}^{\infty} [-jX(f)] \, [+j \, Z^*(f)] \, df$$

$$+ \int_{-\infty}^{0} [+jX(f)] \, [-jZ^*(f)] \, df$$

$$= \int_{-\infty}^{\infty} X(f) \, Z^*(f) \, df \, .$$

It follows that

$$\int_{-\infty}^{\infty} x(t) \, z(t) \, dt = \int_{-\infty}^{\infty} \hat{x}(t) \, \hat{z}(t) \, dt \tag{27}$$

and

$$\int_{-\infty}^{\infty} x^2(t) \, dt = \int_{-\infty}^{\infty} \hat{x}^2(t) \, dt \, . \tag{28}$$

In the same way, it is easy to show that

$$\int_{-\infty}^{\infty} x(t) \, \hat{z}(t) \, dt = - \int_{-\infty}^{\infty} \hat{x}(t) \, z(t) \, dt \tag{29}$$

and

$$\int_{-\infty}^{\infty} x(t)\hat{x}(t)\,dt = 0 \quad . \tag{30}$$

IV. CANONIC FORMS FOR TIME-VARIANT LINEAR FILTERS

It was pointed out in Chapters 4, 5, 6, and 7 that transmission media have time-variant characteristics, and can for most practical purposes be considered linear. We shall therefore consider a general transmission channel as being a linear time-variant filter, and proceed to rederive in the notation of the present chapter two of the canonic forms that were presented in Chapter 6. In the next section, these canonic forms will be used in the description of maximum-likelihood receivers.

One way to characterize a linear time-variant filter is in terms of its impulse response, $h(y, t)$, where

$h(y, t)$ = response at time t to a unit impulse applied at time $t - y$.

Let us first recall (Chapter 3) that for a time-invariant filter, the impulse response $h(y)$ is a function of the elapsed time y only and that by the superposition postulate,

$$z(t) = \int_{0}^{\infty} x(t - y)\,h(y)\,dy \tag{31}$$

where $z(t)$ is the output of the filter when $x(t)$ is the input. The lower limit of the convolution reflects the physical realizability condition that $h(y) = 0$ for $y < 0$. Equation (31) is interpretable physically as stating that the output of a filter at time t is the weighted sum of all previous inputs, where the weighting $h(y)$ is a function only of the *age* of these previous inputs, but *not* a function of the observation time t.

In a similar fashion, we have by superposition for a linear time-variant filter

$$z(t) = \int_{0}^{\infty} x(t - y)\,h(y, t)\,dy \quad . \tag{32}$$

In this case, however, the weighting $h(y, t)$ depends not only upon the age of an input, but also upon the observation instant t. The condition for physical realizability is still that no response should occur before the excitation that gives rise to it: $h(y, t) = 0$ for $y < 0$.

Let us also recall (Chapter 3) that the system function for a time-invariant filter is

$$H(f) = \int_{0}^{\infty} h(y)\, e^{-j2\pi fy}\,dy \tag{33}$$

and that in terms of $H(f)$ and an input spectrum $X(f)$, we have

$$z(t) = \int_{-\infty}^{\infty} X(f)H(f)\, e^{j2\pi ft}\, df \; . \tag{34}$$

In like fashion we may define a time-variant system function as the Fourier transform *with respect to* y of $h(y, t)$:

$$H(f, t) = \int_{-\infty}^{\infty} h(y, t)\, e^{-j2\pi fy}\, dy \; . \tag{35}$$

If $x(t - y)$ in Eq. (32) is replaced by its expression as an inverse Fourier transform, we have

$$z(t) = \int_{0}^{\infty} h(y, t)\, dy \int_{-\infty}^{\infty} X(f)\, e^{+j2\pi f(t-y)}\, df \; .$$

The integration with respect to y yields

$$\boxed{z(t) = \int_{-\infty}^{\infty} X(f)H(f, t)\, e^{j2\pi ft}\, df} \tag{36}$$

which is analogous to Eq. (34). It would not, however, be correct to refer to $X(f)H(f, t)$ as the spectrum of $z(t)$, since $X(f)H(f, t)$ is a function of t as well as of f.

Canonic Form for Band-Limited Inputs

We see directly from Eq. (36) that the value of $H(f, t)$ is unimportant for ranges of f over which $X(f)$ itself is zero. When $X(f)$ is limited to a band $f_0 - W_x/2 < |f| < f_0 + W_x/2$ by an ideal filter $W_x(f)$, we may therefore arbitrarily set $H(f, t) = 0$ for f outside of this range, and still have a filter that is equivalent to the original one over this class of band-limited inputs. If we do this, we can apply the sampling theorem to the representation of $h(y, t)$. Thus, if we first invert Eq. (35), we have

$$h(y, t) = \int_{-\infty}^{\infty} H(f, t)\, e^{+j2\pi fy}\, dy, \tag{37}$$

where $H(f, t)$ is now taken to be band-limited in f. Let $\hat{h}(y, t)$ be the Hilbert transform *on* y of $h(y, t)$:

$$\hat{h}(y, t) = \frac{1}{\pi} \int_{-\infty}^{\infty} \frac{h(\tau, t)}{y - \tau}\, d\tau \; . \tag{38}$$

It then follows directly from Eqs. (19) and (20) that

$$h(y, t) = \mathrm{Re} \sum_{i=-\infty}^{\infty} \left[h\left(\frac{i}{W_x}, t\right) + j\hat{h}\left(\frac{i}{W_x}, t\right) \right] \times \operatorname{sinc}(W_x y - i)\, e^{j2\pi f_0 \left(y - \frac{i}{W_x}\right)} . \tag{39}$$

The major mental hazard in all of the preceding formulas is the realization that in our formulation the transformations are all between the variables y and f, and t is only a parameter. The functions $h(i/W_x, t)$ and $\hat{h}(i/W_x, t)$ are y-sampled values of functions satisfying the Hilbert transform relations on the variable y, not on the variable t. Accordingly, they are linearly independent functions of the absolute time parameter t. In order to avoid confusion, we hereafter denote them as $h(i/W_x, t) = m_i(t)$ and $\hat{h}(i/W_x, t) = m_i'(t)$.

With this change in notation, Eq. (39) can be rewritten in the form

$$h(y, t) = (\cos 2\pi f_0 y \operatorname{sinc} W_x y) \circledast \sum_{i=-\infty}^{\infty} m_i(t)\, \delta\left(y - \frac{i}{W_x}\right) - (\sin 2\pi f_0 y \operatorname{sinc} W_x y) \circledast \sum_{i=-\infty}^{\infty} m_i'(t)\, \delta\left(y - \frac{i}{W_x}\right) . \tag{40}$$

We recognize the term $(\cos 2\pi f_0 y \operatorname{sinc} W_x y)$ as $1/2W_x$ times the impulse response of the ideal filter $W_x(f)$. Similarly, the term $-(\sin 2\pi f_0 y \operatorname{sinc} W_x y)$ is $-1/2W_x$ times the impulse response of the ideal filter $W_x(f)$, cascaded with the Hilbert transforming filter $\hat{H}_1(f)$. The two infinite summations represent delay lines cascaded after these time-invariant filters, with taps spaced $1/W_x$ apart having time-variant tap-gain-multiplier functions $m_i(t)$ and $m_i'(t)$ respectively. Replacing the terms in the mathematical expression of Eq. (40) by their physical equivalents, we have the delay-sampled canonic representation of $h(y, t)$ modeled in Fig. 1. This canonic model, of course, represents the combination of original channel with ideal bandpass filter $W_x(f)$ preceding it. As usual with sampling, we note that the postulation of this unrealizable filter leads to contradiction of the condition $h(y, t) = 0$ for $y < 0$, a difficulty that can be alleviated through the introduction of sufficiently long delay.

For any signal first passed through the ideal band-pass filter $W_x(f)$, our equivalent time-variant filter produces the same output $z(t)$ as does the original filter $H(f, t)$. It is at first distressing, however, to observe that the number of taps on the delay line [as also the limits of summation in Eq. (39)] is infinite. If the original filter $H(f, t)$ did indeed have an impulse response $h(y, t)$ that continued for $y \to \infty$, then our model also must run to infinity. As a practical matter, however, physical channels (although dispersive) have finite memories.

Let us consider the following experiment. By-passing the filter $W_x(f)$, we insert a sharp pulse into the original $H(f, t)$, and measure

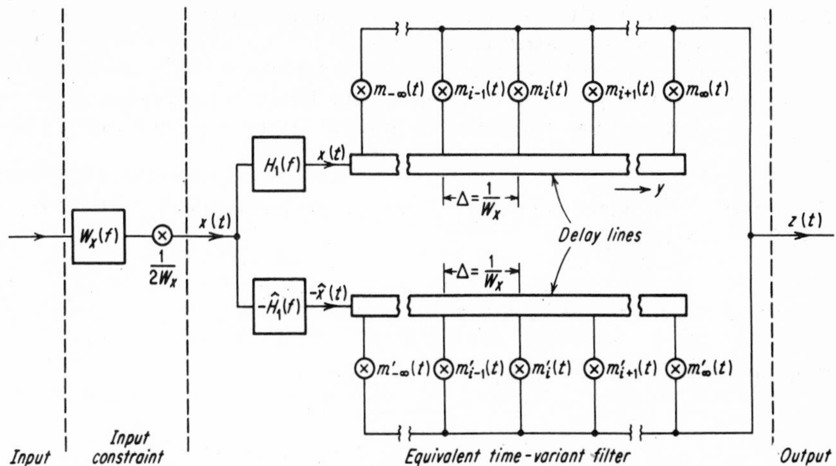

Fig. 1. Delay-sampling canonic form for time-variant linear filters. [$H_1(f) = 1$ for all f; it has been added for symmetry only.]

the response. At some time Y seconds later, the response is substantially zero. If we repeat the experiment many times with the same result, we conclude that the physical process under investigation has an impulse response $h(y, t)$ that is zero for $y > Y$ and any t. We can then approximate the cascade of $W_x(f)$ and $h(y, t)$ as closely as we please by making the delay lines appropriately longer than Y. If "as close as we please" is reasonable in an engineering sense, then "appropriately longer" is also reasonable; $(\sin x/x)^2$ is down 20 db for $x = 10$.

We may in addition place bounds on the bandwidth of the tap gain functions $m_i(t)$ and $m'_i(t)$. Let us measure the original channel again, this time with a sine wave whose frequency f_m lies within the passband of $W_x(f)$. If for every such frequency f_m the spectrum of $z(t)$ is always zero for $|f - f_m| > W_m$, then we conclude that each of the tap-gain functions is a lowpass function with a spectrum equal to zero for $|f| > W_m$. These gain functions can therefore themselves be represented by samples, giving finally a two-dimensional sampling representation for the process $h(y, t)$. Interesting questions arise as to the conditions under which the values of these two-dimensional samples can be determined through input-output measurements,[9] but such questions are beyond the scope of the present treatment.

Canonic Form for Finite Memory Filters

In the preceding analysis we derived a delay-sampled canonic form for a general time-variant linear filter subject to a constraint on the bandwidth of allowable inputs. We then argued that if the memory of the original filter were finite, we could closely approximate it by a finite model. In this paragraph we reverse the arguments, and assume first a finite memory, and afterwards introduce the input bandwidth constraint.

Let us state—on the basis of prior measurements or understanding of the physical process itself—that our filter has a response $h(y, t)$ at a time t to a unit-impulse input at time $t - y$ such that

$$h(y, t) = 0 \quad \text{for } y > Y \tag{41}$$

Since the filter exists physically, we already know that $h(y, t) = 0$ for $y < 0$. Accordingly,

$$h(y, t) = \left[h(y, t) * \sum_{i=-\infty}^{\infty} \delta(y - iY)\right] \text{rect}\left(\frac{y}{Y} - \frac{1}{2}\right)$$

Taking the Fourier transform on y, we have

$$H(f, t) = \left[H(f, t) \cdot \frac{1}{Y} \sum_{i=-\infty}^{\infty} \delta\left(f - \frac{i}{y}\right)\right] * Ye^{-j\pi Yf} \text{sinc } Yf$$

or

$$H(f, t) = \sum_{i=-\infty}^{\infty} H\left(\frac{i}{Y}, t\right) e^{-j\pi(Yf-i)} \text{ sinc } (Yf - i) \tag{42}$$

This is a time-variant frequency-sampling theorem in the f-domain. Taking the inverse Fourier transform on f of both sides of this equation yields

$$h(y, t) = \frac{1}{Y}\left[\sum_{i=-\infty}^{\infty} H\left(\frac{i}{Y}, t\right) e^{j2\pi y \frac{i}{Y}}\right] \text{rect}\left(\frac{y}{Y} - \frac{1}{2}\right)$$

Finally, since $h(y, t)$ is real for all y and t, $H(f, t) = H^*(-f, t)$. Letting

$$A_i(t) = \frac{2}{Y} \text{ Re } H\left(\frac{i}{Y}, t\right) \quad \text{and} \quad B_i(t) = \frac{2}{Y} \text{ Im } H\left(\frac{i}{Y}, t\right)$$

we may pair positive and negative values of the index i to get

$$h(y, t) = \left[\tfrac{1}{2} A_0(t) + \sum_{i=1}^{\infty} \left(A_i(t) \cos 2\pi \frac{i}{Y} y + B_i(t) \sin 2\pi \frac{i}{Y} y\right)\right] \times \text{rect}\left(\frac{y}{Y} - \frac{1}{2}\right) \tag{43}$$

The ith term of Eq. (43) is recognizable as a filter that extracts continuously in time what would be the ith Fourier cosine and sine coefficients of a periodic waveform, each period of which duplicates the preceding Y seconds of the input, and then multiplies these coefficients by $A_i(t)$ and $B_i(t)$, respectively. Such a filter, of course, cannot be built exactly with finite lumped-parameter circuits. It can, however, be approximated in several ways. Conceptually, the most

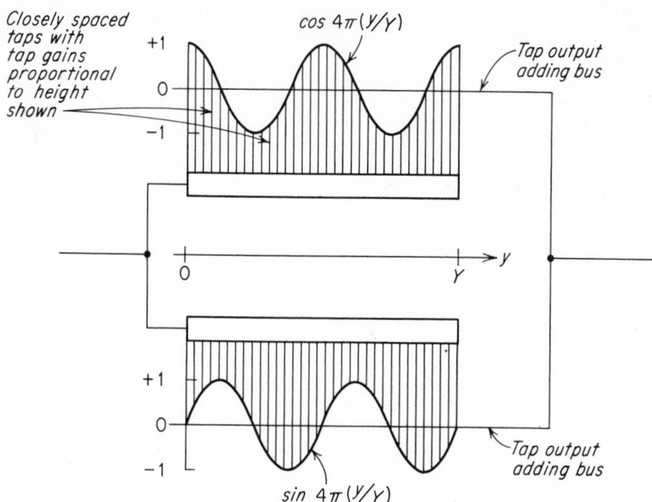

Fig. 2. Continuous Fourier coefficient extracting filter.

straightforward of these is two delay lines of length Y, with dense taps having gains of cos $2\pi(i/Y)y$ and sin $2\pi(i/Y)y$ respectively, where y measures length along the delay line. An illustration of such a filter for $i = 2$ is provided in Fig. 2. However, a more economical (although conceptually more difficult) way to build these continuous Fourier-coefficient-extracting filters in practice would be either through the use of re-circulating delay lines, or through the use of a weighting matrix interconnecting a set of monopole filters.

As illustrated in Fig. 3, the complete equivalent time-variant filter is formed by multiplying the output of each of the infinite number of Fourier extracting filters by the appropriate time function $A_i(t)$ or $B_i(t)$, and adding these weighted outputs together. In the present case, however, we note that a restriction on the input bandwidth to W_x allows us to represent the actual filter $h(y, t)$ exactly by using only $W_x Y$ Fourier-extracting filters, whereas the corresponding representation in the delay sampling model was only approximate. When $A_i(t)$ and $B_i(t)$ are low-pass functions limited to a bandwidth W_m, a two-dimensional sampling analysis is again possible.[9]

V. DETECTION OF TIME-VARIANT DISPERSIVE TRANSMISSIONS

In this section we apply the results of the preceding discussions to an analysis of the detection of band-pass signals transmitted through noisy, linear, time-variant channels having an impulse response $h(y, t)$ that is substantially zero for $y > Y$. We consider first the situation in which the transmitter sends a single particular selection of one out of a finite (but very large) set of possible

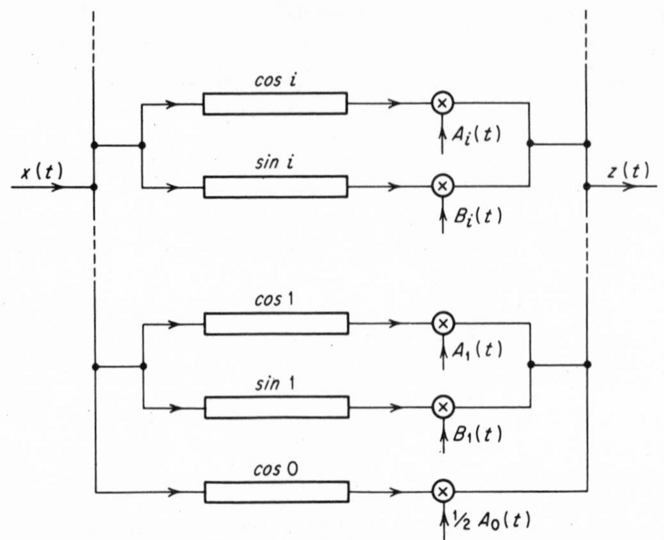

Fig. 3. Frequency-sampling canonic form for time-variant linear filters. The notation cos i denotes a filter whose impulse response $h(y)$ is $[\cos 2\pi (i/Y)y] \times \mathrm{rect}\,(y/Y - 1/2)$.

narrow-bandpass waveforms $x(t)$ of bandwidth W_x, center frequency f_0, and substantial duration T. The transmitter selects a particular waveform in accordance with instructions given to it by an information source. We assume that each of the possible instructions—and hence each of the possible waveforms—is equally likely. We also assume that $TW_x \gg 1$, and that $T \gg Y$.

In this postulated situation, the task of the receiver is to decide on the basis of the received signal which of the finite set of allowed waveforms was actually transmitted. The *a posteriori* probability that a particular waveform $x(t)$ was sent, given that the signal $z(t)$ was received, is given by Bayes' rule

$$P[x(t) \mid z(t)] = \frac{P[x(t)]}{p[z(t)]}\, p[z(t) \mid x(t)] \ . \tag{44}$$

On the average, the receiver will decide correctly most often if it calculates the left-hand-side probability—or a number that is a monotonic function of it—for each allowed $x(t)$, and selects each time that $x(t)$ for which this probability is greatest. This is maximum-likelihood detection, the optimum procedure whenever minimum probability of error is the criterion of goodness. Since $p[z(t)]$ is constant for all $x(t)$ over the set of alternatives, and the $x(t)$'s are equally likely, the receiver need only be concerned with the conditional probability density $p[z(t) \mid x(t)]$.

The Matrix Formulation

We have assumed that the signals $x(t)$ are restricted to a bandwidth W_x, and that the channel impulse response $h(y, t)$ is zero for y greater than some constant Y. We therefore exploit the results of the delay-sampling theorem of section IV, and represent the actual transmission medium by its delay-line equivalent. Since the effect of the dispersion extends only over a range $0 < y < Y$, we need only take L taps in order to obtain a satisfactory approximation, where L is somewhat greater than the product YW_x. From Fig. 1, the received signal $z(t)$ is then given by

$$z(t) = \sum_{\ell=1}^{L} [m_\ell(t)\, x(t + \Delta - \ell\Delta) - m'_\ell(t)\, \hat{x}(t + \Delta - \ell\Delta)] + n(t) \tag{45}$$

where $n(t)$ is a statistically independent noise added at the front end of the receiver, the ^ denotes the Hilbert transform (on the variable t), and $\Delta = 1/W_x$.

Let us now assume that all $m_i(t)$ and $m'_i(t)$ are lowpass bandlimited time functions of bandwidth $W_m < f_0 - W_x/2$. Then there is no product spectrum overlapping across $f = 0$, and each of the terms in the summation above is limited to the bandwidth $W = 2\,W_m + W_x$ cps centered on f_0. We may therefore without loss of information about $x(t)$ consider $z(t)$ to be received through a bandpass filter of bandwidth W.

We now introduce the following notation:

Received signal: $\zeta(t) = z(t) + j\hat{z}(t)$ (46)

Transmitted signal: $\chi(t) = x(t) + j\hat{x}(t)$ (47)

Noise: $\eta(t) = n(t) + j\hat{n}(t)$ (48)

Tap gain: $\mu_\ell(t) = m_\ell(t) + jm'_\ell(t)$ (49)

In terms of these complex quantities, Eq. (45) becomes

$$\operatorname{Re} \zeta(t) = \operatorname{Re}\left[\sum_{\ell=1}^{L} \mu_\ell(t)\, \chi(t + \Delta - \ell\Delta) + \eta(t)\right]. \tag{50}$$

Note that the spectrum of every χ is nonzero only for positive f. Moreover, the μ_ℓ are lowpass and the χ are bandpass. The convolution of these two spectra is therefore nonzero only for positive f. We can therefore apply the property stated in Eq. (8), namely that the imaginary part of each product term $\mu_\ell(t)\,\chi(t + \Delta - \ell\Delta)$ is the Hilbert transform of the real part. The functions $\zeta(t)$ and $\eta(t)$ already meet this condition, by definition. Accordingly, Hilbert-transforming both sides of Eq. (50) yields

$$\operatorname{Im} \zeta(t) = \operatorname{Im}\left[\sum_{\ell=1}^{L} \mu_\ell(t)\, \chi(t + \Delta - \ell\Delta) + \eta(t)\right]. \tag{51}$$

Finally, combining the real and imaginary parts, and writing $\chi(t + \Delta - \ell\Delta)$ as $\chi_\ell(t)$, we have

$$\zeta(t) = \sum_{\ell=1}^{L} \mu_\ell(t)\,\chi_\ell(t) + \eta(t) \tag{52}$$

Both $\hat{z}(t)$ and $\hat{x}(t)$ are obtainable from $z(t)$ and $x(t)$ at the receiver by the reversible operation of passing them through the Hilbert-transforming filter $\hat{H}_1(f)$. It follows that

$$p[z(t) \mid x(t)] = p[\zeta(t) \mid \chi(t)], \tag{53}$$

since the event pairs $z(t)$, $\zeta(t)$ and $x(t)$, $\chi(t)$ are synonomous.

At this point it is convenient to represent the waveforms of Eq. (52) by their sample values, and to adopt a matrix notation. Using Eq. (19), we make the column matrix identifications

$$\zeta(t) \rightarrow \boldsymbol{\zeta} = \begin{bmatrix} \zeta_1 \\ \zeta_2 \\ \vdots \\ \zeta_k \end{bmatrix}; \quad \eta(t) \rightarrow \boldsymbol{\eta} = \begin{bmatrix} \eta_1 \\ \eta_2 \\ \vdots \\ \eta_k \end{bmatrix}; \quad \mu_\ell(t) \rightarrow \boldsymbol{\mu}_\ell = \begin{bmatrix} \mu_{\ell 1} \\ \mu_{\ell 2} \\ \vdots \\ \mu_{\ell k} \end{bmatrix} \tag{54}$$

where $\zeta_i = \zeta(i/W)$, $\eta_i = \eta(i/W)$, and $\mu_{\ell i} = \mu_\ell(i/W)$. The index $k = TW \gg 1$ is assumed to be large enough so that ζ_i can be neglected in the decision process for $i > k$. In order to represent the term $\sum_{\ell=1}^{L} \mu_\ell(t)\chi_\ell(t)$ we use the k by Lk matrix

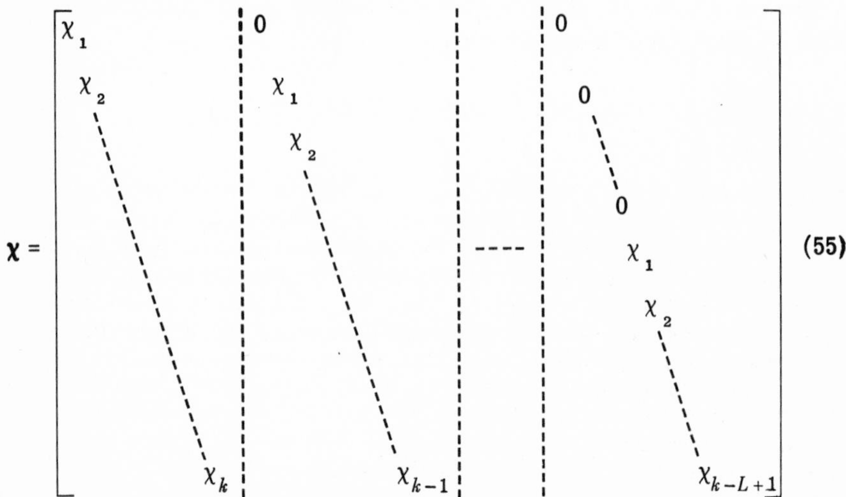

(55)

where $\chi_i = \chi(i/W)$, and all unspecified matrix elements are zero. Then, letting μ be the Lk-element column matrix

$$\mu = \begin{bmatrix} \mu_1(t) \\ \mu_2(t) \\ \vdots \\ \mu_\ell(t) \\ \vdots \\ \mu_L(t) \end{bmatrix} \tag{56}$$

we have the identification

$$\sum_{\ell=1}^{L} \mu_\ell(t)\chi_\ell(t) \to \chi\mu \ . \tag{57}$$

From the form of Eq. (55), it is seen that the identification in (57) amounts to neglecting the trailing part of the output (*i.e.*, the tail of the received signal) which continues after the input signal has been turned off. The approximation is good whenever the duration of the input signal far exceeds the dispersion time of the channel.

In terms of these matrices, it follows that the task of the receiver is to compute

$$p[\zeta(t) \mid \chi(t)] = p(\zeta \mid \chi) \tag{58}$$

for each possible transmitted signal χ, where

$$\zeta = \chi\mu + \eta \ . \tag{59}$$

Calculation of Probabilities

The calculation of $p(\zeta \mid \chi)$ implies knowledge of the statistical description of μ and η. In general,

$$p(\zeta \mid \chi) = \underbrace{\int_{-\infty}^{\infty} \cdots \int_{-\infty}^{\infty}}_{Lk} p(\zeta \mid \chi, \mu)\, p(\mu \mid \chi)\, d\mu_{11} \cdots d\mu_{Lk} \tag{60}$$

which is a formidable integral. In the particular case in which μ and η are both gaussian distributed and independent, however, Price[1,2] first recognized a simple interpretation for the answer, which Kailath[6,10] has extended and generalized. (See Appendix at the end of this chapter.)

We are concerned, in particular, with the situation in which μ represents a set of gaussian variables whose covariance matrix has rank r that is less than its order Lk. This, for instance, is the situation when the tap-gain multipliers $\mu_\ell(t)$ are lowpass functions of time with narrow spectra extending from $-W_m$ to $+W_m$; samples taken at intervals $1/(W_m + W_x)$ cannot then be statistically independent.

If the covariance matrix $\Phi_\mu = E[\mu\, \mu_t]$† has rank r, then it is possible to set

$$\mu = \Gamma \mathbf{q} \tag{61}$$

where $\Gamma = \mathbf{A} + j\mathbf{B}$ is an Lk by r complex matrix of rank r, and $\mathbf{q}$ is an r-element real column matrix representing those r statistically independent random parameters q_i that underlie the tap-gain functions. Since knowledge of the statistics of μ implies Γ, no additional assumption has been introduced. We can, however, now rewrite Eq. (60) more properly as

$$p(\zeta \mid \chi) = \underbrace{\int_{-\infty}^{\infty} \cdots \int_{-\infty}^{\infty}}_{r} p(\zeta \mid \chi, \mathbf{q})\, p(\mathbf{q} \mid \chi)\, dq_1 \cdots dq_r \ . \tag{62}$$

At this point we specialize to the case in which η represents additive white gaussian noise[13] of mean power density N_0 watts/cps and $\mathbf{q}$ represents r zero-mean gaussian variables, and η and $\mathbf{q}$ are both independent of χ.

$$p_\eta(\eta_1, \eta_2, \cdots, \eta_k) = \frac{1}{(\pi N_0 W)^k}\, e^{-\frac{1}{2N_0 W} \eta_t \mathbf{I} \eta^*} \tag{63}$$

$$p_q(q_1, q_2, \ldots, q_r) = \frac{1}{(2\pi)^{r/2}\, |\Phi_q|^{\frac{1}{2}}}\, e^{-\frac{1}{2}\mathbf{q}_t \Phi_q^{-1} \mathbf{q}} \tag{64}$$

where $\mathbf{I}$ is the identity matrix, $\Phi_q = E[\mathbf{q}\,\mathbf{q}_t]$, and the symbol $|\ |$ means determinant.

Before substituting from Eqs. (63) and (64) into Eq. (62), we note from Eqs. (59) and (61) that

$$p(\zeta \mid \chi, \mathbf{q}) = p_\eta(\eta = \zeta - \chi\mu) = p_\eta(\zeta - \chi\Gamma\mathbf{q}) \ . \tag{65}$$

It follows that

$$\begin{aligned} p(\zeta \mid \chi) &= \underbrace{\int_{-\infty}^{\infty} \cdots \int_{-\infty}^{\infty}}_{r} K_1 \exp\left[-\frac{1}{2N_0 W}(\zeta_t - \mathbf{q}_t \Gamma_t \chi_t) \right. \\ &\quad \left. \times (\zeta^* - \chi^* \Gamma^* \mathbf{q}) - \frac{1}{2}\mathbf{q}_t\, \Phi_q^{-1}\, \mathbf{q}\right] dq_1 \cdots dq_r \\ &= \frac{K_2}{\left|\Phi_q^{-1} + \frac{1}{N_0 W}\Gamma_t \chi_t \chi^* \Gamma^*\right|^{\frac{1}{2}}} \\ &\quad \times \exp - \frac{1}{2N_0 W}\, \zeta_t \left[\mathbf{I} - \chi^* \Gamma^* \left(\Phi_q^{-1} + \frac{1}{N_0 W}\Gamma_t \chi_t \chi^* \Gamma^*\right)^{-1} \right. \\ &\quad \left. \times \frac{1}{N_0 W}\Gamma_t \chi_t\right] \zeta^* . \end{aligned} \tag{66}$$

The integration above follows directly[14] when the matrix of the

† The subscript t is used to denote the transpose of a matrix.

Hermitian form in the exponent is diagonalized by means of a unitary transformation.[15] The constants K_1 and K_2 represent terms that are independent of the hypothesis χ. If we now assume that all of the possible signals χ are such that the determinant in the denominator of Eq. (66) is nearly independent of which χ hypothesis is under test, the receiver need only consider the χ-dependent terms in the exponent. This assumption is reasonable when the signals χ are, for instance, themselves taken to be representative samples of gaussian noise, white over the band W_x. Then†

$$p(\zeta \mid \chi) \propto \zeta_t \chi^* \Gamma^* \left(\Phi_q^{-1} + \frac{1}{N_0 W} \Gamma_t \chi_t \chi^* \Gamma^*\right)^{-1} \Gamma_t \chi_t \zeta^* \tag{67}$$

where we have dropped the constant factor $1/[2(N_0W)^2]$.

Interpretation of Results

Kailath[6] and Price[1,2] have pointed out that the ideal receiver can be interpreted as one that first makes the optimum (least-mean-square error) estimate of what the received signal (given χ) would have been in the absence of additive noise, and then cross-correlates this estimate against the actual received signal. It follows that this optimum estimate, ζ_e^*, of ζ^* given χ, varies (to within a factor of $1/[2(N_0W)^2]$) as

$$\zeta_e^* \propto \chi^* \Gamma^* \left(\Phi_q^{-1} + \frac{1}{N_0 W} \Gamma_t \chi_t \chi^* \Gamma^*\right)^{-1} \Gamma_t \chi_t \zeta^* \ . \tag{68}$$

Also, since in the absence of noise ζ^* would equal $\chi^* \Gamma^* \mathbf{q}$, it follows[10] (see Appendix, section AIII) that $\zeta_e^* = \chi^* \Gamma^* \mathbf{q}_e^*$, where $\mathbf{q}_e^*$ is the optimum estimate of $\mathbf{q}^*$ given χ, and

$$\mathbf{q}_e^* \propto \left(\Phi_q^{-1} + \frac{1}{N_0 W} \Gamma_t \chi_t \chi^* \Gamma^*\right)^{-1} \Gamma_t \chi_t \zeta^* \tag{69}$$

The fact that $\mathbf{q}_e$ is complex even though $\mathbf{q}$ is real results from our use of complex notation for the bandpass signals. This complication is avoided if the bandpass transmission problem is handled by the method suggested in the Appendix (Eq. A10).

Finally, if we let the $\mathbf{q}$-estimating (given χ) matrix $\mathbf{H}_{\mathbf{q}^* \mid \chi}$ be defined by

$$\mathbf{H}_{\mathbf{q}^* \mid \chi} = \left(\Phi_q^{-1} + \frac{1}{N_0 W} \Gamma_t \chi_t \chi^* \Gamma\right)^{-1} \tag{70}$$

we have

$$P(\chi \mid \zeta) \propto p(\zeta \mid \chi) \propto \zeta_t \chi^* \Gamma^* \mathbf{H}_{\mathbf{q}^* \mid \chi} \Gamma_t \chi_t \zeta^* \ . \tag{71}$$

The column matrix $\chi_t \zeta^*$ on the right represents all possible shifted products of the received and the hypothesized-transmitted signals.

†Throughout the present chapter, the proportionality sign $\propto$ is used to mean "simply related to" or "essentially determined by" and does not always have its usual meaning of "directly proportional to."

$$\chi_t \zeta^* = \begin{bmatrix} \chi_1 \zeta_1^* \\ \chi_2 \zeta_2^* \\ \vdots \\ \chi_k \zeta_k^* \\ \hdashline 0 \\ \chi_1 \zeta_2^* \\ \chi_2 \zeta_3^* \\ \vdots \\ \vdots \\ \chi_{k-L+1} \zeta_k^* \end{bmatrix} \tag{72}$$

These Lk products are then mapped down by $\mathbf{\Gamma}_t$, fed into the $\mathbf{q}$-estimator, and r estimates $\mathbf{q}_e^*$ come out. The Lk column matrix $\mathbf{\Gamma}^*\mathbf{q}_e^*$ equals μ_e^*, the best estimate of the tap-gain functions. Finally, the k-element column matrix $\mathbf{\chi}^*\mu_e^* = \boldsymbol{\zeta}_e^*$ is the best estimate of the noiseless received signal, and this is premultiplied by $\boldsymbol{\zeta}_t$ to give

$$\boldsymbol{\zeta}_t \boldsymbol{\zeta}_e^* = (\zeta_1 \zeta_{1e}^* + \zeta_2 \zeta_{2e}^* + \cdots + \zeta_k \zeta_{ke}^*) \; . \tag{73}$$

Using Eqs. (21), (27), and (71), we have finally

$$P(\chi \mid \boldsymbol{\zeta}) \propto \boldsymbol{\zeta}_t \boldsymbol{\zeta}_e^* \propto \int_0^T \zeta(t)\, \zeta_e^*(t)\, dt \propto \int_0^T z(t)\, z_e(t)\, dt$$

where $z(t) = \text{Re}\,\{\zeta(t)\}$, and $z_e(t) = \text{Re}\,\{\zeta_e^*(t)\}$ is recognized as the best estimate of $z(t)$.

A block diagram of the receiver is shown in Fig. 4. During the time interval $(0, T)$, the received signal $\zeta^*(t)$ is multiplied against all shifts of $\chi(t)$. At time $t = T$, the best estimate $\mathbf{q}_e^*$ is calculated instantaneously. Thereafter, this estimate is used to construct, over the interval $(T, 2T)$, delayed replicas of the best estimate of the tap gain functions $\mu_\ell(t)$.

Sequential Detection

Thus far we have considered only a single transmission. If, indeed, we define a whole message to be a single transmission, then our problem is solved, at least in principle. A practical difficulty arises, however, when we contemplate the number of χ-hypotheses (messages) that the receiver would then have to test, computing

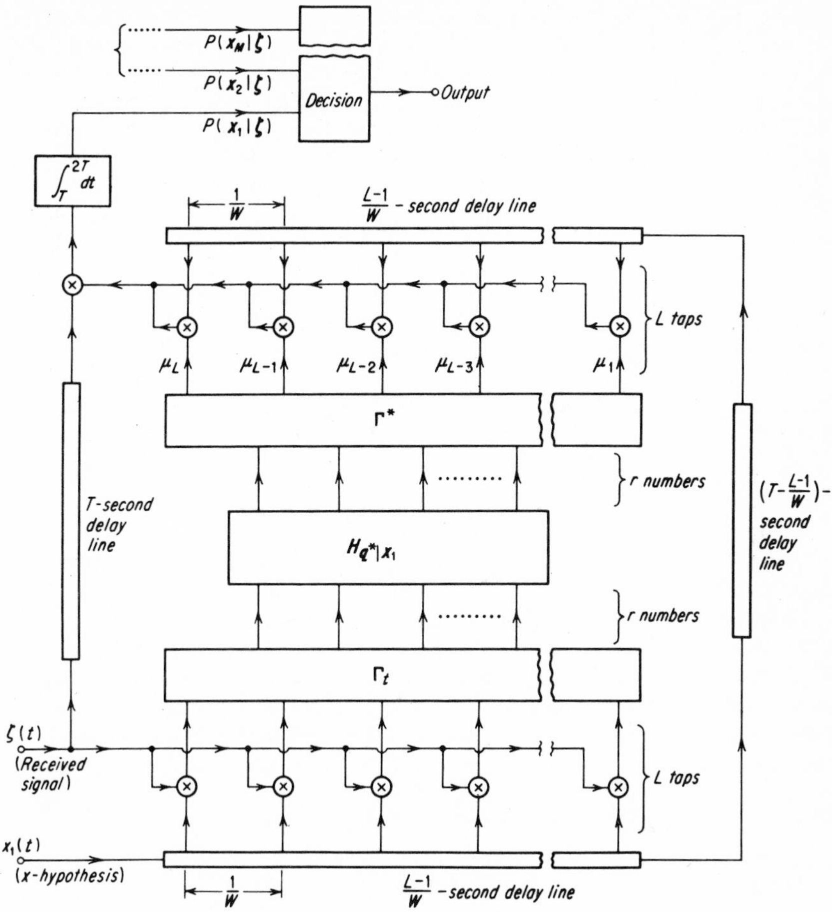

Fig. 4. Functional diagram of optimum receiver. The matrix Γ_t accepts inputs for $0 \leq t < T$ and gives r outputs at $t = T$. The matrix $H_{q^*} \mid X$ operates at $t = T$. The matrix Γ^* accepts r inputs at $t = T$ and gives outputs for $T < t \leq 2T$.

$P(X \mid \zeta)$ for each allowable X. It is clear that for finite-information-rate systems there are advantages to breaking up the transmission into small successive elements, and receiving and deciding about each element as it comes along.

In analyzing this sequential problem, we can take advantage of the previous single-transmission formulation. There were k samples in our matrix ζ; let them be divided into m successive groups, each of k/m samples. This corresponds to dividing our transmission of duration T into m intervals of duration $\tau = T/m$. We shall constrain the transmitter, during each such τ interval, to send one out of a small number M of equally likely signals.

We now define what may be called a "zero-foresight" receiver: At the end of each τ seconds, the receiver must decide which of the M possible signal elements has been transmitted. These decisions are taken to be inviolate, and cannot be changed at a later time. In making these decisions, however, the receiver is permitted to take advantage of its previous decisions and its knowledge of the previously received signal. We presume that the receiver still has *a priori* knowledge of the probability distribution $p(\mu)$ over the entire span T, and consider the problem of detecting the *last* of the m signal elements of duration τ.

In order to express these new constraints mathematically, we use in the sequel the subscript "d" to denote variables describing that portion of the transmission which has already been detected, and the subscript "m" to denote variables describing the current decision process. Since our receiver is permitted to benefit from previous experience, the appropriate decision function for the last τ interval [analogous to Eq. (60)] is

$$P(\chi_m \mid \zeta_m, \chi_d, \zeta_d) \propto \underbrace{\int_{-\infty}^{\infty} \cdots \int_{-\infty}^{\infty}}_{Lm} p(\zeta_m \mid \chi_m, \chi_d, \zeta_d, \mu_m) \cdot p(\mu_m \mid \chi_m, \chi_d, \zeta_d)\, d\mu_{1,k-m+1} \dots d\mu_{L,k} \ . \tag{75}$$

Now,

$$p(\zeta_m \mid \chi_m, \chi_d, \zeta_d, \mu_m) = p_\eta(\zeta_m - \chi_m \mu_m) \tag{76}$$

and

$$\begin{aligned} p(\mu_m \mid \chi_m, \chi_d, \zeta_d) &= \underbrace{\int_{-\infty}^{\infty} \cdots \int_{-\infty}^{\infty}}_{L(k-m)} p(\mu_m \mid \chi_m, \chi_d, \zeta_d, \mu_d) p(\mu_d \mid \chi_m, \chi_d, \zeta_d) \\ &\qquad \times d\mu_{11} \cdots d\mu_{L,k-m} \\ &= \underbrace{\int_{-\infty}^{\infty} \cdots \int_{-\infty}^{\infty}}_{L(k-m)} p(\mu_m \mid \mu_d) p(\mu_d \mid \chi_d, \zeta_d)\, d\mu_{11} \cdots d\mu_{L,k-m} \ . \end{aligned} \tag{77}$$

The second integral follows from the fact that μ_m depends on χ_d and ζ_d only through μ_d, and that μ_d is independent of χ_m. Also,

$$p(\mu_d \mid \chi_d, \zeta_d) = \frac{p(\mu_d) p(\zeta_d \mid \chi_d \mu_d)}{p(\zeta_d \mid \chi_d)} \ . \tag{78}$$

The denominator of Eq. (78) is independent of the present hypothesis χ_m, and of the variables of integration μ_{ij}; accordingly, it may be treated as a constant. Combining Eqs. (76), (77), and (78), we have finally

$$p(\chi_m \mid \zeta_m, \chi_d, \zeta_d) \propto \underbrace{\int_{-\infty}^{\infty} \cdots \int_{-\infty}^{\infty}}_{Lk} p_\eta(\zeta_m - \chi_m \mu_m) \times p(\mu) p(\zeta_d \mid \chi_d, \mu_d) d\mu_{11} \cdots d\mu_{Lk}$$

$$\propto \underbrace{\int_{-\infty}^{\infty} \cdots \int_{-\infty}^{\infty}}_{Lm} p_\eta(\zeta_m - \chi_m \mu_m) p'(\mu_m) d\mu_{1, k-m+1} \cdots d\mu_{L,k} \tag{79}$$

where

$$p'(\mu_m) = \underbrace{\int_{-\infty}^{\infty} \cdots \int_{-\infty}^{\infty}}_{L(k-m)} p(\mu) p_\eta(\zeta_d - \chi_d \mu_d) d\mu_{11} \cdots d\mu_{L,k-m} \quad . \tag{80}$$

This result can also be obtained directly by partially integrating Eq. (60) over the variables μ_d.

The function $p'(\mu_m)$ is, to within a scale factor, the probability density function of μ_m, conditioned by χ_d and ζ_d. It is worthwhile to point out that even if the unconditioned path variables μ_ℓ have zero means and are uncorrelated, the path components of $(\mu_m \mid \zeta_d, \chi_d)$ will in general be correlated, and will in general have non-zero means. Thus, we see that even if the probability distribution $p(\mu)$ is stationary, in the sense that the statistical dependencies in the time-variant path structure over the last T seconds remain the same as this T-second window moves along in absolute time, the sequential receiver itself is non-stationary. At each step of detection, account must be taken of time-variant mean values (specular components) of path gain that depend on the previous received signal and decisions.

In an attempt to avoid requiring that the receiver actually calculate a new $p'(\mu)$ for each τ interval, we may investigate the results of partitioning the matrices ζ and χ of Eqs. (54) and (55). Letting the first $(k-m)$ rows represent the past variables, and the last m rows represent the current variables, we have

$$\zeta = \begin{bmatrix} \zeta_d \\ \hline \zeta_m \end{bmatrix} \quad \text{and} \quad \chi = \begin{bmatrix} \chi_d \\ \hline \chi_m \end{bmatrix} \quad . \tag{81}$$

These partitioned matrices can be substituted directly into the results for the "single-transmission" receiver, Eq. (71). Thus

$$P(\chi \mid \zeta) \propto [(\zeta_d)_t \mid (\zeta_m)_t] \begin{bmatrix} \chi_d^* \\ \hline \chi_m^* \end{bmatrix} \mathbf{\Gamma}^* \mathbf{H}_{q^* \mid \chi} \mathbf{\Gamma}_t [(\chi_d)_t \mid (\chi_m)_t] \begin{bmatrix} \zeta_d^* \\ \hline \zeta_m \end{bmatrix}$$

$$\propto \left[(\zeta_d)_t \chi_d^* + (\zeta_m)_t \chi_m^*\right] \times \mathbf{\Gamma}^* \mathbf{H}_{q^* \mid \chi} \mathbf{\Gamma}_t \left[(\chi_d)_t \zeta_d^* + (\chi_m)_t \zeta_m^*\right] \tag{82}$$

From Eq. (69), we have

$$\mathbf{q}_e^* = \mathbf{H}_{\mathbf{q}^*|\chi} \boldsymbol{\Gamma}_t \left[(\chi_d)_t \zeta_d^* + (\chi_m)_t \zeta_m^*\right] = \mathbf{q}_{e,d}^* + \mathbf{q}_{e,m}^* \tag{83}$$

and therefore

$$P(\chi \mid \zeta) \propto (\zeta_d)_t \chi_d^* \boldsymbol{\Gamma}^* \mathbf{q}_{e,d}^* + (\zeta_d)_t \chi_d^* \boldsymbol{\Gamma}^* \mathbf{q}_{e,m}^* + (\zeta_m)_t \chi_m^* \boldsymbol{\Gamma}^* \mathbf{q}_{e,d}^* + (\zeta_m)_t \chi_m^* \boldsymbol{\Gamma}^* \mathbf{q}_{e,m}^* . \tag{84}$$

Finally, since

$$P(\chi \mid \zeta) = P(\chi_m \mid \chi_d, \zeta_m, \zeta_d) P(\chi_d \mid \zeta_m, \zeta_d) \tag{85}$$

and $P(\chi_d \mid \zeta_m, \zeta_d)$ is constant for all hypotheses χ_m, we have†

$$P(\chi_m \mid \chi_d, \zeta_m, \zeta_d) \propto (\zeta_d)_t \chi_d^* \boldsymbol{\Gamma}^* \mathbf{q}_{e,d}^* + 2\,\mathrm{Re}\left\{(\zeta_m)_t \chi_m^* \boldsymbol{\Gamma}^* (\mathbf{q}_{e,d}^* + \frac{1}{2}\mathbf{q}_{e,m}^*)\right\} \tag{86}$$

where we have taken advantage of the fact that the second and third terms in Eq. (84) are conjugate transposes.

The operation of the zero-foresight sequential receiver is embodied in Eq. (86). Unfortunately, no great simplification has as yet been effected, since from Eqs. (83) and (70) we see that $\mathbf{q}_{e,d}^*$ is not independent of the current hypotehsis χ_m. However, when $m \ll k$, and all of the M possible signals are of nearly equal energy, the term $(1/N_0W)\boldsymbol{\Gamma}_t(\chi_m)_t \chi_m^* \boldsymbol{\Gamma}^*$ can be neglected in comparison with $\boldsymbol{\Phi}_q^{-1} + (1/N_0W)\boldsymbol{\Gamma}_t(\chi_d)_t \chi_d \boldsymbol{\Gamma}^*$ in the determination of $\mathbf{H}_{\mathbf{q}^*|\chi}$. Certainly, in the limit of low signal-to-noise ratio ($N_0 \to \infty$) this is true regardless. To this level of approximation then

$$P(\chi_m \mid \chi_d, \zeta_m, \zeta_d) \propto 2\,\mathrm{Re}\left\{(\zeta_m)_t \chi_m^* \boldsymbol{\Gamma}^* (\mathbf{q}_{e,d}^* + \frac{1}{2}\mathbf{q}_{e,m}^*)\right\} \tag{87}$$

where $\mathbf{q}_{e,d}^*$ is now taken to be independent of χ_m.

We see from Eq. (87) that our now approximately-optimum sequential receiver still cross-correlates $\zeta_m(t)$ against an estimate of what $\zeta_m(t)$ would be in the absence of additive noise, on the hypothesis that χ_m was transmitted. It does this for each of the M possible $\chi_m(t)$, and decides in favor of that one yielding the highest correlation.

Further levels of approximation to the ideal receiver can now also be visualized. For instance, our supposedly χ_m-independent matrix $\mathbf{H}_{\mathbf{q}^*|\chi_d}$ could be used to estimate $\mathbf{q}_{e,d}^*$, and the perturbation term $\mathbf{q}_{e,m}^*$ neglected. This would be a valid approximation in the case in which all of the r independent random parameters determining the channel are effective over the entire time span T. Even in this situation, however, the estimating matrix depends on the previous decisions χ_d. It is only under conditions of small signal-to-noise ratio ($N_0 \to \infty$)

†A result of this form has been obtained by Kailath in unpublished work.

that the matrix is completely independent of all χ, and the connections of the ideal receiver therefore stationary when $p(\mu)$ is stationary.

Rake

The Rake receiver (shown in Fig. 5) can be regarded as a further engineering approximation to the optimum sequential receiver that has been described above, for the special case of a binary alphabet ($M = 2$) and a slowly varying channel. In Rake, the tap gain functions $\mu_\ell(t)$ are each independently estimated by an exponentially weighted cross-correlation of the received signal $\zeta(t)$ against the delayed sum of the two possible transmitted waveforms. The delayed received signal $\zeta(t)$ [instead of the hypothesis $\chi(t)$] is then multiplied by these estimated tap gains, the L resulting products added together, and this sum finally cross-correlated against the $\chi(t)$. In the limit of slow channel variations, this is equivalent to multiplying the delayed $\chi(t)$ by the tap gains, summing, and cross-correlating against $\zeta(t)$; the advantage of the Rake procedure, of course, is in the resulting equipmental simplification.

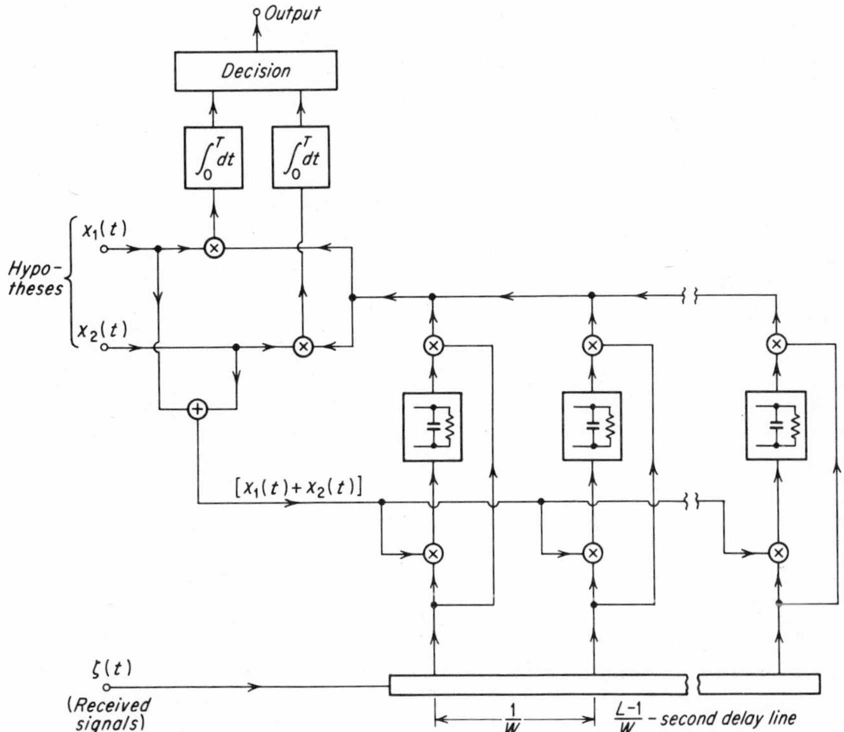

Fig. 5. Functional diagram of Rake.

VI. KINEPLEX

The analysis of section V has dealt with linear time-variant channels in their delay-sampled canonic form. We could just as well, however, have used the frequency-sampled canonic form, and derived an entirely equivalent receiver.

In this section we proceed in a somewhat less general way, and consider a situation in which the transmitted information is localized in particular cells of the $2\,TW_x$ space available. In particular, with the frequency-sampled model of Fig. 3 in mind, we consider first the case in which the transmitter sends as a signal a single pulsed sine wave of duration T and frequency $2\pi f_i$, where $f_i = i/Y$ lies within the allowed band W_x. When T is considerably greater than Y, the ith filter of the channel model provides the only significant response. The received signal is accordingly given by

$$z(t) = \frac{1}{2}A_i(t)\,Y\cos\,(2\pi f_i t + \theta) - \frac{1}{2}B_i(t)\,Y\sin\,(2\pi f_i t + \theta) + n(t), \qquad Y < t \leqslant T \tag{88}$$

when

$$x(t) = \cos\,(2\pi f_i t + \theta), \quad 0 < t \leqslant T. \tag{89}$$

In the Kineplex system, the received signal $z(t)$ is processed in a filter whose effective impulse response is given by

$$h(t) = (\cos\,2\pi f_i t)\,\text{rect}\left(\frac{t}{T} - \frac{1}{2}\right) \tag{90}$$

at the desired observation instant T. The filter is actually a time-variant device itself, consisting of a high-Q circuit at the frequency f_i. The energy in the filter is instantaneously dumped at time instants $\ell T + \epsilon$, and the output observed only at time instants ℓT, where ℓ is an integer and ϵ a time duration small compared to T. The transfer function $H(f)$ is zero at $f = f_i + l/T$, l an integer, on account of the rect function in Eq. (90).

If we restrict our attention to the observation instant $t = T$, and neglect unimportant constants, the output of the receiving filter is [by convolution of (88) and (90)]

$$y(t) = \cos\,(2\pi f_i t + \theta)\int_0^T A_i(\tau)\,d\tau - \sin\,(2\pi f_i t + \theta)\int_0^T B_i(\tau)\,d\tau + \text{noise}\;. \tag{91}$$

So long as $\int_0^T A_i(\tau)\,d\tau = \int_0^T B_i(\tau)\,d\tau$, the phase of the received signal—in the absence of the noise—is uniquely related to that of the transmitted signal.

If $A_i(t)$ and $B_i(t)$ are slowly varying functions of time, we may expect that their integrals from 0 to T and from T to $2T$ will be substantially constant and generally not equal. Under these conditions, the phase difference between two successive transmitted pulses, and between two successive received pulses, will be the same. Kineplex exploits this fact by means of what we may call *progressive* discrete phase modulation. The information to be communicated by each new pulse is used to position the phase of that pulse *relative* to the phase of its predecessor. Demodulation is performed, naturally, by observing this same phase difference.

The existing commercial Kineplex equipment uses quadrature phase modulation—that is, two bits of information are conveyed by each pulse. One, three, or any number k of bits, could be employed by dividing the 2π phase domain into 2^k disjoint sectors. The total number, of course, must be sufficiently small that the probability of error is tolerable.

Errors are introduced into the system by the noise $n(t)$ and/or by the instabilities of $A_i(t)$ and $B_i(t)$. In general, the S/N ratio at the output of the integrating receiver filter is $2E(t)/N_0$, as for any matched filter when the noise is white and gaussian. The energy $E(t)$, of course, reflects the sum of the squares of the integrals of $A_i(t)$ and $B_i(t)$. The probability distribution of phase excursions caused by noise around those produced by $A_i(t)$ and $B_i(t)$ is known.[13]

The channel can upset communications in any of several ways. Most simply, if $A_i(t)$ and $B_i(t)$ do not behave congenially, errors of course result. Rapid fluctuations in these gain functions can also cause the energy from one signal at frequency f_i to spill over into an adjacent receiving filter on frequency $(f_i + 1/T)$. Although frequency multiplexing at intervals of $\Delta f = 1/T$ would be possible in the time-invariant case, this cross-talk in time-variant channels calls for spacing the allowed tones at larger integral multiples of $1/T$. Finally, when T is so short as to be comparable to Y, a single tone-pulse excites more than one Fourier-extracting filter, and the situation becomes more complicated than is appropriate to consider here.

APPENDIX

ESTIMATION AND CORRELATION DETECTION FOR TIME-VARIANT RANDOM CHANNELS*

Thomas Kailath

In this Appendix, we shall derive and elaborate on certain results that were used in the main discussion of the chapter. In particular, we shall show how the concept of correlation detection of deterministic signals (namely signals whose waveform is exactly known at the receiver) in additive gaussian noise can be extended in a natural manner to the detection of signals that are transmitted through a "gaussian" random channel and are also corrupted by additive gaussian noise. Such signals are encountered in communication over scatter-multipath channels (with or without a specular component). In the deterministic case the receiver essentially cross-correlates the received noisy signal with the expected known waveform as modified by the known channel characteristics. When a random channel is present, however, this latter signal (*i.e.*, the output of the random channel in the absence of noise) is not known at the receiver. However, knowing the statistics of the channel and of the noise, the receiver can make an estimate of it from the received signal on the hypothesis that a particular signal was transmitted. The optimum receiver then cross-correlates this estimate with the received signal.

Channel-estimating filters thus play a key role in the synthesis of receivers for optimal detection of time-variant dispersive transmissions. We shall therefore devote considerable attention here to two important types of estimator: the minimum-variance estimator and the maximum-likelihood estimator. We shall first derive the estimating filter on a minimum-variance basis and then prove that this filter is also optimum for gaussian statistics on the basis of a maximum likelihood criterion.

AI. Statement of the Problem

Consider the situation in which one of a finite set of known signals $\{x^{(k)}(t)\}$ of limited duration is transmitted through a random, linear, time-variant channel, A, of finite memory, resulting in a waveform, $y^{(k)}(t)$, which is further corrupted by additive noise, represented by $n(t)$, before being introduced to the receiver (*cf.* Fig. A1). Let $z(t)$ denote the final received signal—that is, $z(t) = n(t) + y^{(k)}(t)$—and let T denote the duration of $z(t)$. Woodward[11] has shown that all of the information in the received signal $z(t)$ is contained in the set of

*This Appendix was written by the Editor using two publications (Refs. 6 and 10) by T. Kailath.

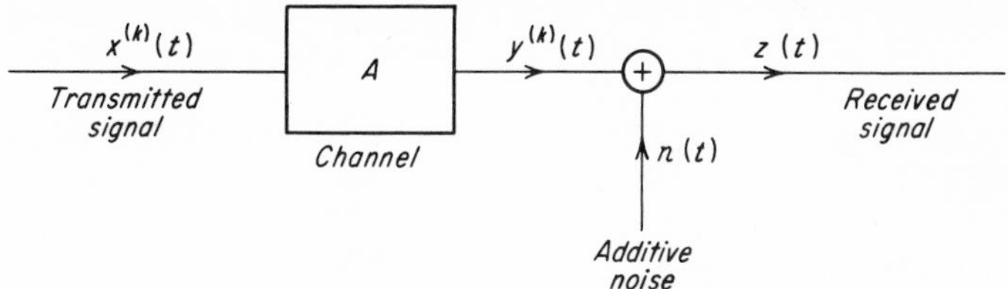

Fig. A1. Model of a channel with additive noise.

a posteriori probabilities $p[x^{(k)}(t) \mid z(t)]$. We therefore define the optimum receiver as being the one that computes the *a posteriori* probabilities $p[x^{(k)}(t) \mid z(t)]$, and our problem here is to determine the functional block diagram of such a receiver.

We assume that the additive noise is gaussian (though not necessarily white) and that the random channel is such that its output $y^{(k)}(t)$, for a particular input $x^{(k)}(t)$, is gaussian. We also assume that the mean and the variance of each of these distributions are known *a priori*; however, the distributions themselves need not be stationary. No further assumption is made about the structure of the channel—that is, whether it consists of a finite number of paths, independent or otherwise, or whether there is only a continuum of paths, etc. Scatter-multipath channels are often of this type, and our model includes the cases of Rayleigh fading with uniform phase distribution, a Rice-fading channel (namely, one whose output is made up of a Rayleigh-fading component having a uniform phase distribution plus a specular component) with arbitrary rates of variation.

In the case of a non-random channel, the problem can be solved by

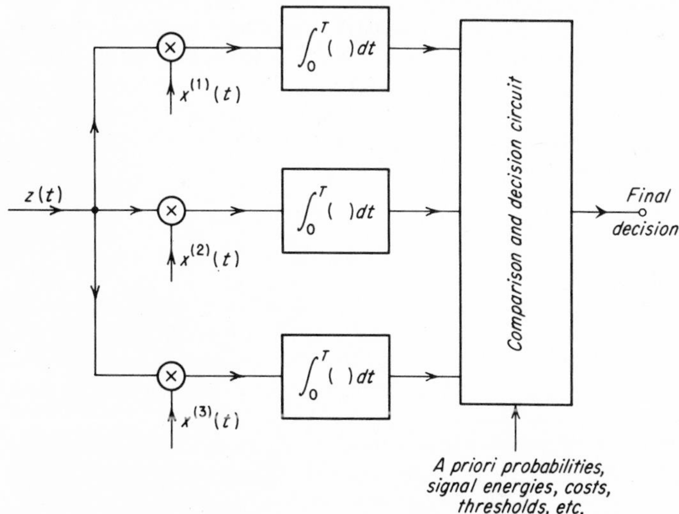

Fig. A2. Fundamental operations of optimum receiver for detection of deterministic signals in white gaussian noise.

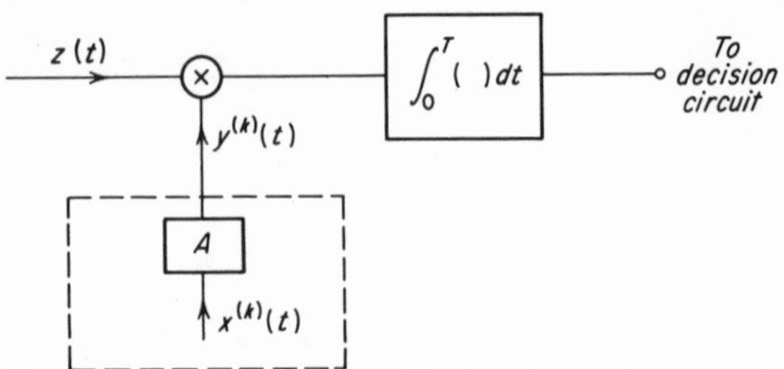

Fig. A3. The kth-signal branch of the optimum receiver when the channel can be simulated by a known filter A.

a trivial extension of a well-known result. It has been shown[11,16,17] that if the waveform of the signal is known at the receiver (a so-called deterministic signal), and if the signal is embedded in white gaussian noise, then the operation performed by an "optimum" receiver is essentially a cross-correlation, as shown in Fig. A2. The receiver cross-correlates the received signal, say $z(t)$, with each possible transmitted signal $x^{(k)}(t)$. This operation can be performed by a multiplier-integrator combination, with readout at time T, where T is the duration of the $x^{(k)}(t)$, or by a matched filter with readout at T. If a non-random channel transforms $x^{(k)}(t)$ to $y^{(k)}(t)$, we need only introduce a channel-simulating filter A at the receiver as shown in Fig. A3.

AII. Analytical Formulation

For convenience, we shall discuss the lowpass transmission problem, and indicate at the end of this section how the same analysis and results can be adapted for the bandpass case.

Consider a channel whose tapped-delay-line model is shown in Fig. A4. Let the excitation $x(t)$ be a pulse of duration $3/2\,W_i$ sec., and let the channel be at rest before the application of $x(t)$ at $t = 0$. If the output $y(t)$ is sampled at times $t = m/2W_i$ sec., $m = 0, 1, 2, \dots,$ and if we measure time in units of $1/2\,W_i$ sec., we have

$$\left.\begin{aligned}
y(0) &= a_0(0)\,x(0) \\
y(1) &= a_1(1)\,x(0) + a_0(1)\,x(1) \\
y(2) &= a_2(2)\,x(0) + a_1(2)\,x(1) + a_0(2)\,x(2) \\
y(3) &= \qquad\qquad\quad a_2(3)\,x(1) + a_1(3)\,x(2) \\
y(4) &= \qquad\qquad\qquad\qquad\qquad a_2(4)\,x(2)
\end{aligned}\right\} \tag{A1}$$

These equations can be presented more compactly in matrix form. For this purpose, we first adopt the convenient notation

$$y_m \equiv y(m),\ a_{km} \equiv a_k(m),\ \text{and}\ x_m \equiv x(m) \tag{A2}$$

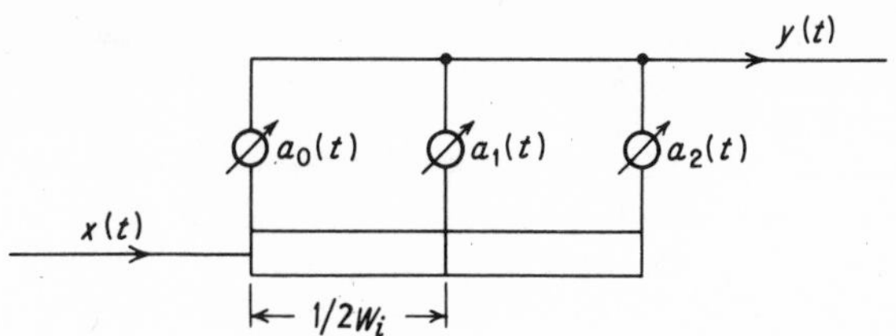

Fig. A4. A simple delay-line model of a low-pass channel.

The set of equations (1) can now be expressed in either of two useful matrix arrangements:

$$\begin{bmatrix} y_0 \\ y_1 \\ y_2 \\ y_3 \\ y_4 \end{bmatrix} = \begin{bmatrix} a_{00} & 0 & 0 \\ a_{11} & a_{01} & 0 \\ a_{22} & a_{12} & a_{02} \\ 0 & a_{23} & a_{13} \\ 0 & 0 & a_{24} \end{bmatrix} \begin{bmatrix} x_0 \\ x_1 \\ x_2 \end{bmatrix}$$

or

$$\begin{bmatrix} y_0 \\ y_1 \\ y_2 \\ y_3 \\ y_4 \end{bmatrix} = \begin{bmatrix} x_0 & 0 & 0 & 0 & 0 & 0 & 0 & 0 & 0 \\ 0 & x_1 & 0 & x_0 & 0 & 0 & x_0 & 0 & 0 \\ 0 & 0 & x_2 & 0 & x_1 & 0 & 0 & x_1 & 0 \\ 0 & 0 & 0 & 0 & 0 & x_2 & 0 & 0 & x_2 \end{bmatrix} \begin{bmatrix} a_{00} \\ a_{01} \\ a_{02} \\ a_{11} \\ a_{12} \\ a_{13} \\ a_{22} \\ a_{23} \\ a_{24} \end{bmatrix}$$

With obvious identifications, we can now write

$$\mathbf{y} = \mathbf{Ax} \quad \text{in the first arrangement} \tag{A3}$$

$$= \mathbf{Xa} \quad \text{in the second arrangement} \tag{A4}$$

The second form is introduced because of its importance in later discussions.

In the notation a_{km}, the first subscript identifies the term as being the kth tap-gain function, and for fixed k, the sequence a_{km}, $m = 0, 1, 2, \ldots$, gives the values of the kth tap-gain function at the instants $t = m/2W_i$. Notice that the number of *columns* in **A** depends on the duration of the $x(t)$ pulse, while the number of rows depends on the sum of the channel memory and the duration of $x(t)$. Therefore **A** is square only in the case of a one-path channel. Finally, we observe that physical realizability of the channel represented in Fig. A4 requires that all the elements in **A** above the diagonal that starts with the first element in the first row be zero.

The representations (A3) and (A4) and the associated discussion apply generally to channels of the type illustrated in Fig. A4 and with an arbitrary number of taps on the delay line. In order to describe random channels having gaussian statistics, we assume the tap-gain functions, $a_i(t)$, in the delay-line model to be sample functions of a gaussian process. We shall also assume that the $a_i(t)$ have zero means and that the correlation matrix

$$\Phi_{AA} = \begin{bmatrix} \overline{a_{00}^2} & \overline{a_{00}a_{01}} & \cdots & \overline{a_{00}a_{11}} & \cdots & \overline{a_{00}a_{22}} & \cdots \\ \overline{a_{01}a_{02}} & \overline{a_{01}^2} & \cdots & \cdot & \cdots & \cdot & \cdots \\ \cdot & \cdot & \cdots & \cdot & \cdots & \cdot & \cdots \\ \cdot & \cdot & \cdots & \cdot & \cdots & \cdot & \cdots \\ \cdot & \cdot & \cdots & \cdot & \cdots & \cdot & \cdots \\ \overline{a_{11}a_{00}} & \overline{a_{11}a_{01}} & \cdots & \overline{a_{11}^2} & \cdots & \overline{a_{11}a_{22}} & \cdots \\ \cdot & \cdot & \cdots & \cdot & \cdots & \cdot & \cdots \\ \cdot & \cdot & \cdots & \cdot & \cdots & \cdot & \cdots \\ \cdot & \cdot & \cdots & \cdot & \cdots & \cdot & \cdots \\ \overline{a_{22}a_{00}} & \overline{a_{22}a_{01}} & \cdots & \overline{a_{22}a_{11}} & \cdots & \overline{a_{22}^2} & \cdots \\ \cdot & \cdot & \cdots & \cdot & \cdots & \cdot & \cdots \\ \cdot & \cdot & \cdots & \cdot & \cdots & \cdot & \cdots \\ \cdot & \cdot & \cdots & \cdot & \cdots & \cdot & \cdots \end{bmatrix} \tag{A5}$$

is known. The matrix Φ_{AA} is of course symmetrical.

With such a channel, the output signal **y** for a given input signal **x** is gaussian distributed with zero mean and covariance matrix

$$\Phi_{yy} = [\phi_{ij}]$$

in which $\phi_{ij} = \overline{y_i y_j}$, the bar denoting an ensemble average over parameters whose randomness in this case is caused by the channel. For the channel of Fig. A4, we have, for example,

$$\begin{aligned} \overline{y_0^2} &= \overline{a_{00}^2 x_0^2} \\ \overline{y_0 y_1} &= \overline{a_{00}a_{01}}x_0x_1 + \overline{a_{00}a_{11}}x_0^2 \\ \overline{y_1 y_2} &= \overline{a_{11}a_{22}}x_0^2 + (\overline{a_{11}a_{12}} + \overline{a_{01}a_{22}})\,x_0x_1 + \overline{a_{11}a_{02}}\,x_0x_2 \\ &\quad + \overline{a_{01}a_{02}}\,x_1x_2 + \overline{a_{01}a_{12}}\,x_1^2 \end{aligned} \tag{A6}$$

And finally, if **y** (for the given **x**) is gaussian, and the additive noise n is gaussian, the received signal

$$\mathbf{z} = \mathbf{A}\mathbf{x} + \mathbf{n} = \mathbf{y} + \mathbf{n} \tag{A7}$$

is also gaussian and we may write (if N samples constitute the components of $\mathbf{z}$)

$$p(\mathbf{z} \mid \mathbf{x}) = \frac{1}{(2\pi)^{N/2}} \frac{1}{|\mathbf{\Phi}_{zz}|^{1/2}} \exp - \frac{1}{2}\{\mathbf{z}_t \ \mathbf{\Phi}_{zz}^{-1}\mathbf{z}\} \tag{A8}$$

where $\mathbf{\Phi}_{zz}$ is the covariance matrix of $\mathbf{z}$ (given $\mathbf{x}$). If we assume the additive noise to be statistically independent of the channel, then

$$\mathbf{\Phi}_{zz} = \mathbf{\Phi}_{yy} + \mathbf{\Phi}_{nn} \tag{A9}$$

One final point: The extension of the analysis to the bandpass case is easily made—consider the matrix $\mathbf{x}_t$ to be in the form

$$\mathbf{x}_t = [\mathbf{x} \vdots \hat{\mathbf{x}}] = [x_0 \ x_1 \cdots \vdots \ \hat{x}_0 \ \hat{x}_1 \cdots]$$

where the $\hat{x}_i$ are samples from the Hilbert transform $\hat{x}(t)$ of $x(t)$. We write the channel matrix $\mathbf{A}$ in similar partitioned form so that

$$\begin{bmatrix} y \\ \hat{y} \end{bmatrix} = \begin{bmatrix} \mathbf{A} & -\hat{\mathbf{A}} \\ \hat{\mathbf{A}} & \mathbf{A} \end{bmatrix} \begin{bmatrix} \mathbf{x} \\ \hat{\mathbf{x}} \end{bmatrix} \tag{A10}$$

Comparison with (A3) for the lowpass case suggests immediately how the results we shall derive for the lowpass case can be adapted to yield the corresponding results in the bandpass situation.

AIII. Channel-Estimating Filters

The assumption of a random channel in the model of Fig. A1 means that the channel response $y(t)$ to a specified input $x(t)$ cannot be determined in advance—it can at best be estimated on the basis of what is known about the channel statistics. So-called channel estimation [or estimation of $y(t)$] is a fundamental operation in optimal reception of random-channel transmissions, as has already been illustrated in the text of the present chapter. We shall therefore show here how to derive estimates of $y(t)$ on a minimum-variance and on a maximum-likelihood basis from a knowledge of statistics of $z(t)$ and $n(t)$ in Fig. 1. For the minimum-variance estimate we shall only need to assume knowledge of the autocorrelation functions of $z(t)$ and $n(t)$; for the maximum-likelihood estimate we have to assume that $z(t)$ and $n(t)$ are gaussian. Under these assumptions, we shall find that the maximum-likelihood estimate coincides with the minimum-variance estimate—a well known result. The relations we shall need have all been presented in the preceding section.

(i) The minimum-variance estimator[18]—We have $\mathbf{z} = \mathbf{y} + \mathbf{n}$ and we want to find the linear filter, $\mathbf{H}$ (not necessarily realizable), for which

$$\mathbf{y}_e = \mathbf{H}\mathbf{z} \tag{A11}$$

and

$$\epsilon = \overline{(\mathbf{y} - \mathbf{y}_e)^2} = \text{a minimum} \tag{A12}$$

z, **n**, **y**, **ϵ** are all column matrices of length proportional to the duration T of z (or n, etc.). If $T = M\Delta t$, then these matrices have M elements. The number of columns in **H** must be equal to the number of rows in **z**. Furthermore we want to have $\mathbf{y}_e$ of length equal to the length of **y**. Therefore **H** must also have at least as many rows as **y** (or **z**). We say "at least" because we could assume **H** to have more rows than this, but all outputs from **H** after **T** seconds would be neglected. Thus all of these additional rows of **H** may be quite arbitrary. This brings out an important point: We want **H** to be an optimum estimator for only the first T seconds of its operation; it is arbitrary at other times. This fact gives us some freedom when it comes to actually building **H**. We shall assume that **H** is a square matrix of order M.

Thus

$$\epsilon_i = y_i - \sum_{j=0}^{M} h_{ij} z_j$$

$$\overline{\epsilon_i^2} = \overline{y_i^2} - 2\sum_{j=0}^{M} h_{ij}\overline{y_i z_j} + \sum_{j=0}^{M}\sum_{k=0}^{M} h_{ij}h_{ik}\overline{z_j z_k}$$

$$= \overline{y_i^2} - 2\sum_{j=0}^{M} h_{ij}\phi_{yz}(i, j) + \sum_{j=0}^{M}\sum_{k=0}^{M} h_{ij}h_{ik}\phi_{zz}(j, k)$$

For a minimum

$$\frac{\partial\overline{\epsilon_i^2}}{\partial h_{ij}} = 0 \qquad j, k = 0, 1, \cdots M$$

Therefore the ith row of **H** must satisfy

$$\phi_{yz}(i, j) = \sum_{k=0}^{M} h_{ik}\phi_{zz}(j, k) \qquad j, k = 0, 1, \cdots M \tag{A13}$$

or, rearranging all of the terms in a matrix equation,

$$\mathbf{\Phi}_{yz} = \mathbf{H}\mathbf{\Phi}_{zz}$$

But since **y** and **n** are statistically independent,

$$\mathbf{\Phi}_{yz} = \mathbf{\Phi}_{yy}.$$

This enables us to write

$$\mathbf{H}\mathbf{\Phi}_{zz} = \mathbf{\Phi}_{yy}.$$

Postmultiplication on both sides by $\mathbf{\Phi}_{zz}^{-1}$ yields

$$\mathbf{H} = \mathbf{\Phi}_{yy}\mathbf{\Phi}_{zz}^{-1}$$

$$= (\mathbf{\Phi}_{zz} - \mathbf{\Phi}_{nn})\mathbf{\Phi}_{zz}^{-1} \tag{A14}$$

where we have used Eq. (A9). An alternative use of Eq. (A9) also leads to

$$\mathbf{H} = \mathbf{\Phi}_{yy}(\mathbf{\Phi}_{yy} + \mathbf{\Phi}_{nn})^{-1}. \tag{A15}$$

It can be shown that this expression for **H** actually minimizes $\overline{\epsilon^2}$.

Notice that the covariance matrix Φ_{yy} of the channel response to **x** is explicitly present in (A15). The computation of Φ_{yy} is conveniently carried out by using the expression (A4) for **y**. Thus

$$\begin{aligned}\Phi_{yy} &= E[\mathbf{y}\mathbf{y}_t] = \overline{\mathbf{y}\mathbf{y}_t} \\ &= \mathbf{X}\,\overline{\mathbf{a}\,\mathbf{a}_t}\,\mathbf{X}_t \\ &= \mathbf{X}\,\Phi_{AA}\,\mathbf{X}_t \quad .\end{aligned} \tag{A16}$$

Substitution into Eq. (A15) leads to

$$\mathbf{H} = \mathbf{X}\,\Phi_{AA}\,\mathbf{X}_t\,(\mathbf{X}\,\Phi_{AA}\,\mathbf{X}_t + \Phi_{nn})^{-1} \quad . \tag{A17}$$

Expression (A15) is a discrete analog of the Wiener-Hopf integral equation.

(ii) The maximum-likelihood estimator—The maximum-likelihood estimate of **y** is obtained by finding the **y** that maximizes the conditional probability, $p(\mathbf{y}\mid\mathbf{z})$. To solve for this **y** is, in general, quite difficult but for the case of gaussian statistics the calculation is readily made. Therefore, here, in contrast with the minimum-variance estimate, we shall specifically assume that **z**, **y**, and **n** are gaussian as described in Eqs. (A5)—(A9). Thus

$$\mathbf{z} = \mathbf{y} + \mathbf{n}$$

where **z**, **y**, and **n** are all gaussian with zero means and covariance matrices Φ_{zz}, Φ_{yy}, Φ_{nn} respectively.

Now, Bayes' rule gives

$$p(\mathbf{y}\mid\mathbf{z}) = \frac{p(\mathbf{z}\mid\mathbf{y})\,p(\mathbf{y})}{p(\mathbf{z})} = k \cdot p(\mathbf{z}\mid\mathbf{y})\,p(\mathbf{y})$$

where k is a constant because $p(\mathbf{z})$ is a constant. From assumption of gaussian statistics for **y** and **n**, we have (if the output is sampled N times)

$$p(\mathbf{z}\mid\mathbf{y}) = p_n(\mathbf{z}-\mathbf{y}) = \frac{1}{(2\pi)^{N/2}\,|\,\Phi_{nn}\,|^{1/2}}\,\exp -\frac{1}{2}\left\{(\mathbf{z}-\mathbf{y})_t\,\Phi_{nn}^{-1}\,(\mathbf{z}-\mathbf{y})\right\}$$

and, assuming Φ_{yy}^{-1} exists (*i.e.*, Φ_{yy} is nonsingular)

$$p(\mathbf{y}) = \frac{1}{(2\pi)^{N/2}}\,\frac{1}{|\,\Phi_{yy}\,|^{1/2}}\,\exp -\frac{1}{2}\,\mathbf{y}_t\,\Phi_{yy}^{-1}\,\mathbf{y} \quad . \tag{A18}$$

Therefore

$$p(\mathbf{y}\mid\mathbf{z}) = k'\exp -\frac{1}{2}\left\{(\mathbf{z}-\mathbf{y})_t\,\Phi_{nn}^{-1}\,(\mathbf{z}-\mathbf{y}) + \mathbf{y}_t\,\Phi_{yy}^{-1}\,\mathbf{y}\right\} \quad .$$

To obtain the maximum-likelihood estimate of **y**, we set

$$\frac{\partial p(\mathbf{y}\mid\mathbf{z})}{\partial \mathbf{y}} = 0$$

or

$$\frac{\partial}{\partial y}\left\{(\mathbf{z}-\mathbf{y})_t\,\Phi_{nn}^{-1}\,(\mathbf{z}-\mathbf{y}) + \mathbf{y}_t\,\Phi_{yy}^{-1}\,\mathbf{y}\right\} = 0$$

which leads to

$$\begin{aligned}\mathbf{y} &= (\Phi_{nn}^{-1} + \Phi_{yy}^{-1})^{-1}\, \Phi_{nn}^{-1}\, \mathbf{z} \\ &= (\mathbf{I} + \Phi_{nn}\, \Phi_{yy}^{-1})^{-1}\, \mathbf{z} = \Phi_{yy}\,(\Phi_{yy} + \Phi_{nn})^{-1}\, \mathbf{z} \\ &= \mathbf{H}_{me}\, \mathbf{z} \end{aligned} \tag{A19}$$

where

$$\mathbf{H}_{me} = \Phi_{yy}\,(\Phi_{yy} + \Phi_{nn})^{-1} \quad . \tag{A20}$$

This expression for the maximum-likelihood estimating filter, $\mathbf{H}_{me}$, is the same as that for the filter derived on a minimum mean-square error basis. This equivalence is a characteristic of gaussian processes and is not a new result.[19] We might also point out that for gaussian statistics, our estimate of $\mathbf{y}$ is optimum for more general criteria, namely, for any function $L(\mathbf{y} - \mathbf{y}_e)$ fulfilling the requirements[20]

$$\begin{aligned} L(0) &= 0 \\ L(-\epsilon) &= L(\epsilon) \\ L(\epsilon_2) &\geqslant L(\epsilon_1) \geqslant 0 \qquad\qquad \text{for } \epsilon_2 \geqslant \epsilon_1 \geqslant 0. \end{aligned} \tag{A21}$$

Recall that our ability to express $p(\mathbf{y})$ as in (A18) depended upon the nonsingularity of Φ_{YY}. Examples in which Φ_{YY} is singular are rare in the real world, but important among these is a time-invariant channel whose output $\mathbf{y}$ matrix is specified as a 1 by N matrix with $N > 1$. But it is interesting to note that Φ_{YY}, singular or nonsingular, can always be expressed in the form (A16) in which Φ_{AA} is nonsingular and $\mathbf{X}$ is generally not a square matrix.

But the result in Eq. (A20) does not involve Φ_{yy}^{-1} and it holds whether or not Φ_{yy} is singular. This can be shown by writing

$$\mathbf{z} = \mathbf{y} + \mathbf{n} = \mathbf{X}\mathbf{a} + \mathbf{n}$$

and seeking first a maximum-likelihood estimate of $\mathbf{a}$ for use in estimating $\mathbf{y}$. Thus, we first write

$$p(\mathbf{a} \mid \mathbf{z}) = \frac{p(\mathbf{z} \mid \mathbf{X}\mathbf{a})\, p(\mathbf{a} \mid \mathbf{X})\, p(\mathbf{X})}{p(\mathbf{z})} = k \cdot p(\mathbf{z} \mid \mathbf{X}\mathbf{a})\, p(\mathbf{a} \mid \mathbf{X})$$

where k is a constant since $p(\mathbf{z})$ and $p(\mathbf{X})$ are constants. If we note that $p(\mathbf{z} \mid \mathbf{X}\mathbf{a}) = p_n(\mathbf{z} - \mathbf{X}\mathbf{a})$ and that $p(\mathbf{a} \mid \mathbf{X}) = p(\mathbf{a})$ because of independence of channel and signal, then assumption of gaussian statistics for channel and for noise, as before, leads to

$$p(\mathbf{a} \mid \mathbf{z}) = k' \cdot \exp - \frac{1}{2} \left\{ (\mathbf{z} - \mathbf{X}\mathbf{a})_t\, \Phi_{nn}^{-1}\, (\mathbf{z} - \mathbf{X}\mathbf{a}) + \mathbf{a}_t \Phi_{AA}^{-1}\, \mathbf{a} \right\} \tag{A22}$$

where k' is independent of $\mathbf{a}$. For a maximum likelihood estimate of $\mathbf{a}$, we set

$$\frac{\partial p(\mathbf{a} \mid \mathbf{z})}{\partial \mathbf{a}} = 0$$

to obtain

$$(\mathbf{a}_{me})_t = \mathbf{z}_t \Phi_{nn}^{-1} \mathbf{X} (\Phi_{AA}^{-1} + \mathbf{X}_t \Phi_{nn}^{-1} \mathbf{X})^{-1}$$

whence

$$\mathbf{y}_{me} = \mathbf{X} \mathbf{a}_{me}$$
$$= \mathbf{X} (\Phi_{AA}^{-1} + \mathbf{X}_t \Phi_{nn}^{-1} \mathbf{X})^{-1} \mathbf{X}_t \Phi_{nn}^{-1} \mathbf{z} \quad . \tag{A23}$$

From this it can be shown that $\mathbf{H}_{me}$ has the expression given in (A20).

Before terminating this discussion, attention should be drawn to the fact that the results of this section reveal various matrix identities, and new arrangements can be adduced from them by matrix manipulations. Some of these matrix arrangements have been valuable as springboards for synthesizing optimum receivers for random channels.[7] In the next section we shall illustrate this by synthesizing a "one-shot" optimum receiver, meaning a receiver whose operation is optimum in any one decision interval T without making use of observations made in other intervals. Optimum sequential receivers have been illustrated in the text of this chapter.

AIV. A "One-shot" Optimum Receiver

As stated earlier, the optimum receiver computes the set of *a posteriori* probabilities $\{p(\mathbf{x}^{(k)} \mid \mathbf{z})\}$. We shall show how to get one of these, say $p(\mathbf{x}^{(k)} \mid \mathbf{z})$.

From Bayes' rule we have

$$p(\mathbf{x}^{(k)} \mid \mathbf{z}) = \frac{p(\mathbf{z} \mid \mathbf{x}^{(k)}) p(\mathbf{x}^{(k)})}{\sum_k p(\mathbf{z} \mid \mathbf{x}^{(k)}) p(\mathbf{x}^{(k)})} \quad . \tag{A24}$$

We shall assume that the $p(\mathbf{x}^k)$ are known; then, since the denominator of Eq. (A24) is a constant, what we essentially have to compute is the "forward" probability $p(\mathbf{z} \mid \mathbf{x}^{(k)})$. This is given by the multivariate gaussian distribution as in Eq. (A8). But notice that since the exponential is a single-valued function of its argument, we might just as well compute the quadratic form

$$\Lambda'^{(k)} = \mathbf{z}_t [\Phi_{zz}^{(k)}]^{-1} \mathbf{z} \quad . \tag{A25}$$

Substitution from Eq. (A14) for $[\Phi_{zz}^{(k)}]^{-1}$ yields

$$\Lambda'^{(k)} = \mathbf{z}_t \Phi_{nn}^{-1} \mathbf{z} - \mathbf{z}_t \Phi_{nn}^{-1} \mathbf{H}^{(k)} \mathbf{z} \quad . \tag{A26}$$

Since the first term on the right-hand side of Eq. (A26) is independent of $\mathbf{x}^{(k)}$ we need only to consider the second term:

$$\Lambda^{(k)} = \mathbf{z}_t \Phi_{nn}^{-1} \mathbf{H}^{(k)} \mathbf{z} \tag{A27}$$

and $\Lambda^{(k)}$, which is also a quadratic form, will determine the operations that the receiver will have to perform. These we shall now discuss.

Consider first the case in which the additive noise is white gaussian, with a noise power of 1 watt per cycle; that is, $\Phi_{nn} = \mathbf{I}$, the identity matrix. Then we have

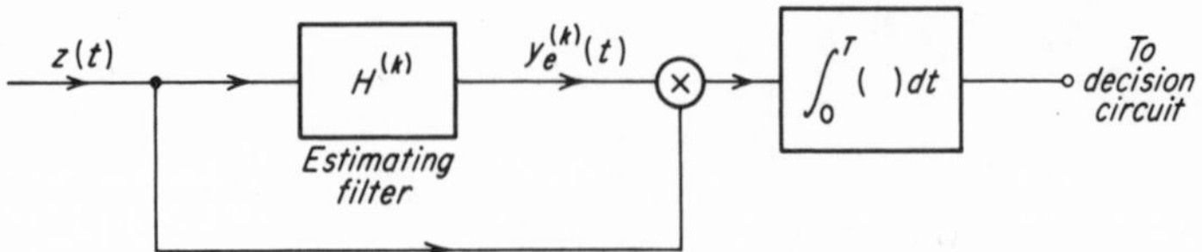

Fig. A5. The kth-signal branch of the optimum receiver for a random channel with additive *white* gaussian noise.

$$\Lambda^{(k)} = \mathbf{z}_t \mathbf{H}^{(k)} \mathbf{z} = (\mathbf{z}_t)(\mathbf{H}^{(k)} \mathbf{z}) \quad . \tag{A28}$$

To compute this we can use the receiver structure that is shown in Fig. A5; that is, we pass $\mathbf{z}$ through the filter $\mathbf{H}^{(k)}$, then multiply the output of $\mathbf{H}$ by $\mathbf{z}$, and integrate over a time T. The output of the integrator at time T is simply related to $p(\mathbf{z} \mid \mathbf{x}^{(k)})$; the multiplier-and-integrator combination is just a cross-correlator. From the preceding section, we recall that $\mathbf{H}^{(k)}$ represents a filter that operates on $\mathbf{z} = (\mathbf{y}^{(k)} + \mathbf{n})$ to give an estimate, $\mathbf{y}_e^{(k)}$ of $\mathbf{y}$ which is optimum in a minimum mean-square error sense and, for gaussian statistics, in a maximum-likelihood sense also.

The filters $\mathbf{H}^{(k)}$ are, in general, not realizable. When we have white gaussian noise, however, the $\mathbf{H}^{(k)}$ are symmetric and therefore we can write

$$\Lambda^{(k)} = \mathbf{z}_t \mathbf{H}'^{(k)} \mathbf{z} \tag{A29}$$

where $\mathbf{H}'^{(k)}$ is a realizable filter which is obtained from $\mathbf{H}^{(k)}$ by omitting all terms above the main diagonal and doubling all terms below it. Therefore, in Fig. A5 the output of the filter $h(\tau, t)$ (which is a realizable filter) is $\mathbf{y}_e^{(k)}$, and hence the receiver effectively cross-correlates $z(t)$ and $y_e^{(k)}(t)$ to give an output that is directly related to $p(\mathbf{x}^{(k)} \mid \mathbf{z})$. Thus we have a rather natural generalization of the situation in which the channel A is known, for which case an optimum receiver is shown in Fig. A3. Finally, note that we can also set up a matched-filter type of receiver to perform the cross-correlation in Eq. (A28).

Now let us return to the case in which the noise is not white and therefore $\mathbf{\Phi}_{nn}^{-1} \neq \mathbf{I}$. In this case

$$\Lambda^{(k)} = \mathbf{z}_t \mathbf{\Phi}_{nn}^{-1} \mathbf{H}^{(k)} \mathbf{z} \tag{A30}$$

Here a receiver structure of the type shown in Fig. A5 can be used. Since $\mathbf{\Phi}_{nn}^{-1} \mathbf{H}^{(k)}$ is symmetric [it is equal to the difference of two symmetric matrices, *cf.* Eq. (A14)], we can again use the method given above, *cf.* Eq. (A29), to make the filter $\mathbf{\Phi}_{nn}^{-1} \mathbf{H}^{(k)}$ realizable. Note that while $\mathbf{\Phi}_{nn}^{-1}$ is symmetric, $\mathbf{H}^{(k)}$ is not necessarily symmetric. In this receiver $\mathbf{H}^{(k)}$ again plays the role of a maximum-likelihood filter that produces as its output the best possible estimate of $\mathbf{y}^{(k)}$, say $\mathbf{y}_e^{(k)}$.

While we thus have a receiver structure for the non-white noise case, we can obtain another structure that is equivalent to this but

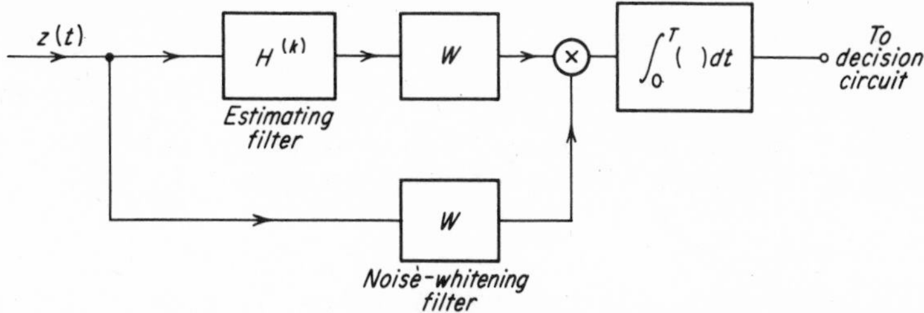

Fig. A6. The kth-signal branch of the optimum receiver for a random channel with additive *non-white* gaussian noise.

has a direct relation to the receiver structure for white noise. We first recall a theorem in matrix algebra[21] which states that a positive-definite matrix can be factored into the product of a triangular matrix and its transpose. Applying this theorem to Φ_{nn}^{-1}, we can write

$$\Phi_{nn}^{-1} = \mathbf{W}_t \mathbf{W} \tag{A31}$$

where **W** is a matrix whose elements above the main diagonal are all zeros. Using Eq. (A31) we can write

$$\Lambda^{(k)} = z_t \mathbf{W}_t \mathbf{W} \mathbf{H}^{(k)} \mathbf{z} = (\mathbf{W}\mathbf{z})_t (\mathbf{W}\mathbf{H}^{(k)} \mathbf{z}) \tag{A32}$$

A receiver structure for implementing Eq. (A32) is shown in Fig. A6. The filter **W** has an interesting effect upon the noise. Notice that if $\mathbf{n}_0$ represents the noise output from **W** when **n** is at its input, then $\mathbf{n}_0 = \mathbf{W}\mathbf{n}$ and $\Phi_{n_0 n_0} = \mathbf{W}\Phi_{nn} W_t$. Substitution from (A31) gives $\Phi_{n_0 n_0} = \mathbf{W}\mathbf{W}^{-1}\mathbf{W}_t^{-1}\mathbf{W}_t = \mathbf{I}$. This shows that the filter **W** acts as a "whitening" filter for the noise component of the received signal **z**. The action of the receiver is now clear: To reduce the non-white-noise case to the white-noise case we pass **z** through a "noise-whitening" filter **W**. However, **W** distorts the signal portion $\mathbf{y}^{(k)}$ of **z**, and to compensate for this distortion we pass $\mathbf{y}_e^{(k)}$ (which is the output of the filter $\mathbf{H}^{(k)}$) through the same filter **W**. We are now in the same situation as in the case for white noise, and the optimum operation, once again, is the cross-correlation of **z** and $\mathbf{y}_e^{(k)}$.

Thus we have seen in Figs. A5 and A6 how the concept of correlation detection extends in a rather natural fashion to the case of transmission through a random channel. However, the extension is incomplete in one respect: We cannot now assume that A is not random and obtain the result shown in Fig. A3. This is because, here, **y** is no longer random and **z** (although still gaussian distributed) does not have *zero* mean; therefore Eq. (A8) is not true. But the situation is easily remedied. We shall assume that channel A is such that $\mathbf{y}^{(k)}$ is gaussian with a mean $\overline{\mathbf{y}^{(k)}}$ which is known *a priori*. Then $\mathbf{y}^{(k)}$ can be written as the sum of a random component $\mathbf{y}_r^{(k)}$ and a constant component $\overline{\mathbf{y}^{(k)}}$

$$\mathbf{y}^{(k)} = \mathbf{y}_r^{(k)} + \overline{\mathbf{y}^{(k)}} \tag{A33}$$

and similarly we can write

$$\mathbf{y}^{(k)} = \mathbf{A}\mathbf{x}^{(k)} = \mathbf{A}_r\mathbf{x}^{(k)} + \overline{\mathbf{A}}\mathbf{x}^{(k)} \ . \tag{A34}$$

With these additional assumptions and definitions it can readily be seen that $\mathbf{z}$ is gaussian with mean $\overline{\mathbf{y}^{(k)}}$ and covariance matrix

$$\mathbf{\Phi}_{zz}^{(k)} = \mathbf{\Phi}_{y_r y_r}^{(k)} + \mathbf{\Phi}_{nn} \ . \tag{A35}$$

Since we have already gone through the derivations in detail for the case in which $\overline{\mathbf{y}^{(k)}}$ is zero, we can proceed by analogy without much further explanation.

Thus

$$\Lambda'^{(k)} = (\mathbf{z} - \overline{\mathbf{y}^{(k)}})_t \, [\mathbf{\Phi}_{zz}^{(k)}]^{-1} (\mathbf{z} - \overline{\mathbf{y}^{(k)}}) \tag{A36}$$

$$= (\mathbf{z} - \overline{\mathbf{y}^{(k)}})_t \, \mathbf{\Phi}_{nn}^{-1} (\mathbf{z} - \overline{\mathbf{y}^{(k)}}) - (\mathbf{z} - \overline{\mathbf{y}^{(k)}})_t \, \mathbf{\Phi}_{nn}^{-1} \mathbf{H}_r^{(k)} (\mathbf{z} - \overline{\mathbf{y}^{(k)}}) \tag{A37}$$

where

$$\mathbf{H}_r^{(k)} = \mathbf{\Phi}_{y_r y_r} [\mathbf{\Phi}_{y_r y_r} + \mathbf{\Phi}_{nn}]^{-1} \tag{A38}$$

and then, if we assume that the transmitted signals $\mathbf{x}^{(k)}$ all have the same energy, and that the noise is white, with power of 1 watt per cycle per second, we have

$$\Lambda^{(k)} = +2\overline{\mathbf{y}_t^{(k)}}\mathbf{z} + (\mathbf{z} - \overline{\mathbf{y}^{(k)}})_t \, \mathbf{H}_r^{(k)} (\mathbf{z} - \overline{\mathbf{y}^{(k)}}) \ . \tag{A39}$$

$\Lambda^{(k)}$ determines the receiver structure shown in Fig. A7.

Now notice that if $\mathbf{y}_r^{(k)} = 0$—that is, there are no random components in the channel—we have the receiver that is shown in Fig. A3. Modifications can be made as before when the noise is not white and/or when the transmitted signals are not of equal energy.

In conclusion, it should be pointed out that the method of reception discussed in this section is but one interesting example of various useful forms[7] that are suggested by rearrangements of the basic matrix equations derived in the preceding section. One of these re-

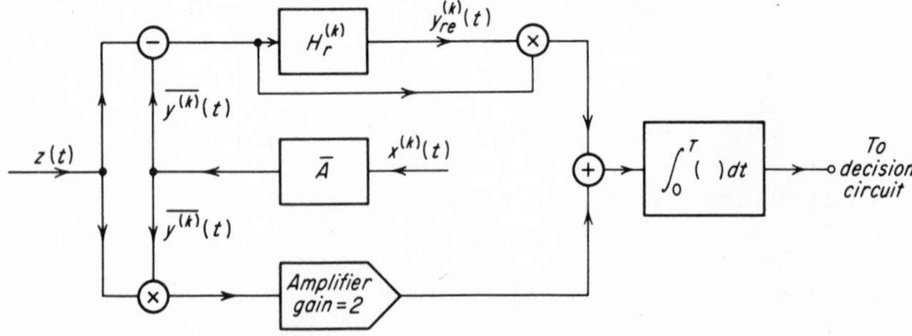

Fig. A7. The kth-signal branch of the optimum receiver for a channel whose output consists of a specular component and a random component with additive *white* gaussian noise.

arrangements [(67) of the main text] has served as the basis for the discussion of the sequential reception problem in the main text.

REFERENCES

1. R. Price, "Notes on Ideal Receivers for Scatter Multipath," Group Report 34-39, Lincoln Laboratory, Massachusetts Institute of Technology, May 1955.
2. R. Price and P. E. Green, "A Communication Technique for Multipath Channels," *Proc. IRE,* vol. 46, pp. 555-570, March 1958.
3. G. L. Turin, "Communication through Noisy, Random-Multipath Channels," Technical Report No. 116, Lincoln Laboratory, Massachusetts Institute of Technology, May 1956.
4. G. L. Turin, "Review of Statistical Multipath-Communication Theory." Presented at the Second National Symposium on Global Communication, St. Petersburg, Fla., December 1958.
5. R. M. Fano, "On Matched-Filter Detection in the Presence of Multipath Propagation," Informal Memorandum, Research Laboratory of Electronics, Massachusetts Institute of Technology, 1956.
6. T. Kailath, "Correlation Detection of Signals Perturbed by a Random Channel," *Trans. IRE, PGIT, Matched-Filter Issue,* pp. 361-366, June 1960
7. T. Kailath, "Optimum Receivers for Randomly Varying Channels.' To be published in *Proc. Fourth London Symposium on Information Theory,* Butterworth's Scientific Publications, London, 1960.
8. M. L. Doelz, E. T. Heald, and D. L. Martin, "Binary Data Transmission Techniques for Linear Systems," *Proc. IRE,* vol. 45, pp. 656-661, May 1957.
9. T. Kailath, "Sampling Models for Linear Time-Variant Filters," Technical Report 352, Research Laboratory of Electronics, Massachusetts Institute of Technology, May 1959. (Chapter 6 of the present volume is an adaptation of this report by the Editor).
10. T. Kailath, "Estimating Filters for Linear Time-Variant Channels," Quarterly Progress Report, Research Laboratory of Electronics, Massachusetts Institute of Technology, April 15, 1960.
11. P. M. Woodward, *Probability and Information Theory with Applications to Radar,* Pergamon Press, London, 1953.
12. C. E. Shannon, "Communication in the Presence of Noise," *Proc. IRE,* vol. 37, pp. 10-21, January 1949.
13. W. B. Davenport, Jr., and W. L. Root, *Introduction to Random Signals and Noise,* McGraw-Hill Book Company, Inc., New York, 1958.
14. H. Cramér, *Mathematical Methods of Statistics,* Princeton University Press, Princeton, N.J., 1946.

15. R. Courant and D. Hilbert, *Methods of Mathematical Physics*, vol. 1, Interscience Publishers, Inc., New York, 1953.
16. D. O. North, "An Analysis of the Factors Which Determine Signal/Noise Discrimination in Pulsed-Carrier Systems," Technical Report PTR-6C, RCA Laboratories, Princeton, N.J., 1943.
17. J. H. Van Vleck and D. A. Middleton, "Theoretical Comparison of the Visual, Aural, and Meter Reception of Pulsed Signals in the Presence of Noise," *J. Appl. Phy.*, vol. 17, pp. 940-971, November 1946.
18. B. Friedland, "Theory of Time-Varying Sampled-Data Systems," Technical Report T-19/B, Electronics Research Laboratories, Columbia University, April 1957.
19. G. W. Preston. "The Equivalence of Optimum Transducers and Sufficient and Most Efficient Statistics," *J. Appl. Phy.*, vol. 24, pp. 841-844, July 1953.
20. S. Sherman, "Non-Mean-Square Error Criteria," *Trans. IRE, PGIT-4,* pp. 125-126, September 1958.
21. E. A. Guillemin, *The Mathematics of Circuit Analysis*, John Wiley & Sons, Inc., New York, 1949.

CHAPTER 13

Coding and Decoding

Peter Elias

I. INTRODUCTION

Preceding chapters have discussed what channels are like, how noise can be described, how to make decisions as to which signal has been sent over a noisy channel, and how to choose which signals to send. We will discuss here additional steps that can be taken between the information source and the transmitter, and between the decision-maker and the recipient, namely, *coding and decoding.*

The typical problems in decision making which have been discussed assume that two waveforms have been selected for signalling purposes and that during each use of the channel, the receiver knows that one of these two has been sent. The receiver must then decide, on the basis of the received noisy waveform, which is more likely *a posteriori*. These decisions will from time to time be incorrect, so that the output of the decision device is a stream of binary digits which agrees with the stream of binary digits going into the transmitter most of the time, but differs occasionally. If we consider the modulator, transmitter, transmitting antenna, medium, receiving antenna, receiver, and decision-making device all together as a channel that accepts binary input digits and produces binary output digits, then this channel can be represented as in Fig. 1. Here p_c is the probability of a "crossover" or error, and $q = 1 - p_c$ is the probability of correct transmission. We assume that the decision maker operates symmetrically, so that ones and zeros are equally likely to be received in error. This is a plausible assumption in communications, where zeros and ones are likely to be more or less equiprobable as inputs to the transmitter, unlike the radar situation in which the presence of a signal may be much less likely than its absence.

If the signalling rate has been set, and optimum signals and detection procedures are in use, then p_c can be reduced only by increasing transmitter power, or by installing additional equipment

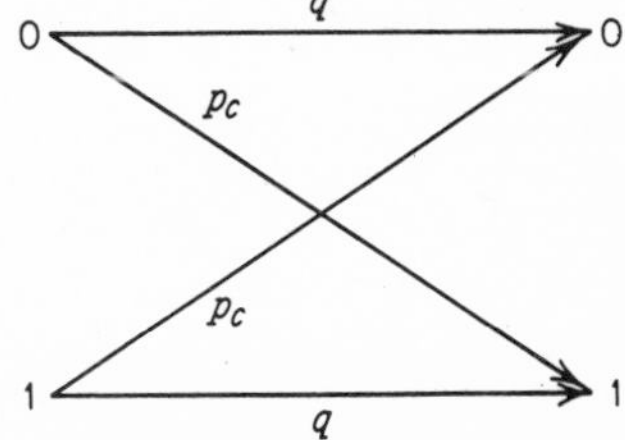

Fig. 1. Binary symmetric channel .

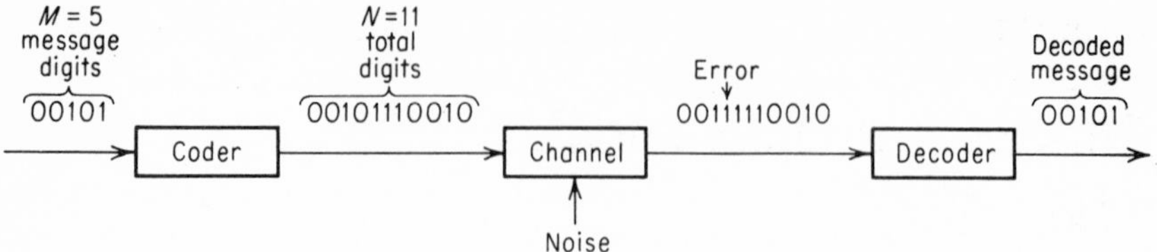

Fig. 2. Check-digit code for binary symmetric channel.

and using a diversity system, or by using a receiver with a lower noise figure, or by other modifications in the design of the system. On the other hand, given a fixed channel like that in Fig. 1, it is possible to precede it by a coding device, and to follow it by a decoding device, so as to produce in effect another binary channel in which the signalling rate is slower, but the crossover probability is much smaller. If it is desired to keep the data rate constant then it will be necessary to speed up the signalling rate in the original system. Apart from this, however, this option does not require any modification of the channel, transmitter, or other equipment in the original system. But it does require additional digital data-processing equipment before the transmitter and after the receiver, as is illustrated in Fig. 2.

As can be seen in Fig. 2, the coding and decoding also introduce two new parameters into the design situation. The continuous stream of digits coming into the coder is segmented into blocks, each of M consecutive digits. To each block is added a number of check digits, whose values are determined by the values of the message digits, bringing the total number of digits in the code block up to $N > M$. Each digit, message or check, is transmitted as a waveform, and the receiver and decision-maker produces an output stream of binary digits which differs from time to time from the input stream. The decoder examines each block of N successive message and check digits, and makes use of the check digits to correct some of the decisions which were made earlier.

It can be seen that this procedure involves a reduction in the rate of transmission, since the system can only accept M message digits during the length of time required to transmit N waveforms over the channel. Thus the rate $R = M/N$, of binary digits transmitted per access to the channel, is one parameter of a code. The other is the block size N, which is a measure of the delay introduced by the coding. Since the decoder in this scheme does not operate until all N digits in the block have been received, there is a delay of N channel-access times between the time when the first message digit in a block is received and the time when the decoder can start to compute and decide whether the value of the digit should be altered. Other more continuous coding and decoding procedures have been discussed[2,14] but they all involve a delay of this sort, and a reduction in the rate of transmission.

It is a fundamental result in information theory[5,10,11] that if the rate of transmission $R = M/N$ is less than a quantity called the capacity C of the channel of Fig. 1, then by increasing M and N indefinitely but keeping R fixed, it is possible to make the probability of error for message digits coming out of the decoder as small as is desired. If the channel has no memory—*i. e.*, if the crossover probability p_c is independent of the past history of the channel and of the signal—then the channel capacity C is given by

$$C = 1 + p_c \log_2 p_c + q \log_2 q \,. \tag{1}$$

(Note that since p_c and q are both less than 1, both logarithms are negative and C is less than 1. C has a minimum value of zero which occurs when $p_c = q = 1/2$). If there is memory in the channel, but p_c is the correct average probability of crossover, then C is larger than the value given in Eq. (1) but it is still less than 1.

The ability to attain arbitrarily small error probability while still transmitting at a fixed positive rate, with no increase in transmitter power, makes coding appealing for purposes of reliable communication, particularly for the transmission of digital information with extremely high reliability. But of course there is a price for this result.

First, there is the delay already mentioned. If M and N become large, then the delay between the transmission of a message digit and the reception of a decoded version of it grows. This limitation is inherent and fundamental—it is impossible to attain high reliability without having a large sample of received digits to work on. However, this price may not always be high: in a millisecond communication system a delay of $N = 1000$ is a delay of one second, and for many digital data transmission applications this is of no concern.

Second, the amount of digital data processing which must be done by the coder and the decoder increases as N increases, and this is a more severe limitation than the first in most applications. It is hard to prove theorems about how inherent this computation is in the decoding problem—it is conceivable that with sufficient ingenuity it could be reduced a great deal. In the present state of development the coder in Fig. 2 requires an amount of computation per digit which grows linearly with N. It would be easy to construct a coder for a millisecond communication system with $N = 1000$, and it might be possible to do the same for a microsecond system. The coding part of the problem therefore is not the major obstacle, since $N = 100$ is already a sufficiently large block size to give valuable results. The decoder, however, requires more computation. For the simple block coding scheme illustrated in Fig. 2 (for the channel of Fig. 1) the only known *general* decoding procedures that work for *any* block code are procedures whose computations grow exponentially with N. It is necessary to store or to generate a list of: (a) all 2^N possible received sequences; or (b) all 2^{NR} possible transmitted sequences; or (c) all $2^{N(1-R)}$ possible sets of crossovers that can be corrected.

The received sequences of N digits or a sequence of $N(1-R)$ modified check digits derived from it must be compared with all of the entries in one of the preceding lists. This requires exponential growth, either in equipment or in computing speed, and it becomes impractical when N is large enough to be of any real interest.

Reed[9] has discussed promising decoding procedures for certain block codes. The amount of computation required for these is manageable, and work is being done at Lincoln Laboratory[15] in constructing coding and decoding devices for the implementation of one of these codes, with $M = 64$ and $N = 128$. However, there are limitations on the R and N values for which these codes are efficient in correcting errors. Wozencraft[14] has discussed a sequential decoding procedure for use in conjunction with a coding procedure that generates output digits in a continuous rather than a block fashion. For this scheme the average amount of computation per received digit grows somewhat more slowly than N^2. This procedure is efficient for any R and any N (where N now measures not a block size, but the delay—measured in channel-access times—between the transmission of any one binary digit and the generation of a decoded version of it at the receiver); but the *average* amount of decoding computation per digit grows slowly only for R less than about one-half of the channel capacity. For both the Reed and the Wozencraft procedures it is possible, as Wozencraft has put it, for microsecond digital circuitry to keep up with a millisecond communication system. There are other coding and decoding schemes (all designed for the binary symmetric channel of Fig. 1) which have not been investigated in detail for computational requirements, but which look feasible at about the same complexity for N not too large.

None of these schemes will be considered here. Instead, we shall present a modification of the decision process in the system of Fig. 1, which is easy to implement and which intrinsically simplifies the decoding problem. This modification also increases the channel capacity under certain circumstances. But when used for maximal simplification of decoding, it is more likely to reduce the channel capacity slightly. We shall then discuss the procedure of coding and decoding for the modified channel, and evaluate the probability of successful decoding. Finally we shall assume a particular model for the physical channel, and evaluate the overall behavior of the system using block coding.

II. ERASURES

When the composite channel of Fig. 2 is viewed from end to end, (including the coder and decoder), it simulates a device that accepts a selection of one of the 2^M possible input sequences of M message digits and, after a delay of N channel access times, reproduces that selection at the output of the decoder with a small probability of error. However, the actual course of events is as follows: The input sequence of M binary digits generates the $(N-M)$ check digits; each of the resulting N digits then selects one of the two waveforms to be transmitted during a channel access time; thereafter, the sequence of N waveforms is received and the decision-maker makes a preliminary decision about each one to produce a sequence of binary digits; the decoder then imposes the constraint that only 2^M of the possible 2^N sequences of length N can in fact have been transmitted, and chooses the one of these which on the basis of the preliminary decisions on individual digits looks most probable.

From the statistical viewpoint, this rather complex procedure is obviously not an optimum thing to do. First, although the two waveforms used for transmitting digits may be optimum for binary signalling, the 2^M sequences of N of them which are in fact used as a larger alphabet with a longer signalling time may not be an especially good set of signals under the conditions of the channel. Second, given the transmitted waveforms actually in use, the procedure of making preliminary decisions destroys information. The receiver would do better if, instead of making decisions on individual digits, the *a posteriori* probabilities were computed and saved until all N digits became available. The decoder could then determine which of the possible 2^M sequences had the highest *a posteriori* probability on the basis of the received signal, and thereby could make an optimum decision. Special systems of this sort have been discussed.[12]

There are reasons of practicality for following the procedure of Fig. 2. It is not tempting to think of selecting an optimum set of 2^{100} waveforms, or constructing 2^{100} cross-correlators or other devices in order to make an optimum decision on them. We shall therefore not change the waveform-generating process. However, we will permit the decision maker to present a little more *a posteriori* probability information than is done in the case of a binary decision. When the receiver receives a waveform and computes *a posteriori* probabilities for the two possible transmitted waveforms, then if the ratio of the computed probabilities is very large or very small the receiver makes a decision and prints an output zero or one, as before. However, we now permit the receiver to refuse to guess if the ratio of *a posteriori* probabilities is not sufficiently extreme. Instead of a 0 or 1, the receiver then prints out an X, indicating that the transmitted digit was "erased" by the channel. This gives a uniform floor to the *a posteriori* probabilities in the case of the decisions which *are* made. The combination of channel, transmitter, receiver, and decision maker then looks like the model of Fig. 3, rather than that of Fig. 1. Here p_c is, as before, the probability that an input digit will be received incorrectly, and is again assumed symmetric, q is the probability that an input digit will be correctly received, and $p_x = 1-q-p_c$ is the probability that an input digit will not be received at all—*i.e.*, that the channel was noisy or faded enough so that a decision of sufficient reliability could not be reached.

By changing a threshold in the receiver (which is an easy operation to perform) it is possible to reduce p_c at the expense of increasing

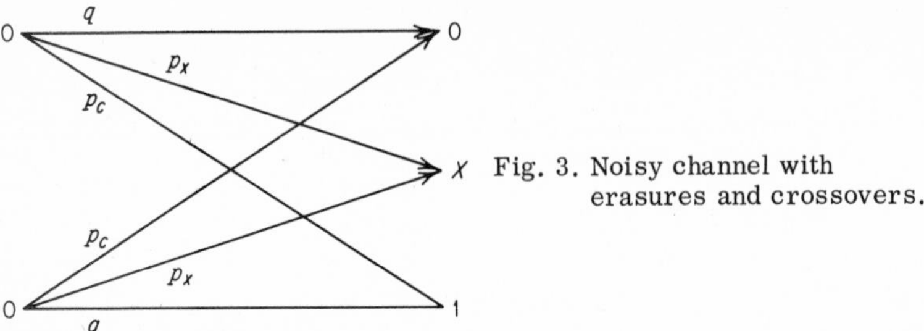

Fig. 3. Noisy channel with erasures and crossovers.

p_x. But it is possible to decrease *both* of them by using more transmitter power or otherwise improving the received signal-to-noise ratio or the channel statistics.

The detection procedure that gives the channel of Fig. 3 is appealing in the case of fading when FSK or some such constant-energy transmission scheme is used. For in the absence of fading, it is possible to make decisions with very small p_c; but when the fading is bad it would take fantastic amounts of transmitter power to guarantee small p_c in the channel of Fig. 1. One possibility in using the channel of Fig. 3 is to make p_c so small that it can be ignored in terms of the overall reliability requirements for the system. The channel can then make erasures only, and no errors. Such a channel model has been discussed under the name of the *binary erasure channel.* Block coding and decoding procedures have been given[2,3] and sequential decoding procedures analogous to those used by Wozencraft in the binary symmetric case have been investigated by Epstein.[4] However, the restriction of negligible p_c becomes more severe as the block size or constraint length N grows. A single crossover in a block may cause many errors in message digits, and p_c must be so small that the probability of a single crossover in a sequence of N digits is also negligible—*i.e.*, not only p_c but Np_c must be negligible, and N will be 100 or more in the cases of interest. We shall relax this requirement. We shall consider coding procedures that will handle any number of erasures in a block, and will also permit the detection and correction of some crossovers. However, the decoding computation, which requires of the order of N^2 operations per digit for dealing with erasures alone, becomes substantially greater than this if three or more crossovers are to be corrected. Thus, we shall restrict the decoding operation to the correction of one or two crossovers per block, along with any number of erasures.

III. PARITY-CHECK CODES

The codes that we shall discuss are block parity-check codes. They have been widely discussed,[3,6,7,13] but not very much of the published work deals with codes for large N and their use in channels having erasures. An example of such a code is given in Fig. 4.

Message digits

I_k = 00101

$$\text{Coding matrix} \rightarrow [A_{jk}] \quad \begin{bmatrix} 01001 \\ 10111 \\ 00101 \\ 11010 \\ 01101 \\ 10010 \end{bmatrix} \quad \left.\begin{matrix} 1 \\ 0 \\ 0 \\ 0 \\ 0 \\ 0 \end{matrix}\right\} \text{Check digits } C_j = \sum_{k=1}^{5} A_{jk} I_k, \quad 1 \leq j \leq 6$$

Coded message = 00101100000

Received message = 00XX110X000

Decoding equations

Initial form	Unknowns isolated	Solution
$0 + 0 + 0 + 0 + 1 = 1$		
$0 + 0 + I_3 + I_4 + 1 = 0$	$I_3 + I_4 = 1$	$I_3 = 1$
$0 + 0 + I_3 + 0 + 1 = X$	$I_3 = 1 + X$	$I_4 = 0$
$0 + 0 + 0 + I_4 + 0 = 0$	$I_4 = 0$	
$0 + 0 + I_3 + 0 + 1 = 0$	$I_3 = 1$	
$0 + 0 + 0 + I_4 + 0 = 0$	$I_4 = 0$	

Fig. 4. Decoding erasures by parity-check equations.

For block length N and rate R, the code has $M = NR$ message digits and $N - M = N(1 - R)$ check digits. We denote the M message digits by $I_1, I_2, \ldots, I_M$ and the $N(1 - R)$ check digits by $C_1, C_2, \ldots, C_{N(1-R)}$. Then the values of the check digits are given by the $N(1 - R)$ equations

$$\sum_{k=1}^{M} A_{jk} I_k = C_j, \quad 1 \leq j \leq N(1 - R), \tag{2}$$

where the summation is modulo 2, and $[A_{jk}]$ is an $N(1 - R)$ by M matrix whose entries are 0 or 1, as illustrated in Fig. 4. That is, each check digit C_j checks a subset of the information digits whose positions are the values of k for which A_{jk} has the value 1. Equation (2) means that if among this subset there is an odd number of message digits having the value 1, then C_j is made equal to 1; if there is an even number of message digits with value 1 in the subset, then C_j is made equal to 0. The check digit C_j is called a *parity-check* digit because it checks the parity (evenness or oddness) of a set of digit values. Addition modulo two follows the rules for the addition of even and odd numbers, with 0 representing even and 1 representing odd. Thus $0 + 0 = 1 + 1 = 0$ (the sum of two even numbers or two odd numbers is even), and $0 + 1 = 1 + 0 = 1$ (the sum of an even number and an odd number is odd).

The code is specified completely by the matrix $[A_{jk}]$, which is assumed known to both the transmitter and the receiver. The formation of the check digits is a straightforward operation by conventional digital techniques. It could be realized, for example, by taking the logical product (the "and") of the M-digit message sequence with the first row of the matrix, $[A_{jk}]$, and shifting the resultant M-digit sequence through a flip-flop to count evenness or oddness of the number of ones in the logical product, and thus to generate C_1. Repeating this process with the other rows of the matrix forms the full set of $N(1 - R)$ check digits as successive outputs of the flip-flop.

IV. DECODING ERASURES

The block of N coded digits is now transmitted over the noisy channel of Fig. 3, first the M message digits and next the $N(1 - R)$ check digits. We assume for the moment that the crossover probability p_c is so small that the receiver can ignore the possibility of crossovers.

If no erasures occur in the received sequence, then the decoding operation just consists in throwing away the check digits and reproducing the received message digits. If any number of erasures have occurred among the check digits, but no message digits have been erased, then the receiver could regenerate the check digits again by making use of the equations (2), as the coder did to generate the check digits in the first place. This is unnecessary, however, since the decoder is ultimately interested only in the message digits: if none of *them* have been erased, the decoder may ignore the check digits.

If a single message digit I_k has been erased, then the receiver can replace it by inspecting the *kth* column of the matrix $[A_{jk}]$ and finding a row j in which the coefficient $A_{jk} = 1$, and for which the check digit C_j has not been erased; that is, the receiver must find any unerased check digit that checks the erased message digit. Having done so, the receiver can fill in all the values in the *jth* equation of the set (2), replacing all the known information digits by the received values 0 or 1 and the check digit C_j by its received value, leaving only I_k as an unknown quantity with coefficient $A_{jk} = 1$. Thus I_k is determined as the value that makes the *jth* equation correct—*i.e.*, makes C_j equal to the parity (0 for even, 1 for odd) of the number of 1's on the left-hand side of the equation. This decoding procedure fails only if *all* of the check digits that check I_k have been erased in transmission.

When more than one erasure occurs, decoding is carried out by solving a set of linear simultaneous equations in modulo two algebra. Since the decoder knows the coefficient matrix $[A_{jk}]$, it can generate the equations (2), using the known numerical values (0 or 1) for the coefficients and for those message digits and check digits which have not been erased. The erased message digits whose coefficients A_{jk} are not 0 in a particular equation remain in that equation on the left as unknowns. The remainder of the terms on the left are just 0's and 1's that can be added up modulo 2 and added modulo 2 to both sides of the equation to leave each equation with a subset of the erased message digits on the left and a 0 or 1 on the right. (Note that adding a digit to itself modulo 2 always gives 0, so that addition and subtraction are identical in modulo 2 arithmetic.) Those equations for which the check digits have been erased during transmission also have an unknown check digit on the right, and may be thrown away by the decoder, which then proceeds to solve the simultaneous set of equations.

This process is illustrated in Fig. 4 for a particular set of erasures. It can be described more formally. Suppose that k_1 erasures have occurred among the message digits and k_2 among the check digits. Let K be the set of k_1 integers labelling the positions of the erased message digits, and let K' be the set of M-k_1 integers labelling the positions of those left unerased. Thus I_k is erased for k in K, and is not erased for k in K'. Let J be the set of k_2 integers that label the positions of the erased check digits, and let J' be the set of $N(1-R)-k_2$ integers that label the other check digits. Then the set of $N(1-R)-k_2$ simultaneous equations which the decoder uses is

$$\sum_{k \text{ in } K} A_{jk}I_k = \sum_{k \text{ in } K'} A_{jk}I_k + C_j, \text{ for all } j \text{ in } J'. \tag{3}$$

The matrix of coefficients for the k_1 unknowns which appears on the left in (3) is obtained from the original matrix $[A_{jk}]$ by selecting and assembling those columns in the original matrix which correspond to erased message digits, and then striking out those rows which correspond to erased check digits.

The integers modulo 2 form a field, and the operation of solving a set of simultaneous linear equations in modulo 2 algebra follows precisely along the lines of doing the same thing for a set of unknown real numbers.[1] Equations may be added to one another to produce a final diagonal set in which each unknown appears isolated on the left, as shown in Fig. 4. The conditions for solubility of the set are also the same: there must be a set of independent equations which is as large as the number of unknowns. A *necessary* condition for this is that the number of equations be at least as large as the number of unknowns; *i.e.* that $k_1 \leq N(1-R)-k_2$, or $k = k_1 + k_2 \leq N(1-R)$, so that the total number of erasures in the block is less than or at most equal to the total number of check digits that were originally provided. A necessary *and sufficient* condition is that the set of columns corresponding to erased information digits, after crossing out the rows corresponding to erased check digits, be linearly independent under addition modulo 2.

To solve a set of linear equations requires on the order of N^3

multiplications and additions. In the modulo 2 case, if the modified coefficient matrix of (3) is first assembled and then each row is represented as one word in a register, the operation of adding one row to another modulo two is just one computer operation, provided that the computer word length available is as large as the largest number of erasures that the system can handle, and about N^2 such operations (times a bookkeeping factor independent of N) are needed to solve for all of the erasures in the received block of N digits.

V. DECODING CROSSOVERS

In decoding erasures the only question as to the decodeability of a received block of N digits is whether the equations provided by the constraints (2) are sufficient to determine the missing message digits. No question of consistency of the equations can arise. For if no crossovers have occurred, then the equations (3) are obviously consistent: the original set of values for the erased message digits satisfy all the equations (2), and thus certainly all of (3). It is just necessary to be sure that no other set of values also satisfies them. But if the probability p_c of crossover is not negligible, and if in fact some crossovers have occurred in a block that reaches the decoder, then questions of consistency arise.

Suppose that some erasures have occurred in transmission, and that there is also a crossover among the message digits. If the decoder proceeds as described above to assemble a set of equations for the unknown message digits, unaware of the crossover, then the equations which it assembles will have right-hand sides that are incorrect for every equation that checks the incorrectly received digit. If there are more equations than unknowns, this will usually mean that the set of equations becomes inconsistent and cannot be satisfied by any set of values for the erased message digits. The receiver will then be alerted to the fact that one or more crossovers have occurred. However, if the coefficient column for the message digit that has crossed over is linearly dependent on the columns corresponding to the erased message digits in Eq. (3), the set will not be inconsistent: there will be some set of values for the erased digits which satisfies the constraints without changing the digit that has crossed over. The decoding process will find this set, and will fill in the erased digits, and there will be no indication that a crossover has occurred. About half of the values for the erased digits will be incorrect, and a decoding failure will have occurred. The situation is similar if the crossover has occurred in a check digit. If C_j is incorrectly received, the decoder will have an inconsistent set of equations unless the appropriate column (consisting of all zeros except for a 1 in the *jth* row) is linearly dependent on the set of columns corresponding to the erased message digits, in which case the decoder will not know that a crossover has occurred and it will decode incorrectly.

Thus the receiver can usually *detect* the presence of one or more

Coded sequence

00101100000

Matrix $[B_{jk}]$

$$\begin{bmatrix} 01001100000 \\ 10111010000 \\ 00101001000 \\ 11010000100 \\ 01101000010 \\ 10010000001 \end{bmatrix} \qquad \sum_{k=1}^{11} B_{jk} D_k = 0, \; 1 \leqslant j \leqslant 6$$

Received sequence (D_3, D_4 and D_8 erased: D_9 crossed over)

00XX110X100

Matrix $[F_{jk}]$

$$\begin{bmatrix} 01001100000 \\ 01000010011 \\ 01000001010 \\ 01000000101 \\ 01101000010 \\ 10010000001 \end{bmatrix}$$

Obtained from $[B_{jk}]$ by adding last two rows to other rows to clear 3rd and 4th columns.

Decoding equations $\displaystyle\sum_{k=1}^{11} F_{jk} D_k = 0$

$$\begin{aligned} 0 &= 0 \\ 0 &= 0 \\ D_8 &= 0 \\ 1 &= 0 \\ D_3 &= 1 \\ D_4 &= 0 \end{aligned}$$

The fourth equation $1 = 0$ is inconsistent. We inspect $[F_{jk}]$ for a column in which the first and second entries are 0 and the fourth is 1. The 9th is the only such column, so we change D_9 from the received value 1 to the correct value 0. This affects only the fourth equation: adding the 9th column to the right hand sides gives $D_8 = 0$, $D_3 = 1$, $D_4 = 0$. Note that if a crossover had occurred in D_5, the decoder would not have been able to tell whether D_5 or D_6 was in error, since changing the value of either one would give a consistent set of equations.

Fig. 5. Decoding erasures and crossovers.

crossovers by the inconsistency of the set of equations (3). If the crossover is *not* detected, however, it can cause errors in the decoding of the erased digits. Recall that when only erasures occur the worst that can happen is that the decoder may not be able to fill in the erased digits because the set of equations (3) is not soluble.

If the decoder is not merely to detect crossovers but to correct them, it is necessary to modify the decoding procedure somewhat. In principle this can be done by having the decoder set up the equations (3), try to solve them, and if it finds them inconsistent, proceed to change the unerased digit values, one at a time, to see whether any such change will produce a consistent set of equations. If not, the decoder then proceeds to try changing the values of all the digits by pairs, and so forth, until it has found the smallest number of crossovers that would produce a consistent set of equations. These crossovers will be the most probable set, and the decoder now changes the values of those digits and solves the resulting consistent equations for the erased message digits.

However, in practice this would mean trying to solve the set of equations once for each set of crossovers that was being tried out. For correcting single crossovers, the total computation would then be the number of possible single crossovers (about N) times the number of computations required to solve the set of equations. A more economical procedure is shown in Fig. 5.

The decoder now considers the message and check digits in a more homogeneous way. In order to write equations more conveniently, we will introduce a new notation. Let $D_k = I_k$ for $1 \leqslant k \leqslant M$, and let $D_k = C_{k-M}$, $M+1 \leqslant k \leqslant N$. Then the original constraint equations (2) can be written in homogeneous form:

$$\sum_{k=1}^{N} B_{jk} D_k = 0, \quad 1 \leqslant j \leqslant N(1-R). \tag{4}$$

The matrix $[B_{jk}]$ in (4) is identical with the matrix $[A_{jk}]$ of Eq. (2) in its first M columns, but it has an additional $N(1-R) = N - M$ columns that belong to a square unit matrix. Thus the equations (4) are identical with the equations (2), except that the check digits have been brought over to the left side of each equation, as shown in Fig. 5.

The decoder starts with the matrix $[B_{jk}]$ and notes which columns correspond to erased digits. By successive elimination—*i.e.*, the addition of rows of the matrix to one another—the matrix is brought into a form in which each column corresponding to an erased digit has just one entry which is 1, all the rest being 0. If it is not possible to do this for all columns corresponding to erased digits, then the set of equations is indeterminate and it is not possible to solve for all of the erasures. We will assume that this is not the case for the moment. The decoder then wants to test whether the equations are consistent. Let $[F_{jk}]$ be the matrix obtained from $[B_{jk}]$ by the elimination process. The decoder then forms the set of equations

$$\sum_{k=1}^{N} F_{jk} D_k = 0, \quad 1 \leq j \leq N(1-R), \tag{5}$$

and evaluates them by replacing all the unerased D_k by their numerical values. The equations (5) then all have one of two forms. Either an equation has an erased digit plus a constant (0 or 1) equal to 0, or it has a constant (0 or 1) equal to zero. If all of the equations that do not contain erased digit values are 0 = 0, then the set of equations is consistent and the decoder prints out the erased digit values given by the other equations. If, however, there are equations of the form 1 = 0 in the set (5), the decoder can correct a single crossover by noting which column corresponding to an unerased digit has 1's in all the equations of the form 1 = 0 and 0's in all the equations of the form 0 = 0. Changing the value of this digit will make the set consistent and will give the values of the erased digits via the other equations in the set.

From the point of view of computation, the manipulation of the matrix $[B_{jk}]$ requires the same number of row operations as the manipulation of the $[A_{jk}]$ matrix does in solving for erasures alone. The operations are now performed on longer rows, so that there is an increase in the number of individual digit multiplications and additions that are needed, but the order is still N^3 and it grows no more rapidly with block size than before. Having converted the $[B_{jk}]$ matrix into the $[F_{jk}]$ matrix in this many operations, it then takes N inspections of columns (or N^2 digit operations) to correct a single crossover, and $N(N-1)/2$ inspections of column pair sums to correct a double crossover, etc. In principle, it is possible to correct any number of crossovers with such a code, providing that enough check digits have been used in coding. However, the amount of computation required increases rapidly, and we will stop with the correction of double crossovers, since at this point the order of computation required for the correction of crossovers is about equal to that required to correct erasures alone. Correcting triple crossovers would require about N times as much work.

VI. PROBABILITY OF DECODING FAILURE

To compute how well a given code performs in a given channel we could in principle examine the matrix $[A_{jk}]$ and discover exactly which combinations of crossovers and erasures can be correctly decoded, which combinations leave the decoder with some of the erased digit values still undetermined, and which cause actual errors to be present in the decoded sequence. We could then multiply the probability of each combination of erasures and errors (as determined by the channel) by the number of digits in the output block which are not correct, and sum, to get an average probability that an input message digit will not be received correctly. But for appreciable N and p_x, the actual computation would be extremely tedious and in fact quite impractical: there are just too many different patterns of erasures and errors to be considered. The knowledge of the statistics of the channel which would be required for the computation is for the same reason effectively unattainable.

For these reasons, and also because we do not know specific codes that are extraordinarily good for arbitrary large N and arbitrary R, we do not compute the behavior of any single code but rather the average behavior of all possible codes. That is, we consider the set of all possible distinct matrices $[A_{jk}]$, and for each particular pattern of erasures and crossovers we ask what fraction of the codes will be correctly decodeable. This procedure is known as *random coding*, although that name is somewhat misleading.[2,3,10,11] A major simplification immediately results. The fraction of codes that decode a given pattern of erasures and errors correctly turns out to be essentially independent of where the erasures and crossovers occur within the block, and depends only on the number of each. To simplify things further, we count as a decoding failure any decoding that does not lead to correct values for *all* of the message digits in a block, even though many may have been decoded correctlv.

The result of this computation is a conditional probability $Q_m(k)$, the probability (for given N and R) that a pattern containing k erasures and m crossovers will lead to a decoding failure. We will give bounds for $Q_0(k)$, $Q_1(k)$ and $Q_2(k)$, since we are discussing decoding procedures which can deal with at most two crossovers. In order to evaluate the average performance of these codes in a given channel, it is then necessary only to know the probability of a given number of erasures and crossovers among N digits.

The set of all possible check-digit codes of length N and rate R has a very simple probability structure. The matrix $[A_{jk}]$ has $M(N-M) = MN(1-R) = N^2R(1-R)$ entries, each a 0 or 1. There are therefore just $2^{N^2R(1-R)}$ possible matrices, and the same number of possible codes. We give equal weight to each of these codes in taking averages, so it is easy to compute the fraction of the codes whose matrices have specified values for particular entries. For example, in picking a code from this set the probability that its first column is all zeros is just $2^{-N(1-R)}$since there are $2^{N^2R(1-R)}$ codes in all, and only $2^{(NR-1)N(1-R)}$ that have an all-zero first column. In general, in the ensemble of possible codes, one may think of the probability of a particular code as being the product of $N^2R(1-R)$ factors of 1/2, which is the product of the probabilities for its individual entry values; or as the product of NR factors each $2^{-N(1-R)}$in value, these being the probabilities of its individual columns; or as the product of $N(1-R)$ factors each 2^{-NR} in value, these being the probabilities of its rows. Since any region of a matrix in the ensemble of codes is statistically independent of other regions, the probabilities multiply.

Let us consider erasures first, and assume that a total of k of them have occurred k_1 in message positions and k_2 in check positions. If in each code we cross out the k_2 rows corresponding to the erased check digits, then this particular pattern of erasures will be soluble in all codes for which the k_1 columns corresponding to the erased message digits are linearly independent. Each of these columns now contains $N(1-R)-k_2$ coefficients. In order for the set to be linearly independent, it is necessary and sufficient that the first of the k_1 columns be not all zeros, that the second be not all zeros nor equal to the first column, that the third column be not all zeros nor the first column nor the second column nor the modulo 2 sum of the first and second columns, and so on; the $k_1 th$ column must not be any of the 2^{k_1-1} linear modulo 2 combinations of the earlier k_1-1 columns already chosen. Since the coefficients in each column are statistically independent in the ensemble, the probability of avoiding dependence is just the probability of avoiding one event of probability $2^{-N(1-R)+k_2}$ in choosing the first column, 2^1 events of the same probability in choosing the second column, 2^2 such events in choosing the third column and so forth. This gives the probability of successful decoding as a product of k_1 terms:

$$\begin{aligned} \prod_{j=0}^{k_1-1} (1-2^{-N(1-R)+k_2+j}) &\geq 1-\sum_{j=0}^{k_1-1} 2^{-N(1-R)+k_2+j} \\ &\geq 1-(2^{-N(1-R)+k_2})\sum_{j=0}^{k_1-1} 2^{+j} \\ &\geq 1-2^{-N(1-R)+k_2+k_1} . \end{aligned} \tag{6}$$

Note that $k_1+k_2=k$, and that the probability of successful decoding when k erasures and no crossovers have occurred is just $1-Q_0(k)$, where $Q_0(k)$ is the probability of decoding failure. Thus from (6) we have the bounds

$$\begin{aligned} Q_0(k) &\leq 2^{-N(1-R)+k}, \quad k \leq k_0 = N(1-R) \\ &\leq 1, \; k > k_0 \end{aligned} \tag{7}$$

where the second bound ($Q_0(k) \leq 1$) follows from the fact that $Q_0(k)$ is a probability, and k_0 is the value of k above which the second bound becomes smaller than the first. In fact, for $k > k_0$ there are fewer equations than there are unknowns in the set (3), and complete solution for the values of the erased digits is not possible.

Next, we bound $Q_1(k)$, the conditional probability of decoding failure when exactly k erasures and one crossover have occurred. In this case it is more convenient to talk about the matrix $[B_{jk}]$ of Eq.(4). The probability of success, $1-Q_1(k)$, is bounded below by the probability that each of the $(N-k-1)$ set of $k+2$ columns that include the k columns corresponding to the erased digits, the one column corresponding to the digit that has crossed over, and any other single column, be linearly independent.

The probability of linear dependence for one set of $(k+2)$ columns each with $N(1-R)$ entries has an upper bound of $2^{-N(1-R)+k+2}$. The argument is similar to that leading to (7) above. A decoding failure will occur if any one of the $N-k-1$ such sets is linearly dependent, and the probability of this is bounded by $N-k-1$ times the probability of dependence for a single set. Thus

$$Q_1(k) \leqslant (N-k-1)\, 2^{-N(1-R)+k+2}\ ,\ k \leqslant k_1 \qquad (8)$$
$$\leqslant 1,\ k > k_1.$$

Here k_1 is the value of k above which the second bound is smaller than the first, and the second bound follows again from the fact that $Q_1(k)$ is a probability.

Finally, $Q_2(k)$, the probability of decoding failure when k erasures and two crossovers have occurred in transmission, is the probability that one or more of the $(N-k-2)(N-k-3)/2$ sets of $k+4$ columns including the k erasures and the 2 crossovers, and any other 2 columns, will be linearly dependent. By the same type of argument, this is bounded by

$$Q_2(k) \leqslant \frac{(N-k-2)(N-k-3)}{2}\, 2^{-N(1-R)+k+4},\ k \leqslant k_2 \qquad (9)$$
$$\leqslant 1,\ k > k_2.$$

where k_2 is the value of k above which the first bound exceeds unity.

VII. AVERAGE BEHAVIOR OF A CODE IN USE

The preceding results tell us how, on the average, a block code of given rate and block size will handle sets of erasures and crossovers. In order to specify the average probability of decoding failure for the code in use over a channel, we need to make use of the channel statistics. We also need to decide whether the decoder will attempt to correct erasures only, or single crossovers as well, or double crossovers too.

For the purposes of carrying out the computation in examples, we will assume that successive erasures and crossovers are statistically independent, so that each digit is erased or crosses over with probability p_x or p_c independently of how the preceding digits have been treated by the channel. This makes the probability of a set of k erasures and 0, 1 or 2 crossovers independent of where these have occurred in the block of N digits. Any statistics which make it possible to compute the average probability of a set of a given number of erasures and crossovers, averaged over positions in the block, could be used instead in order to compute the behavior of a code of this sort in a channel that has some memory. However, the decoding procedure may no longer be optimum in such a channel if the crossovers tend to clump. That is, it may not be true that the *a priori* probability of a set of crossovers is a monotonically decreasing function of the number of the crossovers in the set; clumps of adjacent crossovers may have higher probability than sets of the same number of crossovers more widely separated in time. In this case, the receiver should search for sets of crossovers which will make the decoding equations consistent in order of decreasing probability rather than in order of increasing number. Although this assures optimum receiver performance, it may represent a severe problem in the binary symmetric channel. However, for the erasure channel derived by using a threshold in comparing the 0 and the 1 detector outputs, correlation between successive crossovers is unlikely. It will result from correlated noise, but correlated fading will produce very little correlation among crossovers.

On the assumption of independence, then, we give bounds on the probability of decoding failure when the decoder is ignoring crossovers, attempting to correct single crossovers, or attempting to correct double crossovers.

Case 0: No Crossovers

When the decoder makes no attempt to correct crossovers, a decoding failure will occur whenever there are one or more crossovers in a block of N digits. The probability of this event is bounded by Np_c. If there are no crossovers, then the probability of decoding failure is bounded by taking a binomially weighted average of $Q_0(k)$. The total probability of failure is bounded by the sum of these two quantities. Using the bounds of Eq. (7) on $Q_0(k)$ gives

$$Q_0 \leq Np_c + \sum_{k=1}^{k_0} \binom{N}{k} p_x^k (1-p_x)^{N-k} \cdot 2^{k-N(1-R)} + \sum_{k_0+1}^{N} \binom{N}{k} p_x^k (1-p_x)^{N-k}, \tag{10}$$

where $k_0 = N(1-R)$ is given by the inequality (7), and $\binom{N}{k}$ is the binominal coefficient.

Case 1: Single Crossovers

If the decoder attempts to correct single crossovers, there will be a decoding failure if two or more crossovers occur in the block of N transmitted digits. The probability of this is less than $N(N-1)p_c^2/2$. If there are not more than two crossovers, then there is either one or none. The probability of k erasures along with a single crossover among the $N-k$ unerased digits is less than $(N-k)p_c$ times the (binomial) probability of k erasures, so that the two last terms may be bounded by a common sum with binomial weights. Thus Q_1, the average probability of decoding failure in this case, is bounded by the sum:

$$Q_1 \leq N(N-1)\, p_c^2/2 + \sum_{k=0}^{N} \binom{N}{k} p_x^k (1-p_x)^{N-k} [Q_0(k) + (N-k)p_c Q_1(k)]. \tag{11}$$

To make full use of the bounds (7) and (8), it is necessary to separate the sum, breaking the range of summation for $Q_0(k)$ at k_0 and for

$Q_1(k)$ at k_1. However, if it is desired to make Q_1 small, then the erasure threshold must be set so that Np_c is small in order to keep the probability of a double crossover sufficiently low. In that case the quantity $(N-k)p_c Q_1(k)$ may stay smaller than the quantity $Q_0(k)$ even for k values larger than k_1, and up to k_0. If so, the bound will not be appreciably weakened by breaking the sum for both terms at k_0 only, which simplifies hand computation a bit, although the simplification would not be worthwhile for machine computation.

Case 2: Double Crossovers

If double crossovers are to be corrected by the decoder, then there will in general be decoding failure when triple crossovers occur, an event whose probability is bounded by $N(N-1)(N-2)p_c^3/6$. If the probabilities of failure for k erasures alone, k erasures and one crossover, and k erasures and two crossovers are all included under a single summation sign (as in (11) for Case 1), we can write

$$Q_2 \leq N(N-1)(N-2)p_c^3/6 + \sum_{k=0}^{N} \binom{N}{k} p_x^k (1-p_x)^{N-k} \, [Q_0(k) + (N-k)p_c Q_1(k) + (N-k)(N-k-1)p_c^2 Q_2(k)/2]. \tag{12}$$

Here again, for accurate bounding it is necessary to break each of the sums over the three terms in square brackets at a different point—at the values given by k_0, k_1 and k_2 in (7), (8) and (9) respectively. Again, however, if the threshold of the decision device is set for small p_c in order to make the probability of triple crossovers sufficiently small to make Q_2 small, then the second and third terms in brackets in (12) may be smaller than the first for all values of k up to k_0, and a single break point can be used.

VIII. CONCLUSIONS ON CODING

We have discussed block parity-check codes for use in a binary-input channel in which erasures occur with appreciable probability p_x, and crossovers occur with non-negligible probability p_c. We have seen that with about N^3 operations on binary digits, or N^2 operations on words of length N, it is possible to decode many erasures and one or two crossovers in such a block. We have derived expressions that bound the probability for decoding failure when averaged over all possible such codes, as a function of the block size N and the rate of transmission R. Of course, we are actually interested not in the average behavior of all possible codes but in the actual behavior of some particular code—preferably the best one we can use for given N and R, or one that makes the decoding particularly easy. However, the decoding for any such code is already easy enough, in the sense that it is within reach of current digital circuit techniques without requiring fantastic amounts of equipment or time. And the behavior of the best possible code can be shown to be not very much better than the average behavior of all codes, so that we need not be too choosy: we can fill in a large matrix at random, do a little checking to make sure that we have not selected a particularly bad code, and be quite sure that the average probabilities will apply. In particular, there must be many codes whose probability of decoding failure is not much worse than average, as Shannon has pointed out.[10,11]

Coding is therefore feasible. The next question, of course, is how valuable it might be in practice. To sketch an indication of an answer to this question, we now consider a particular continuous channel model, a selection of waveforms and a decision procedure that gives this channel a binary input and a ternary output, and do some rough bounding to show what coding could achieve in this case. We compare the results with what could be done with the same channel model and more conventional techniques; *i.e.*, using time-division diversity before making a decision, and then making a statistically optimum binary decision on each message digit separately.

It would not be difficult to compute bounds on decoding failure more precisely, and to prepare tables relating N, R and Q for a given channel. However, since our upper bounds, though rough, *are* upper bounds, such a computation would only strengthen the general conclusion that coding will indeed permit the reliable transmission of digital data over such a channel at a lower cost in transmitter power than will other techniques, and that its use must seriously be considered in situations in which very high reliability is required.

IX. CHANNEL MODEL

We consider a communication system that transmits FSK signals over a channel in which they are subjected to Rayleigh fading. There are two receivers, one for each of the two signals. Each signal is received with additive gaussian noise of power N_0 watts per cps, the noises in the two receivers being independent. The fading of successive bauds is assumed to be statistically independent, and it is also assumed that there is no phase coherence between successive bauds. Envelope detection (*i.e.*, summing the squared outputs of two correlation detectors in quadrature and sampling the sum at the time of peak signal correlation) is used in each channel. This is optimum on the assumption that there is no phase drift during a baud, which is not quite consistent with the assumption of phase independence between successive bauds, but which makes the computation easier. Of course we could make more effective use of the channel by using some of the phase coherence which in fact must exist between bauds in order to make better decisions, while still retaining the statistical independence of successive digits in a code block by time scrambling. And in fact we would do so by means of one of the systems of the preceding chapter if we were attempting to use the channel as efficiently as possible. This would improve the channel whether or not coding were used. But since we shall be comparing behavior with coding to behavior without, it is fair to say that the comparison is not too distorted by the limitations of the model. Any channel that does have Rayleigh fading, independent or not, would give the same sort of results after optimum detection followed by time scrambling or interlace to produce independence between adjacent output digits.

This channel model has been discussed in detail by Pierce[8] who compares the outputs of the two receivers and chooses the larger as representing the transmitted signal. This procedure is optimum under the assumptions, and it leads to a binary symmetric channel with no erasures and with a crossover probability given by

$$p_c = \frac{1}{2 + E/N_0} \ . \tag{13}$$

Here N_0 is the noise power per cps at each receiver input and $E = S_0 T$ is the total energy in each signal, where S_0 is the average transmitter power and T is the baud duration.

Pierce also considers the use of diversity in this channel model. We shall take this to be time diversity in which the transmitter always sends the same signal for two successive bauds, and the receiver adds up the detector output samples from each receiver for two bauds before comparing them. This reduces the rate of transmission to 1/2 its former value, but reduces the crossover probability to

$$p_c = \frac{3}{(2 + E/N_0)^2}\left(1 - \frac{2/3}{2 + E/N_0}\right) . \tag{14}$$

Using triple time diversity, the rate is reduced to 1/3 of its original value since each input digit is transmitted three times, but the crossover probability is reduced further to

$$p_c = \frac{10}{(2 + E/N_0)^3}\left(1 - \frac{3/2}{2 + E/N_0} + \frac{3/5}{(2 + E/N_0)^2}\right) . \tag{15}$$

Pierce gives general expressions for diversity of arbitrary order, but we shall restrict our comparisons to double and triple diversity.

Now we wish to modify the decision procedure so that the baud is called an erasure unless *a posteriori* one of the transmitted waveforms has much greater probability than the other. It turns out that the required optimum decision procedure in this case is just to compare the outputs of the two channels and to call the baud an erasure if the magnitude of the difference is below a threshold value. If the threshold is exceeded, the receiver producing the larger signal is taken to indicate the transmitted waveform, as before.

We define w^2 as the sum of the squares of the two correlator outputs for one of the receivers and z^2 as the corresponding quantity for the other. It is convenient to normalize by the noise power density in defining the threshold variable V_{th}. That is, the receiver calls a received signal an erasure if

$$|w^2/2N_0 - z^2/2N_0| < V_{\text{th}}, \tag{16}$$

otherwise it picks the stronger of the two receiver outputs.

A straightforward integration, very similar to that used by Pierce to evaluate the crossover probability in his case, but with the limits changed to take the threshold region into account, gives the following expressions:

$$q = \left(1 - \frac{1}{2 + E/N_0}\right) \exp\left(-\frac{V_{\text{th}}}{1 + E/N_0}\right)$$

$$p_c = \frac{1}{2 + E/N_0} \exp(-V_{\text{th}}) \tag{17}$$

$$p_x = 1 - q - p_c$$

These relationships enable us to compute what V_{th} and E/N_0 values are required in order to meet requirements on p_x and p_c. Together with the equations that bound the probability Q of decoding failure in terms of N, p_x, p_c and R, they enable us to find combinations of rate, block length, and E/N_0 that will provide a given reliability--*i.e.*, a given small value for Q. It is not possible to give explicit solutions, since the equations are not simple. However, the different expressions have very different sensitivities to the different parameters in the problem, so that it is possible to make trial solutions converge rapidly.

X. EFFECT OF CODING ON TRANSMITTER POWER REQUIREMENTS

Table I shows the results of computation for the channel model just discussed. It gives the E/N_0 ratios required at the receiver (in decibels) in order to attain average error probabilities, after processing, of 10^{-6} and 10^{-9}. For rate $R = 1$, the only transmission scheme available is simple transmission with binary decision-making. For rate 1/2, double time-division diversity followed by binary decision making is compared with no diversity, coding, ternary decision making to produce some erasures, and decoding of erasures and single or double crossovers. The coding scheme is evaluated for $M = 50$, $N = 100$ and for $M = 100$, $N = 200$. For rate 1/3, triple-time-division diversity is compared with coding for the two cases $M = 34$, $N = 100$ and $M = 67$, $N = 200$. The E/N_0 requirements for diversity are computed from the expressions (13), (14), and (15). For coding, given M and N the expression (12) is used to determine a pair of values p_c and p_x that give a value of Q_2 less than the reliability requirement. Then (17) is used to find the smallest E/N_0 that (with appropriate V_{th}) will give the p_c and p_x values required.

The table leads to the following conclusions. First, coding does

TABLE I

E/N_0 Requirement (decibels) for Time-Division Diversity and for Coding.

p or Q_2	10^{-6}	10^{-9}
Simple transmission	60 db	90 db
Rate $R = 1/2$		
Double diversity	32.5	47.5
Coding, $N = 100$	16	18.5
Coding, $N = 200$	14	15.5
Rate $R = 1/3$		
Triple diversity	23.5	33.3
Coding, $N = 100$	13	15
Coding, $N = 200$	12	13

lead to significant reductions in transmitter power required for a given reliability, giving a 10 db advantage over triple diversity for 10^{-6} error probability. Second, this advantage increases as the reliability requirement becomes more stringent. Third, although the reduction in transmitter power obtainable by doubling the block length at fixed reliability is small—1 to 3 db—the reduction in error probability obtained by doubling the block length at fixed transmitter power is large—from 10^{-6} to 10^{-9} at 13 db and rate 1/3.

XI. CONCLUSION

The type of coding we have discussed is practical and useful. However, before someone builds it into a system, it must be pointed out that the selection of this particular code and decoding procedure was in part pedagogically motivated. There are other procedures which might be better, but which are somewhat harder to explain.

In practice, in a communication system in which transmitter power is an important consideration, and in which there is appreciable fading in the transmission medium, one would probably use some space or polarization diversity first, and then use coding on the resulting improved channel. It would undoubtedly be worthwhile to introduce erasures at the reciever, and the kind of block coding we have discussed would be a candidate for consideration. However, a sliding code[2] in which the different rows of the matrix $[A_{jk}]$ are all derived by sliding an M-digit window along a sequence of N randomly selected binary digits would be preferable to the random matrix code we used, since it requires less information storage at transmitter and receiver. We did not discuss it because it makes the random coding argument more difficult, but it leads to the same bounds on probability of decoding failure.

There would also be competing coding systems that would need careful consideration, however. One would be a Reed-Muller code, with a modified decoding procedure to allow for erasures as well as crossovers. The suitability of this code would depend on the precise N and R to be used, but for the kinds of numbers we have considered such a code should be quite efficient. Another candidate would be an iterated version of a simple code. For example, adjacent groups of 16 digits might be Hamming-coded, using 11 message digits and 5 check digits in each group. After 11 such groups, 5 more groups of second-order check could be sent, the five initial digits in these groups being Hamming checks on the 11 initial digits of the preceding groups, and so on. Decoding procedures for codes of this sort have been discussed for the binary symmetric channel[16] and for the erasure channel with no crossovers.[17] They have not been investigated in detail for the type of channel we have been using which has both erasures and crossovers. Finally, the convolutional codes and the sequential decoding procedures introduced by Wozencraft[14] for the binary symmetric case and investigated by Epstein[4] for the erasure channel could be used in the mixed case too.

Not only the channel and the code, but the communications practice in the system might be modified to advantage. If in fact the communication system is two-way, then the receiver need not correct all sets of erasures and errors. Instead, the receiver may stop after a reasonable amount of decoding computation and call for a repeat of a particularly noisy block. It is easy to construct codes with very small probability of an undetected set of errors. If this is done, and then once every 10^4 blocks or so the receiver asks for repeats, the decoding computation is never very severe and the final reliability can be very high, while the cost in channel capacity of the occasional repeats is negligible. As Wozencraft has pointed out,[18] the sequential decoding procedure is particularly adapted to repeat requests, but any decoding scheme can use them to advantage.

The object in pointing out these alternatives is to show that there are now a variety of procedures that can be used to code information for transmission over noisy channels; that several of these are quite practical in terms of equipment requirements; and that coding theory is now at a stage in which it can not only prove theorems, but also can be used for the design of coding and decoding procedures for use in practical communication systems.

REFERENCES

1. Birkhoff and Maclane, *A Survey of Modern Algebra* (rev. ed.), The Macmillan Company, New York, 1953.

2. P. Elias, "Coding for Noisy Channels," *IRE Conv. Record,* pt. 4, pp. 37-46, March, 1955.
3. P. Elias, "Coding for Two Noisy Channels," in C. Cherry (ed.) *Information Theory,* Butterworth and Co. (Publishers) Ltd., London, 1956.
4. M. Epstein, "Algebraic Decoding for a Binary Erasure Channel," *IRE Conv. Record,* pt. 4, pp. 56-69, March, 1955. See also Sc. D. Thesis, "Coding for the Binary Erasure Channel," Electrical Engineering Department, Massachusetts Institute of Technology, September, 1958.
5. A. Feinstein, "A New Basic Theorem in Information Theory," *Trans. IRE, PGIT-4,* pp. 2-22, September, 1954.
6. M. J. E. Golay, "Binary Coding," *Trans. IRE, PGIT-4,* pp. 23-28, September, 1954.
7. R. W. Hamming, "Error Detecting and Error Correcting Codes," *Bell System Tech. J.,* vol. 29, pp. 147-160, 1950.
8. J. N. Pierce, "Theoretical Diversity Improvement in Frequency-Shift Keying," *Proc. IRE,* vol. 46, pp. 903-910, May, 1958.
9. I. S. Reed, "A Class of Multiple Error-Correcting Codes and the Decoding Scheme," *Trans. IRE, PGIT-4,* pp 38-49, September, 1954.
10. C. E. Shannon, *The Mathematical Theory of Communication,* University of Illinois Press, Urbana, Ill., 1949.
11. C. E. Shannon, "Certain Results in Coding Theory for Noisy Channels," *Information and Control,* vol. 1, pp. 6-25, September, 1957.
12. R. A. Silverman and M. Balser, "Coding for Constant-Data-Rate Systems," *Trans. IRE, PGIT-4,* pp 50-63, September, 1954.
13. D. Slepian, "A Class of Binary Signalling Alphabets," *Bell System Tech. J.,* vol. 35, pp. 203-234, January, 1956.
14. J. M. Wozencraft, "Sequential Decoding for Reliable Communication," *Technical Report 325,* Research Laboratory of Electronics, Massachusetts Institute of Technology, 1957.
15. K. E. Perry, "An Error-Correcting Encoder and Decoder for Phone Line Data," *IRE Wescon Conv. Record,* pt. 4, pp. 21-26, August, 1959.
16. P. Elias, "Error-Free Coding," *Trans. IRE, PGIT-4,* pp. 29-37, September, 1954.
17. P. Elias, "Information Theory" (Chap. 16) in Grabbe, Ramo, and Wooldridge, (eds.) *Handbook of Automation, Computation and Control,* vol. 1, John Wiley and Sons, Inc., New York, 1958.
18. J. M. Wozencraft, *Sequential Decoding,* to be published in the Technology Press Research Monograph Series.

CHAPTER 14

Feedback Communication Systems

Paul E. Green, Jr.

I. INTRODUCTION

In our discussions up to now, we have considered various aspects of the problem of communicating via a single one-way link. In practice, one is apt to be confronted with a situation that is more complicated. The opportunity or even necessity may exist for arranging a number of such links into topologically more complex structures or networks embodying cascades, parallel connections, and feedback or feed-forward connections. Extensions of the elegant theories of the single one-way link to networks of communication facilities have been sought persistently but have so far proved to be most difficult to construct. There is one direction however in which some progress can be reported—the simple special case of two one-way links interconnecting two stations in opposite directions. This special case—a system utilizing a forward and a feedback link simultaneously—is the topic to be discussed in this chapter.

There are many practical communication situations in which information can be made available at the transmitter on the current status of the transmitter-receiver link. This may be because a return link from receiver to transmitter is already available for other purposes or can be added without too much difficulty, or it may be that there is some other source capable of supplying the information. In either event, when such a situation exists, there is the possibility of significantly increasing the reliability of the forward transmission of information by suitably exploiting the fed-back channel information at the transmitter. We shall use the term feedback systems to include all those in which the transmitter uses information regarding the performance of the forward link.

Not only is feedback a useful possibility in the design of reliable communication systems, but also it is an implied necessity in "flexible rate" systems, in which channel conditions are made to influence not just the performance at a fixed data rate, but the data rate too.

In recent years these possibilities have received a fair amount of attention, and the information theory of certain aspects of feedback systems has been studied in detail. Concurrently, but quite independently, several operating systems have been built around the feedback principle and have achieved a large measure of success in practical operation.

As was pointed out in Chapter 1, we can distinguish between "analog" communication systems, in which the criterion of performance is some sort of "fidelity," and "digital" systems in which an overall error probability is the pertinent measure of performance. We shall confine our discussion of feedback systems to the "digital" case since this is the only one for which significant results have been obtained.

As we have seen in preceding chapters, the communication theory of simple one-way digital links divides naturally into two categories. The first of these treats that part of the communication system concerned with what signals should be sent through the continuous channel itself, and, knowing something about the signals and the channel, what kind of receiver operations should be used to make a suitable decision from the signal received as to which signal was transmitted. This might be loosely labelled "decision theory". The emphasis is usually on a single typical message element or character, without regard to the manner in which these elements are arranged in time sequence. The other half of the picture involves "coding theory", the manipulation of successions of choices among signals at the transmitter and successive decision results at the receiver, without going into the explicit form of the signals, the propagating medium or the receiver decision operation. To the decision theorist the word "channel" implies some mathematical model, possibly derived from the physics of the propagation process; to the coding theorist the channel is a set of probabilities describing the average decision results.

The same sort of division occurs naturally in the study of feedback systems. There are techniques that supply to the transmitter data on the continuous channel itself and there are those that supply information on the results of individual receiver decisions or strings of decisions. We shall call these two classes of feedback systems "predecision feedback" and "post-decision feedback", respectively. The distinction is specified in Fig. 1, which is merely the digital communication system block diagram of Chapter 1 with feedback added.

To date, most contributions to the theory of communication systems with feedback have emphasized postdecision feedback. In this chapter we will briefly call attention to this literature and its principal results and then go on to a discussion of predecision feedback, presenting some hitherto unpublished results. The correspondences between these results and those for postdecision feedback will be pointed out. An interesting study by Elias has also been included as an Appendix. Brief mention is made of two successful operating systems, the Janet system, and the ARQ system, as examples of predecision and postdecision feedback, respectively.

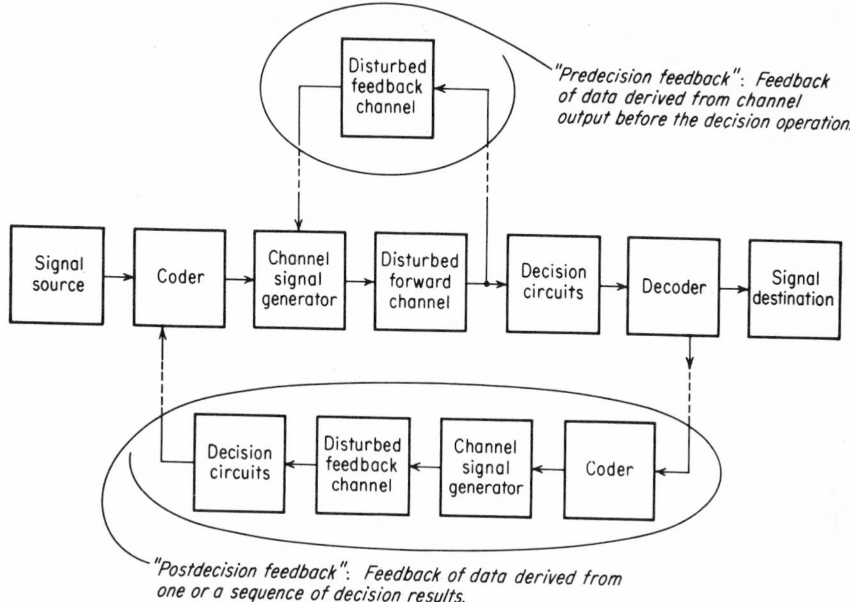

Fig. 1. Two classes of communication systems using feedback.

II. POSTDECISION FEEDBACK

The possibility of improving system performance by using feedback was included in Shannon's earliest investigations.[1] He showed that under certain conditions complex coding operations could be virtually eliminated if feedback were available. Specifically he considered the following situation. There is a noisy forward channel, say a binary symmetric channel of capacity $1 + p \log_2 p + (1 - p) \log_2 (1 - p)$ bits per second (p is the transition probability). Supplementing this are two noiseless channels. The first of these is a feedback channel and is used to convey all the received digits back to the transmitter so that the erroneous digits can be located in the sequence. The second is a forward link used to send to the receiver the locations of these erroneous digits, which are then automatically converted to correct digits. Shannon showed that if this forward link has a capacity of at least $-p \log_2 p - (1 - p) \log_2 (1 - p)$, all errors can be corrected. Thus an error-free rate of one bit per second (the sum of the two capacities) is achieved with no coding of the noisy forward channel and only rudimentary coding and decoding operations on the noiseless forward link.

In subsection III-1 of this chapter, we will discuss a scheme of predecision feedback devised by Elias which does much the same thing as this early postdecision feedback example of Shannon's.

Note that the addition of the feedback link did not allow transmission over the noisy forward channel alone at a rate exceeding its capacity in the absence of feedback. Indeed Shannon has since shown[2] that if there are only two channels, a noisy one in the forward direction and a noiseless one in the reverse direction, the presence of the latter cannot increase the capacity in the forward direction, provided the forward channel has no memory (*i.e.* there is no statistical dependence of errors in the successive decisions).[3] However, he found that the maximum rate at which information can be sent with no errors whatsoever (the zero-error capacity) can be increased by using feedback. Without going into a detailed analysis he pointed out that in the case of memory allowed, there can be some situations in which there is an increase of capacity and some in which there is not.

Chang[4] treated the case in which the forward channel is memoryless and the feedback channel is allowed to be noisy (with the noises in both channels independent). In order that the demands on the feedback channel might be less severe than for the forward channel, Chang allowed the possible transmitted symbols to be divided into groups with the receiver sending back not which symbol was decided on in the decision operation, but which group it lay in. He postulated a class of ways of handling the fed-back information at the transmitter ("information feedback" systems*), and then went on to analyze several particular forms. In all such systems the indication sent back from the receiver is compared with the transmitted symbol and if there is a discrepancy, a repetition or some other form of correction is sent. With the feedback channel error-free, error-free forward transmission is possible, using simple repetition rather than coding. Even when the feedback channel is noisy, one can achieve the same performance with simple coding that would have required more elaborate coding in the absence of feedback.

In the case of a noisy feedback channel, Chang conjectured that the best procedure would be to choose the correspondence between received and feedback symbols so that pairs of feedback symbols that are *most* easily confused with each other correspond to pairs of forward channel symbols that are *least* easily confused with each other. An interesting example of what happens when this is not done has been given by Bishop and Buchanan.[5] They show that when the transition probabilities between symbols are completely identical** in the two channels, redundant coding is *less* costly in terms of total number of digits sent than is the use of feedback.

All these studies assumed that the disturbances in the two channels were independent. If the disturbances are not independent, then constraints exist between the receiver decision results in the forward and

*In some publications, the possible forms of feedback manipulations have been divided into "information feedback" and "decision feedback" types. We prefer a different breakdown into "predecision" and "postdecision" systems.

**That is, for all pairs of possible transmitted symbols i and j the probability that i is erroneously received as j in the forward transmission is the same as the probability that when the receiver signals that j was received the transmitter will get the erroneous indication that i was received.

feedback directions. If it is known what these constraints are, then it would seem plausible that one could gain an increase in performance over that available with independent disturbances.

The case in which forward and feedback channels are perturbed dependently and use is made of this dependence at the transmitter, is identical to the situation in which the transmitter is provided information (by some third party) about the state of the forward channel. Shannon[6] has called this knowledge of channel conditions "side information" and has investigated several interesting cases of memoryless forward channels about which various degrees of knowledge are available at the transmitter. He shows that the use of this information allows the forward channel capacity to be increased and the coding to be simplified.

We shall investigate in subsection III-2 a very simple example of predecision feedback, and will see that it has some of the properties we have just listed for postdecision feedback. In particular it will turn out that the forward channel capacity is not increased by use of the feedback link, even when the latter is noiseless. If the feedback link is noisy, channel capacity is only decreased unless the noises in the two channels are correlated, in which case the forward capacity can be increased by using the feedback connection.

One simple alternative to making a binary decision at the receiver is to make a ternary decision out of it by using instead of one decision threshold a pair of thresholds. Received signals falling in the "null zone" between thresholds result in no decision, and a "blank" appears in the output sequence.

Harris, *et al.* have investigated a number of cases in which the transmitter is notified of each "blank" and asked for a repeat via a feedback channel that may or may not be error-free. They have investigated[7] the effect of terminating the process after a certain number of repeats, of various choices of permanent adjustments of the two thresholds, and of having time-variant threshold adjustments. A gaussian distribution for the predecision noise was assumed. They also investigated the case in which the predecision signal-to-gaussian-noise ratio varies slowly as a function of time, requiring a continual readjustment of threshold levels.[8] Cascades of such systems have also been treated.[9]

So far we have spoken of postdecision feedback of individual decision results. Some work has also been published on the use of coding into short strings (*e.g.* Hamming codes), and then using the feedback circuit to ask for a repeat of the string whenever an error is detected.[10] A number of variants of this scheme are possible; one is employed by the ARQ system to be described in the next subsection. Feedback of the results of decoding a sequence of symbols is a technique worth much further study. As Elias has pointed out in Chapter 13, this stratagem offers great possibilities in the use of very-long-block-length codes. Coding schemes such as the Wozencraft sequential code seldom make an error, but when they do, errors tend to propagate. A feedback channel to signal such occurrences would require a tiny fraction of the forward capacity.

1. An Operational Postdecision Feedback System—The ARQ System[11]

This is a binary radio teletype system designed to correct errors automatically by requesting a repeat via a feedback link from receiver to transmitter.

Each letter of the text is sent by means of a 7-bit character. A repeat is requested whenever the check digits used signify an error. The automatic feedback is employed in a 2-way scheme in which information flows in both directions simultaneously. An error in either direction causes a hold until it is satisfactorily corrected.

This system has the effect of adjusting the information rate automatically to conform to channel conditions. It has been widely used with great success on high-frequency radio teletype circuits[12] where modest delays are not so disastrous as errors.

III. PREDECISION FEEDBACK

We turn now to predecision feedback, the class of situations in which the information supplied the transmitter is about the analog channel itself. That is, we will deal with that part of the system of Fig. 1 that follows the signal-selection operation at the transmitter and precedes the decision-making operation at the receiver. Decision making is inherently destructive of information about the most likely transmitted signal and the most likely channel condition, and therefore one expects that exploitation of this type of feedback might be particularly useful.

This class of problems has been almost completely neglected in published work. The one exception is a study made by Elias,[13] which is reproduced in the Appendix.

Elias devised a method of dividing up a wide-band forward channel and a wide-band feedback channel and then interconnecting the subchannels so obtained in a particular way. His results will now be described briefly, the full text being given in Appendix A. We will then go on to analyze (1) a simple scheme in which the receiver sends back the received signal and then the transmitter adds the feedback channel output to the input signal, and (2) a method of using information fed back on multiplicative channel disturbances.

1. Elias' Channel-Division Feedback Scheme

Elias uses K forward channels (each of bandwidth W and gaussian noise power density N_{01}) and $K-1$ feedback channels (each of bandwidth W and noise power density N_{02}) in the manner shown in Fig. 2. The second forward channel from the top is fed with a weighted combination of the input and the output of the first channel, and then the

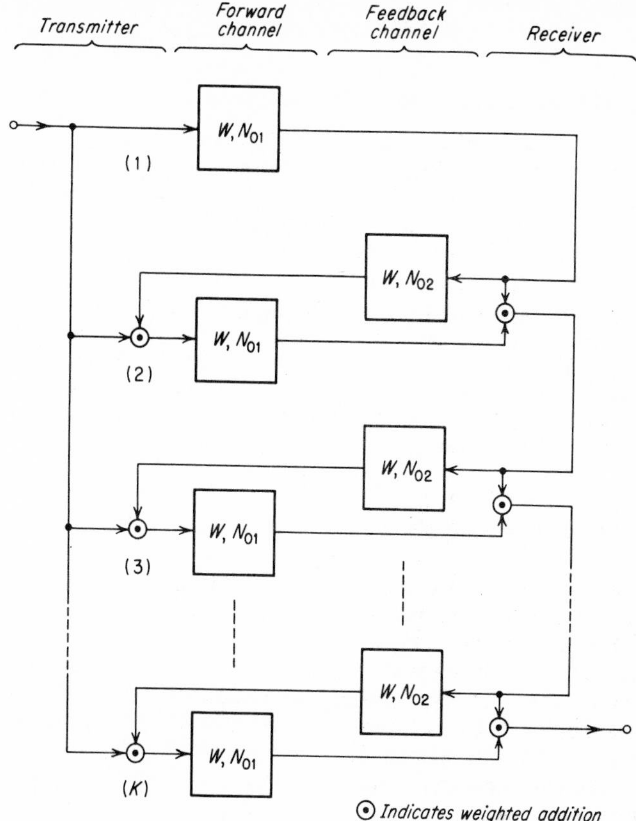

Fig. 2. Elias's channel-division feedback scheme.

outputs of these first two forward channels are combined on a voltage basis (with suitable weighting) to form a new output. The same operation is now repeated on the input and the composite output of the first two forward channels, using the third forward channel and the second feedback channel, and so forth.

Elias proves that if the feedback channels are noiseless ($N_{02} = 0$), and if we let $K \to \infty$ keeping W fixed, information can be sent about the input at a rate equal to the limiting value of

$$C = KW \log_2 \left(1 + \frac{S}{N_{01}KW}\right) \qquad (1)$$

bits per second (where S is the average transmitted power), namely $(S/N_{01}) \log_2 e$. Yet even though the capacity appropriate to a bandwidth KW is achieved, the bandwidth of the input and output signals is only W. Compare this with the situation without feedback, Fig. 3, in which the same capacity can be obtained by widening the bandwidth to KW, this

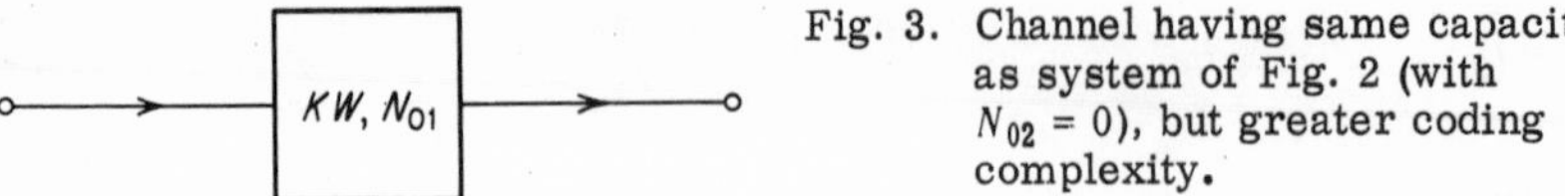

Fig. 3. Channel having same capacity as system of Fig. 2 (with $N_{02} = 0$), but greater coding complexity.

being the input and output signal bandwidth. The output signal-to-noise ratios of the two schemes are equal, but the bandwidths are different by the factor K. Thus the coding and decoding complexity for the feedback scheme (Fig. 2) becomes an arbitrarily small fraction of that required without feedback (Fig. 3), as K is increased.

2. Simple Addition of Input and Fed-Back Signals

Another possible predecision feedback procedure is one in which the received mixture of signal and noise is fed back, suitably weighted, and then added to the transmitted signal. This is illustrated in Fig. 4. A linear combination of forward and feedback signals is made at the transmitter, hopefully for purposes of correcting the transmitted signal for more effective use of the channel. Both channels are perturbed by multiplicative and additive disturbances. We shall shortly assume that the latter are gaussian noises, not necessarily uncorrelated, and see what this implies.

Time-invariant, multiplicative disturbances representable as the effects of linear filters $M_1(\omega)$ and $M_2(\omega)$ are also included in both channels. The transmitter and receiver are allowed the use of weighting system functions $C_1(\omega)$ and $C_2(\omega)$. It is desired to determine the filter transfer functions $C_1(\omega)$ and $C_2(\omega)$ and the complex spectrum $X(\omega)$ at the transmitter that maximize the overall capacity in the forward direction. It is assumed that M_1, M_2, C_1, and C_2 permit only a one-way flow of energy.

The first step is to replace the network of Fig. 4 with an equivalent one-way channel whose channel capacity can be more readily computed. With reference to Fig. 4, we find that

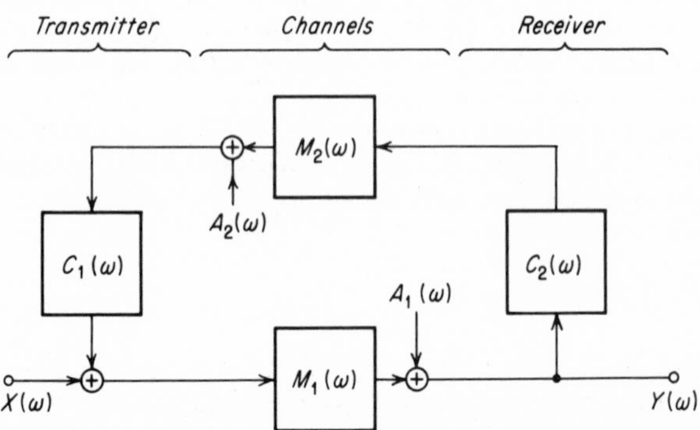

Fig. 4. Feedback scheme using simple addition of signals.

$$Y(\omega) = \frac{A_1(\omega) + M_1(\omega)\, C_1(\omega) A_2(\omega) + X(\omega) M_1(\omega)}{1 - M_1(\omega)\, M_2(\omega)\, C_1(\omega)\, C_2(\omega)} \tag{2}$$

But this also holds for the equivalent one-way link of Fig. 5, where

$$A(\omega) = A_1(\omega) + M_1(\omega)\, C_1(\omega)\, A_2(\omega) \tag{3}$$

and

$$Q(\omega) = [1 - M_1(\omega)\, M_2(\omega)\, C_1(\omega)\, C_2(\omega)]^{-1} \tag{4}$$

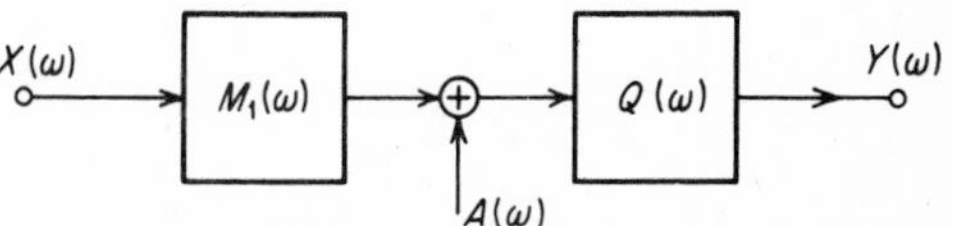

Fig. 5. Equivalent one-way channel.

According to Shannon, the maximum rate of reception of information about the input of the one-way system of Fig. 6 is

$$R = \frac{1}{2} \int_{-\infty}^{\infty} \log_2 \left(1 + \frac{|S(\omega)|^2}{N(\omega)}\right) d\omega \tag{5}$$

bits per second, where $S(\omega)$ is the complex spectrum of the signal and $N(\omega)$ is the power spectral *density* of the added gaussian noise. If $S(\omega)$ happens to be that function that maximizes R under a suitable constraint, say total average power $\int_{-\infty}^{\infty} |S(\omega)|^2 d\omega$ equal to some fixed value P, then and only then is R equal to the channel capacity, defined as the maximum rate of error-free reception for the prescribed P and $N(\omega)$. From Figs. 5 and 6 and Eq. (4), it is clear that if the additive signal of Fig. 5 is gaussian with power spectral density $N(\omega)$ then

$$R = \frac{1}{2} \int_{-\infty}^{\infty} \log_2 \left(1 + \frac{|X(\omega)|^2\, |M_1(\omega)|^2}{N(\omega)}\right) d\omega \tag{6}$$

(and we can henceforth disregard $Q(\omega)$, since it drops out in the ratio).

We now assume the additive time functions $a_1(t)$ and $a_2(t)$ (represented by their Fourier transforms $A_1(\omega)$ and $A_2(\omega)$ in Fig. 4) to be stationary gaussian noises with power spectral densities $N_1(\omega)$ and $N_2(\omega)$, respectively, where

$$N_1(\omega) = \int_{-\infty}^{\infty} R_1(\tau)\, e^{-j\omega\tau} d\tau \tag{7}$$

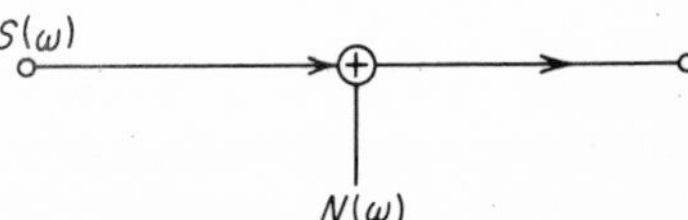

Fig. 6. Simple one-way channel.

with the autocorrelation function

$$R_1(\tau) = \lim_{T\to\infty} \frac{1}{2T} \int_{-T}^{T} a_1(t)\, a_1(t+\tau)\, dt \tag{8}$$

and similarly for $N_2(\omega)$.

The statistical dependence of $a_1(t)$ and $a_2(t)$ is expressed by the cross power spectral density

$$N_{12}(\omega) = \int_{-\infty}^{\infty} R_{12}(\tau)\, e^{-j\omega\tau} d\tau \tag{9}$$

and

$$R_{12}(\tau) = \overline{a_1(t)\, a_2(t+\tau)} \tag{10}$$

where the bar denotes the time average (as in Eq. 8). With these definitions, the power spectral density $N(\omega)$ of the equivalent additive disturbance $A(\omega)$ of Fig. 5 is

$$N(\omega) = \int_{-\infty}^{\infty} R(\tau)\, e^{-j\omega\tau} d\tau \tag{11}$$

with

$$R(\tau) = \overline{a(t)\, a(t+\tau)}\ . \tag{12}$$

From Eq. (3)

$$a(t) = a_1(t) + \int_{-\infty}^{\infty} m_1(\sigma)\, d\sigma \int_{-\infty}^{\infty} c_1(\rho)\, a_2(t-\sigma-\rho)\, d\rho, \tag{13}$$

so that

$$\begin{aligned} R(\tau) &= \overline{a_1(t)\, a_1(t+\tau)} \\ &+ \int_{-\infty}^{\infty} m_1(\sigma)\, d\sigma \int_{-\infty}^{\infty} c_1(\rho) \left[\overline{a_1(t)\, a_2(t+\tau-\sigma-\rho)} + \overline{a_1(t+\tau)\, a_2(t-\sigma-\rho)}\right] d\rho \\ &+ \int_{-\infty}^{\infty} m_1(\sigma) d\sigma \int_{-\infty}^{\infty} c_1(\rho)\, d\rho \int_{-\infty}^{\infty} m_1(\mu) d\mu \int_{-\infty}^{\infty} c_1(\nu)\, \overline{a_2(t-\sigma-\rho)\, a_2(t+\tau-\mu-\nu)}\, d\nu \end{aligned} \tag{14}$$

Substituting in (11), interchanging order of integration, and making use of relations (7) and (9), we have

$$\begin{aligned} N(\omega) &= N_1(\omega) + M_1(\omega)\, C_1(\omega)\, N_{12}(\omega) + M_1^*(\omega)\, C_1^*(\omega)\, N_{12}^*(\omega) \\ &\quad + |M_1(\omega)|^2\, |C_1(\omega)|^2\, N_2(\omega) \\ &= N_1(\omega) + 2\,\mathrm{Re}\, [M_1(\omega)\, C_1(\omega)\, N_{12}(\omega)] + |M_1(\omega)|^2\, |C_1(\omega)|^2\, N_2(\omega) \end{aligned} \tag{15}$$

where "Re" means "real part of", and "*" means "complex conjugate".

Equations (6) and (15) place in evidence the things that can be done to maximize the rate of information reception, R, that the channel will support. First of all, note the absence of $C_2(\omega)$ in the expressions.

Since $C_2(\omega)$ is the system function of the correcting network at the receiver, one concludes that the presence of such a network has no effect on R, and so it might as well be omitted. The only effective corrective action is that taken at the transmitter.

Second, the multiplicative disturbance $M_2(\omega)$ in the feedback path has no effect on R. It is interesting to note, however, that in the situation treated in the next subsection, $M_2(\omega)$ does affect the result, and, in particular, identity of the two multiplicative disturbances helps considerably.

Third, if the noises $n_1(t)$ and $n_2(t)$ are non-zero and uncorrelated ($N_{12}(\omega) \equiv 0$), then the presence of the feedback loop cannot increase R [since all factors in the last term of (15) are non-negative]. When the feedback is noiseless [$N_2(\omega) \equiv 0$], performance is neither improved nor degraded. In what way the coding problem is simplified (if indeed it is) cannot be determined from this analysis.

Fourth, if both additive disturbances are non-zero and correlated, there exists the possibility of increasing R. Assuming a fixed signal spectrum $|X(\omega)|^2$, the function $C_1(\omega)$ that will maximize R can be found by determining its phase and magnitude separately. The absence so far of any integral constraint (on transmitter power for example) allows a maximization of (6) by looking at each frequency separately. The integral (6) will be greater if at each frequency the quantity $N(\omega)$ is made as small as possible. A necessary condition is that the middle term in (15) take on the most negative value possible. Writing this term as

$$2|M_1(\omega)|\ |C_1(\omega)|\ |N_{12}(\omega)| \cos(\alpha + \beta + \gamma) \tag{16}$$

where α, β, and γ are the phase angles of M_1, C_1, and N_{12}, respectively, we see that β should be adjusted for

$$\beta = \pi - \alpha - \gamma \quad \text{(modulo } 2\pi) \tag{17}$$

so that the cosine factor is always -1. This leaves

$$N(\omega) = N_1(\omega) - 2|M_1(\omega)|\ |C_1(\omega)|\ |N_{12}(\omega)| + |M_1(\omega)|^2 |C_1(\omega)|^2 N_2(\omega). \tag{18}$$

Differentiating with respect to $|C_1(\omega)|$ and equating to zero leads to

$$|C_1(\omega)|_{\text{opt}} = |N_{12}(\omega)| / |M_1(\omega)| N_2(\omega) \tag{19}$$

so that we have finally

$$C_{1\text{opt}}(\omega) = -N_{12}^*(\omega)/M_1(\omega) N_2(\omega). \tag{20}$$

In words, knowing the spectral density N_2 of the feedback noise, the cross-spectral density N_{12} between noises $n_1(t)$ and $n_2(t)$, and the forward multiplicative disturbance M_1, the transmitter should set the correcting filter C_1 to (a) de-emphasize those frequencies at which the feedback noise passes through the forward multiplicative element M_1 with high intensity, and at the same time (b) emphasize those frequencies at which the two additive disturbances are statistically dependent, and (c) adjust the phase angle of the filter for maximum cancellation of the two noises.

This exercise illustrates several points. For example, channel capacity can in fact be increased by feedback if there is a statistical dependence between the two disturbances, a point that is sometimes overlooked. Stated in another way, the feedback channel noise (which would at first appear to be just so much more interference) actually can be used to increase the capacity. Not many real channels would be expected to have correlated gaussian noises at both ends, but several examples come to mind. Simultaneous noise jamming of two links is one example; noise from radio stars of small angular size is another.

There are several respects in which the above analysis falls short of describing a real situation. First, it would be nice to impose the condition of physical realizability (*i. e.*, no response before excitation) on the functions $M_1(\omega)$, $M_2(\omega)$, $C_1(\omega)$, and $C_2(\omega)$ and in fact to go further and require that the impulse responses $m_1(t)$ and $m_2(t)$ of each of the two channels be zero prior to some fixed positive value of t that represents the propagation time of a real channel.

Second, it would be valuable to go beyond a discussion of maximization of R, the information-bearing capacity for a prescribed input signal $x(t)$, and find the channel capacity itself, namely, the maximum value of R for all possible values of $x(t)$, $C_1(\omega)$ and $C_2(\omega)$ under a dual constraint on the average forward transmitter power and the feedback transmitter power.

Both of these problems present formidable mathematical difficulties that have not yet been dealt with.

3. Optimizing both Transmitter and Receiver for Channels with Slowly Varying Multiplicative Disturbances

The preceding two subsections have considered situations in which a signal is propagated in the forward direction, and then back in the reverse direction, retransmitted forward, and so forth. We shall now look at a slightly different use of predecision feedback, namely the situation in which the nature of the multiplicative forward channel disturbance is continually made known to the transmitter and this data is to be used in some initially unspecified way to optimize the transmitter parameters. There have been numerous treatments of the question of modifying the receiver parameters only. Here we shall take a brief look at modifying the transmitter only, and then at modifying both transmitter and receiver simultaneously.

Consider the simple channel depicted in Fig. 7, consisting of a multiplicative disturbance representable as a linear time-variant filter, followed by added gaussian noise of constant spectral density $N_0/2$ watts per cps (for a double-sided spectrum). The transfer function of this filter, $M(\omega, t)$ is a function of real time t, as is its impulse response $m(\tau, t)$.

Price[14] has derived the optimum receiver (the one that minimizes

Fig. 7. Channel with both additive and multiplicative disturbances.

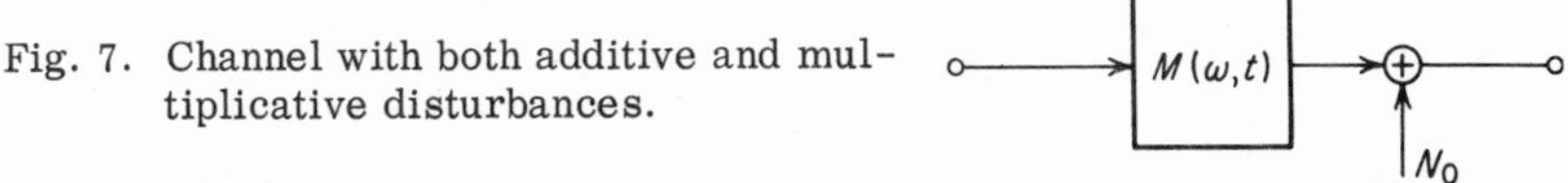

the probability of erroneously deciding which transmitted symbol waveform was sent) for receiving a single symbol which could be much longer than the time during which $M(\omega, t)$ undergoes important changes. It appears that this receiver embodies a measurement or estimation of the current value of the hypothetical transmitted signal as perturbed by $M(\omega,t)$. The Rake receiver[15] is essentially the experimental counterpart of Price's theoretically optimum one.

Recall from Chapter 12 that in the limit of *slow* random-channel variation it is sometimes possible to view the operation of such an optimum receiver as a cascade of two matched filter operations: one filter whose impulse response is the time reverse of that of the estimated channel filter, followed by a paralleled set of individual filters whose impulse responses are the time reverses of the possible transmitted signals.

We shall start with this convenient model of the receiver and, using the known fact that a matched filter maximizes the ratio of peak signal to rms noise, we shall investigate the possibilities of the type of feedback that we have postulated. For simplicity, it will be assumed that the channel filter is changing so slowly compared to the signaling rate that we can make a quasistationary analysis in which the filter is fixed during each message element. It will also be assumed that the duration in τ over which the impulse response $m(\tau, t)$ has significant values is less than T the duration of each signal.

We shall show that moving the receiver front-end matched filter [the one matched to $M(\omega)$] to the transmitter (which actually makes the receiver non-optimum but improves transmitter performance) leaves the overall system performance substantially unaffected. Then, returning to the use of a receiver that is optimum, we ask what measures the transmitter can take to maximize the system performance. Here a considerable improvement turns out to be possible since the signals degenerate into simple sinusoids, the optimum receiver degenerates into a series of filters matched to sinusoids, and the information needed by the transmitter is not $M(\omega)$ but simply the frequency at which $|M(\omega)|$ is greatest (a drastic reduction in the amount of data to be fed back).

The transmitter can obtain information on the channel by having the results of measurement at the receiver sent back to it. Or if the channel is very nearly reciprocal* (meaning that it has very nearly identical multiplicative disturbances in both directions), the transmitter can make the measurement on some signal from the receiver. This signal may be a standard test signal (such as a pulse), or it

*Not to be confused with the usage sometimes employed in network theory in which the product of two "reciprocal" functions is a constant.

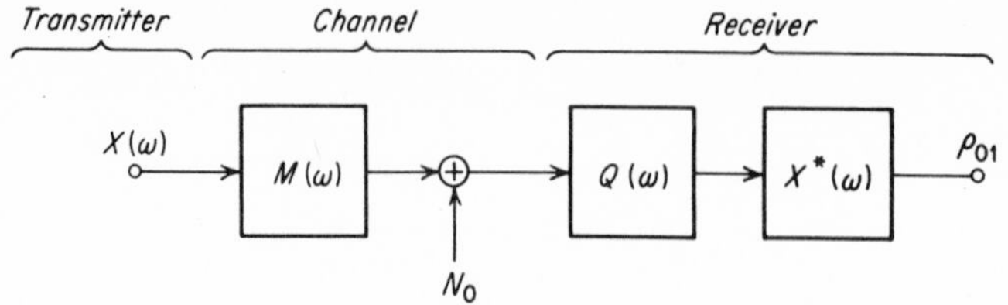

Fig. 8. System with optimum receiver.

may even be derived from the energy in an information-bearing transmission in the other direction, as is done in the forward direction with the present Rake system. In any case, the transmitter has a measurement or estimate of $M(\omega)$, not the actual $M(\omega)$. Nevertheless, to allow presentation of a simple analysis it will be assumed that the transmitter knows the actual $M(\omega)$. We will not be able to prove here that the end results of operations with the *exact* $M(\omega)$ that we find to be optimum carry over into identical operations with estimates of $M(\omega)$.

First consider the one-way system we have spoken of, shown in Fig. 8. If we assume equiprobable, equal-energy transmitted signals with identical spectra, only one signal need be shown, with no loss of generality. This is denoted $x(t)$ with complex spectrum $X(\omega)$.

The second filter at the receiver is matched to the transmitted signal. We already know that the first filter should be matched to the channel filter, that is, $Q(\omega)$ should be equal to $M^*(\omega)$, so that the composite filter formed by Q and X^* is matched to the signal formed by X and M. This maximizes the output signal-to-noise ratio, defined as the ratio of the square of the output voltage at some fixed time, say $t = 0$, to the output noise power,

$$\rho_{01} = \frac{2\left|\int_{-\infty}^{\infty} |X(\omega)|^2 M(\omega)\, Q(\omega)\, d\omega\right|^2}{N_0 \int_{-\infty}^{\infty} |Q(\omega)|^2\, |X(\omega)|^2\, d\omega} \,. \tag{21}$$

(The Schwarz inequality allows proof by inspection of the fact that (21) is maximized if $Q = M^*$). The non-realizability of Q (non-zero response before $t = 0$) can obviously be avoided by maximizing the output not at $t = 0$ but at a positive value of t that exceeds the duration of the impulse response of the channel.

Now consider what happens if this first channel-matched filtering operation is carried out at the transmitter instead of at the receiver so as to predistort rather than post-distort the signal, retaining at the receiver the bank of filters that are matched to the transmitted signals. This might be expected to make more effective use of transmitter power by concentrating it in the more favorable frequency regions. The situation is depicted in Fig. 9. The output signal-to-noise ratio is

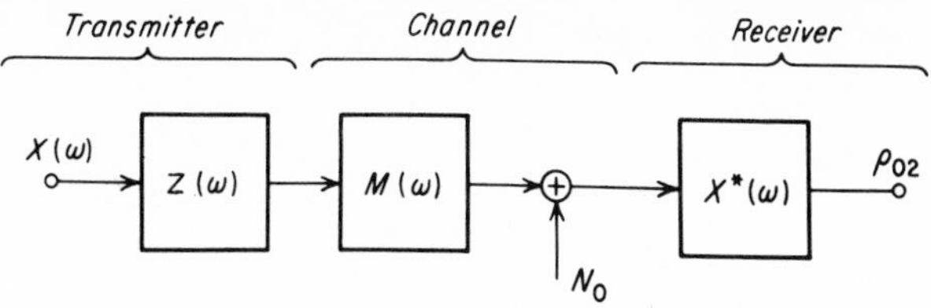

Fig. 9. System with optimum transmitter.

$$\rho_{02} = \frac{2\left|\int_{-\infty}^{\infty} |X(\omega)|^2 Z(\omega) M(\omega)\, d\omega\right|^2}{N_0 \int_{-\infty}^{\infty} |X(\omega)|^2\, d\omega} \tag{22}$$

and we should like to determine the $Z(\omega)$ that will maximize this ratio for a given average transmitter power

$$P_{T2} = \int_{-\infty}^{\infty} |X(\omega)|^2\, |Z(\omega)|^2\, d\omega\ . \tag{23}$$

Since the denominator of (22) does not depend on $Z(\omega)$, this is equivalent to maximizing the ratio of the numerator of (22) to (23), namely

$$\frac{\left|\int_{-\infty}^{\infty} |X(\omega)|^2 Z(\omega)\, M(\omega)\, d\omega\right|^2}{\int_{-\infty}^{\infty} |X(\omega)|^2\, |Z(\omega)|^2\, d\omega}\ . \tag{24}$$

From the similarity of (24) to the ratio (21) it is seen that the optimum value of $Z(\omega)$ is again $M^*(\omega)$. Thus moving the first filter to the transmitter does not change the desired characteristics of the filter.

That the performance of the system is not affected by moving the channel-matched filter from receiver to transmitter can be seen from an examination of the ratio $(\rho_{01}/\rho_{02})/(P_{T1}/P_{T2})$, where P_{T1} is the transmitter power for the scheme of Fig. 8.

$$P_{T1} = \int_{-\infty}^{\infty} |X(\omega)|^2\, d\omega \tag{25}$$

This ratio is unity, a result that is perhaps surprising until one realizes that the improvement that transplanting the filter to the transmitter causes (by diverting the signal energy into the high-transmissivity regions of the spectrum) is exactly equal to the degradation caused by not using an ideal receiver. For non-white noise this equivalence is no longer true. In the system of Fig. 8, the ideal receiver accentuated those regions of the arriving signal spectrum having greater intensity.

It is conceivable that in some practical situation the odds might be slightly in favor of placing the filter at the transmitter because if it is at the receiver some of the received signal energy must somehow go into measurement of $M(\omega)$. In the experimental Rake

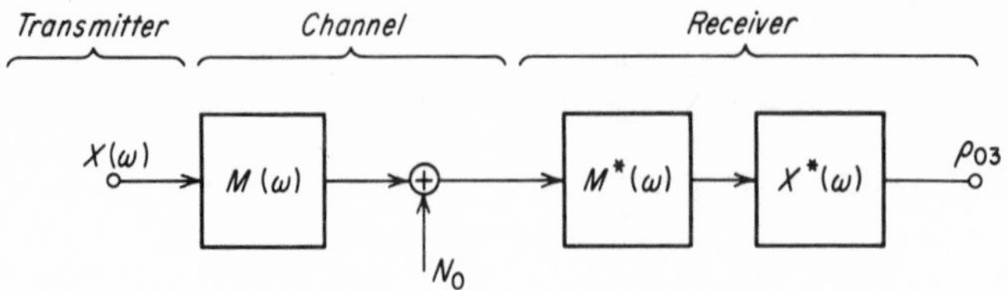

Fig. 10. System with optimum transmitter and receiver.

system $M(\omega)$ is estimated and decision between alternatives is made, both from the same incoming signal. If the estimate had been provided independently at no cost in transmitter power, the output signal-to-noise ratio would have been slightly higher. The whole question of how best to share the transmitted power between conveying data and conveying information on the channel is very poorly understood at present.

So far, we have discussed a system in which the receiver was optimum for a given transmitter (transmitting a signal $x(t)$), and one in which the transmitter was optimized for a given receiver (a matched filter of impulse response $x(-t)$). Let us now try to optimize both transmitter and receiver simultaneously. The situation is depicted in Fig. 10.

We again assume that whatever the transmitted signal $x(t)$, the desired receiver is the cascade of the two matched filters shown. Assuming white noise also, we would like to find the $X(\omega)$ that maximizes

$$\rho_{03} = \frac{2}{N_0} \int_{-\infty}^{\infty} |X(\omega)|^2 \, |M(\omega)|^2 \, d\omega \tag{26}$$

for a given

$$P_{T3} = \int_{-\infty}^{\infty} |X(\omega)|^2 \, d\omega \, . \tag{27}$$

The solution is that $|X(\omega)|^2$ should be a delta function at the frequency ω_{max} (in the operating band) for which $|M(\omega)|$ is the greatest.*

However, a signal of arbitrarily narrow bandwidth conveys information at a zero rate (in the presence of any non-zero amount of noise) and we are obliged to bring in the question of signaling rate in order to see what our result means. If the multiplicative disturbance is such that the impulse response $m(t)$ approaches zero after $t = T$, then changes in $|M(\omega)|$ with ω will be no more rapid than $1/T$. Thus if the duration of each signaling element is substantially greater than T, the above solution is still correct—the transmission should be

*That this is truly a maximum can be proved by allowing $|X(\omega)|^2$ to deviate from a single impulse in any way. Since $|M(\omega)|^2$ is either concave downward or flat about the frequency ω_{max} of a maximum, the value of Eq. (27) is either less than or equal to $(2P_{T3}/N_0)\,|M(\omega_{max})|^2$. Equality means that there is a plurality of equally good frequencies.

made with a pulse of sine wave at ω_{max}, the frequency for which the multiplicative disturbance gives the greatest transmissivity. If the duration of each signaling element is less than T, time smearing or "inter-symbol interference" occurs anyhow, and since this factor was ignored in setting up the present problem one can be quite certain that the present form of solution is no longer optimum. Intersymbol constraints are difficult to include in any decision theory analysis and very little analytical study of this problem has been done. The form of general solution for the optimum signal of arbitrary duration with respect to T, and intersymbol effects ignored, has been outlined by Price.[16] In the limit of large signal duration the solution degenerates into the sinusoids mentioned above.

The required number of alternative transmitted signals might be provided either by using various phases at the same frequency (*e.g.*, 0° and 180° for a binary system) or by using the second highest peak of $|M(\omega)|$, the third highest, and so forth.

One consequence of the simplicity of the optimum form of transmitter-receiver combination is that the feedback channel does not have to provide $M(\omega)$ (or an estimate of it) after all—it need only say at which frequency (or frequencies) $|M(\omega)|$ is a maximum.

In contemplating a possible practical embodiment of these notions, and in particular the problem of supplying the required information to the transmitter, the use of soundings from the receiver has particular appeal. This requires that the two channels be reciprocal to the extent that ω_{max} is the same for both directions. For ionospheric propagation in particular, $m(t)$ consists essentially of a series of impulses at various delays corresponding to ray paths usually involving different ionospheric layers. The required high degree of reciprocity requires that the amplitude and phase of the signal via each path vary with time in an identical manner for the two propagation directions. If one or more of the component paths is not reciprocal in this sense, ω_{max} will not be the same in both directions. Balser and Smith[17] have performed two-way pulse experiments at the same frequency simultaneously and find that although reflections near the MUF have highly correlated amplitudes, this dependence disappears as the frequency drops. This negative result would tend to discourage confidence in this means of supplying information on ω_{max}.

As a final note it should be remarked that although the form of optimum transmitter signal is easy to determine in our simple feedback situation where the transmitter has knowledge of the channel, the situation is not nearly so clear in the one-way case. The problem of finding the optimum signal waveform given the form of optimum receiver, has not been solved, although one would think that the signal energy should be spread uniformly over the available band if the high-transmissivity regions of $M(\omega)$ are apt to occur equiprobably at any frequency.

4. A Practical Predecision Feedback System—Janet

Of the many new forms of communication system developed in recent years, perhaps only the Janet system[18] represents a serious attempt to exploit what we have called here predecision feedback (the use at the transmitter of information on the state of the analog channel). In the Janet system a very simple parameter is fed back to the transmitter, namely the times at which the transmissivity of the multiplicative disturbance at the operating frequency is adequately high. Burst transmission of stored data then takes place during such intervals, with data piling up in storage at the transmitter between intervals.

There is a superficial similarity between this notion and that of the optimum system just discussed; Janet concentrates the transmission at favorable times; the optimum system of the preceding section concentrates the transmission at favorable frequencies. But this is the extent of the similarity.

The reason for using so different a procedure with Janet becomes apparent when one considers the unusual type of channel employed. In the optimization described in the preceding subsection, we sought to maximize the ratio of output S/N to transmitted signal energy, for a single typical transmission. The channel was thus tacitly assumed to have stationary statistics. The Janet system, however, employs VHF frequencies and seeks to capitalize on the fact that VHF propagation exhibits large enhancements of transmission above the scatter-mode background, these enhancements being caused by meteor-induced ionization. The magnitude of the multiplicative disturbance $|M(\omega, t)|$ is then quite flat in ω but very variable with t. If continuous transmission were employed, each signaling element sent during low signal level periods would have high error probability due to low signal-to-noise ratio (ratio of signal energy to noise density). The enhancements of received signal strength occur often enough and are so large that the ratio of received signal energy to noise power density for each message element is actually much greater if the elements are transmitted rapidly during enhanced periods than if they are transmitted slowly during weak-signal periods. This is true even if the transmitter is peak-power limited rather than average-power limited.

In its practical embodiment, the Janet system employs a two-way information transmission, both links serving to convey message data as well as to feed back data on the channel. The many interesting details of this type of system will be found in the series of papers in Reference 18.

IV. CONCLUSIONS

It is hoped that the preceding pages have suitably emphasized that the broad class of notions collectively called feedback systems represents still another in the bag of tricks that can be used in designing more reliable communication systems.

Among other things we have considered the idealized information-bearing capability of a given one-way link, namely, its channel capacity, and we have seen that the addition of a feedback connection may or may not make possible an increase in this capacity. As we have learned from the preceding chapter, channel capacity is just an upper limit to the attainable reliable transmission rate, a goal that cannot usually be approached without elaborate coding and decoding operations. Yet, when a reverse feedback connection is available, it often becomes possible to use much less elaborate coding to achieve a given level of performance, say the error rate at a given transmission rate, and as a matter of fact in certain special situations the forward link can be used at very close to capacity with only the simplest of coding procedures.

It seems to be almost universally true that effective use of a feedback connection leads either to a simplification of the system or an improvement in performance or both. For example, the analysis of subsection III-3 suggests that the normally difficult problems of communicating through dispersive channels become markedly simplified and improved if a feedback connection is available to provide a small amount of information on the current state of the channel.

It is disappointing that there have been so few experimental communication systems built using a feedback link to augment the forward link. Perhaps our growing understanding of the theory of this rudimentary form of "communication network", plus the success achieved by the ARQ and Janet systems will soon lead to further exploitation of the many possibilities.

APPENDIX

CHANNEL CAPACITY WITHOUT CODING*

by P. Elias

A-I. INTRODUCTION

Kelly[19] recently gave an illustration of a gambling situation in which channel capacity has a meaning independent of any requirement to code the signals that are to be transmitted over the channel. Shannon[1] gave a "cheating channel" example of a procedure which, given a noisy forward channel of capacity C_1, a noiseless feedback

*Adapted from *Quarterly Progress Report, Research Laboratory of Electronics, M.I.T.*, pp. 90-93, October 15, 1956.

channel, and a noiseless forward channel of capacity C_2, would permit transmission at a rate $C_1 + C_2$ over the combination of the two forward channels with a simple, constructive coding procedure that would be easy to implement, as opposed to the complex coding procedures that are required to transmit over a single noisy channel with low error probability, in the absence of feedback. (It has been shown[2] that for a channel without memory, the presence of the noiseless feedback channel does not affect the capacity of the forward channel.)

For channels with additive white gaussian noise, it is possible to strengthen Shannon's example. Two such forward channels, both noisy, of equal bandwidth W and capacities C_1 and C_2, can be used to obtain in analog fashion, without substantial coding or delay, one channel of capacity $C_1 + C_2$, by making use of a noiseless feedback channel. Reiterating this procedure leads to the interesting result that, if a noiseless feedback channel is available, a single forward channel of large bandwidth (many times W), perturbed by additive white gaussian noise of power density N_0 watts/cps, can transmit an analog signal of bandwidth W with transmitter power S which will be received with an effective signal/noise power ratio ρ_0^2 that is given by

$$\rho_0^2 = e^{\rho_i^2} - 1$$

where

$$\rho_i^2 = S/(N_0 W)$$

is the signal/noise power ratio obtainable by simple transmission without coding or feedback, and

$$\rho_0^2 = S/(N_0' W)$$

is the signal/noise power ratio of the received signal after a detection operation, still in bandwidth W and identical to the transmitted signal except for the added noise of power density N_0' watts/cps and a delay of about $1/2W$ sec. Thus, a 10-db signal-noise ratio in band W is equivalent to a signal/noise ratio of $e^{10} - 1 = 22{,}000$, or approximately 43.5 db, if the available forward channel is wideband and a noiseless feedback channel is available.

This behavior is not quite as exceptional as it sounds: pulse-code modulation achieves the same character of behavior without the noiseless feedback channel, but an extra 8 db or so is required,[20] which would make it useless in a channel with an initial signal/noise ratio as low as 10 db.

A-II. PARALLEL GAUSSIAN CHANNELS

Consider two channels of unit bandwidth, with additive gaussian noise, and signal/noise power ratios ρ_1^2 and ρ_2^2, respectively. Their capacities (in nats/sec) will be

$$C_1 = \ln(1 + \rho_1^2)$$
$$C_2 = \ln(1 + \rho_2^2) \tag{A1}$$

If the same signal is applied to both channels, we recall from Eq. (43), Chapter 7, that the optimum way to combine the two signals gives a received signal/noise power ratio of $\rho_0^2 = \rho_1^2 + \rho_2^2$, and thus an effective total capacity for the two channels which are used in this way, of

$$C_0 = \ln(1 + \rho_1^2 + \rho_2^2) . \tag{A2}$$

However, the sum of the capacities of the two channels, which is the total capacity available for forward transmission, is

$$C = C_1 + C_2 = \ln(1 + \rho_1^2) + \ln(1 + \rho_2^2) = \ln(1 + \rho_1^2)(1 + \rho_2^2)$$
$$= \ln(1 + \rho_1^2 + \rho_2^2 + \rho_1^2\rho_2^2) \tag{A3}$$

Now, Eq. (A3) implies that the attainable $(S/N)_0$ at the receiver should be

$$\rho^2 = \rho_1^2 + \rho_2^2 + \rho_1^2\rho_2^2 \cdot \tag{A4}$$

which is not much greater than $\rho_0^2 = \rho_1^2 + \rho_2^2$ if $\rho_1^2 < 1, \rho_2^2 < 1$. But if both channels have good and equal signal/noise ratios, then ρ_0^2 is approximately equal to $2\rho_1^2$, but from (A4) ρ_1^2 and ρ_2^2 should then multiply, not add, which suggests that better behavior may be obtainable.

To obtain a received signal/noise ratio ρ^2 as in (A4), we send the noisy output of the first channel back to the transmitter over the noiseless feedback path, and send a signal over the second channel which is a linear combination of the original signal and the first-channel noise. This is added (with appropriate weighting) to the first received signal. The net result, using optimum linear combinations at both ends, is a received signal at the signal/noise ratio given by Eq. (A4), which gives the channel capacity $C = C_1 + C_2$. The process is illustrated in Fig. A-1. The fact that this is a maximum in received signal/noise power ratio is a consequence of the channel capacity theorem: it can be proved, with patience, by substituting undetermined coefficients at the two adders and varying in order to maximize the received signal/noise ratio.

The statements in the introduction of this Appendix now follow, if a channel of wide bandwidth is turned into many channels, each of bandwidth W, by frequency-multiplexing. The capacity of the sum channel, iterating the procedure given above, is the sum of the channel capacities, the signal power available being divided among the

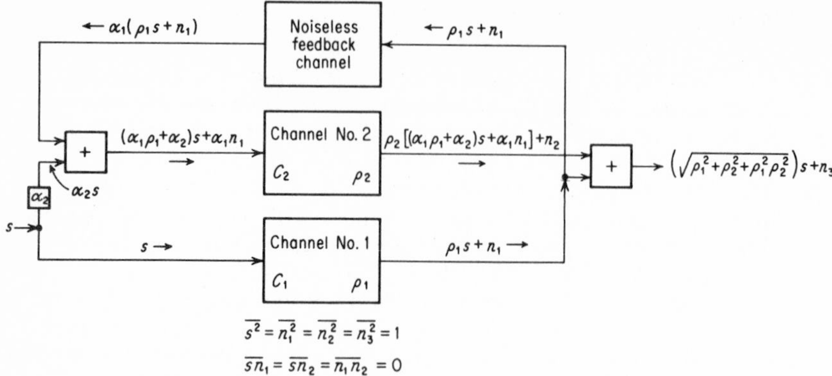

Fig. A-1. Combination of two noisy forward channels using noiseless feedback channel.

channels. In the limit, this gives

$$C = \lim_{K\to\infty} KW \ln(1 + S/KN_0W) = S/N_0 \text{ nats/sec}$$

Then, ρ_0^2, the effective received signal/noise power ratio, is given by

$$C = W \ln(1+\rho_0^2) = S/N_0$$

$$\ln(1+\rho_0^2) = S/N_0W = \rho_i^2$$

$$\rho_0^2 = e^{\rho_i^2} - 1 .$$

If noise is added to the feedback channel, the optimum behavior attainable by the addition of two forward channels, making use of feedback, gives a forward capacity that is less than $C_1 + C_2$, and a ρ_0^2 that is less than $\rho_1^2 + \rho_2^2 + \rho_1^2\rho_2^2$. In fact, if ρ_3^2 is the signal/noise power ratio in the feedback channel, then the output signal/noise power ratio becomes

$$\rho_0^2 = \rho_1^2 + \rho_2^2 + \frac{\rho_1^2\rho_2^2\rho_3^2}{(1+\rho_1^2)(1+\rho_2^2)+\rho_3^2} \tag{A5}$$

which approaches the no-feedback result when ρ_3^2 is small, approaches the noiseless case when ρ_3^2 is large, and shows that, for any value of ρ_3^2, it would always be more advantageous to use the feedback channel as an additional forward channel, if this were possible, and the signal/noise power ratio in it could be kept unchanged. That is, for all ρ_1^2, ρ_2^2, $\rho_3^2 > 0$, we have

$$\rho_1^2 + \rho_2^2 + \rho_3^2 > \rho_1^2 + \rho_2^2 + \frac{\rho_1^2\rho_2^2\rho_3^2}{(1+\rho_1^2)(1+\rho_2^2)+\rho_3^2} \tag{A6}$$

REFERENCES

1. C. E. Shannon and W. Weaver, *The Mathematical Theory of Communication,* University of Illinois Press, 1949, pp. 37, 38.
2. C. E. Shannon, "The Zero-error Capacity of a Random Channel," *P. G. I. T. Trans.,* vol. IT-2, no. 3, pp. 8-19, September, 1956.
3. This point is investigated further by R. L. Dobrushin, "Transmission of Information over a Channel with a Feedback Connection," *Theory of Probabilities and its Applications (Moscow),* vol. 3, no. 4, pp. 395-412, 1958.
4. S. S. L. Chang, "The Theory of Information Feedback Systems," *P. G. I. T. Trans.,* vol. IT-2, no. 3, pp. 29-40, September, 1956.
5. W. B. Bishop and B. L. Buchanan, "Message Redundancy versus Feedback for Reducing Message Uncertainty," *IRE Conv. Record,* pt. 2, 1957, pp. 33-39.
6. C. E. Shannon, "Channels with Side Information at the Transmitter," *I. B. M. J.,* vol. 2, pp. 289-293, 1958.
7. B. Harris, A. Hauptschein, and L. S. Schwartz, "Optimum Decision Feedback Circuits," *IRE Conv. Record,* pt. 2, pp. 3-10, 1957. See also *Operations Research,* vol. 5, pp. 680-692, 1957.
8. B. Harris, A. Hauptschein, K. C. Morgan, and L. S. Schwartz, "Binary Decision Feedback Systems for Maintaining Reliability under Conditions of Varying Field Strength," *Proc. Nat. Elec. Conf.,* vol. 13, pp. 126-140, 1957.
9. J. J. Metzner, "Binary Relay Communication with Decision Feedback," *IRE Conv. Record,* pt. 4, pp. 112-119, 1959.
10. B. Harris and K. C. Morgan, "Binary Symmetric Decision Feedback Systems," *Commun. and Electronics,* no. 38, pp. 436-443, 1958.
    H. B. Voelcker, Jr., "Simple Codes for Fading Circuits," *P. G. C. S. Trans.,* vol. CS-6, no. 2, pp. 47-52, 1958.
    A. B. Brown and S. T. Meyers, "Evaluation of Some Error Correction Methods Applicable to Digital Data Transmission," *IRE Conv. Record,* pt. 2, pp. 37-55, 1958.
11. H. C. A. Van Duuren, U. S. Patent 2, 313, 980 (1947). Also *Tijdschr. Ned. Radiogenoot.,* vol. 16, pp. 53-67, 1951.
12. J. B. Moore, "Signal Mutilation and Error Prevention on Shortwave Radio-Teleprinter Circuits," *IRE Conv. Record,* pt. 8, pp. 127-131, 1957.
    J. K. Given, "Recent Advances in International Radio Communications," *P. G. C. S. Trans.,* vol. CS-2, no. 3, pp. 86-92, 1954.
13. P. Elias, "Channel Capacity without Coding (Abstract only)," *IRE Conv. Record,* pt. 2, p. 49, 1957.
14. R. Price, "Optimum Detection of Random Signals in Noise, with Application to Scatter-multipath Communication, I, *P. G. I. T. Trans.,* vol. IT-2, no. 4, pp. 125-135, 1956.
15. R. Price and P. E. Green, Jr., "A Communication Technique for Multipath Channels, *Proc. IRE,* vol. 46, no. 3, pp. 555-570, 1958.

16. R. Price, "Studies of Analog Channels Using Feedback," *Lincoln Lab. Div. III Q: P. R.*, Section IV-B-2, October 15, 1959.
17. M. Balser and W. B. Smith, "Experiments to Test HF Ionospheric Reciprocity," in preparation.
18. *Proc. IRE*, December, 1957, thirteen papers on Janet and related systems.
19. J. L. Kelly, "A New Interpretation of Information Rate," *Bell System Tech. J.*, vol. 35, pp. 917-926, 1956.
20. B. M. Oliver, J. R. Pierce, and C. E. Shannon, "The Philosophy of P. C. M.," *Proc. IRE*, vol. 36, pp. 1324-1331, 1948.

CHAPTER 15

Characterization of Noise in Receiving Systems*

Robert P. Rafuse

I. INTRODUCTION

A basic limitation on the maximum range of a communication system is imposed by the presence of receiver noise and antenna noise. The development of the maser and parametric amplifiers has reduced the limitation imposed by front-end noise to the point where the planning of new systems must involve a close examination of other sources of noise, as well as a careful analysis of the behavior of receiving systems that include negative-resistance devices (*i.e.*, devices with negative input and/or output impedances). Inadequecies in the earlier theories have necessitated a reassessment of the basic concepts. An approach to this problem has recently been developed by Haus and Adler.[1,2,3]

The present discussion is primarily concerned with the analysis of the noise performance of a receiving system. The theoretical framework presented here will be restricted to situations in which the noise has gaussian statistics (*e.g.* thermal and shot noise). Moreover, only linear operations will be considered. In particular, we shall consider the effect of various components on overall system signal-to-noise ratio and the conditions under which *system* signal-to-noise ratio can be optimized before any detection process is attempted.

II. CONCEPTUAL STRUCTURE

The parameters that characterize the noise performance of any amplifier are noise figure and gain. Perhaps one of the best concise treatments of this subject will be found in Chapters 4 and 5 of Refer-

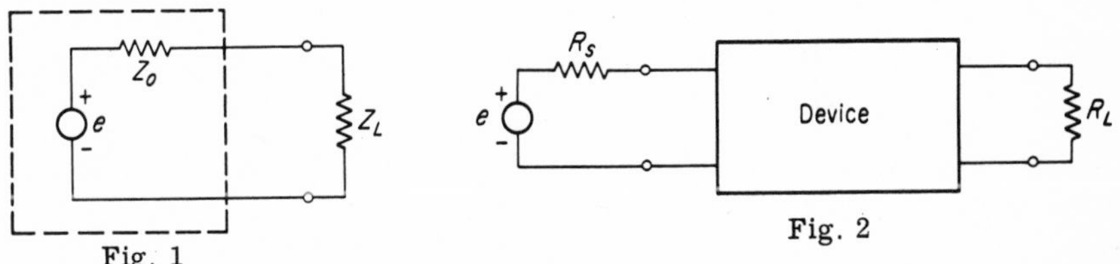

Fig. 1. Thevenin equivalent representation of a one-terminal-pair device with external load Z_L.
Fig. 2. Two-terminal-pair device with source and load connected.

*Written by the Editor from rough notes by R.P.R.

ence 4. The earlier treatments did not include the case of negative resistance devices. This inconvenience has been removed by extensions of the theory by Haus and Adler. We shall start with a discussion of basic definitions and concepts.

A. Available and Exchangeable Power

Figure 1 illustrates a one-terminal-pair network in Thévenin representation. If the source impedance Z_o has $\mathrm{Re}\{Z_o\} > 0$, then the available power at the output is simply the maximum value of power that the source can deliver to a load of impedance Z_L. The combination of terminal voltage and current for which the maximum power is delivered by the source occurs when $Z_L = Z_o^*$. This maximum power, called the *available power*, is

$$P_a = \frac{1}{2}\,\frac{\overline{e \cdot e^*}}{Z_o + Z_o^*} = \frac{\overline{e^2}}{4R_o} \tag{1}$$

where,

$$Z_o = R_o + jX_o,\ R_o > 0\ .$$

But if the $\mathrm{Re}\{Z_o\} < 0$, the available power definition gives $P_a = \infty$, a rather useless result. If we consider the nature of the maximum when $\mathrm{Re}\{Z_o\} > 0$, we see that the available power, P_a, is a *stationary maximum* $\left(i.e., \dfrac{\partial P_a}{\partial Z_L} = 0, \dfrac{\partial^2 P_a}{\partial Z_L^2} < 0\right)$, but the value of $P_a = \infty$ for $\mathrm{Re}\{Z_o\} < 0$ is not. There is, however, a stationary maximum for power returned by *the load* to the source for $\mathrm{Re}\{Z_o\} < 0$ given by Eq. (1) with the restriction on $\mathrm{Re}\{Z_o\}$ removed. Thus, the maximum value of power "exchanged" by the load and the source is

$$P_e = \frac{1}{2}\,\frac{\overline{e \cdot e^*}}{Z_o + Z_o^*} = \frac{\overline{e^2}}{4R_o} \tag{2}$$

where,

$$Z_o = R_o + jX_o, R_o \lessgtr 0\ .$$

It should be noted that the exchangeable power, P_e, will be positive if $R_o > 0$ (and would, therefore, be the available power) and is negative if $R_o < 0$. This one critical extension of the available power concept will now allow us to extend all other noise concepts to include negative resistance devices.

B. Exchangeable Power Gain

Figure 2 illustrates a two-terminal-pair device. If we define the exchangeable power gain as the ratio of exchangeable power of the network output, P_{eo}, to the exchangeable power of the source, P_{es}, then

$$G_e = \frac{P_{eo}}{P_{es}} \; . \tag{3}$$

Thus, if the output impedance of the device is $Z_o = R_o + jX_o$ and the source impedance is $Z_s = R_s + jX_s$ then,

$$G_e > 0 \text{ if } [R_s/R_o] > 0 \tag{4a}$$

$$G_e < 0 \text{ if } [R_s/R_o] < 0 \; . \tag{4b}$$

It is interesting to note that G_e would reduce to the available gain of the device if $R_s > 0$ and $R_o > 0$. The concepts of available-power gain and exchangeable-power gain are artificial, and one should not confuse them with the concept of actual power gain. They are not the same thing, except, of course, when the input and output terminals of the device are conjugate matched—a condition that is seldom achieved *or desired* in practice. In any case, the behavior of signals and additive noise in a system is normally characterized by a signal-to-noise ratio that is unaffected by the gain of any *single* device (both signal and noise being acted on in like manner). Note that the exchangeable-power gain of a cascade of n amplifiers is simply the product of the individual exchangeable-power gains:

$$G_{e,\text{cascade}} = \prod_{k=1}^{n} G_{ek} \; . \tag{5}$$

Example 1: A conventional neutralized triode operated as an amplifier in the common-cathode connection has the high-frequency model shown in Fig. 3. Here,

$$G_e = \frac{P_{eo}}{P_{es}} = \frac{\mu^2 \overline{e_g^2}/4 r_p}{\overline{i_s^2}/4 G_s} \tag{6}$$

or, since

$$\overline{e_g^2} = \overline{i_s^2}/(G_s + g_i)^2 ,$$

$$G_e = \frac{\mu^2 G_s}{r_p (G_s + g_i)^2} \; . \tag{7}$$

The actual power gain is

$$G_{\text{actual}} = \frac{\mu^2 \overline{e_g^2} \dfrac{R_L}{[r_p + R_L]^2}}{\overline{i_s^2}/4G_s} = \frac{4\mu^2 G_s R_L}{(G_s + g_i)^2 [r_p + R_L]^2} \tag{8}$$

Example 2: A negative-resistance amplifier may be characterized as in Fig. 4.

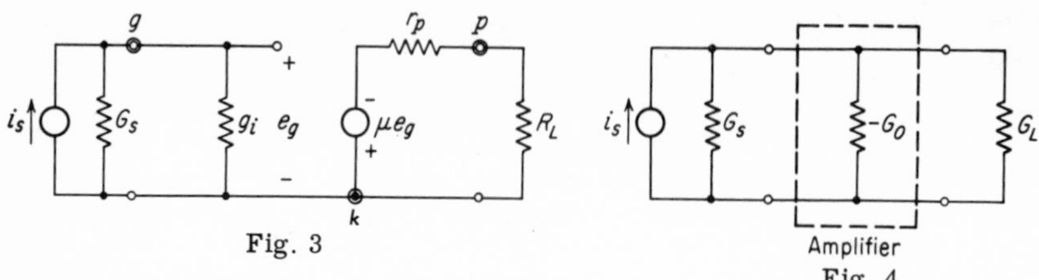

Fig. 3. Model of a neutralized triode amplifier. All reactances are assumed to be tuned out.

Fig. 4. A negative-resistance amplifier with source and load attached.

Here we have

$$G_e = \frac{P_{eo}}{P_{es}} = \frac{\overline{i_s^2}/4(G_s - G_o)}{\overline{i_s^2}/4G_s} \tag{9}$$

or

$$G_e = \frac{G_s}{G_s - G_o} \; . \tag{10}$$

Note that $G_e = \infty$ for $|G_s| = |G_o|$. However, the insertion gain of the device can be expressed as the ratio of power delivered by the source to the load, G_L, with the amplifier "turned on" ($-G_o$ in place) to the power delivered by the source to the load with the amplifier "turned-off" ($G_o = 0$). This results in

$$G_{insertion} = \frac{\overline{i_s^2}\, G_L/(G_s + G_L - G_o)^2}{\overline{i_s^2}\, G_L/(G_s + G_L)^2} \tag{11}$$

$$= \left[\frac{G_s + G_L}{G_s + G_L - G_o}\right]^2 \; . \tag{12}$$

It is obvious that $G_{insertion} \neq G_e$.

Example 3: The expression for the exchangeable power gain of a cascade of amplifiers given by Eq. (5) may be demonstrated by considering the cascade of three negative-resistance amplifiers shown in Fig. 5.

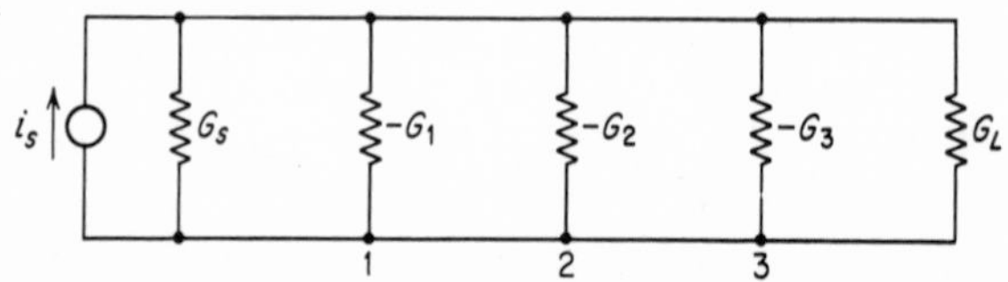

Fig. 5. Cascade of three negative-resistance amplifiers.

From the preceding example, the exchangeable power gain of amplifier 1 is

$$G_{e1} = \frac{G_S}{G_S - G_1} \,. \tag{13}$$

For amplifier 2 the source conductance is $G_S - G_1$. Therefore

$$G_{e2} = \frac{G_S - G_1}{G_S - G_1 - G_2} \,. \tag{14}$$

Similarly, for amplifier 3

$$G_{e3} = \frac{G_S - G_1 - G_2}{G_S - G_1 - G_2 - G_3} \,. \tag{15}$$

Using Eq. (5), we obtain

$$G_{e,cascade} = G_{e1} \cdot G_{e2} \cdot G_{e3} = \frac{G_S}{G_S - G_1 - G_2 - G_3} \tag{16}$$

which is exactly the same result that we would have obtained had we taken the amplifier cascade as a whole and lumped the negative conductances together as $-(G_1 + G_2 + G_3)$.

C. Noise Figure and Noise Temperature

A logical criterion of noise performance of a receiving system might be the total degradation in signal-to-noise ratio experienced in passing through the system, as measured by the ratio

$$\frac{\dfrac{\textit{exchangeable signal power at the system input}}{\textit{exchangeable noise power at the system input}}}{\dfrac{\textit{exchangeable signal power at the system output}}{\textit{exchangeable noise power at the system output}}} \,. \tag{17}$$

Unfortunately, the value of this ratio depends upon many factors, such as signal bandwidth, source temperature, noise bandwidth, etc. However, one disadvantage can be removed by considering the system performance in frequency intervals so small that the ratio given above remains constant over the frequency range considered. This is normally called *"spot" noise figure* and may well be a function of frequency. A total *integrated noise* figure may be obtained for other situations.[4]

If we now express the ratio given in Eq. (17) in the form

$$F = \frac{(S/N)_{in}}{(S/N)_{out}} \tag{18}$$

and remember that exchangeable gain acts on signal and noise in exactly the same way, we can write

$$F = \frac{S_{in}/N_{in}}{S_{in} \cdot G_e/(N_{in} \cdot G_e + N_{internal,\ at\ out})} \qquad (19)$$

or

$$F = 1 + \frac{N_{internal,\ at\ out}}{N_{in} \cdot G_e} \ . \qquad (20)$$

An ideal receiver is one that has no internal noise sources and for it $F = 1$. We shall define a term which is somewhat more useful than F itself. This we shall call the *"excess" noise figure*

$$F - 1 = \frac{\textit{Noise power exchangeable at the output from internal sources}}{\textit{Noise power exchangeable at the output from the signal source}}$$

$$= \frac{N_{eoi}}{N_{eos}} \ . \qquad (21)$$

If we replace all internal noise sources in the system by equivalent noise sources at the input of the system, the exchangeable power gain, G_e, will act on source noise and equivalent internal noise in like manner. If N_{ei} denotes the input-exchangeable-power equivalent of the internal noise, then

$$F - 1 = \frac{N_{ei} \cdot G_e}{N_{es} \cdot G_e} = \frac{N_{ei}}{N_{es}} \ . \qquad (22)$$

If the source is resistive and at a thermal-equilibrium temperature T_s,

$$N_{es} = \pm\, kT_s \Delta f \qquad (23)$$

where k is Boltzman's constant, 1.38×10^{-23} joules/°K, and Δf is the noise bandwidth in cps. N_{es} is positive or negative depending on whether the source conductance is positive or negative. If we let

$$N_{ei} = k\, T_a \Delta f \qquad (24)$$

we can write

$$F - 1 = \pm \frac{T_a}{T_s} \qquad (25)$$

where T_a can be termed the "amplifier temperature". Note that ac-

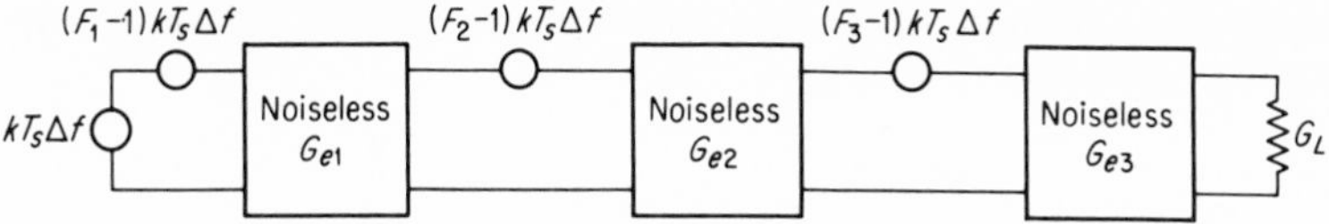

Fig. 6. A cascade of noisy amplifiers.

cording to Eq. (25) $(F-1)$ can be either positive or negative; this will be explained in a later section. We might add here that F or $(F-1)$ is normally measured in terms of a standard source temperature of 300° K (or 290° K, to be more exact) which we shall call T_o. Thus, an amplifier with a measured noise figure of 3 would have $(F-1) = 2$ or an amplifier temperature of 300 °K.

D. The Cascade Formula

Figure 6 illustrates a cascade of three amplifiers in which the internal exchangeable noise power has been referred to the input of each amplifier. Figure 7 shows a single-block equivalent of Fig. 6. The total exchangeable noise power at the output is the sum of

$$N_{eos} = kT_s\,\Delta f\,G_{e1}G_{e2}\,G_{e3} \tag{26}$$

which is caused by the signal source, and

$$\begin{aligned} N_{eoi} &= (F_1-1)kT_s\Delta f\,G_{e1}G_{e2}G_{e3} \\ &+ (F_2-1)kT_s\Delta f\,G_{e2}G_{e3} + (F_3-1)kT_s\,\Delta f\,G_{e3} \end{aligned} \tag{27}$$

which is caused by the internal noise sources. Consequently,

$$F_{total} - 1 = \frac{N_{eoi}}{N_{eos}} = (F_1-1) + \frac{(F_2-1)}{G_{e1}} + \frac{(F_3-1)}{G_{e1}G_{e2}} \quad . \tag{28}$$

By extension, the total excess noise figure of a cascade of n amplifiers is

$$F_{total} - 1 = F_1 - 1 + \frac{F_2-1}{G_{e1}} + \frac{F_3-1}{G_{e1}G_{e2}} + \dots + \frac{F_n-1}{\prod_{k=1}^{n-1} G_{ek}} \tag{29}$$

It should be noted here that the various excess noise figures are defined on the basis of *exchangeable* power and that the gains are *ex-*

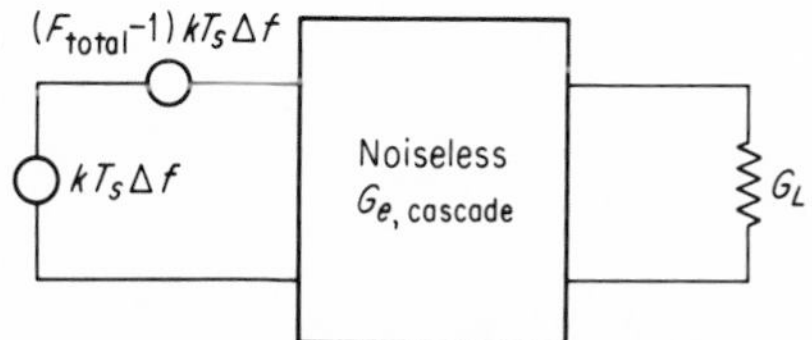

Fig. 7. Single-block equivalent of Fig. 6.

changeable power gains and not transducer gains or insertion gains. Also, each $F_k - 1$ is referred to the original source temperature, T_s.

E. Noise Measure

We can see from Eq. (29) that for high *exchangeable* power gain in the first few stages, $F_n - 1$ can be approximated by $F_1 - 1$, which means that the noise figure of the first stage is most important in this case. Unfortunately, this criterion is not always fulfilled (*e.g.* crystal mixers). Evidently, a stage with unity exchangeable gain would be a very poor choice for first stage. Consider, for example, two amplfiers with exchangeable excess noise figures of $F_1 - 1$ and $F_2 - 1$ and exchangeable power gains of G_{e1} and G_{e2}. These amplifiers can be cascaded in two possible orders. Let us examine the resultant overall excess noise figures

$$F_a - 1 = F_1 - 1 + \frac{F_2 - 1}{G_{e1}} \tag{30a}$$

and

$$F_b - 1 = F_2 - 1 + \frac{F_1 - 1}{G_{e2}} \quad . \tag{30b}$$

If we want $F_a - 1 < F_b - 1$ then

$$F_1 - 1 + \frac{F_2 - 1}{G_{e1}} < F_2 - 1 + \frac{F_1 - 1}{G_{e2}} \quad . \tag{31}$$

Collecting terms belonging to each amplifier on each side of the inequality, we have

$$M_1 = \frac{F_1 - 1}{1 - 1/G_{e1}} < M_2 = \frac{F_2 - 1}{1 - 1/G_{e2}} \quad . \tag{32}$$

The significance of the quantity

$$M = \frac{F - 1}{1 - 1/G_e} \tag{33}$$

was first realized by Haus and Adler, who termed it the *noise measure* of the amplifier. For very high *exchangeable* gain, the expression for noise measure reduces to the excess noise figure, and a cascade of n amplifiers having equal values of M results in an amplifier of the same M as each of the individual stages.

The importance of the concept of noise measure rests in the fact that the optimization procedure for minimum noise measure does not, in general, lead to the same results as the optimization procedure for minimum excess noise figure.[2]

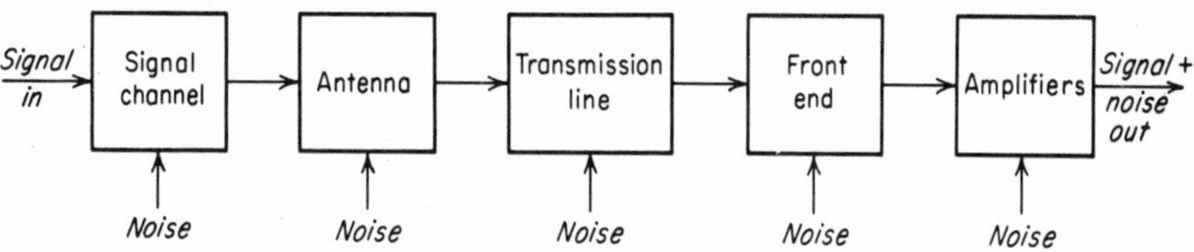

Fig. 8. Block diagram of a conventional receiving system.

III. RECEIVING SYSTEM NOISE

A simple model of a typical receiving system is shown in Fig. 8. Each individual contributor to the overall system performance has been isolated for examination. We shall examine the system piece by piece and show how various factors influence the performance optimization procedure.

A. Signal Channel

We shall consider a very-much-simplified model of a signal channel; namely, one in which we assume a linear addition of a signal and gaussian noise. The signal channel will consist of the major lobe of the antenna pattern and its resultant noise environment.

If we consider a lossless angenna, with a radiation resistance R_o, directed so that its major lobe is at an angle θ with the zenith (as shown in Fig. 9), the noise temperature of R_o will be largely determined by three factors: (a) atmospheric absorption (mainly due to water vapor), (b) ionospheric absorption, and (c) sources of noise of

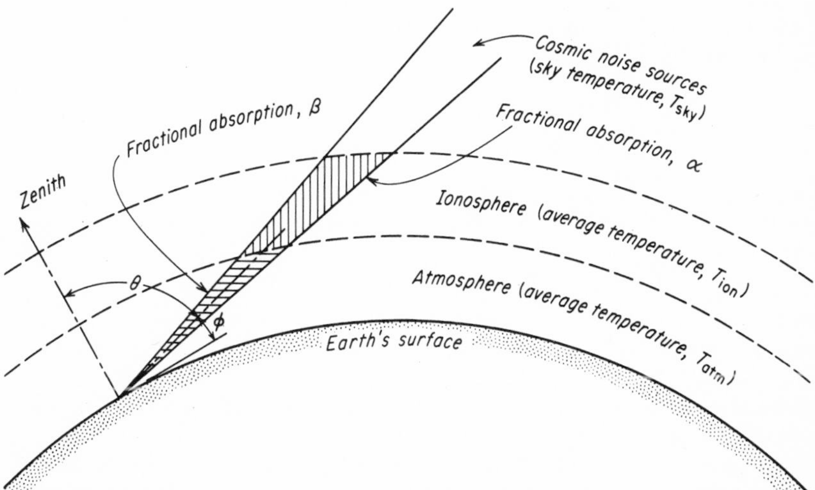

Fig. 9. Sources of noise contributing to the effective noise temperature of an antenna.

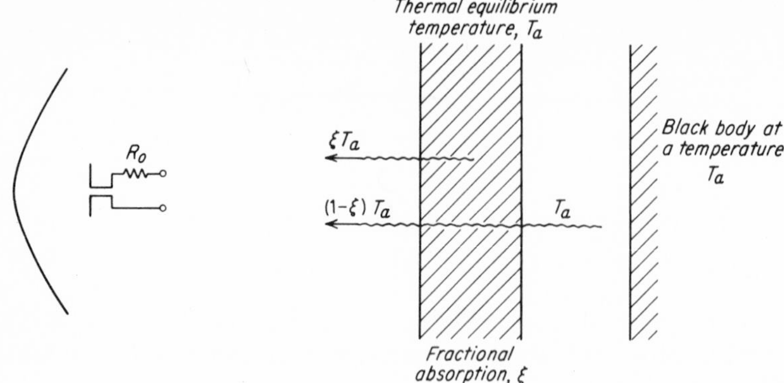

Fig. 10. Illustration of antenna temperature.

galactic origin. The manner in which these three factors contribute to the effective temperature of the radiation resistance is illustrated in Fig. 10. This figure shows an antenna with a radiation resistance R_o coupled electromagnetically to a black-body radiator (and absorber, as well), at a thermal temperature T_a, through an absorbing region whose fractional absorption is ξ and whose thermal-equilibrium temperature is T_a. The radiation resistance of the antenna has its temperature totally determined by the thermal equilibrium temperature of its surroundings. It should then have a total exchangeable noise power, at its output terminals, of

$$P_{e,total} = kT_a\Delta f \tag{34}$$

with contributions of

$$P_{e,black} = k(1-\xi)\,T_a\Delta f \tag{35}$$

from the black body, and

$$P_{e,absorb} = k\xi T_a\Delta f \tag{36}$$

from the absorbing region. In the absence of the black body, the antenna temperature would be

$$T_{antenna} = \xi T_a \,. \tag{37}$$

Thus with reference to Fig. 9, we may express the total antenna temperature from major-lobe contributions as

$$T_{antenna} = \beta T_{atm} + \alpha T_{ion} + (1-\alpha)(1-\beta)\,T_{sky}. \tag{38}$$

It should be emphasized here that both β and α are strong functions of frequency and of antenna elevation—an antenna pointed at the

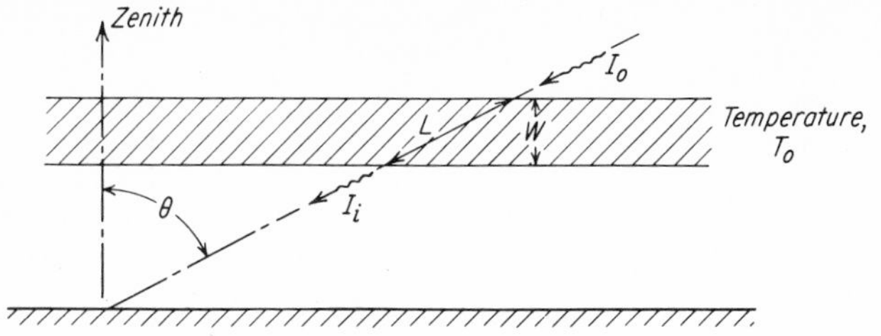

Fig. 11. Plane-earth geometry.

zenith has the shortest path through the atmosphere and ionosphere and, consequently, the lowest temperature contributions from these sources.

To illustrate the effect of antenna elevation, let us note that if the width of the absorbing layer is W and the absorption per unit length is γ, the "plane-earth" model in Fig. 11 gives, to a first approximation,

$$\frac{I_i}{I_o} = \epsilon^{-\gamma L} \tag{39}$$

where

$$L = W \sec\theta \ .$$

The absorption fraction is then

$$\alpha = \frac{I_o - I_i}{I_o} = 1 - \epsilon^{-\gamma W \sec\theta} \ . \tag{40}$$

If the absorbing medium has a thermal temperature T_o,

$$T_\theta = \alpha T_o = T_o\left[1 - \epsilon^{-\gamma W \sec\theta}\right] \tag{41}$$

and

$$T_{\text{zenith}} = T_o\left[1 - \epsilon^{-\gamma W}\right]$$

whence

$$\frac{T_\theta}{T_o} = 1 - \left(1 - \frac{T_{\text{zenith}}}{T_o}\right)^{\sec\theta} \ . \tag{42}$$

The frequency dependence of α is only partially known.[5,6] At frequencies well above 100 mc, αT_{ion} is only a few degrees (five or so).

The dependence of β on frequency is somewhat better known. The major absorbing constituents of the atmosphere are oxygen and water vapor (oxygen by virtue of its permament magnetic dipole moment and water vapor by virtue of its electric dipole moment). The absorption is particularly important at frequencies in excess of 1000 mc, reaching one maximum at approximately 23,000 mc (water vapor) and a

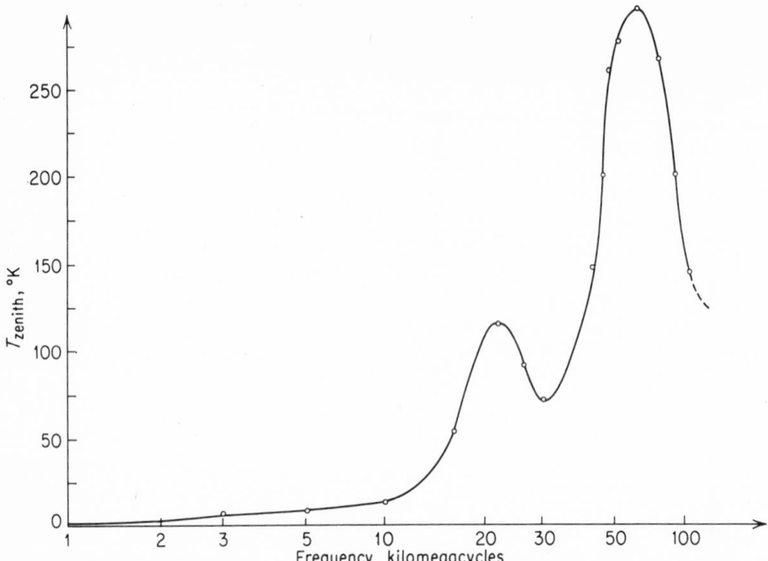

Fig. 12. Zenith temperature as a function of frequency for a standard reduced atmosphere of 10 Km depth with 66% relative humidity at 290°K. (From data in Ref. 7.)

much larger maximum at approximately 60 Kmc (oxygen). Assuming a 10-Km-deep atmosphere at standard pressure and temperature (a "reduced" atmosphere) with 10 gms water/m^3 (66% relative humidity at 18°C), we get the plot of zenith temperature as a function of frequency shown in Fig. 12. One can be sure that communication with space vehicles would not be economical at frequencies much in excess of 10 Kmc, because the minimum detectable signal level would be severely restricted by thermal noise generated by atmospheric absorption to say nothing of the attendant attenuation of the transiting signal (which can exceed 100 db in vertical transit of atmosphere at 60 Kmc).

Equation (42) does not hold for values of θ near 90° (*e.g.* elevation angles near zero). A more accurate form based on a spherical earth of radius R with a reduced atmosphere of depth W gives the temperature at all elevation angles, including zero, as

$$\frac{T_\phi}{T_\circ} = 1 - \left(1 - \frac{T_{\text{zenith}}}{T_\circ}\right)^{\sqrt{(R/W)^2 \sin^2\phi + 2(R/W)} - (R/W)\sin\phi} \tag{43}$$

where T_ϕ is the temperature at an elevation angle of ϕ° and $T_\circ$ is the mean effective thermal temperature of the atmosphere. For a 4/3-earth model with a standard reduced atmosphere, $R = 7700$ Km, $W = 10$ Km, and $R/W = 770$.

We can see that for frequencies below 3 Kmc and for elevation

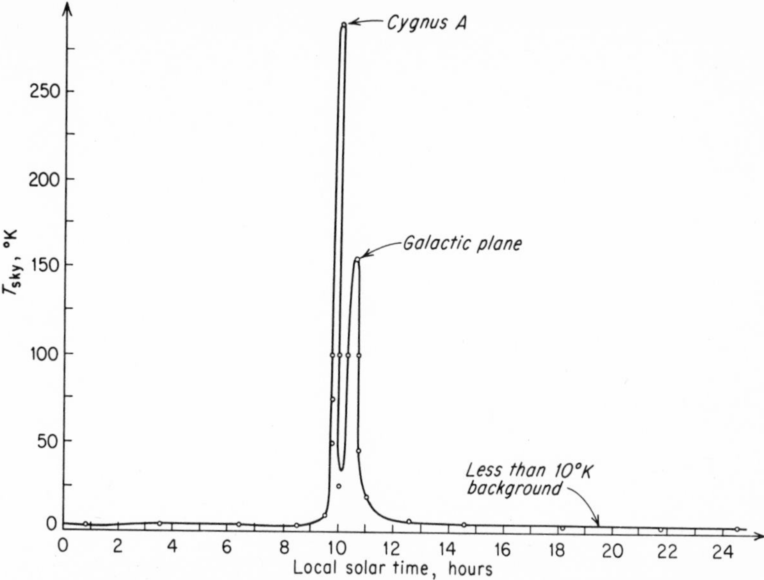

Fig. 13. Diurnal variation of sky temperature at 600 mc with a 2° major-lobe width, 0° elevation, 30° E azimuth, and antenna location at 42° N lat. (for October 1).

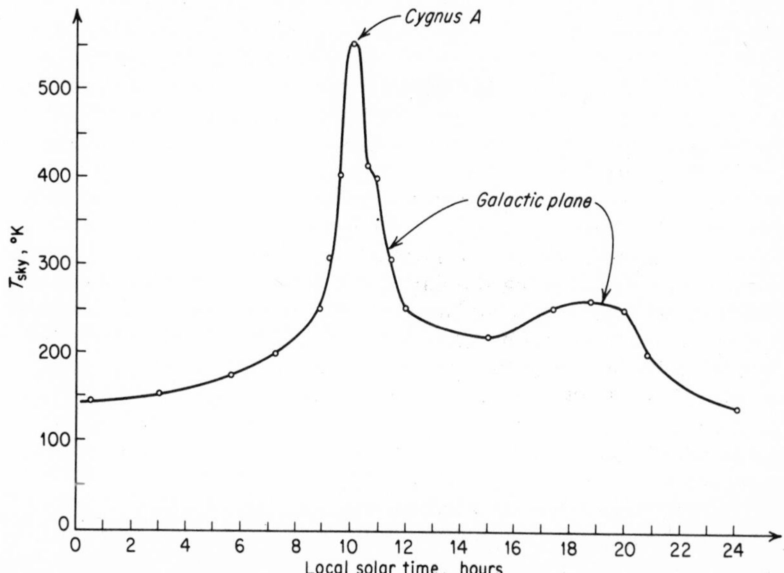

Fig. 14. Diurnal variation of sky temperature at 200 mc with a 10° major-lobe width, 0° elevation, 30° E azimuth, and antenna located at 42 N lat. (for October 1).

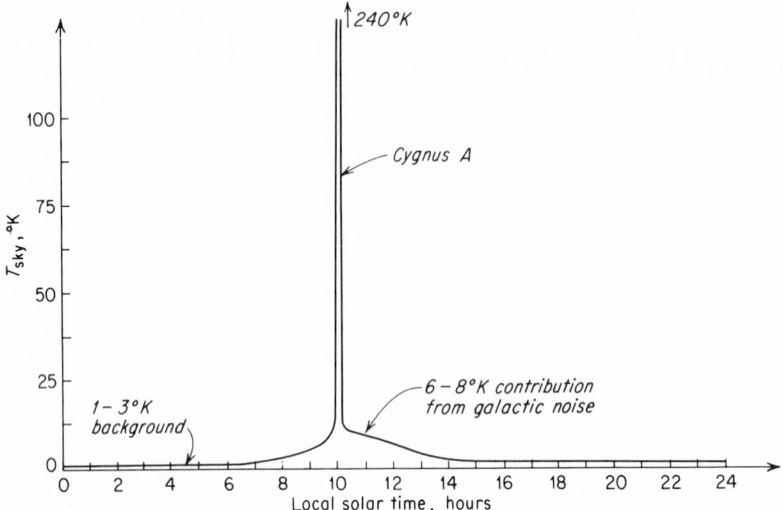

Fig. 15. Diurnal variation in sky temperature at 1000 mc with 1° major-lobe width 0° elevation, 30° E azimuth, antenna located at 42° N lat. (for October 1).

angles in excess of 0.1 radian, the atmospheric-absorption contribution to antenna temperature is less than 70°K.

The third major source contributing to the effective noise temperature of an antenna is of cosmic origin. Cosmic noise is of greatest intensity in antennas directed at the galactic plane. Therefore, there will be a diurnal variation in intensity superimposed on a yearly cycle as the earth rotates and orbits around the sun. Figure 13* shows a representative plot of cosmic noise contribution in °K for October 1 at a frequency of 600 mc and antenna located at 42° N lat., with a major lobe 2° wide beamed at 30°E azimuth and 0° elevation. The azimuth and elevation of the antenna have been purposely chosen so that the "point source" of noise in the constellation Cygnus will appear in the antenna beam at some time during the day. Figure 14 shows the antenna temperature at 200 mc with a 10° major-lobe width and the same orientation as before. It should be noted that the average background sky temperature at 200 mc is in the neighborhood of 200°K as contrasted with less than 10°K at 600 mc. Figure 15 shows the diurnal variation of sky temperature under the same conditions as before but with a 1° antenna beam width at 1000 mc. The total background temperature is now 1-3°K but the point source in Cygnus A still contributes strongly. If we take a rough average of 200°K for sky noise at 200 mc, the variation of sky temperature with frequency appears as shown in Fig. 16.

If the contribution of atmospheric absorption to the noise tempera-

*Cosmic noise data taken from sky temperature charts produced by D. H. Menzel of the Harvard College Observatory under Dept. of Defense Contract No. 49-170-SC-2386.

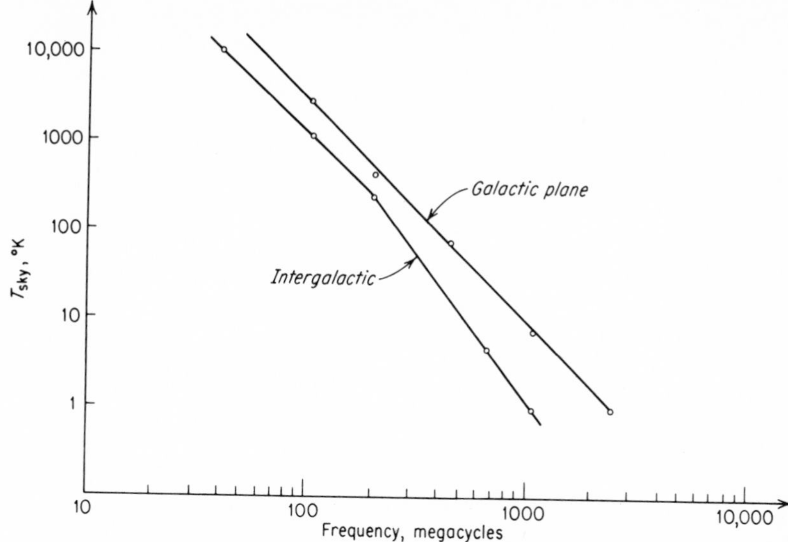

Fig. 16. Mean sky temperature vs. frequency.

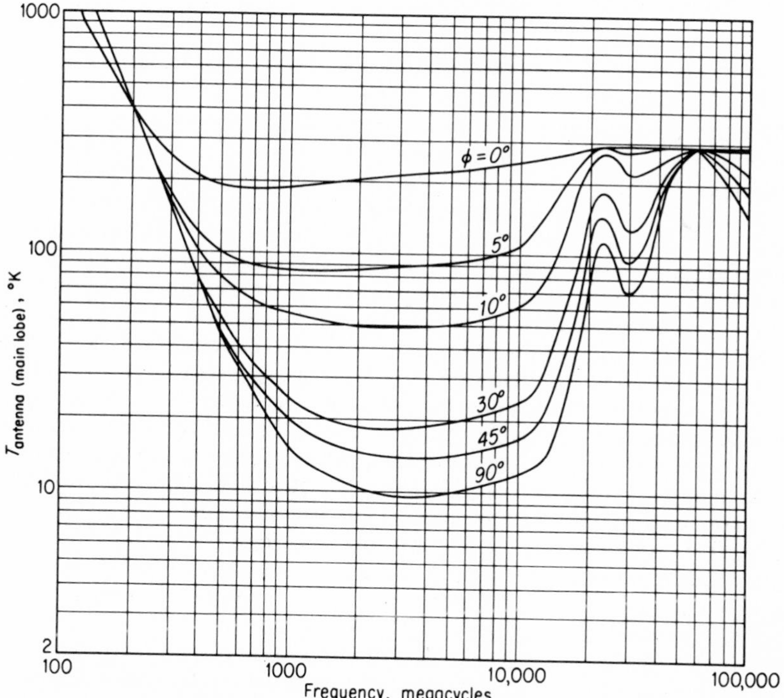

Fig. 17. Antenna temperature vs frequency and antenna elevation. Ionospheric absorption neglected. Antenna orientation is towards the galactic plane.

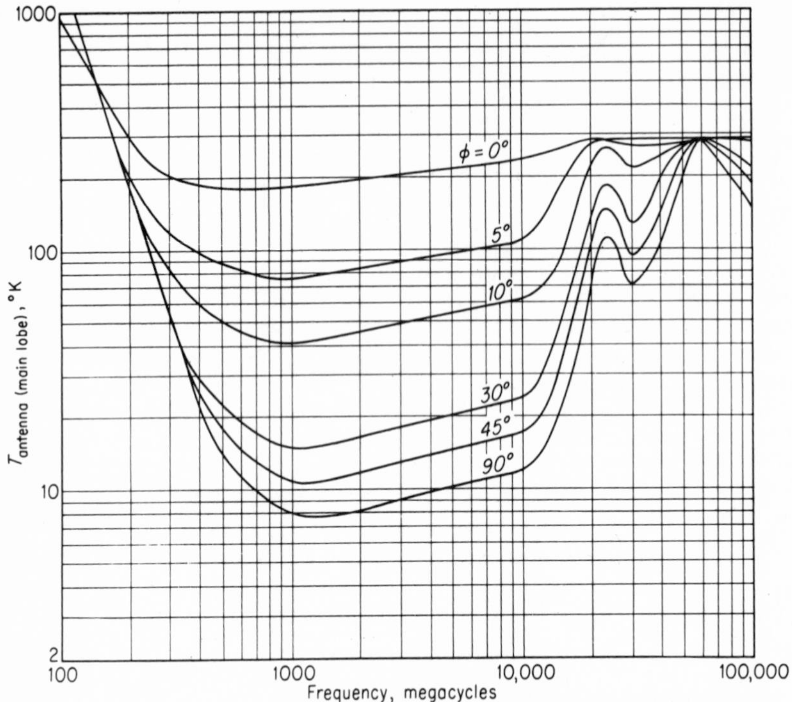

Fig. 18. Antenna temperature vs frequency and antenna elevation. Ionospheric absorption neglected. Antenna orientation is away from the galactic plane.

ture [as given by Eq. (43) for various elevation angles] is added to the cosmic-noise contribution plotted in Fig. 12, we obtain the total major-lobe antenna temperature plotted vs. frequency in Figs. 17 and 18.

If the signal source is terrestrial, we will not be unduly concerned with atmospheric absorption insofar as the attenuation of the signal itself is concerned—this attenuation can be considered a part of the path loss. However, if the signal source is extra-terrestrial, the signal-channel noise figure must be considered. For a receiving antenna located outside the atmosphere, the noise temperature is relatively independent of aperture (except for discrete noise sources) and the total signal power abstracted and delivered by the antenna depends directly upon antenna aperture. Therefore the noise figure of the channel is inversely proportional to antenna aperture. The noise temperature of the extra-terrestrial antenna is determined by cosmic noise alone. However, the same antenna located at the surface of the earth would see added noise from atmospheric absorption and would deliver a total signal power that is decreased by the amount of atmospheric absorption. Using the definitions in Eqs. (18) and (38), we have

$$F_{\text{signal channel}} = \frac{(S/N)_{in}}{(S/N)_{out}} = \frac{\dfrac{S_e}{kT_{sky}\Delta f}}{\dfrac{(1-\beta)S_e}{(1-\beta)kT_{sky}\Delta f + k\beta T_{atm}\Delta f}} \tag{44}$$

whence

$$F_{\text{signal channel}} - 1 = \frac{\beta T_{atm}}{(1-\beta)T_{sky}} \; . \tag{45}$$

Figures 17 and 18 give $\beta T_{atm} + T_{sky}$ for $T_{atm} = 290\,^\circ\mathrm{K}$ and for various antenna elevation angles. Using this data, we can find $F_{\text{signal channel}} - 1$ as a function of antenna elevation angle and frequency. But more useful information is afforded by the maximum range at which one watt of isotropically radiated signal will have a unity signal-to-noise ratio in a 1 cps bandwidth at the terminals of a terrestrial antenna of fixed dimensions. Using the standard range formulation, we can show that the range R is

$$R = \sqrt{\frac{A(1-\beta)}{4\pi k\, T_{antenna}}} \text{ meters} \tag{46}$$

where

A = effective antenna aperture in sq. m
k = Boltzmann's constant, 1.38×10^{-23} joules/°K

and (from Eq. 43)

$$(1-\beta) = \left(1 - \frac{T_{zenith}}{T_\circ}\right)^{\sqrt{(R/W)^2 \sin^2\phi + 2R/W} - R/W \sin\phi} \; .$$

Representative plots of range vs. frequency and elevation angle are given in Fig. 19.

It is interesting to note that with an elevation of 90°, the best choice of frequency is any value in the range between 1000 and 10,000 mc. At elevation angles near zero the maximum range shifts downward to 300 mc with a two-to-one drop in range from 300 to 10,000 mc This effect is easily attributed to increased atmospheric absorption. The range at 23 Kmc is even more radically affected by water vapor absorption and the elevation-angle effect is strongly pronounced. At 100 Kmc, the range is 4.4×10^7 Km at 90° elevation, but it drops to 53 Km (off the graph) and is not even out of the atmosphere at 0° elevation.

Figure 20 shows a plot of maximal-range frequency vs. elevation angles for an antenna oriented at the galactic plane and away from the galactic plane. The effect of increased sky noise is seen to push the maximal-range frequency upward when atmospheric absorption is not too important.

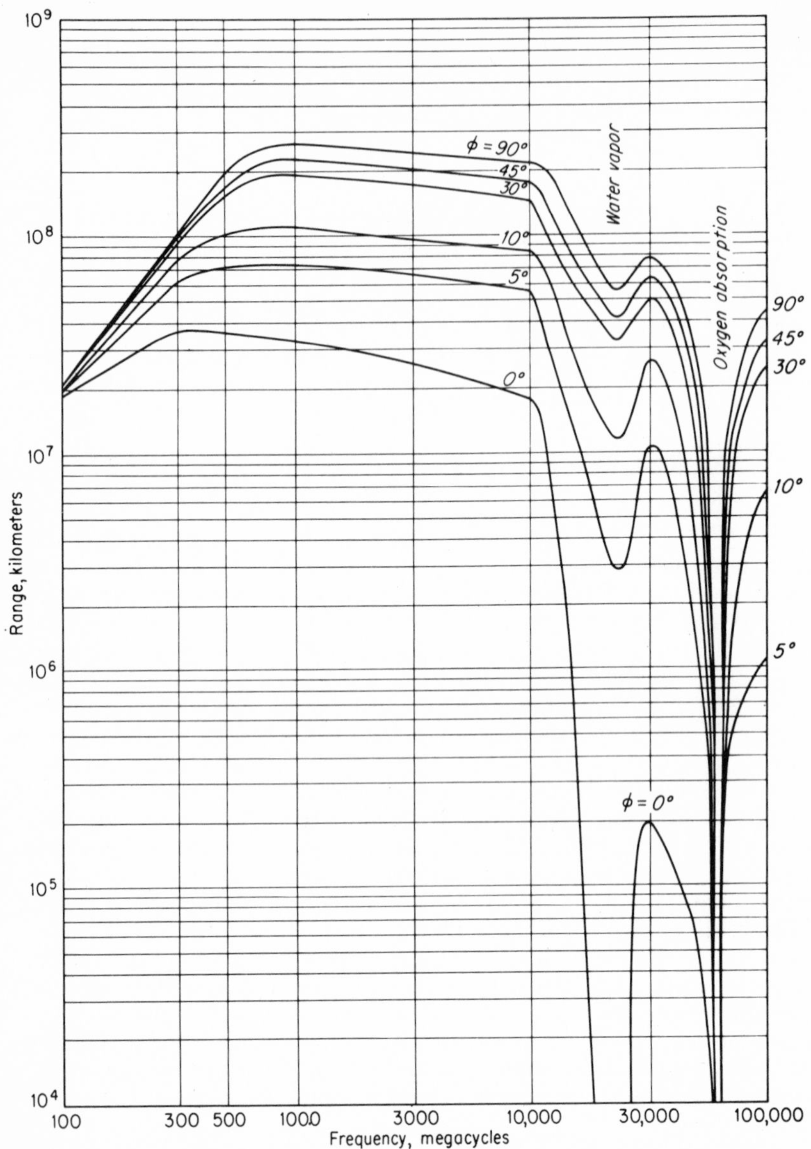

Fig. 19. Maximum range of a 1 watt of isotropically radiated signal, for unity signal-to-noise ratio at antenna terminals in 1 cps band-with. Cosmic noise contribution is considered to be from off the galactic plane with an antenna aperture 100 m^2.

B. The Antenna

Other sources of noise in an antenna may be attributed to physical I^2R losses and noise picked up by minor lobes. Most antennas are

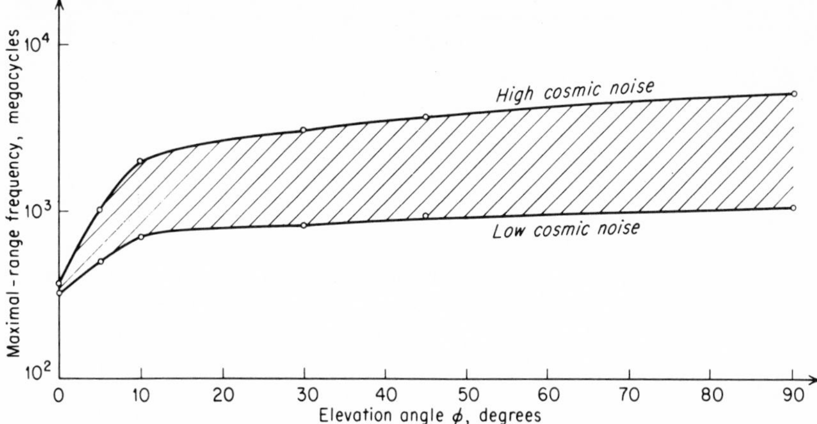

Fig. 20. Maximal-range frequency vs. elevation angle with cosmic noise level as a parameter.

relatively efficient. For antennas whose physical dimensions closely approximate their effective apertures (parabolic reflectors, broadside arrays, etc.) the efficiency may be nearly 100%. Note that 90% efficiency will add roughly 30°K to 90% of the major-lobe antenna temperature and lose 10% of the captured signal. This would not be very important if the antenna temperature from the main lobe were 300°K or higher. But at 90° elevation and 1 Kmc the main-lobe antenna temperature is only 10°K. On the other hand for antennas whose physical dimensions are small compared with their effective apertures (so-called "super-gain" antennas such as long Yagis, ferrite-loaded structures, etc.) the resultant high Q and large I^2R losses may result in efficiencies of 50% or less, and the consequent contribution to antenna temperature may be considerably larger than the main-lobe temperature.

The problem of minor lobes is not a simple one. High-gain antennas inherently have minor lobes and any attempt to reduce them will compromise the main-lobe gain.[8] For various elevation angles some of the forward minor lobes will be pointing at the ground. Depending on the amount of absorption at the operating frequency that a radio wave would experience upon reflection at the ground surface, the minor lobes will contribute a total antenna temperature of

$$T_{\text{minor lobes}} = \sum_{k=1}^{n} \gamma_k \zeta_k T_k \tag{47}$$

where

γ_k = total fractional attenuation of the kth minor lobe compared with the main lobe,

ζ_k = total fractional absorption of the reflected, scattered, and transmitted minor lobe in a medium whose mean temperature is T_k.

If one minor lobe has $T_k = 300°$ and $\zeta_k \gamma_k = -15$ db (1/30), $T_{\text{minor lobes}} = 300/30 = 10°$K.

The rear lobe of the antenna will always point at the ground (except, perhaps at 0° elevation) and may be only 20 db down (or less). We can, therefore, expect as much as 3° of antenna noise from the rear lobe (or lobes). Although this does not seem to be much, it should be remembered that the lobe contribution is most important at high elevation angles where the forward minor lobes and the major lobe have T_k's ≈ 10° at suitable frequencies.

We can, in fact, characterize the excess noise figure of the antenna proper by using Eq. (18). Thus

$$F = \frac{(S/N)_{\text{in}}}{(S/N)_{\text{out}}} = \frac{\dfrac{S_{e,\text{in}}}{k\,T_{\text{major lobe}}\,\Delta f}}{\dfrac{S_{e,\text{in}}\cdot\epsilon}{kT_{\text{major lobe}}\Delta f\cdot\epsilon + k\,T_{\text{minor lobes}}\,\Delta f\cdot\epsilon + kT_o\,\Delta f\cdot(1-\epsilon)}} \tag{48}$$

$$= \frac{k\,T_{\text{major lobe}}\,\Delta f\cdot\epsilon + k\,T_{\text{minor lobes}}\,\Delta f\cdot\epsilon + kT_o\,\Delta f\cdot(1-\epsilon)}{k\,T_{\text{major lobe}}\,\Delta f\cdot\epsilon} \tag{49}$$

where T_o = ambient temperature (~300°K)

and ϵ = antenna efficiency .

The excess noise figure of the antenna is

$$F_{\text{antenna}} - 1 = \frac{T_{\text{minor lobes}}}{T_{\text{major lobe}}} + \frac{T_o\,(1-\epsilon)}{\epsilon\,T_{\text{major lobe}}} \; . \tag{50}$$

C. The Transmission Line

All transmission lines have loss. The unavoidable consequence of this loss is another temperature contribution. The excess noise figure of a transmission line may be found by an argument that is similar to that in Fig. 10. Figure 21 illustrates this argument. A transmission line at a thermal temperature T_o is driven with a generator of impedance Z_o and temperature T_o (antenna). The line has a fractional loss factor γ. The exchangeable noise power in the termination Z_o is

$$P_e = kT_o\Delta f\cdot(1-\gamma) + \text{Noise generated in line} \; . \tag{51}$$

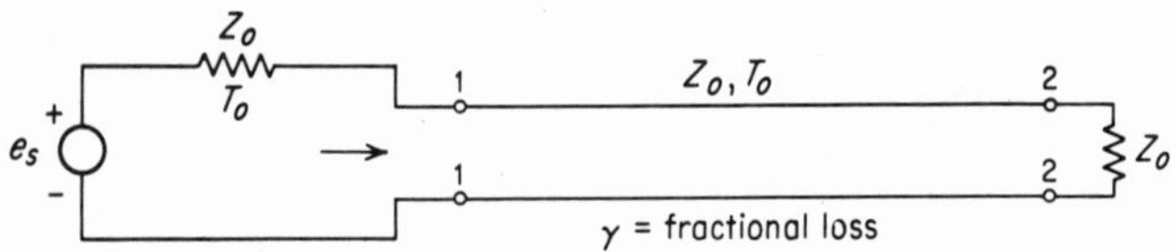

Fig. 21. A transmission line at thermal equilibrium.

But, since the terminals 2-2 may be assumed as looking back into a medium of impedance Z_o and temperature T_o,

$$P_e = kT_o\Delta f \;. \tag{52}$$

Combination of (51) and (52) yields

$$T_{line} = \gamma T_o \;. \tag{53}$$

We can generalize this to the case in which the source impedance is at a temperature other than T_o. Specifically we shall *define* the source temperature as the main-lobe antenna temperature, so that the total exchangeable noise power at the output of the line becomes (for a completely efficient antenna)

$$P_{e,total} = kT_{major\ lobe}\,\Delta f \cdot (1-\gamma) + k\gamma\, T_o\, \Delta f \,. \tag{54}$$

With the transmission line exchangeable power gain of $G_e = (1-\gamma)$ we can write the excess noise figure of the transmission line as

$$F_{line} - 1 = \frac{\gamma T_o}{(1-\gamma)T_s} \tag{55}$$

where the "source temperature" $T_s = T_{major\ lobe}$ and T_o = ambient temperature (290 – 300°K).

D. The Front End

The first stage (or stages) of amplification and/or frequency conversion in the receiving system immediately following the transmission line are normally termed the "front end" of the system. If the front end has sufficient exchangeable power gain the following stages will contribute very little to the overall noise performance except, of course, in determining the system bandwidth. In the treatment of spot (or per-unit-bandwidth) noise figure, bandwidth effects need not be considered. If we define the front-end noise performance by using the definitions in Eq. (21), we can express the front-end exchangeable excess noise figure as

$$F_{front\,end} - 1 = \frac{N_{eoi}}{N_{es} \cdot G_e} \;. \tag{56}$$

Recall that N_{es} is defined as the total exchangeable noise power from an ideal source at a thermal temperature T_s; *i.e.*

$$N_{es} = kT_s\Delta f \,. \tag{57}$$

But N_{eoi} is yet to be determined.

The previous sections dealt with passive devices (antenna and transmission line) where the optimization procedures normally be-

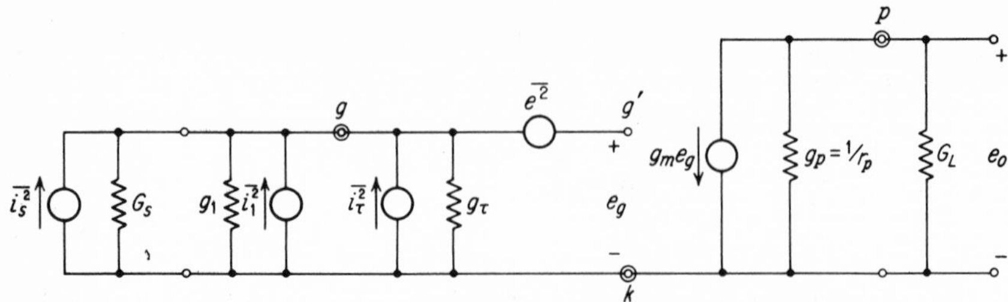

Fig. 22. A noise characterization of a common-cathode, neutralized triode amplifier.

come obvious upon inspection of the excess-noise characterizations. The optimization procedure simply consists of minimizing all losses and the minimum excess noise figure is zero. (Antenna minor lobes are also considered as "losses" here.) Unfortunately, we do not usually have such a control over the noise environment of active devices, but there is normally a *bona fide* minimum excess noise figure (or noise measure) achievable through some realizable optimization procedure. It turns out that the optimization program is usually quite simple but not necessarily intuitive.

Example 1. Figure 22 is an equivalent noise-circuit model for a high-frequency grounded-cathode triode amplifier. In this figure

(58a) $\overline{i_s^2} = 4kT_s G_s \Delta f$, G_s = source conductance

(58b) $\overline{i_1^2} = 4kT_1 g_1 \Delta f$, g_1 = input circuit loss

(58c) $\overline{i_\tau^2} = 4kT_\tau g_\tau \Delta f$, g_τ = transit-time loading

(58d) $\overline{e^2} = 4kT_o R_{eq} \Delta f$, R_{eq} = equivalent shot noise resistance

and

T_s = source temperature

T_1 = temperature of input-circuit loss $\cong T_o$

$T_\tau \cong 5\ T_o$ (normal oxide cathode temperature), from ref. 9,

T_o = 290°K.

The exchangeable power gain is

$$G_e = \frac{\mu^2 G_s}{r_p (G_s + g_1 + g_\tau)^2} \tag{59}$$

and

$$N_{es} = kT_s \Delta f \tag{60}$$

so that

$$N_{eos} = N_{es} \cdot G_e = \frac{\mu^2 k T_s G_s \Delta f}{r_p (G_s + g_1 + g_\tau)^2} \,. \tag{61}$$

Now,

$$N_{\text{eoi}} = \frac{\overline{(\mu e_g')^2}}{4 r_p} \tag{62}$$

where

$$e_g' = \frac{i_T + i_1}{G_s + g_1 + g_T} + e \ . \tag{63}$$

Using relations (58a) to (58d) we obtain

$$N_{\text{eoi}} = \frac{\mu^2 \overline{[i_T + i_1 + e(G_s + g_1 + g_T)]^2}}{r_p(G_s + g_1 + g_T)^2} \tag{64}$$

The evaluation of N_{eoi} may be simplified by realizing that

$$\overline{i_1 \cdot i_T} = \overline{i_1 \cdot e} = 0$$

$$\overline{i_T \cdot e} \neq 0$$

But in general this is the correlation function of the induced grid noise and the shot noise.[9] Therefore, we have

$$N_{\text{eoi}} = \frac{\mu^2[\overline{i_T^2} + \overline{i_1^2} + \overline{e^2}(G_s + g_1 + g_T)^2 + 2\overline{\{i_T \cdot e\}}(G_s + g_1 + g_T)]}{r_p(G_s + g_1 + g_T)^2} \tag{65}$$

and

$$F - 1 = N_{\text{eoi}}/N_{\text{eos}}$$

$$= \frac{g_1 T_1 + g_T T_T + R_{\text{eq}}(G_s + g_1 + g_T)^2 T_o}{G_s T_s} + 2\rho \frac{\sqrt{T_o T_T R_{\text{eq}} g_T}(G_s + g_1 + g_T)}{G_s T_s} \tag{66}$$

where[10]

$$\rho = \frac{E[i_T \cdot e]}{\sigma_T \sigma_e} = \frac{\overline{i_T \cdot e}}{\sigma_T \sigma_e}$$

$$\sigma_T \sigma_e = k \Delta f \sqrt{T_o T_T R_{\text{eq}} g_T} \ .$$

Let us examine the first term,

$$\frac{g_1 T_1 + g_T T_T + R_{\text{eq}}(G_s + g_1 + g_T)^2 T_o}{G_s T_s} \ . \tag{67}$$

This term goes to ∞ for $G_s \to 0$ and $G_s \to \infty$. We therefore expect this term to have a minimum at some intermediate value of G_s. Differentiation with respect to G_s and equating to zero gives

$$G_{s,opt} = \pm\sqrt{\frac{g_1 T_1 + g_\tau T_\tau}{R_{eq} T_o} + (g_1 + g_\tau)^2} \quad . \tag{68}$$

For $G_{s,opt} > 0$ the minimum value of (67) is

$$\left(\frac{T_o}{T_s}\right) 2\, R_{eq} \left\{ g_1 + g_\tau + \sqrt{(g_1 + g_\tau)^2 + \frac{t_1 g_1 + t_\tau g_\tau}{R_{eq}}} \right\} \tag{69}$$

where, $t_1 = T_1/T_o$, and $t_\tau = T_\tau/T_o$, the noise temperature ratios of the input circuit loss and the transit-time loading.

Some approximations can be made here. Under usual circumstances

$$t_1 g_1 \ll t_\tau g_\tau \text{ and } G_{s,opt} \gg g_1 + g_\tau, \text{ also } \frac{t_1 g_1 + t_\tau g_\tau}{R_{eq}} \gg (g_1 + g_\tau)^2$$

so that (69) can be approximated by

$$\left(\frac{T_o}{T_s}\right) 2\, R_{eq} \left\{ g_1 + g_\tau + \sqrt{\frac{t_\tau g_\tau}{R_{eq}}} \right\} \quad . \tag{70}$$

Under these circumstances

$$(F-1)_{\substack{\text{minimum} \\ G_{s,opt} > 0}} \cong 2\left(\frac{T_o}{T_s}\right)\left\{ R_{eq}\,(g_\tau + g_1) + (1+\rho)\sqrt{t_\tau g_\tau R_{eq}} \right\} \quad . \tag{71}$$

Note that if $G_{s,opt} < 0$, then

$$(F-1)_{\substack{\text{minimum} \\ \text{magnitude} \\ G_{s,opt} < 0}} \cong -2\left(\frac{T_o}{T_s}\right)\left\{ R_{eq}(g_1 + g_\tau) + (1-\rho)\sqrt{t_\tau g_\tau R_{eq}} \right\} \quad . \tag{72}$$

Example 2. The excess noise figure of a two-tank parametric amplifier (Fig. 23), expressed in scattering-matrix[11] notation, is given by

$$\begin{aligned} F - 1 = \frac{T_o}{T_s} \Bigg\{ & \frac{\omega_s}{\omega_i} \frac{T_i}{T_0} \left[1 - \frac{1}{G_e} \right] + \left(\frac{\omega_s}{\omega_i} \frac{T_i}{T_o} + 1 \right) \left| \frac{S_{23}}{S_{21}} \right|^2 \\ & + \left(\frac{\omega_u T_i}{\omega_i T_o} + 1 \right) \left| \frac{S_{26}}{S_{21}} \right|^2 + \left(\frac{T_o - T_i}{T_o} \right) \left| \frac{S_{24}}{S_{21}} \right|^2 \Bigg\} \left[G_e = \frac{|S_{21}|^2}{1 - |S_{22}|^2} \right] \end{aligned} \tag{73}$$

where

ω_s = signal frequency
ω_i = idler frequency = $\omega_p - \omega_s$
ω_p = pump frequency
ω_u = $\omega_p + \omega_s$ the upper sideband frequency
T_i = idler-termination temperature
T_o = room temperature (290 °K)
T_s = antenna (or source) temperature

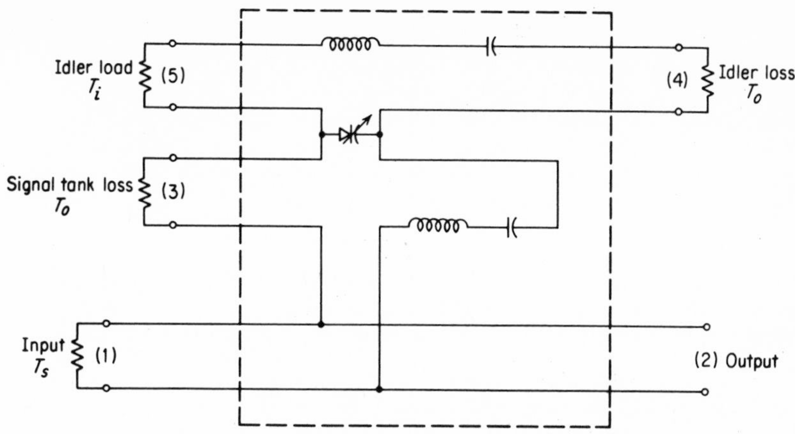

Fig. 23. Model of a two-tank parametric amplifier.

and

S_{nk} = scattering matrix between the two terminal pairs n and k.

It is clear from this expression that $(F-1)$ will be minimized if

$\left|\frac{S_{23}}{S_{21}}\right|^2$, $\left|\frac{S_{26}}{S_{21}}\right|^2$, and $\left|\frac{S_{24}}{S_{21}}\right|^2$ are made as small as possible. The term

$\left|\frac{S_{23}}{S_{21}}\right|^2$ is a measure of the coupling to the room temperature loss in the signal tank. This can be minimized by insuring that the signal tank is very heavily loaded by the source and by the load. The term $\left|\frac{S_{26}}{S_{21}}\right|^2$ will depend on coupling from the output terminals to the upper side-band and it can be made very small by careful attention to geometry and coupling. Similarly, $\left|\frac{S_{24}}{S_{21}}\right|^2$ is a measure of the coupling from the output terminals to the idler loss and it can be reduced by similar methods. The excess noise figure of the parametric amplifier with the necessary measures taken can then be written as

$$F - 1 \cong \frac{\omega_s}{\omega_i}\frac{T_i}{T_s}\left[1 - \frac{1}{G_e}\right]. \tag{74}$$

If we substitute for G_e from Eq. 10, we obtain

$$F - 1 \cong \frac{\omega_s}{\omega_i}\frac{T_i}{T_s}\left[\frac{G_o}{G_s}\right]. \tag{75}$$

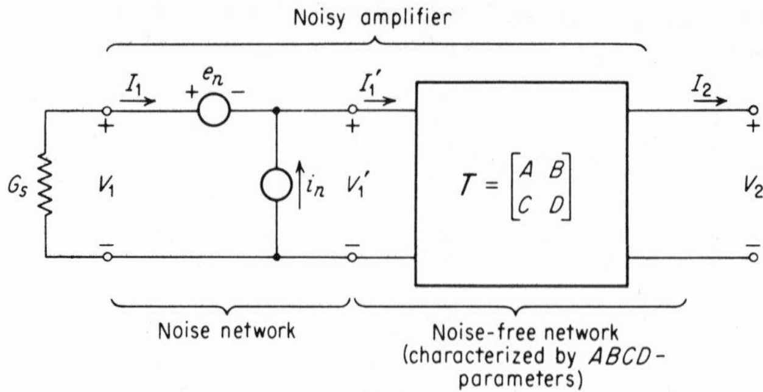

Fig. 24. A general representation for linear two-terminal-pair noisy networks.

From Eq. (74) it is clear that a further minimization of $(F-1)$ is achieved by making G_e very large. Thus

$$(F-1)_{\text{minimum}} = \frac{\omega_s}{\omega_i} \frac{T_i}{T_s} \ . \tag{76}$$

As an illustration let $f_s = 1000$ mc, $f_i = 10{,}000$ mc ($f_p = 11{,}000$ mc) and let T_s have the likely value of 10 °K. Under these conditions,

$$\underset{T_i = 290^\circ\text{K}}{(F-1)_{\text{minimum}}} = \frac{1}{10} \cdot \frac{290}{10} = 2.90 \ . \tag{77}$$

If, however, we terminate the idler in its own *tightly coupled* antenna pointed at the zenith, T_i becomes 12 °K (with no minor-lobe contributions, 100% efficiency, and zero transmission-line loss). Under these conditions

$$\underset{T_i = 290^\circ\text{K}}{(F-1)_{\text{minimum}}} = \frac{1}{10} \cdot \frac{12}{10} = 0.12 \ . \tag{78}$$

Actually, however, this procedure is not necessary since the amplifier can be optimized by appropriate choice of pump frequency along with proper idler termination.[12]

Example 3. A general representation[3] for linear noisy two-terminal-pair networks is shown in Fig. 24. The two noise sources e_n and i_n account for the fact that noise is present at the output when the input terminals are open-circuited as well as when they are short-circuited.

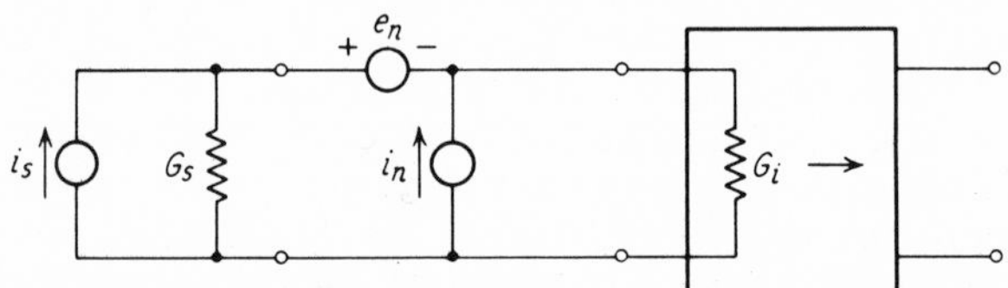

Fig. 25. Representation of Fig. 24 for unilateral amplifier having input conductance G_i.

If the noise-free network is unilateral and has an input conductance G_i, the model can be reduced to the form shown in Fig. 25. For this model

$$N_{eos} = \Lambda \frac{\overline{i_s^2}}{(G_s + G_i)^2} G_i \tag{79}$$

where $\Lambda = P_{eo}$/power delivered to G_i

$$N_{eoi} = \Lambda \cdot \overline{\left[\frac{e_n G_s}{G_s + G_i} + \frac{i_n}{G_s + G_i}\right]^2} \cdot G_i \cdot \tag{80}$$

Thus

$$F - 1 = \frac{N_{eoi}}{N_{eos}} = \frac{\overline{[e_n G_s + i_n]^2}}{\overline{i_s^2}} \tag{81a}$$

$$= \frac{T_o}{T_s}\left[R_n G_s + \frac{G_n}{G_s} + 2\rho\sqrt{R_n G_n}\right] \tag{81b}$$

where we have used Eq. (65), and

$$\overline{e_n^2} = 4kT_o R_n \Delta f\,, \quad \overline{i_n^2} = 4kT_o G_n \Delta f\,,$$

$$\overline{i_s^2} = 4kT_s G_s \Delta f\,, \quad \rho = \frac{\overline{i_n \cdot e_n}}{\sqrt{\overline{i_n^2}\;\overline{e_n^2}}} \quad .$$

The value of G_s that minimizes $(F - 1)$ is

$$G_{sopt} = \pm \sqrt{\frac{G_n}{R_n}} \quad . \tag{82}$$

Substitution leads to

$$(F-1)_{\substack{\text{minimum}\\ \text{magnitude}}} = \frac{T_o}{T_s}\left[2(1 \pm \rho)\sqrt{R_n G_n}\right] \quad . \tag{83}$$

The resemblance to the expressions obtained in Example 1 is not accidental, nor is the fact that $(F - 1)$ can be minimized entirely by mismatch at the input. There is a theorem which states that any unilateral amplifier with a unilateral gain greater than one can be optimized by input mismatch alone. This theorem is proved along with several other interesting theorems by Haus and Adler in Reference 3.

Example 4: The minimization of the overall excess noise figure of a number of stages in cascade is not in general achieved by minimizing the individual excess noise figures. As an example, consider a cascade composed of a negative-resistance amplifier followed by a linear two-terminal-pair noisy network as shown in Fig. 26. In this figure,

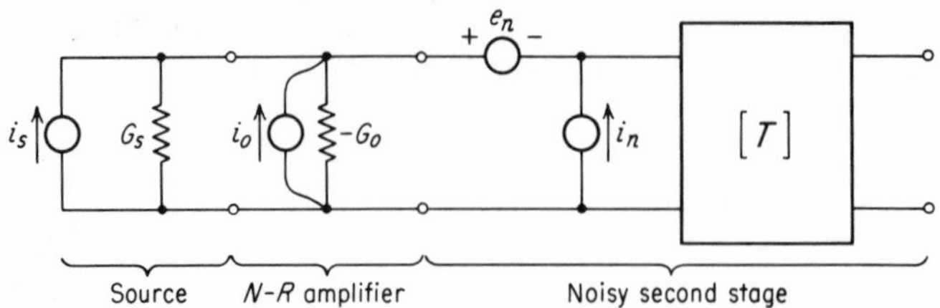

Fig. 26. Cascade of a negative-resistance amplifier and a linear two-terminal-pair noisy network.

$$\overline{i_s^2} = 4kT_s G_s \Delta f$$

$$\overline{i_o^2} = 4kT_a G_o \Delta f$$

$$T_a = \frac{\omega_s}{\omega_i} T_i$$

The excess noise figure of the negative-resistance amplifier is then

$$F_1 - 1 = \frac{\omega_s}{\omega_i}\frac{T_i}{T_s}\left(\frac{G_o}{G_s}\right) \tag{84a}$$

and

$$G_{e1} = \frac{G_s}{G_s - G_o}\,. \tag{84b}$$

The expression for $(F_2 - 1)$ can be obtained from Eq. (81b) by replacing G_s by $G_s - G_o$ since $G_s - G_o$ is now the effective source conductance for the second stage. But since the second stage is driven from the output of the negative-resistance amplifier, a question may be raised as to what the source temperature in the expression for $(F_2 - 1)$ should be. For convenience in the manipulation of the general cascade formula (Eq. 29) the *same* source temperature T_s is chosen as a reference for all stages and the equivalent noise R's or G's are defined accordingly for each stage. Thus the source temperature chosen for each stage is usually the same T_s as that of the *first* stage. Using this definition, we have from Eq. (81b)

$$F_2 - 1 = \frac{T_o}{T_s}\left[R_n(G_s - G_o) + \frac{G_n}{G_s - G_o} + 2\rho\sqrt{R_n G_n}\right] \tag{85}$$

and the cascade formula leads to

$$F_{total} - 1 = \frac{T_o}{T_s}\left[\frac{\omega_s}{\omega_i}\frac{T_i}{T_o}\left(\frac{G_o}{G_s}\right) + \frac{R_n(G_s - G_o)^2}{G_s} + \frac{G_n}{G_s} + \frac{2\rho\sqrt{R_n G_n}(G_s - G_o)}{G_s}\right] \tag{86}$$

Now one may think that in order to minimize $(F_{total} - 1)$ one must make $G_{e1} \to \infty$ by choosing $G_o = G_1$ in order to minimize $(F_1 - 1)$ and reduce $(F_2 - 1)/G_{e1}$ to zero simultaneously. But although

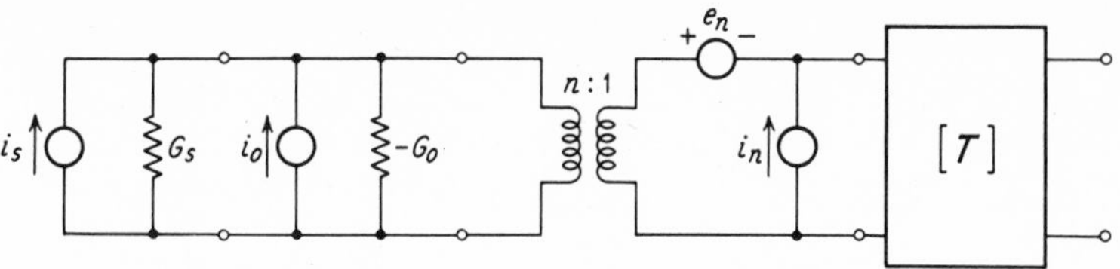

Fig. 27. Impedance transformation that optimizes $[F_{\text{total}} - 1]$.

$G_{e1} \to \infty$ minimizes $(F_1 - 1)$, it turns out that $(F_2 - 1)/G_{e1} \to G_n/G_s$ as $G_{e1} \to \infty$. Thus

$$\left[F_{\text{total}} - 1\right]_{G_o = G_s} = \frac{T_o}{T_s}\left[\frac{\omega_s}{\omega_i}\frac{T_i}{T_o} + \frac{G_n}{G_s}\right] . \tag{87}$$

That this is not the minimum value of $(F_{\text{total}} - 1)$ is evident from the fact that if

$$\frac{G_n}{G_s} \ll \frac{\omega_s}{\omega_i}\frac{T_i}{T_o} \tag{88}$$

a smaller value

$$\left[F_{\text{total}} - 1\right]_{\text{minimum}} = \frac{\omega_s}{\omega_i}\frac{T_i}{T_s} \tag{89}$$

is achieved. Therefore, here, unlike the choice indicated in Eq. (82) we must make G_s as large as possible compared with G_n. We can achieve this result by the use of a transformer as shown in Fig. 27 in order to obtain

$$\left[F_{\text{total}} - 1\right]_{G_o = G_s} = \frac{T_o}{T_s}\left[\frac{\omega_s}{\omega_i}\frac{T_i}{T_o} + \frac{G_n}{n^2 G_s}\right] \tag{90}$$

For very large n

$$\left[F_{\text{total}} - 1\right]_{G_o = G_s} \cong \frac{\omega_s}{\omega_i}\frac{T_i}{T_s} = \left[F_{\text{total}} - 1\right]_{\text{minimum}} . \tag{91}$$

This same formulation applies for Example 1 as is readily verified.

Experimental verification of the relations expressed in Eqs. (86) through (90) has been obtained. The agreement between experimental and theoretical results fully justifies the optimization procedure.[13]

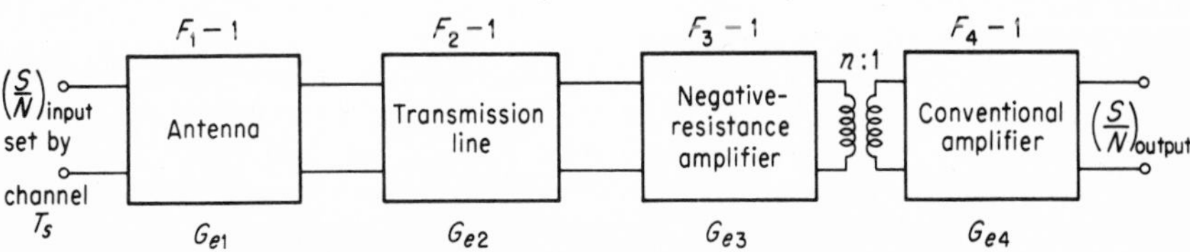

Fig. 28. Complete input section of a receiving system.

IV. OVERALL-ALL SYSTEM PERFORMANCE

The results of this chapter can be combined to give the excess noise figure of the overall receiving system. The complete input section of a receiver is illustrated in Fig. 28. With reference to this figure

$$F_{\text{total}} - 1 = F_1 - 1 + \frac{F_2 - 1}{G_{e1}} + \frac{F_3 - 1}{G_{e1}G_{e2}} + \frac{F_4 - 1}{G_{e1}G_{e2}G_{e3}} . \tag{92}$$

If the appropriate expressions for the various excess noise figures and exchangeable gains are substituted

$$F_{\text{total}} - 1 = \frac{T_\circ}{T_s}\left\{\begin{array}{l} \underbrace{\frac{T_{\text{minor lobes}}}{T_\circ}}_{\text{antenna}} + \frac{1-\epsilon}{\epsilon} + \underbrace{\frac{\gamma}{(1-\gamma)\epsilon}}_{\text{feed line}} + \\ \underbrace{\frac{\omega_s}{\omega_i}\frac{T_i}{T_\circ}\frac{1}{(1-\gamma)\epsilon}}_{\text{neg. res. amp.}} + \underbrace{\frac{G_n}{n^2 G_s}\cdot\frac{1}{(1-\gamma)\epsilon}}_{\text{amplifier}} \end{array}\right\} \tag{93}$$

where

- $T_\circ$ = 290 °K
- T_s = main-lobe antenna temperature
- ϵ = antenna efficiency (I^2R losses)
- γ = fractional loss in the transmission line
- ω_i = idler frequency in parametric amplifier
- ω_s = signal frequency in parametric amplifier
- G_n = equivalent conductance characterizing noise current source in amplifier
- n = turns ratio of transformer
- G_s = source conductance seen at end of transmission line.

V: CONCLUDING REMARKS

In conclusion we see that a useable concept of receiving-system noise performance requires a rigid set of definitions and interpretations on which we can base a comprehensive analysis. The importance of careful definition and interpretation cannot be too strongly emphasized. Once a theory is developed for adequately characterizing the class of devices of interest, the process of system optimization does not necessarily become intuitive. It only becomes so when *all* the parameters characterizing *each* device are included in the theoretical structure and the interrelationships between devices are known. Moreover, the actual optimization of any single device may not necessarily bring very startling improvements in overall system signal-to-noise performance. Only if the entire system is considered as a complete entity can we decide in general which devices must be optimized and in what manner. Any compromises that must be made should be decided upon only after an examination of their effect on overall *system* performance and *not* device performance.

REFERENCES

1. H. A. Haus and R. B. Adler, "An Extension of the Noise Figure Definition," *Proc. IRE*, vol. 45, p. 690, 1957.
2. H. A. Haus and R. B. Adler, "Optimum Noise Performance of Linear Amplifiers", *Proc. IRE*, vol. 46, p. 1517, 1958.
3. H. A. Haus and R. B. Adler, *Circuit Theory of Linear Noisy Networks*, Technology Press and John Wiley and Sons, Inc., New York, 1959.
4. J. L. Lawson and G. E. Uhlenbeck, (eds.), *Threshold Signals*, M. I. T. Radiation Laboratory Series, vol. 24, McGraw-Hill Book Company, Inc., New York, 1950.
5. B. Lovell and J. A. Clegg, *Radio Astronomy*, Chapman and Hall, Ltd., London, 1952.
6. S. K. Mitra, *The Upper Atmosphere*, 2d ed., The Asiatic Society, Calcutta, India, 1952.
7. *Reference Data for Radio Engineers*, 4th ed., International Telephone and Telegraph Corporation, New York, 1956.
8. S. A. Schelkunoff and H. T. Friis, *Antennas: Theory and Practice*, John Wiley and Sons, Inc., New York, 1952.
9. G. E. Valley, Jr., and H. Wallman (eds.), *Vacuum Tube Amplifiers*, M.I.T. Radiation Laboratory Series, vol. 18, McGraw-Hill Book Company, Inc., New York, 1948.
10. W. B. Davenport, Jr., and W. L. Root, *An Introduction to the Theory of Random Signals and Noise*, Lincoln Laboratory Publications, McGraw-Hill Book Company, Inc., New York, 1958.
11. H. A. Haus, "On the Noise Performance of Parametric Amplifiers," R. L. E.-M. I. T. internal publication, Cambridge, Mass., March 13, 1959.
12. P. Penfield, Jr., "Interpretation of Some Varactor Amplifier Noise Formulas," unpublished memorandum, Microwave Associates, Burlington, Mass., September 1, 1959.
13. R. P. Rafuse, "Measurement of Absolute Noise Performance of Parametric Amplifiers," presented at the 1960 Solid-State Circuits Conference, Philadelphia, Pa., February 12, 1960.

CHAPTER 16

Microwave Applications of Semiconductors

Arthur Uhlir, Jr.

I. INTRODUCTION

Nearly all microwave semiconductor devices are diodes. Transistors are just beginning to penetrate the lower microwave frequencies and only a few devices make use of bulk semiconductor properties. One of the most important developments in the last few years has been the recognition of several distinct types of diode behavior at microwave frequencies. The best performance can be obtained by selecting the right type of diode for a given function.

Previously, the point-contact crystal rectifier was universally used, with only minor modifications, in all kinds of microwave circuits: rectifiers, superheterodyne receiving mixers, modulators, frequency shifters, harmonic generators, and switches.

Of the newer types of diodes, the variable capacitance of "varactor" type is of special consequence. It introduces the new possibility of low-noise microwave amplification by a semiconductor device. Its success brings into prominence a type of circuit that has not been fully exploited heretofore in electronics. This general type of circuit involves the interaction of electromagnetic energy of various frequencies, describable (if one wishes) by the photon concept. In an electron tube, on the contrary, the power supply is derived from d-c voltages and passes through an intermediate stage as the kinetic energy of electrons. "Electronics" is so named because it is largely a consequence of the latter type of action. We can now expect to see substantial if not equally profound consequences of the utilization of photon interactions. These effects will not be confined to semiconductors alone; ferrite devices provide somewhat analogous action, and maser amplifiers utilize photon interactions in a somewhat different way, as will be explained in the next chapter.

In addition to varactor amplifiers, this chapter will discuss the use of the conventional mixer type of diodes alone and in combination with varactors, and will mention the PIN junction attenuator diode and the negative-resistance Esaki (or tunnel) diode.

II. EQUIVALENT CIRCUITS OF THE VARIOUS DIODES

In Fig. 1 is shown an equivalent circuit for a varactor diode. Measurements have indicated that this circuit can be applied over a wide range of frequencies without the need for altering the values of the parameters (otherwise the equivalent circuit would not be so useful).

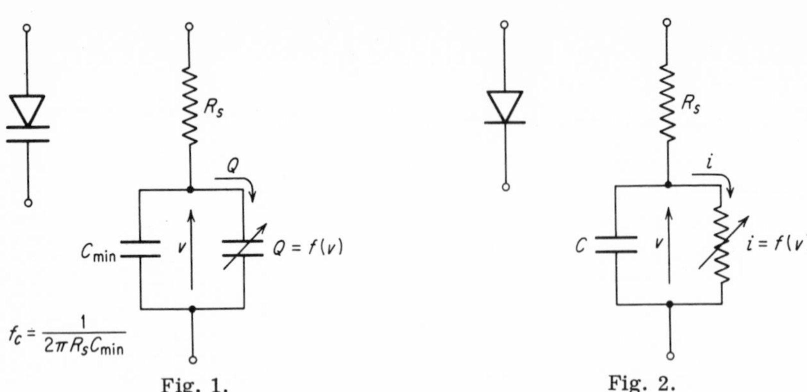

Fig. 1. Fig. 2.

Fig. 1. Varactor symbol and equivalent circuit.
Fig. 2. Equivalent circuit for mixer or rectifier diode.

The assumption that charge is an instantaneous nonlinear function of junction voltage is confirmed by the measurements over a wide range of frequencies. The minimum junction capacitance is not physically distinct from the variable junction capacitance; it is drawn separately to emphasize its importance as a limitation on the ultimate performance of the varactor. The minimum capacitance is obtained at "maximum reverse bias". It is possible, of course, that the maximum reverse bias set by low-frequency conduction current is not identical to the maximum bias that may be usable in a given microwave circuit, particularly where low noise is required. However, in most junctions, the capacitance for voltages substantially less than the breakdown voltage is only a small amount larger than the capacitance at the breakdown voltage.

Figure 2 shows the equivalent circuit of the point-contact diode used as a detector or a superheterodyne mixer. The capacitance in shunt with the nonlinear resistance is physically similar to the capacitance of the varactor junction and, indeed, is variable with voltage. However, for satisfactory rectifier action, one hopes to make the nonlinear conductance predominant over the capacitance so that an average value of the capacitance may be used as a first approximation. At frequencies up to several hundred megacycles, special junction diodes can be used which adhere reasonably well to this equivalent circuit.

Figure 3 illustrates the tunnel or Esaki diode, which exhibits a negative resistance or, one might better say, a negative conductance (because it can be stabilized by shunt loading). A negative conductance is obtained only for certain ranges of forward voltage bias; it is in this range that the diode is of interest as an oscillator or amplifier. In its ability to generate oscillations from a d-c power source, this diode is unique among those discussed here. As in Fig. 2, a capacitance is indicated which is voltage dependent but here an average value at the operating point is used as an approximation. A cutoff

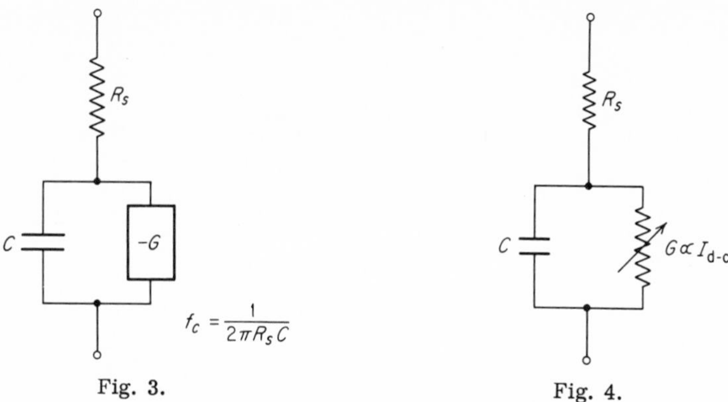

Fig. 3. Fig. 4.

Fig. 3. Equivalent circuit of Esaki (or tunnel) diode.
Fig. 4. Equivalent circuit of PIN diode for small high-frequency signals.

frequency may be defined on the basis of this capacitance, but it, of course, has a different significance from the cutoff frequency defined at breakdown voltage for the varactor diode.

Figure 4 shows the equivalent circuit of a PIN diode. The microwave conductance is approximately proportional to the d-c current. This diode also has a series resistance and a capacitance. For a given microwave capacitance, the junction area is much larger than for the other three types of diodes (all of which have much narrower junctions than the PIN). Because of the large area, the series resistance is very small, so that in switching uses at high frequencies, the PIN can have less insertion loss than existing varactors.

III. VARACTOR AMPLIFIERS

First, we shall consider what can be done with an ideal lossless varactor having the simple circuit shown in Fig. 5; later another approach will be outlined for obtaining detailed information and including the effect of losses. Some general equations (over and above the obvious equation of conservation of energy) have been developed for

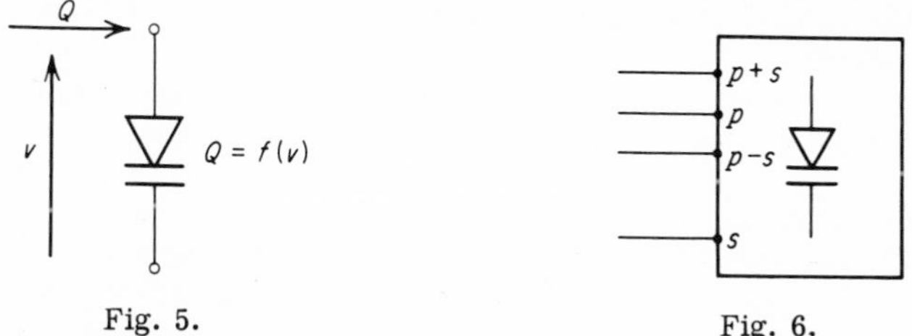

Fig. 5. Fig. 6.

Fig. 5. Lossless varactor.
Fig. 6. Four-frequency varactor "black box."

an element of this type.[1] Their usefulness will be illustrated in a particular set of cases symbolized in Fig. 6. This figure represents a "black box" containing a lossless varactor (or a number of lossless varactors connected by any lossless passive circuits). It is assumed that power may enter or leave the black box at the four frequencies p, s, $(p+s)$, and $(p-s)$, and at no others. The Manley-Rowe equation applicable to this situation is

$$\frac{P(s)}{s} + \frac{P(s+p)}{s+p} - \frac{P(p-s)}{p-s} = 0 . \tag{1}$$

Note that the pump power $P(p)$ is not involved in this equation; an additional equation can be written (which we do not need) which includes $P(p)$ and affirms the conservation of energy.

As an initial application of this equation, consider the upper-sideband up-converter diagrammed in Fig. 7. Here the port for the frequency $(p-s)$ is blocked by a lossless filter, so that power neither enters nor leaves at this frequency; neither can it be dissipated within the box, because all the elements are lossless. In this example, the input power is $[-P(s)]$ and the power out is $[+P(s+p)]$. $P(p-s)$ is zero, so, from Eq. (1),

$$\text{output/input} = -P(s+p)/P(s) = (s+p)/s \tag{2}$$

For example, when p is 10,000 mc and s is 500 mc, a gain of 13 db is possible—enough to reduce substantially, but not eliminate the effect of a typical 10,000-mc receiver noise figure of 7 db.

Unlimited gain can be obtained in two ways from the arrangement illustrated in Fig. 8. Here, $P(s+p)$ is zero. Then Eq. (1) requires that if a net power is to emerge at either $p-s$ or s, it must emerge at *both* of these frequencies. Since the equation refers only to the *net* power at these frequencies, it is possible to have a signal enter at the frequency s and have an output at $p-s$, as long as more power leaves at s than enters with the input signal. This is an interesting and useful arrangement; it can serve as an amplifier in either of two ways.

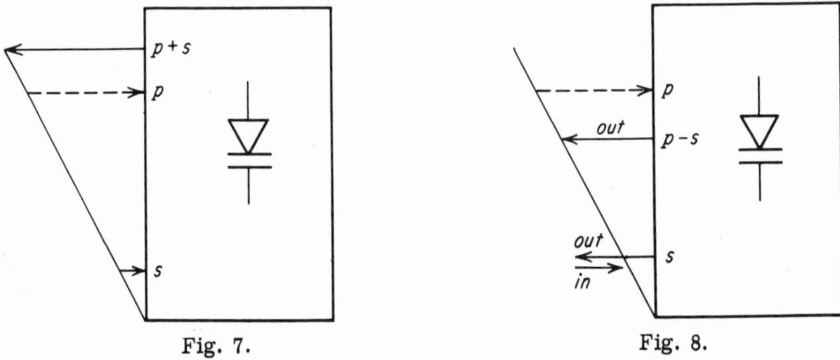

Fig. 7.　　Fig. 8.

Fig. 7. Upper-sideband up-converter. Arrows are proportional to powers (for lossless varactor).

Fig. 8. Negative-resistance amplifier and/or lower-sideband up-converter.

An amplified signal having the same frequency as the input may be obtained from the reflected wave at s. Alternatively, an amplified output may be obtained at $p - s$. The fact that the reflected wave is larger than the incident wave at the frequency s means that the device presents a *negative impedance* at this frequency. Such negative-resistance amplifiers can provide very low noise figures, and they preserve the exact input frequency in spite of any drifts in pump frequency p. The other type of amplifier is the lower-sideband up-converter, in which the output power is taken at $(p - s)$ and a negative resistance is again present at s. The power output at $(p - s)$ must be absorbed by an "idler" termination in order for negative-resistance amplification to take place at s. Whatever the absorbing termination may be, it is liable to serve as a noise source. Noise from the idler proceeds into the varactor and is converted to the signal frequency. The effect of idler noise will be discussed later on in this section.

Another arrangement for amplification by varactors makes use of all three signal frequencies. In the arrangement indicated in Fig. 9, any amount of gain can be obtained without necessarily incurring a negative resistance at the input frequency s. To show that this possibility exists, consider the special case in which

$$P(s + p) = \frac{p + s}{p - s} P(p - s) \ . \tag{3}$$

Then Eq. (1) indicates that $P(s) = 0$, so that the power gain for a signal input at s is infinite. The gain can be made large but finite by adjusting the circuit so that $P(s + p)$ is a little larger, relative to $P(p - s)$, than is indicated by Eq. (3). The second stage following this double-sideband up-converter may receive the upper or lower sideband or both.

Some possible systems using the above types of varactor amplifiers will now be illustrated. Figure 10 shows a negative-resistance

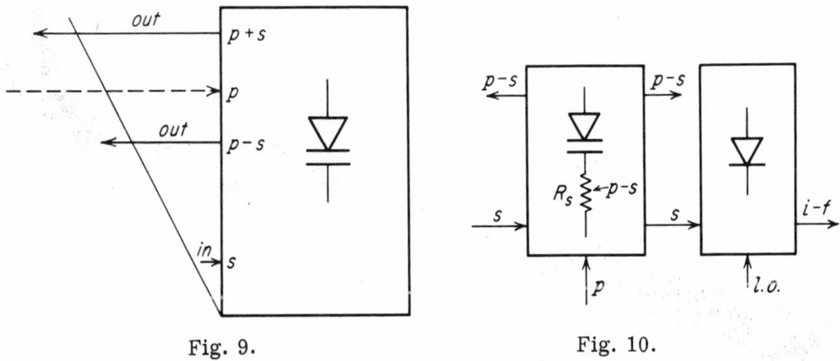

Fig. 9. Fig. 10.

Fig. 9. Double-sideband up-converter.

Fig. 10. Negative-resistance amplifier with superheterodyne second stage (crystal mixer). l.o. stands for local oscillator, i-f for intermediate frequency.

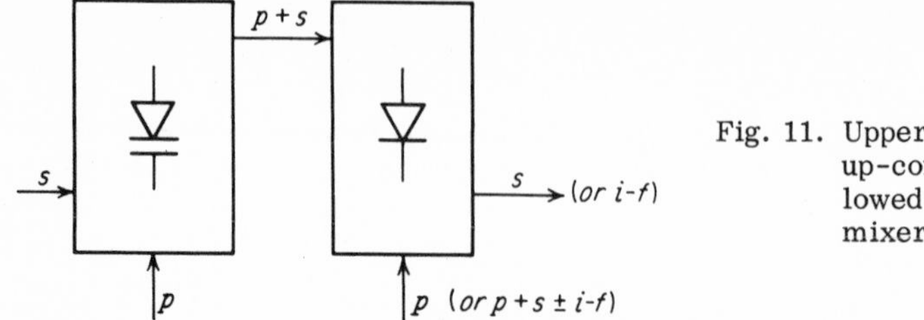

Fig. 11. Upper-sideband up-converter followed by crystal mixer.

amplifier followed by a more-or-less conventional mixer that uses nonlinear resistance action. The negative-resistance-type amplifier has also been used successfully with low-noise electron tube triode receivers in place of the crystal mixer. In Fig. 10, it is indicated that the varactor may have a series resistance. Some of the idler power at a frequency $p - s$ may be absorbed in the series resistance. The rest of the idler power may be delivered to the antenna and/or the second stage. As far as gain is concerned, it does not matter where the idler power is dissipated. Since these various possible terminations in general have different effective noise temperatures, the idler-frequency circuits have an effect on the noise performance.

Figure 11 illustrates an upper-sideband up-converter in combination with a down-converter. When the same frequency as for the pump is used with a local oscillator of the down-converter, the original frequency will be restored despite small variations in pump frequency. Most experiments have used a slightly different system in which the local oscillator is chosen so that the output is at a desired intermediate frequency. If this local oscillator is derived from the pump by frequency shifting, cancellation of pump frequency drifts can still be obtained.

The double-sideband up-converter can be used to special advantage when followed by a crystal mixer whose pump is derived from the original pump in such a way that both sidebands are utilized by the mixer (Fig. 12). The additional gain obtained by utilizing both sidebands is helpful in overcoming the noise of the second stage. One of the most effective utilizations of present varactors was based on a

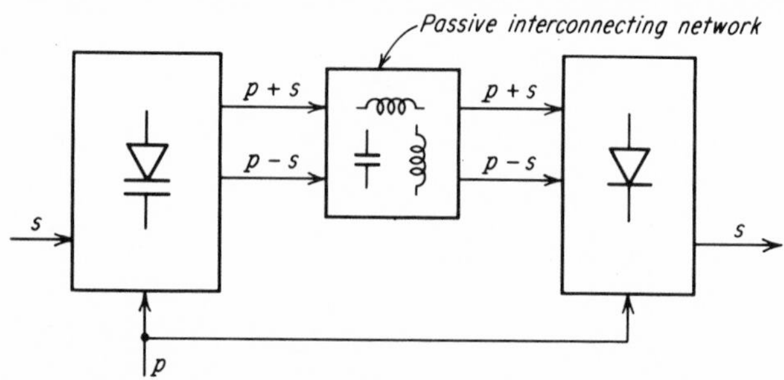

Fig. 12. Double-sideband up-converter with recombination of sidebands in a crystal mixer.

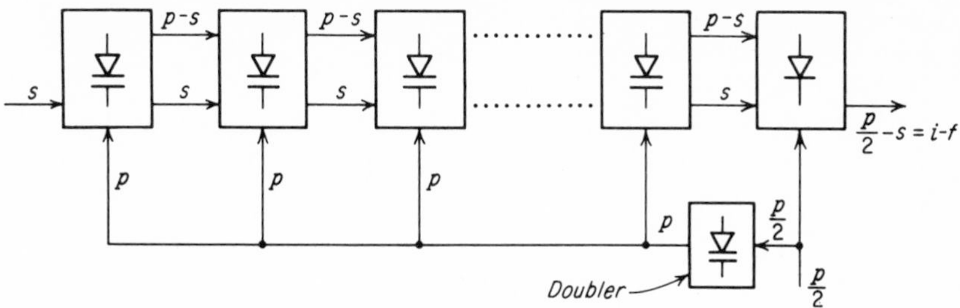

Fig. 13. Traveling-wave varactor amplifier with recombination of signal and idler in a crystal mixer.

double-sideband system; a noise figure of 0.25 db at an input signal frequency s of 400 mc was reported by Peppiat.[2]

A powerful attack on the problems of bandwidth and unilateral gain has been made in the traveling-wave varactor amplifier. Such an amplifier is a cascade of negative-resistance amplifiers, although one may perhaps distinguish between cascading of complete amplifiers (a useful procedure) and the installation of a closely-spaced sequence of varactors in such a way that they approximate in some measure a continuous line. The original work on traveling-wave amplifiers was done by Engelbrecht, who also contemplated the use of both sidebands in a final crystal mixer, as shown in Fig. 13.

The noise equivalent circuit of the varactor is shown in Fig. 14. The main source of noise at high frequencies is believed to be thermal noise of the series resistance. The shot noise of the thermally generated "saturation current" is negligible at microwave frequencies for silicon varactors, even at appreciably elevated temperatures. Under the assumptions that shot noise is negligible and that the series resistance exhibits thermal noise, the noise figure for a given diode temperature depends only on the cutoff frequency.

The Manley-Rowe equations are so general that their validity does not depend upon assumptions of linearity. The most useful applications of varactor amplifiers are as essentially linear circuits at the signal frequencies. By restricting attention to this case, one can make a much more detailed analysis of any particular circuit—an

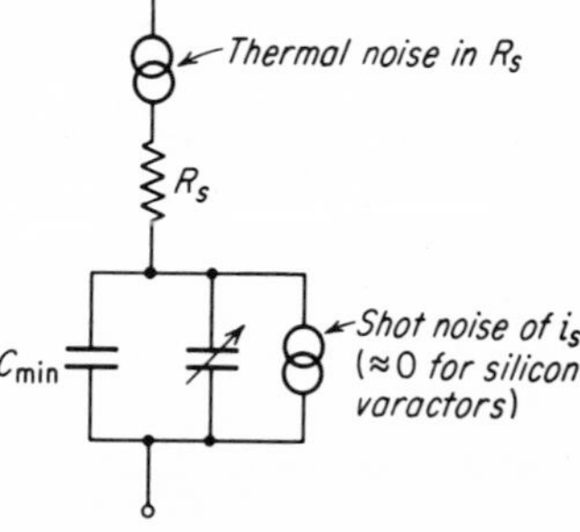

Fig. 14. Noise equivalent circuit of varactor.

analysis that gives the gain, noise, and impedances at the signal frequencies, for given pumping.

The only source of nonlinearity in the varactor circuit is the nonlinear capacitance of the junction, which can be described by the equation

$$Q = f(v) \tag{4}$$

relating the instantaneous charge and voltage. The voltage v in this equation is the sum of the pump voltage v_o and all of the voltages (input, output, idler, etc.) due to the signal. Similarly, the charge Q is the sum of the charge $Q(v_o)$ due to the pump and the charges δQ that are consequences of the applied signal. To calculate the linear signal properties, one may write

$$Q = Q(v_o) + \delta Q \approx Q(v_o) + \left.\frac{dQ}{dv}\right|_{v = v_o} \times \delta v$$

or

$$\delta Q = \left.\frac{dQ}{dv}\right|_{v = v_o} \times \delta v = C(v_0(t))\,\delta v. \tag{5}$$

The "small-signal capacitance" C of a nonlinear capacitor is dQ/dv, by definition. Thus, the linear aspects of the relation between the signal charges and voltages, as they appear at the junction, is completely determined by the small-signal capacitance as a function of time under the influence of the pump. The relation, Eq. (5), is indistinguishable from that which would apply if the junction were replaced with a linear but somehow time-variant capacitor. For analysis by conventional techniques, one obtains the signal currents as time-derivatives of the signal charges. In principle, then, one can analyze any multifrequency linear circuit (including the varactor series resistance) that may be connected to the junction.

Two factors keep the circuit theory of varactor amplifiers from being a closed book. One is the need for a nonlinear analysis to determine what $C(t)$ waveform* results from a pump oscillator of given characteristics applied to the varactor through a network with specified impedances at the pump frequency and its harmonics.

The other factor is that the basic need is for synthesis and optimization, not analysis. Analysis of specific circuits serves the basic need laboriously and only partially; it can establish (changeable) boundaries that *include* the possible, but fail to *exclude* the impossible.

The gain and noise of the upper-sideband up-converter have been studied by Leenov,[3] who avoids the common error of supposing some frequencies to be short-circuited at the junction which, in fact, does not have accessible terminals. The effects of the series resistance are included, of course, since the analysis would otherwise give only

*It is equally valid to speak of an elastance waveform $S(t) = 1/C(t)$. Because the varactor losses are represented by a series resistance, and because S is bounded by $S_{max} = 1/C_{min}$, elastance is more convenient than capacitance in analysis of varactor circuits.

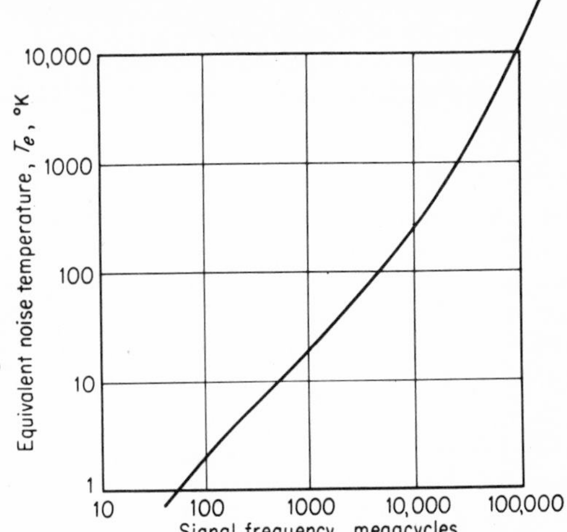

Fig. 15. Equivalent noise temperature for negative-resistance varactor amplifier with varactor and idler at 290°K (f_c = 100 Kmc). (Theoretical, after Penfield.)

Eq. (2) for the gain and no noise at all. The terminations for maximum gain and minimum noise are different, and the gain for minimum noise figure can be considerably below the maximum gain.

A study of noise figure and gain for the negative-resistance amplifier has been carried out by Haus and Penfield.[4,5] In order to obtain general results, the analytical technique employed did not fail to consider, as far as possible, the effect of arbitrary variations in terminations and $C(t)$ waveforms. One of the interesting results is that amplification may be obtained at arbitrarily high signal frequencies with a varactor of given cutoff frequency. However, at high frequencies, the noise performance is poor and the allowable pump frequency is narrowly restricted. The equivalent noise temperature T_e as a function of frequency is shown in Fig. 15 for optimal use of a varactor having a 100-Kmc cutoff frequency, with varactor and idler at 290° K. Since varactors in practice will not be used with all conditions fully optimized, it would be realistic to divide the frequency scale by two. By definition, $T_e = 290(F - 1)$.

The general result is conveniently expressed in terms of the noise measure, M_e:

$$M_e = \frac{F_e - 1}{1 - 1/G_e} \geqslant \frac{T_i}{290} \frac{s}{(p - s)} \tag{6}$$

where T_i is the effective noise temperature of the idler termination.

The gain-bandwidth relations for varactor amplifiers have been the subject of a number of preliminary analyses as well as circuit experiments. These analyses have typically given the result that (Power Gain)$^{1/2}$ times bandwidth was a constant for a given ratio of pump-to-signal frequency. This relation is not general; Herrmann and Seidel have shown that, for a given finite bandwidth, there is no upper limit on the power gain, provided sufficient circuit sophistication is invoked.[6] They explain that the above approximate result is true for single-tuned circuits (which are likely to turn up both in approximate theories and in preliminary experiments). A distinct advantage remains for amplifiers using a plurality of varactors: nonreciprocal characteristics can be obtained without the use of auxiliary ferrite devices.

IV. VARACTORS AND VARACTOR MEASUREMENTS

Voltage-dependent capacitance is exhibited by practically all semiconductor diodes. In approximate chronological order, the types that have been tested as amplifiers are: gold-bonded germanium, point-contact silicon, diffused-junction silicon, diffused-junction germanium, point-contact germanium, point-contact gallium arsenide, and diffused-junction gallium arsenide. Virtually all equipment presently designed for reliable systems makes use of the diffused-junction silicon varactors, because of their ability to operate (and give low noise) at higher temperatures than germanium. Gallium arsenide varactors should be operable at higher temperatures than silicon, but are not yet generally available.

For all of the diode types, the functions $Q = f(v)$ and $C = dQ/dv$ are monotonic functions of voltage. The small-signal junction capacitance can be varied from C_{min} to infinity. To say the same thing, but in a less extravagant-sounding way: the elastance S can vary from zero to $S_{max} = 1/C_{min}$. The capacitance can be well approximated by

$$C = \frac{C_0}{(1 - v/\phi)^{1/3}} \tag{7}$$

for diffused junctions, and by

$$C = \frac{C_0}{(1 - v/\phi)^{1/2}} \tag{8}$$

for most of the other types. These equations can be derived theoretically. However, careful measurements on diffused silicon varactors seem to disagree significantly with the theoretical relation between capacitance per unit area and the constant ϕ.

The above equations apply for appreciable forward biases ($v > o$) in the case of good varactors, which, indeed, may be used advantageously with a pumping arrangement that applies forward voltage. Hence it is misleading to speak of varactors as "back-biased" semiconductor diodes.

The measurement of varactors may be separated into two parts. One is the low-frequency measurement of capacitance as a function of voltage. There is some evidence that the junction capacitance is almost independent of frequency. The series-resistance loss can be measured accurately only at very high frequencies. The most advantageous way of measuring a varactor series resistance is based on the assumed equivalent circuit.[7] Small-signal impedance is measured at several values of junction capacitance. The capacitance of the junction is varied by varying the d-c bias. No matter what transformation stands between the measuring device and the varactor (as long as transformation losses are negligible) the results can be interpreted to give the series resistance in terms of the junction capacitance (which can be measured at low frequencies). The experimental plot must fall on a segment of a constant-resistance circle of a Smith chart which could be placed on the reflection coefficient diagram by suitable choice of phase. The most accurate results are obtained if low-loss transformations are used to make the characteristic impedance of the overall transformation equal to or of the same order of magnitude as the series resistance.

V. MIXER DIODES

The noise equivalent circuit of a mixer diode is shown in Fig. 16. For this type of diode, it is not possible to neglect the shot noise associated with forward conduction, nor is series-resistance thermal noise negligible at high frequencies. (The steady shot noise associated with the saturation current is probably negligible for the better diodes.) The instantaneous mean-square shot noise current of forward conduction is proportional to the instantaneous current. At the same time, the conductance of the junction is approximately proportional to the instantaneous current. Analysis indicates that in such a situation it is theoretically possible for the conductance to short-circuit a large part of the shot-noise current flowing at the high current peaks of a pulsed waveform. In Fig. 17(a), such a pulsed waveform is shown, and it is indicated symbolically that the current is made up of shot events that nearly all occur at the very time that conductance is high. Only in this way can the low noise figures of crystal mixers be understood. If, on the contrary, a sinusoidal current would flow as shown in Fig. 17(b), appreciable noise would result for those shot events which occurred when the conductance of the junction was relatively high, permitting the shot current to be de-

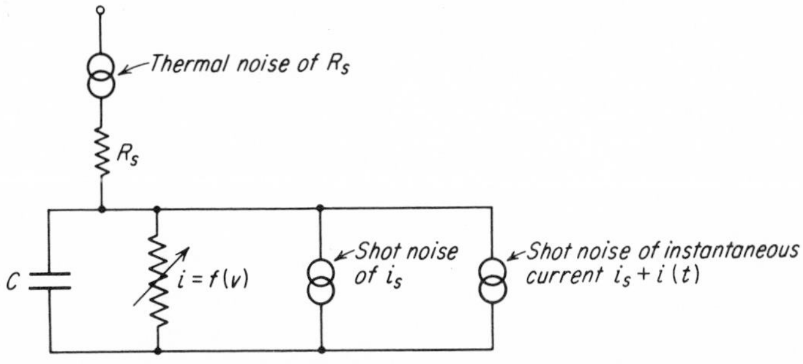

Fig. 16. Noise equivalent circuit of mixer crystal.

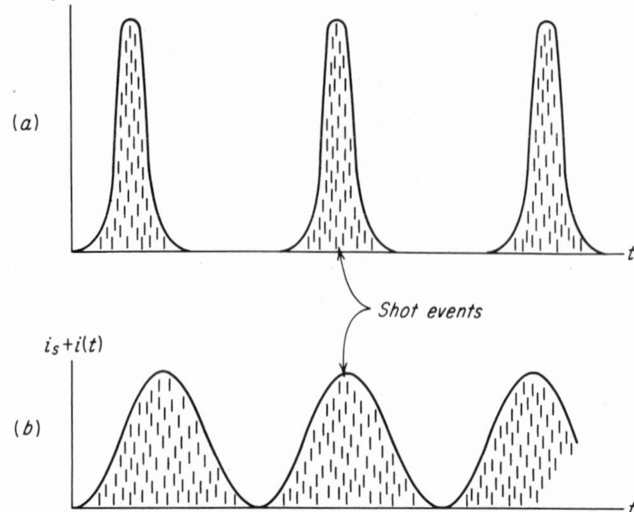

Fig. 17. Local-oscillator waveforms made up of electronic shot events. (a) Pulsed, leading to low noise. (b) Sinusoidal, nonvanishing shot noise.

livered to the load conductance.

The insistance that the local-oscillator waveform is important in determining the noise performance of crystal mixers is equivalent to saying that the impedances at the harmonics of the local oscillator frequency can have large influence on the noise. In addition, it is conceivable that auxiliary diodes could be used to inject an initially nonsinusoidal local oscillator into the mixer.

VI. ESAKI DIODES

A noise equivalent circuit of the Esaki diode is shown in Fig. 18. The published noise studies of such diodes have been concerned primarily with the shot noise associated with the d-c bias current required to put the diode into the negative-conductance region. It does seem inevitable that this current will generate shot noise. Until there

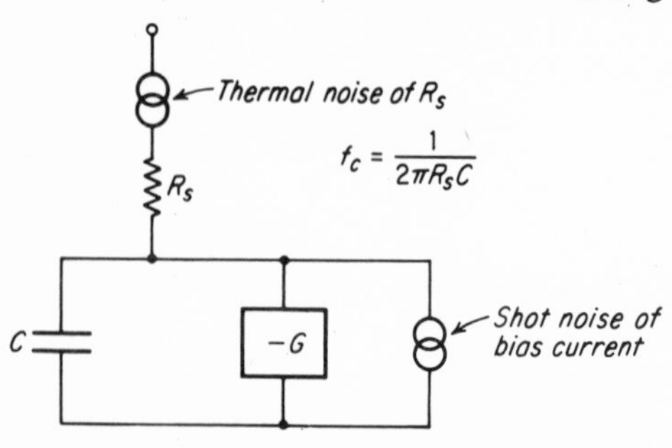

Fig. 18. Noise equivalent circuit of Esaki diode.

is a more certain knowledge of what, if any, necessary relation there is between the magnitude of the negative conductance and the magnitude of the d-c bias current, no evaluation can be made of the ultimate limit on how small this noise contribution may be.

Even if the shot-noise contribution is neglected, one must contend with the thermal noise of the series resistance, which becomes increasingly important at high frequencies. A simple analysis has been made on the basis of the circuit shown in Fig. 19. One result, quite apart from the question of noise, is that the maximum frequency for amplification or oscillation is equal to $f_c/2$, where f_c is the cutoff frequency as defined in Fig. 18. The noise figure, with shot noise neglected, also depends on the ratio of amplified frequency to the cutoff frequency. It is possible to trade noise figure for gain at any frequency below the limiting frequency of amplification.

The noise figure F can be calculated at once from Fig. 19. By definition

$$F = 1 + \frac{\text{noise delivered to load by sources within amplifier}}{\text{noise that would be delivered to load by source impedance at } 290^\circ\text{K}} \tag{9}$$

Obviously, then

$$F = 1 + \frac{R_s}{R_g} \quad \text{(neglecting shot noise)} \tag{10}$$

if the diode temperature is 290°K. To calculate gain, one may convert the parallel combination of capacitance to an impedance with a negative real part $[-G/(G^2+\omega^2C^2)]$. Assume that the inductive reactance is chosen to cancel the capacitive reactance; then the circuit is as shown in Fig. 20. The exchangeable gain is

$$G_e = \frac{R_g}{R_g + R_s - (G/G^2+\omega^2C^2)} \tag{11}$$

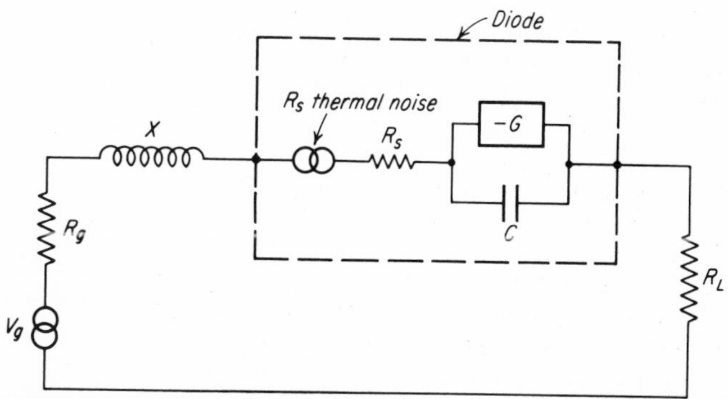

Fig. 19. Circuit for analyzing Esaki diode amplifier.

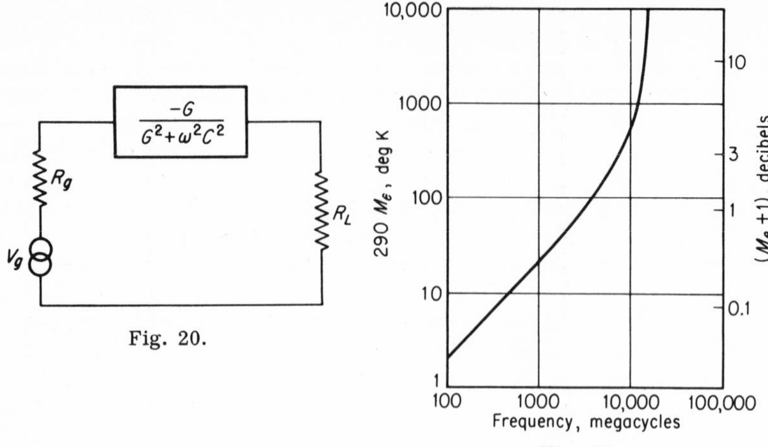

Fig. 20. Series representation of tuned Esaki diode amplifier.

Fig. 21. Minimum noise measure obtainable with Esaki diode with a cutoff frequency of 30 Kmc, neglecting shot noise and considering only series resistance thermal noise.

and the noise measure is

$$M_e = \frac{R_s}{[G/(G^2 + \omega^2 C^2)] - R_s} \cdot \tag{12}$$

Now, G, R_s, and C are probably interrelated in some way. In the absence of a detailed device design theory, however, let us give the diode the best possible chance by varying G arbitrarily to minimize M_e. The minimum occurs for $G = \omega C$ and is given by

$$M_e = \frac{1}{(f_c/2f) - 1} \cdot \tag{13}$$

At $f = f_c/2$, M_e becomes infinite, reflecting the fact that gain is not possible above this frequency.

The cutoff frequency of an Esaki diode is not likely to be as high as that of a varactor, for an equal development of fabrication techniques, simply because varactor design can be directed solely to high cutoff frequency, whereas the Esaki diode must first of all exhibit negative conductance. Thus, it seems fair to compare the 100-Kmc varactor considered in Fig. 15 with a 30-Kmc Esaki diode. Figure 21 gives 290 M_e for such an Esaki diode. Even with shot noise neglected, the Esaki diode does not appear likely to be as good as the varactor as a low-noise amplifier. The possibility of using Esaki diodes as pumps for varactor amplifiers is, of course, attractive. The cutoff frequencies of both varactors and Esaki diodes can be expected to increase as design and fabrication are perfected.

REFERENCES

1. J. M. Manley and H. E. Rowe, "Some General Properties of Nonlinear Elements—Part I. General Energy Relations", *Proc. IRE*, vol. 44, pp. 904-913; July, 1956.
2. H. J. Peppiatt and J. R. Poppe, "Design and Field Test of Two Different Types of Reactance Amplifiers", PGMTT National Symposium, Harvard University, June 3, 1959.
3. D. Leenov, "Gain and Noise of a Variable-Capacitance Upconverter", *Bell System Tech. J.*, vol. 37, no. 4, pp. 989-1008, July, 1958.
4. H. A. Haus and Paul Penfield, Jr., "On the Noise Performance of Parametric Amplifiers," M.I.T., Dept. of E. E., Energy Conversion Group, Internal Memorandum No. 19, August 11, 1959.
5. Paul Penfield, Jr., "The High-Frequency Limit of Varactor Amplifiers," unpublished memorandum, Microwave Associates, Inc., Burlington, Mass.; August 27, 1959.
6. H. Seidel and G. F. Herrmann, "Circuit Aspects of Parametric Amplifiers," 1959 IRE WESCON Convention Record, Part 2 (Circuit Theory), pp. 83-90, August 18-21, 1959.
7. N. Houlding, "Measurement of Varactor Quality," *Microwave Journal*, vol. 3, pp. 40-45, January, 1960.

CHAPTER 17

Masers and Low-Noise Systems

Robert H. Kingston

I. THE SOLID-STATE MASER

I-1. General Principles

The word *maser* is an acronym that stands for *m*icrowave *a*mplification by *s*timulated *e*mission of *r*adiation. Before discussing the solid state maser in particular, it is well first to consider the general process of stimulated emission which is radically different from previous concepts of amplification such as that of the vacuum tube.[1,2]

Most of us are familiar with the idea of absorption in a resonant system. The simplest case, of course, is an *LC* circuit that absorbs energy at a frequency determined by the circuit constants. Similarly, in atomic systems one can obtain absorption if there are two allowed energy levels—that is, if an electron can exist in two separate energy states. If a solid, for instance, in which there are electrons having two discrete energy levels is exposed to electromagnetic radiation, one will observe absorption of energy if the separation between these levels equals the product of Planck's constant, h, and the frequency of the radiation. Schematically, referring to Fig. 1, one can describe the electron distribution by two possible levels with most of the electrons in the lower level. A simple but incorrect method of looking at the absorption is to consider that the incident photons excite electrons from the lower state to the upper state. That is, one assumes that the photons wish to yield energy to the electron system and preferentially excite electrons to a higher energy state. Actually, a detailed analysis of the behavior of the system does not yield such a picture but gives a very important modification which is the

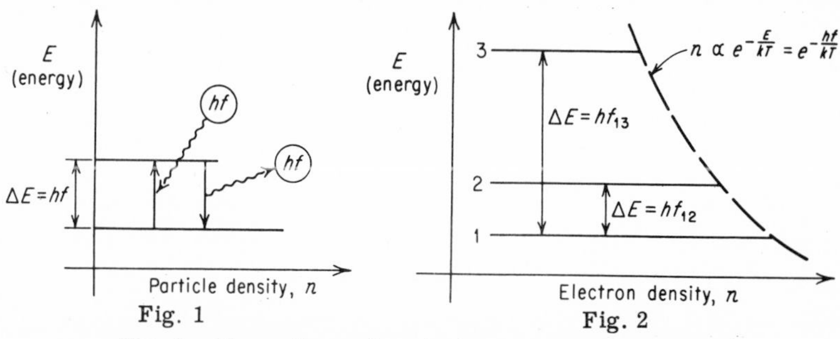

Fig. 1. Absorption and emission in a two-level system.
Fig. 2. Three-level system at thermal equilibrium.

basis of the operation of the maser. This is that photons of the proper frequency actually cause an induced transition between the states with equal probabilities for upward transitions (electrons gaining energy from the photons), and downward transitions (electrons losing energy to the photons or emitting radiation). The fact that all normal physical systems absorb is associated with the difference in occupation of the two energy levels. Under equilibrium conditions there are always more particles in the lower energy state; therefore, the impinging radiation always produces more transitions to the upper state and therefore a net loss in energy. If one could obtain a distribution of electrons in which there were more particles in the upper energy state, then more electrons would be induced to make transitions downward and the result would be a net radiation of photons or electromagnetic energy. It is this process, called stimulated emission, that is the basis of operation of the maser. Not only may more photons be yielded in this process but it may be shown both theoretically and experimentally that the resulting photon flux consists of a coherent train of electromagnetic radiation. Historically, the first operational maser[3] utilized, not electrons but, molecules of ammonia gas which could exist in two possible energy states. A normal beam of gas was separated into the two possible states by the action of an inhomogeneous electric field. The higher-energy particles were then sent into a microwave cavity at which point they tended to seek a lower energy level resulting in emission of photons. These photons in turn stimulated further emission and it was possible to obtain either a direct generation of microwaves from the gas system or, by proper manipulation of the equipment, the amplification of a small incident signal by the cavity. We shall be concerned with electrons in our discussions since for broadband low-noise amplification in communication systems, the magnetic properties of the electron turn out to be most suitable for application.

The key to the operation of the solid state maser is the technique of inverting the electron population, that is, obtaining two states wherein the particle density is greater in the higher energy state. The key to such an arrangement was proposed by Blombergen[4] in 1956. He utilized a paramagnetic salt, a crystal wherein the energies of the electrons could be manipulated by applied magnetic fields. This material was to have at least three allowed energy levels for the electrons. Figure 2 shows such a system in which the three energy levels for the electrons are determined by the properties of the crystal and the intensity and direction of the applied magnetic field. The particle density in each state is indicated by the length of the horizontal bars. In this figure, the electrons are shown in thermal equilibirum and behave according to the normal Boltzmann distribution. Now let us assume that we wish to make the number of particles in state 2 greater than the number in state 1. This may be accomplished by applying electromagnetic energy at a frequency that corresponds to the energy difference between states 1 and 3. As in our previous discussion of stimulated emission, we shall use the fact that the electromagnetic radiation causes an induced transition probability for particles in either direction. In this case the electrons in state 1 and state 3 will make transitions so rapidly that states 1 and 3 will become equal in occupation. That is, the normal equilibration processes that maintain the Boltzmann distribution are overridden by the induced transitions caused by the "pumping" field as this electromagnetic radiation is called. Now if states 1 and 3 are equal and the normal thermally induced transitions between states 3 and 2 and 1 are both small, then state 2 will in general maintain its initial population density. As may be seen in Fig. 3 this will yield a density of electrons in state 2 which is greater than the density in state 1. This fairly simple process is the essence of the operation of the solid state maser. Once power is supplied at the pumping frequency, f_{13}, the material is placed in such a state that incident photons of f_{12} will now produce stimulated emission. To be more descriptive, one might call the system a photon multiplier. There are, of course, practical limitations in the operation of such a device. These are: (1) in order to obtain the large difference in populations as shown in Fig. 2, it is necessary to operate the system at a very low temperature, otherwise the initial difference in level densities will be too small to give reasonable amplification; (2) it is necessary to contain the paramagnetic crystal in a cavity that enhances the electromagnetic fields at the two frequencies of interest; and (3) the crystal must be at low temperature so that the thermal vibrations of the lattice will not produce enough competing transitions to wipe out the effects of the pumping field. In addition to the above factors, which dictate a low-temperature medium for the crystal, the noise generated by the amplifier is also determined by the temperature.

I-2. Noise Properties

A convenient way of characterizing the difference in populations in the solid state maser is by the introduction of an effective temperature. Under equilibrium conditions the electron temperature is, simply, the physical temperature of the crystal lattice. After inversion of the spins, however, a new temperature may be defined as follows:

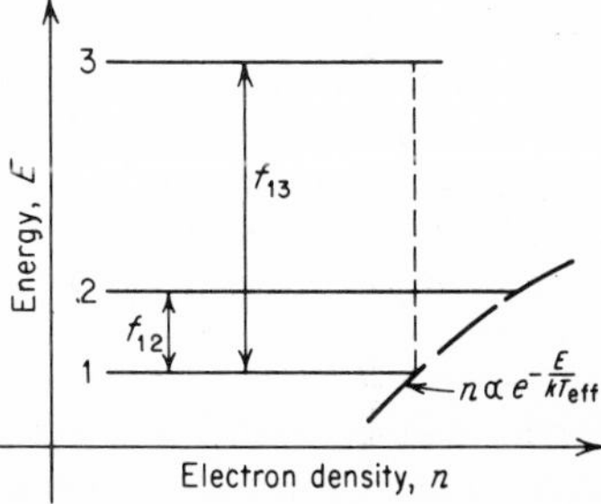

Fig. 3. Three-level system with the f_{13} transition saturated.

Normal statistics require that the ratio n_2 to n_1 be given as:

$$\frac{n_2}{n_1} = e^{-\frac{\Delta E}{kT}} = e^{-\frac{hf_{12}}{kT}} \tag{1}$$

where k is Boltzmann's constant. It turns out that one may similarly describe the non-equilibrium maser system by the same formula but T now becomes a negative quantity, as shown in Fig. 3. We shall now see that the magnitude of the quantity T is also directly related to the noise generated in the maser system.

Let us consider a general set of spins that can exist in either of the two states. In the absence of any external radiation, there will be power generated by this system but it will be caused by spontaneous emission, that is, by transitions from state 2 to state 1. In true thermal equilibrium, this power would be equal to the absorbed energy from the radiation field at the given temperature. (Transitions due to lattice collisions are non-radiative and will not concern us in this treatment). Let us now imagine that this two-level system is placed in a resonant structure whose terminals are available as a single port. We know from the previous discussion that the terminal-pair characteristics will be those of a negative conductance when the system is operating as a maser. What we also wish to determine is the short-circuit noise current which is produced at the terminal pair. This may be approached as follows in a method originally suggested by Blombergen. We know first of all that the square of the noise current should be proportional to n_2, the number of systems in the upper state. We, therefore, write

$$\overline{i_n^2} \propto n_2 = \frac{n_1 - n_2}{\frac{n_1}{n_2} - 1} \tag{2}$$

where the last form is a rearrangement that leads to a simple analysis of the noise behavior. Now the numerator, $(n_1 - n_2)$, is proportional to the conductance g of the system, because it is the difference between the number of systems in the upper and lower levels. The denominator of the expression is simply the Boltzmann factor connecting the two states minus one. Therefore, we can write

$$\overline{i_n^2} = C \times \frac{g}{e^{hf/kT} - 1} \tag{3}$$

where C is an unknown constant. Note that g is negative if n_2 is greater than n_1, and similarly, the exponential factor is less than unity if the maser is in the amplifying state. We must now evaluate the constant, C, that gives us the absolute magnitude of the mean-square noise current. This may be done by referring to the normal equilibrium situation. Specifically, let us assume that T is large and positive or that kT is much larger than hf, the quantum energy for the frequency concerned. Then under these restrictions, Eq. (3) should reduce to the normal Johnson noise formula,

$$\overline{i_n^2} = 4kTgB \tag{4}$$

where B is the effective noise bandwidth in cps. But, with $kT \gg hf$, Eq. (3) actually reduces to

$$\overline{i_n^2} = C \times \frac{kTg}{hf}$$

which by comparison with Eq. (3) leads to

$$C = 4hfB.$$

Therefore, the expression for the mean-square noise current of the maser cavity is

$$\overline{i_n^2} = \frac{4hfgB}{e^{hf/kT} - 1}. \tag{5}$$

This derivation applies equally well to negative temperatures. In particular, as long as hf is small compared with kT, the standard Johnson noise expression still holds. Note that when g is negative the exponential is less than unity and the kT term is also negative. Thus, the negative conductance and the negative temperature yield a positive mean-square noise current. Just as in the case of Johnson noise, the simple noise formula breaks down when hf is comparable to or greater than kT. Specifically, for $kT \ll hf$, the mean-square noise current is given by

$$\overline{i_n^2} = 4hfgBe^{-\frac{hf}{kT}}, \quad T > 0 \tag{6}$$

$$\overline{i_n^2} = 4hf\,|g|\,B \quad, \quad T < 0 \; (g < 0). \tag{7}$$

These expressions follow from Eq. (5) when the specified restrictions are imposed. For the case in which T is small and negative, it is seen from Eq. (7) that the least possible noise temperature of the maser is given by

$$T_{\text{noise}} = \frac{hf}{k}. \tag{8}$$

Actually, this lower limiting case is not too surprising since it expresses the limitation in signal detection produced by the discrete nature of photons. Thus, for instance, if one were operating with a system having a 1-cps bandwidth, it would turn out that the limiting noise power would be 1 photon per second. This is just another way of saying that it is impossible to measure a signal whose power content is such that one would have to measure a fraction of a photon in a specific time interval.

In practice the noise generated in the maser turns out to be negligible compared with the rest of the system contributions. The magnitude of the negative temperature in most operating masers is of the order of the liquid-helium bath temperature although it may be several times smaller or larger in some cases. The photon limitation is also not a serious one in present-day systems, because the limiting photon noise in a one-cm maser would correspond to an effective noise temperature of approximately 1°K. Needless to say, the effective temperature limitation becomes much more serious if one talks in terms of masers in the infrared or submillimeter regions.

I-3. Practical Maser Configurations

A solid-state maser consists of a crystal mounted in a doubly resonant cavity that supports both the signal- and pump-frequency modes. The whole assembly, with appropriate coupling connections, is immersed in a double dewar system containing liquid helium in the inner chamber. In addition, an external magnetic field is supplied by a permanent or wire-wound magnet. From a circuit point of view, the cavity maser may be represented by a single terminal-pair negative resistance with the consequent system problems described in Chapter 15. Although it is possible to operate such an element without recourse to non-reciprocal circuit elements, the instabilities and loss of bandwidth are serious shortcomings. As of the present time, ferrite circulators are available at frequencies from 400 mcps to the millimeter range with insertion losses of the order of 0.5 db or less. This loss corresponds to an added system noise temperature of about 30 – 40°K and is generally not a hindrance in practical systems. The general circuit arrangement using a circulator is shown in Fig. 4. The ferrite device is either a three-port or four-port element which transmits with low insertion loss in the preferred direction shown and attenuates (20 db or more) any signal in the reverse direction. This system arrangement not only prevents receiver noise from entering the maser, but also directs all the amplified signal to the receiver rather than back to the antenna terminals. The coupling techniques utilizing simple reciprocal elements generally result in a high value of amplified signal on the input line with a consequent excessive sensitivity of gain to antenna reflection coefficient.

More recent versions of the maser utilize a traveling-wave structure.[2] In this technique a waveguide is loaded with the paramagnetic

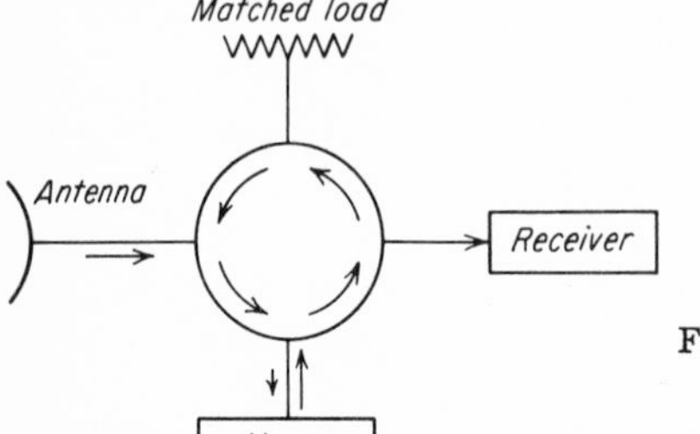

Fig. 4. Circulator connection for maser.

crystal, and the spins in the material are inverted by the propagation of the pump frequency along the structure. The signal frequency is now amplified as it moves down the waveguide in a manner similar to that in the cavity maser. The difference, however, is that large gains can be achieved by making the structure as long as is required by the constants of the material. In contrast, the cavity maser achieves high gain by high Q—that is, the incident signal is built up to a large amplitude by narrow-banding the cavity and thus creating the highest possible r-f magnetic field at the crystal. Thus, although the width of the electron energy levels corresponds to approximately 25—30 mc, appreciable gain is only obtained over the cavity bandwidth, which is usually in the 50-kilocycle to several-megacycle region. Since the waveguide structure is inherently a broadband system, there is no such limitation associated with the microwave design, and only the finite width of the electron energy levels limits the bandwidth. The gain in such a structure can be shown to be inversely proportional to the group velocity of the wave traveling through the structure. Physically this means that the longer the wave stays in a certain region of the guide the more photons are induced or more gain per unit length becomes available. As a result of this relationship, it is possible (by utilizing slow-wave structures) to design traveling-wave masers of small enough dimensions to fit inside a helium dewar.

One point of special significance should be emphasized. This is the inherent non-reciprocity of a traveling-wave structure, resulting from the gyromagnetic property of the electron spins. As a simple example of this phenomenon, consider the structure shown in Fig. 5, which consists of a simple waveguide with the maser material placed on only one side of the guide approximately 1/4 of the distance from the wall. If the dc magnetic field is now perpendicular to the broad face of the guide, the wave that will be amplified is the one that moves in such a direction as to produce circular polarization in the same sense as the spin precession. A wave traveling in the reverse direction will interact negligibly with the crystal. As a result, the guide will amplify in only one direction. In practice, although slow-wave structures are much more complicated than waveguides, they have definite regions of opposite circular polarization which can be uti-

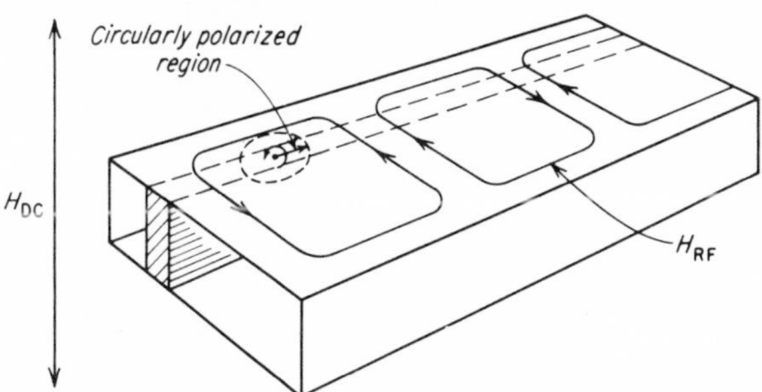

Fig. 5. Traveling-wave maser.

lized for this non-reciprocal behavior. Forward-to-reverse gain ratios as high as 10 to 1 can be obtained by use of the gyromagnetic properties of the maser material alone. In addition, it has been found quite practical to load the guide with heavily doped maser material which does not amplify, or with ferrite material placed in such a position that it absorbs the reverse wave.

Two typical slow-wave structures are shown in Fig. 6. The first is a comb structure developed by Bell Telephone Laboratories.[5] The second is the meander line developed at Stanford University.[6] The comb structure was initially designed and operated at 6000 megacycles while the meander-line version has been operated at 3000 megacycles. There is, however, no physical limitation on the frequency of operation since the structures can be scaled, assuming that appropriate maser crystals can be obtained which have the proper level spacing.

The traveling-wave maser has many advantages over the cavity maser in addition to its much wider bandwidth. In particular, the non-reciprocal behavior of the device results in appreciably reduced noise, which means that a circulator is not necessary for its use in low-noise circuits. Second, the growing-wave type of amplification is much more stable than the single-element, negative-resistance type. As an example, consider two masers operating with 20 db gain, one a cavity maser and the other a traveling-wave maser, and then allow a one-per-cent increase in amplification efficiency (caused by temperature fluctuation, for example). Then the cavity maser gain would increase by 0.8 db while the traveling-wave maser gain would only increase by 0.2 db. In the extreme case of a 10-per-cent change in efficiency, the cavity maser would approach infinite gain or oscillate while the traveling wave maser gain would only increase to 22 db.

The general characteristics of typical experimental masers are

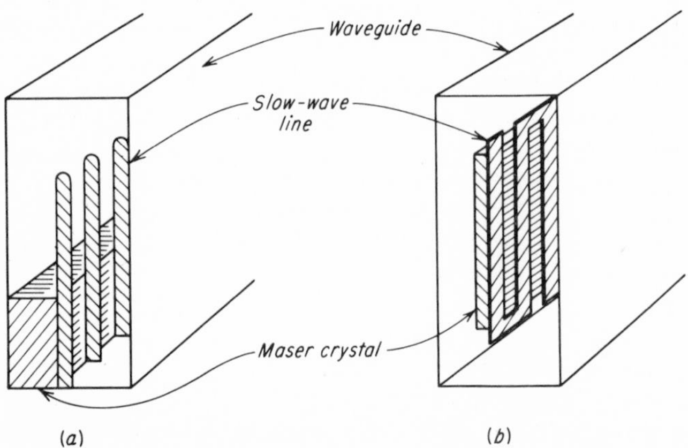

Fig. 6. Two slow-wave maser structures. a) Comb structure. b) Meander line.

TABLE I. Characteristics of Typical Experimental Masers

Freq. (mc)	Structure	Bandwidth (@ 20 db Gain)	Noise Temperature
440	cavity	50 kc	70°K
2800	cavity	100 kc	25°K
2800	TW	≈10 mc	—
6000	TW	>20 mc	17°K
9000	cavity	10 mc	30°K

shown in Table I. Note that the theoretical maser temperature as derived from the treatment in the previous section is well below the system temperature obtained in practice. The 2800-mc and 9000-mc cavity masers utilized a ferrite circulator for coupling, but the 440-mc device used a directional-coupler connection with a resultant high reflected signal intensity on the input line and also higher noise.

In conclusion, it is well to point out some of the difficulties in maser operation which may or may not bear on the design of long-range communication systems. First, there is the inconvenience of using and handling liquid helium for the cooling of the system. There is no immediate hope of developing materials that will operate at higher temperatures with practical bandwidths and reasonably low noise, but the possibility of a closed-cycle, helium-temperature refrigerator does offer some prospect of improvement in the situation. A second factor is related to our initial discussion of the technique of saturation of levels 1 and 3. In practical materials, such as ruby or potassium chromicyanide, the normal relaxation time of the lattice transitions is of the order of 1/10 of a second so that it is quite easy to overcome this normal rate by pump-induced transitions. This same factor, however, can be extremely serious in the signal transition system since the incoming signal may be so large that it saturates the f_{12} energy level configuration. In this case, it will require approximately a tenth of a second for level 2 to return to its quasi-equilibrium state. In this way, maser amplification is lost for a sufficiently long time that use in a radar system would be seriously impaired. Since the average power that will saturate the amplifying levels is the order of microwatts, it becomes necessary to design a radically different form of duplexer for protecting the maser from the radar leakage pulse. The attendant losses and possible noise generation add to the difficulties of utilizing the maser in such a system.

II. LOW-NOISE AMPLIFIER SYSTEMS

In this section we shall describe some practical operating systems and indicate the choice of different low-noise amplifiers for specific applications.

II-1. UHF Region

Since the nominal background temperature of cosmic noise below 300–400 mc is higher than 300°K, there is a real need for low-noise receivers only at frequencies in excess of 400 mc. Two typical applications in the 400-mc range are tropospheric scatter and long-range radar. In 1958, when the initial Venus radar experiments were performed, the only available low-noise receiver with noise temperatures of 100°K or less was the solid state maser. Although it performed satisfactorily in this experiment, there were several serious shortcomings; specifically, a narrow bandwidth of approximately 30 kc, critical tuning, and the usual problems in handling liquid helium. In addition, it was necessary to use an extremely unstable method of connection since there were no low-loss non-reciprocal devices at this frequency. Since that time, the parametric amplifier has been developed to such a stage that it is now quite competitive at these frequencies and it offers greater bandwidth and ease of operation. At this frequency it is possible to use either the up-conversion scheme of operation or the single-port negative resistance mode. The up-converter offers somewhat better stability and more bandwidth; however, it does not promise as low a noise temperature as the negative-resistance method. Although operating experience at this time is not sufficient for a complete comparison, it seems perfectly feasible to plan on systems that have bandwidths of several mc and noise temperatures in the 50–100°K range. Since sky noise and noise due to antenna loss is of the 50–100°K order of magnitude, it is doubtful that more sensitive receivers would have a practical system advantage. The same arguments may be applied for radar with the additional fact that the parametric amplifier does not saturate on such small signals as the maser. The UHF maser used in the Venus experiment normally saturates at a 10^{-9}-watt level. This makes the duplexing problem extraordinarily difficult. Parametric amplifiers, on the other hand, do not saturate until the milliwatt level and even under these conditions their recovery is quite rapid.

The electron-beam parametric tube developed by Adler[7] represents a new type of parametric amplifier that is particularly interesting at UHF. For normal-communications reception this tube yields noise temperatures in the 200°K range, but this higher temperature is compensated by bandwidths of the order of 20–30 mc, and an inherent non-reciprocity that eliminates many of the antenna coupling problems present in the usual parametric amplifier and the maser. The Adler tube also shows promise of successful operation at the higher frequencies.

II-2. L Band

One of the most interesting applications of low-noise receivers in the L-band region is the detection of the hydrogen line radiation at approximately 1420 mc. At present, results with either the maser or the parametric amplifier have not been reported; however, many groups are building and preparing to operate such systems. The difficulty here lies in the bandwidth and exceptional gain stability required. The cavity maser at 1400 mc has only a marginal bandwidth for the application, specifically, about 1 or 2 mc at the requisite gain. In addition, the regenerative mode of operation of the cavity maser leads to inherent instability in the gain. In comparison, the traveling-wave maser structure offers, much broader bandwidth (up to 20 or 30 mc) and a much superior gain stability. The parametric amplifier also shows some promise in this region, and although its noise temperature is not comparable with that of the maser, it does have an inherent bandwidth that is much greater than that of the cavity maser structure. Certainly, for many communications and radar applications the parametric amplifier would be the logical choice where antenna and sky temperatures are 100°K and higher and where saturation would be a serious shortcoming. Receiver noise temperatures in the 50–100°K region are presently feasible in such amplifiers.

II-3. S and C Bands

The frequency range from approximately 3000 to 6000 mc is of special interest because it is in this range that sky temperatures are 10°K or less. This is also the range in which the parametric amplifier noise temperatures are far from competing with those of the maser. Traveling-wave maser structures may be built at these frequencies with overall system noise temperatures in the 10–20°K region. The bandwidths to be expected are also in the 20–30 mc range. Perhaps the most significant experiment along these lines is the use of a 6000 mc maser structure on a 28-foot antenna at the Bell Laboratories.[8] The overall system noise including the antenna and amplifier was measured to be approximately 20°K. This is, undoubtedly, the lowest system noise temperature reported to date. The parametric amplifier still offers some advantages in the lower part of the 3–6 Kmc frequency spectrum and it is expected that in the near future it may be competitive with masers in the 6000-mc and higher range. In particular, for radar applications, where the noise associated with the duplexer and antenna transmission line is the limiting factor, a parametric amplifier having 100–200°K noise temperature offers many advantages. Recently, complete systems have been operated with an overall noise less than 300°K, which is still a marked improvement over conventional receivers using crystal mixers.

II-4. X-Band and Higher Frequencies

At the present time, parametric amplifiers have not been used successfully at these higher frequencies, although noise figures as low as 3db have been reported at X-band. Maser structures, in contrast, yield noise temperatures in the 20 to 30°K range even at these frequencies, although transmission-line losses are more serious and waveguide connections are a necessity. In addition, much higher bandwidths are available in cavity structures because of the higher quantum energies and more sophisticated pumping techniques. Certainly, for the immediate future the maser offers the best low-noise system, until better varactor diodes or more radical parametric methods are developed.

Above X-band, masers are still in the early development stages. The most recent results indicate operation at wavelengths of several milimeters, but detailed systems have not been reported.

REFERENCES

1. J. Weber, "Masers", *Rev. Mod. Phys.*, vol. 31, pp. 681-710, July, 1959.
2. J. R. Singers, *Masers*, John Wiley and Sons, New York, 1959.
3. J. P. Gordon, H. J. Zeiger, and C. H. Townes, "The Maser—New Type of Microwave Amplifier, Frequency Standard, and Spectrometer," *Phys. Rev.*, vol. 99, pp. 1264-1274; August 15, 1955.
4. N. Bloembergen, "Proposal for a New Type Solid State Maser", *Phys. Rev.*, vol. 104, pp. 324-327; October 15, 1956.
5. Ref. 2, Chapter 7.
6. J. Cromack and A. Siegman, (to be published).
7. R. Adler, G. Hrbek, and G. Wade, "The Quadripole Amplifier, a Low-Noise Parametric Device'', *Proc. I.R.E.*, vol. 47, pp. 1713-1723, October, 1959.
8. R. W. DeGrasse, D. C. Hogg, E. A. Ohm, and H. E. D. Scovil, "Ultra-Low-Noise Measurements Using a Horn Reflector Antenna and a Traveling-Wave Maser," *Journ. App. Phys.*, vol. 30, p. 2013, December, 1959.

CHAPTER 18

Performance Criteria of Speech Systems

Irwin Pollack

I. INTRODUCTION

In this chapter, an attempt is made to characterize communication channels in terms of criteria of effective performance from the point of view of the human operators employing the systems. The discussion will, thus, be concerned primarily with terminal criteria of performance rather than sub-system criteria. A further restriction is that speech communication systems will be primarily considered, despite the well-documented publications in the photographic and television systems areas.

The plan is, first, to examine criteria of effective performance of communication systems; and, second, to consider calculation procedures for predicting the effectiveness of a speech communication system from a consideration of the available acoustical characteristics.

II. CRITERIA OF PERFORMANCE

Criteria of communication system performance can be artibrarily classified in the following manner:

a. *Source reproducibility* or the intelligibility of the materials—to what extent are the materials at the source duplicated at the location of the receiver;
b. *Source identification*—to what extent can the receiver identify the source;
c. *Source quality*—to what extent are factors other than the first two, such as the mood or intent of the source, effectively communicated.

Let us consider each criterion in some detail.

A. Source Reproducibility

The basic task of a communication system is to reproduce, at the location of the receiver, materials available at the source. Indeed, communication systems that fail in this task usually will fail to meet all other criteria imposed upon the system.

1. Fidelity vs reproducibility—Reproducibility, however, is not necessarily equivalent to the fidelity of reproduction. It is of little interest whether a teletype message that originates with one type-face terminates with another type-face. The problem of reproducibility essentially boils down to the definition of the functional unit of communication.

Consider first the example of a long-distance radio teletype system. If the individual alphabetic character is adopted as the unit of this system, the performance of such a system may be specified in terms of the percentage of alphabetic characters that are successfully transmitted.

What criterion of performance, in terms of alphabetic units, should be demanded of the teletype code? From the point of view of the human operators employing the system, the question may be rephrased: What percentage of the alphabetic units can be distorted, with a satisfactory reproduction of the materials available to the source? This question has been put to experimental test by Miller and Friedman.[1] They introduced five types of distortion at random upon English text, and instructed observers to recreate the original text. Among the types of distortion employed were the insertion of extra alphabetic characters, and the deletion and substitution of alphabetic characters with and without marking of the point of deletion or substitution.

The results obtained by these investigators can be summarized as follows: nearly 10% of the alphabetic characters can be mutilated under any of the procedures with nearly perfect reconstruction. On the other hand, some procedures are more effective than others. In terms of increasing resistance to reconstruction, the procedures ranked as follows: insertion, deletion, indicated substitution, abbreviation, and substitution.

It may be noted that we have begged the question of what constitutes a satisfactory performance level for reproduction of the source materials. The actual criterion selected will depend, in large measure, upon operational criteria outside of the communication system. In any event, the decision will be based upon a unit of measurement appropriate to the system.

The importance of the definition of the unit of measurement for the reproduction of speech materials was recognized from the earliest days of articulation testing at the Bell Telephone Laboratories.[2] Test scores were obtained for individual speech sounds, nonsense syllables, monosyllabic words and sentences. It was observed, for example, that a score of 93% correct reproduction of sentences could be achieved under conditions that yielded only 35% correct reproduction of nonsense syllables. As a further illustration, one design criterion often employed for speech communication systems (an Articulation Index of 0.5) aims for a monosyllabic word reproduction of 70% correct which is equivalent to a sentence intelligibility of about 98% correct.

2. Information of the message source—The differences in reproducibility among the various materials are, of course, related to the informational uncertainty of the source of possible materials. The role of the size of the message source has been examined in detail by Miller, Heise, and Lichten for speech materials.[3] They employed a large pool (1,000) of monosyllabic words and selected, at random,

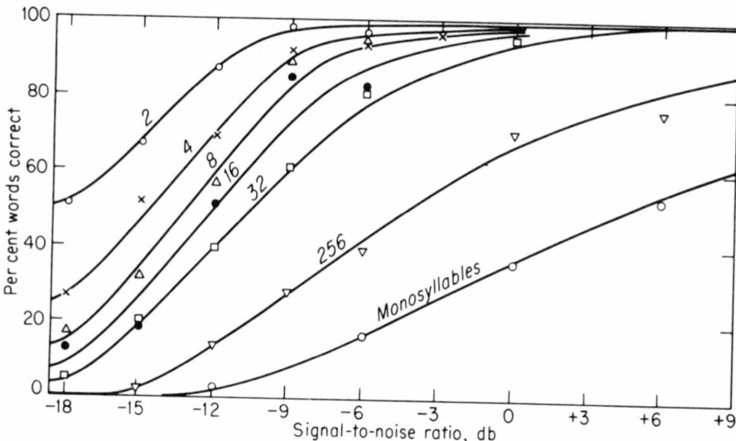

Fig. 1. The effect of size of message set on word intelligibility in noise. The parameter is the number of equally likely monosyllabic words that comprised the message and response sets. Data have not been corrected for effects of chance response. (After Miller, Heise, and Lichten, Reference 3.)

several sets of 2, 4, 8, 16, 32 and 256 words from the pool. Each message set was known to both the listeners and the speakers. The average results obtained with the restricted message sets, as well as the initial pool of words, are presented in Fig. 1. The abscissa is the speech-to-noise ratio under test. The ordinate is the average percentage of words correctly reproduced. The parameter is the size of the message set. It is noted that, for a given communication channel condition, nearly perfect monosyllabic word intelligibility can be achieved with small message sets, whereas nearly zero intelligibility was obtained with the same words within large message sets. Several additional studies have since verified the major conclusion of the Miller, Heise, and Lichten paper: namely, the word intelligibility achieved with a communication system is sensitive to the information of the set of materials employed. It has been shown that the index of signal detectability—a measure closely related to the information measure—is invariant over the size of the message set.[4]

A practical application of the informational characteristics of the materials may be found in a now classical human engineering analysis of Air Defense Command communications. The question to be resolved by an Air Force-Bell Telephone team was whether the Air Defense Command should employ standard telephone lines or should employ extended-range, high-fidelity lines for long-distance transmission of routine fix information. Preliminary analysis showed that the desired intelligibility could not be achieved over the required distances with standard telephone lines, on the assumption that messages were composed of isolated monosyllabic words or their equivalent. Dr. Frederick Frick, now of the Lincoln Laboratory, analyzed the communications traffic over the Air Defense lines and found that actual information transmitted over the lines was extremely limited. The reduced vocabulary size was sufficient to change the preliminary recommendation of high-fidelity lines to the recommendation in favor of the standard long-distance lines. The resultant savings to the taxpayer was many millions of dollars per year.

3. Other considerations—Two extremely important aspects of speech communication systems in considering the criterion of reproducibility have been ignored. First, a joint time-accuracy criterion upon the system is usually desired rather than an accuracy criterion alone. Under favorable communication conditions, indeed, the number of requested repeats, or the total channel utilization required to complete a given set of messages, may be an extremely useful measure of communication system performance.[5] The difficulty encountered with such a joint time-accuracy criterion of system performance is that the measure of performance is critically dependent on the criterion of accuracy demanded by the receiver. Thus, the procedure does not lend itself to engineering specification as directly as the intelligibility testing procedure previously considered.

Another aspect of speech communication system performance that has been ignored here is that speech communication systems exist primarily to provide direct feed-back between source and receiver. In fact, if two-way communication is not required, speech communication systems may be quite wasteful in bandwidth. The reproducibility of the source at the location of the receiver, previously considered, regards communications only as a one-way link. And, thus, the approach is unrealistic. However, the difficulties encountered in the analysis of two-way communications situations (*e.g.*, the criterion demanded by each receiver)[6] are usually sufficiently great that, for purposes of engineering specification, the standard intelligibility testing procedure is preferred.

B. Source Identification

The second criterion of interest is that of identifying the source of communications. Even for certain military speech communication systems, it may be desirable for security purposes to identify the speaker. Speaker identification is demanded by the telephone user. In fact, one of the prime objections to initial versions of the Vocoder (which lacked a pitch channel) was that speaker identification was nearly impossible although its source reproducibility was fair. Requirements for voice identification have also been considered for military speech communication systems on the basis of security and identification.

The available experimental evidence on speaker identification is scanty. The little experimental data that are available, however, indicate that the factors that determine the source reproducibility of speech systems (*e.g.*, frequency range) similarly determine source identification.[7] In addition to specification of the communication system configuration, it is important to specify: (1) the number of talkers to be identified; (2) the duration of the speech sample available for identification; and, (3) the speaker's voice level.

C. Source Quality

We now turn to a set of criteria for communication systems for which easily specified yardsticks of measurement are not available. Little may be known about the system factors that determine the absolute accuracy of source identification, but, at least, a given level of source identification performance can be specified. But, how do we specify a given level of performance in identifying the naturalness, mood, etc., of the source?

The problem is not trivial. If it is desired that the President of the United States broadcast a message to the peoples of the world, as with a satellite-relay system, we might demand something more than he be identified and understood. We might also demand that he be able to project his unique personality and that he be able to transmit an intended mood. It is difficult even to define such terms satisfactorily.

For the most part, we have been unsuccessful in specifying the aspects of source quality. One notable exception is recent work in Japan[8] on the scaling of naturalness of communications. At best, we must rely upon transfer standards. That is, a reference system is chosen, degraded in specific ways, and all other systems are then equated to the reference system. This method is not unlike that of the early specification of the hardness of minerals.

In partial summary, the reproducibility of materials of the source at the location of the receiver has been found to be a useful and reliable terminal criterion of communication system performance. Of course, the materials employed and the unit of measurement must be specified. And, furthermore, speech communication systems that perform well with respect to the criterion of reproducibility usually also perform well with respect to other criteria of performance. It should be pointed out, however, that complex speech processing systems may violate the interrelationship of criteria. For example, one of the most ambitious narrow-band speech communications systems attempts to recognize individual speech sounds, transmit the information by teletype channels, and to recreate speech by a canned library at the receiver. Nearly perfect source reproducibility (as defined here) might possibly be achieved by the system, but source identification and source quality may be totally absent.

III. CALCULATION PROCEDURES FOR SPEECH REPRODUCIBILITY

We now turn to the description of calculation procedures for predicting the reproducibility of speech communication systems. Since the procedure is described in step-by-step detail in several publications,[9,10] the primary aim of the present discussion will simply be to outline the basis of the procedure.

A. The Articulation Index

The Articulation Index procedure for predicting communication system performance reflects two important parameters of communication system design: frequency range and gain. This procedure, developed at the Bell Telephone Laboratories,[11] is based upon two points: first, some speech frequencies are more important for intelligibility than others; and second, speech must be heard to be understood. These points are reflected in the procedure by differentially weighting the various speech frequencies and by determining how much of the speech can be heard above interfering noise.

The weighting of the speech frequency range was initially obtained by running intelligibility tests under various restrictions of the speech frequency range. These data permit the division of the speech frequency range into bands of equal intelligibility. The speech frequency range is divided into 20 frequency bands for the Articulation Index procedure. The weighting of the gain factor was obtained by running tests at different speech-to-noise ratios. It has been found that the contribution to intelligibility is nearly complete when the long-time speech spectrum level exceeds the noise spectrum level by 18 db in the entire band. Similarly, little contribution to intelligibility is observed when the noise spectrum level exceeds the speech spectrum level by 12 db in the entire band. Between the extremes of the 30-db range, each decibel improvement is associated with approximately an equal gain in intelligibility.

The combination of 20 frequency bands and 30 speech-to-noise ratios yields a domain of 600 possible combinations. The Articulation Index is simply that proportion of the entire 600 combinations available to the communication system under consideration. As such, the Articulation Index is simply a frequency-weighted speech-to-noise ratio.

A useful rule of thumb for design specification is that an Articulation Index of about 0.5 is associated with a monosyllabic word score of about 70% correct and a sentence intelligibility score of about 98% correct. Stated differently, this says that if one can achieve a speech-to-noise ratio, measured on a spectrum level basis, of 3 db in each of the 20 speech frequency bands, the communication system should be capable of yielding nearly perfect reproducibility upon connected discourse. (These calculations assume that the speech signal has been measured on a "long-time" basis. If a VU meter is employed to measure speech levels, the preceding estimate must be increased by about 4 db).

B. Extensions of the Articulation Index

There are many parameters other than frequency range and signal-to-noise ratio that must be considered in the design of a system. However, if one is willing to extend the computation procedure (and thus complicate it), additional factors may be evaluated. Let us look briefly at three of these:

1. **Amplitude distortion**—Speech comes in a very inefficient package in that the instantaneous amplitude distribution of speech extends over an extremely wide range[12]. Furthermore, the consonant sounds that primarily determine speech intelligibility are considerably weaker than the vowel sounds. It seems reasonable, therefore, that a repackaging of the speech waveform might improve intelligibility in noise. Indeed, it does[13]. With symmetrical peak clipping imposed on "noise-free" speech, the improvement achieved is nearly exactly the improvement in speech power achieved for a given peak output[14]. For example, 24 db of symmetrical peak slipping with subsequent reamplification to the initial peak level increases the speech power by 12 db, and this is about the improvement achieved with 24 db of peak clipping. Furthermore, it may be noted that not all forms of amplitude distortion will buy gain in intelligibility. In fact, symmetrical peak clipping may be contra-indicated if speech is mixed with strong low-frequency noise components before clipping.

2. **Sharp discontinuities in the noise spectrum**—Noise affects a receiver to the extent that it denies the system, machine or human, ability to make the required discriminations. Thus, we should be concerned with the *masking* spectrum of the noise rather than its acoustical spectrum. For broad-band noises with no sharp discontinuities, the two spectra are nearly equivalent. For noises with sharp discontinuities in frequency, the masking spectrum may extend far beyond the acoustical spectrum. The "spread of masking" depends on the level of the noise and tends to be greater toward the higher speech frequencies than toward the lower speech frequencies. The rules for determining "spread of masking" have recently been codified[15].

3. **Temporal intermittancy of speech and noise**—One of the prime problems of long-distance radio communications is the temporal variation in the signal-to-noise ratio, whether achieved by fading in the transmission path or by intermittant noise bursts in the medium.

Extensive laboratory investigations of the effect of speech intermittancy and noise intermittancy (both regular and random) have been reported[16]. It is difficult to summarize all the results because of the necessary specification of a large number of parameters. Among these are: the fraction of the time the speech is available; the rate of intermittancy of the speech; the fraction of the time the noise is available; the rate of intermittancy of the noise; the speech-to-noise ratio; and the temporal patterning of the intermittancy.

Among the generalizations that are warranted are:

(1) Intelligibility improves as the rate of speech intermittancy increases and as the rate of noise intermittancy decreases. Moreover, there is a range of speech and/or noise interruption rates between 10 and 20 interruptions per second in which intelligibility is relatively high.

(2) Intelligibility improves as the speech-time fraction increases or the noise-time fraction decreases.

(3) Extremely rapid rates of noise intermittancy (200 per second or higher) act effectively as a continuous noise source of the equivalent average noise level.

(4) Extremely slow rates of speech or noise intermittancy (1 per second or less) act effectively as distributed sources. That is, one can obtain the mean intelligibility by calculating the separate intelligibilities of each of several states and weighting the states in terms of their relative occurrence. For example, assume that we are faced with a noise situation that, on the average, is in State A for 80% of the time and in State B for the other 20% of the time and that these periods are well distributed in time. We would simply calculate the Articulation Index for the 80% interval and the 20% interval separately, and weight the two states to get the average Articulation Index. However, the usual transformations between nonsense syllables, words and sentences, observed under continuous noise may be seriously disturbed under intermittant conditions.

IV. CONCLUDING REMARKS

Specification of what is wanted from a speech communication system will *not* build the system. If sufficient factors are known, however, specification may assist the engineering design. A graded series of criteria may be organized in the order of our state of knowledge: source reproducibility, source identification, and source quality. Most of the discussion of this chapter has been spent with the criterion of source reproducibility for two reasons. First, more data are available with respect to this criterion than any others. Second, at least for systems not involving extreme speech processing operations, source reproducibility is closely related to other criteria.

We have also discussed a rationale for computing the efficiency of a speech communication system to transport materials to a human receiver. We have looked at some of the limitations of the procedure and have indicated to what conditions the procedure might be profitably extended. One word of caution: The procedures have been worked out primarily for direct-wire audio communication systems or for audio systems without extensive speech processing. We know very little about how processed speech stands up to additional channel distortions.

REFERENCES

1. G. A. Miller and E. A. Friedman, "The Reconstruction of Mutilated English Messages," *Information and Control*, vol. 1, pp. 38-55, 1957.
2. H. Fletcher, *Speech and Hearing in Communication*, D. Van

Nostrand, Inc., Princeton, N.J., 1953. Especially Chap. 15 and references cited therein.
3. G. A. Miller, G. A. Heise, and W. Lichten, "The Intelligibility of Speech as a Function of the Context of the Test Materials," *J. Expt. Psychol.*, vol. 41, pp. 329-335, 1951.
4. D. M. Green and T. G. Birdsall, "The Effect of Vocabulary Size on Articulation Score," Electronic Defense Group, University of Michigan, AFCRC TR 57-58, January, 1958.
5. I. Pollack, "Message Procedures for Unfavorable Communication Conditions," *J. Acoust. Soc. Am.*, vol. 30, pp. 196-201, 1958.
6. J. P. Egan, F. R. Clarke, and E. C. Carterette, "On the Transmission and Confirmation of Messages in Noise," *J. Acoust. Soc. Am.*, vol. 28, pp. 536-550, 1956.
7. I. Pollack, J. M. Pickett, and W. H. Sumby, "On the Identification of Speakers by Voice," *J. Acoust. Soc. Am.*, vol. 26, pp. 403-406, 1954.
8. T. Koshikawa, "The Factors of Transmitting Systems Affecting the Materialness of Speech" (in Japanese, English summary), *J. Acoust. Soc. Japan*, pp. 164-169, 1958.
9. L. L. Beranek, "The Design of Speech Communication Systems," *Proc. IRE*, vol. 35, pp. 880-890, 1947.
10. M. E. Hawley and K. D. Kryter, "Effects of Noise on Speech," Chap. 9 in C. M. Harris (ed.), *Handbook of Noise Control*, McGraw-Hill Book Company, Inc., New York, 1957.
11. N. R. French and J. C. Steinberg, "Factors Governing the Intelligibility of Speech Sounds," *J. Acoust. Soc. Am.*, vol. 19, pp. 90-119, 1949.
12. W. B. Davenport, "Speech-wave Probability Distributions," *J. Acoust. Soc. Am.*, vol. 24, pp. 390-399, 1952.
13. J. C. R. Licklider, "Effects of Amplitude Distortion upon the Intelligibility of Speech," *J. Acoust. Soc. Am.*, vol. 18, pp. 429-434, 1946.
14. W. Wathen-Dunn and D. W. Lipke, "On the Power Gained by Clipping Speech in the Audio Band," *J. Acoust. Soc. Am.*, vol. 30, pp. 36-40, 1958.
15. K. D. Kryter, "Human Engineering Principles for the Design of Speech Communication Systems," AFCRC TR 58-62, U.S. Department of Commerce, Office of Technical Services, Washington, D.C., 1958.
16. G. A. Miller and J. C. R. Licklider, "The Intelligibility of Interrupted Speech," *J. Acoust. Soc. Am.*, vol. 22, pp. 167-173, 1950.

CHAPTER 19

Analog Modulation Systems

Elie J. Baghdady

I. INTRODUCTION

One of the most important steps in the design of a communication system is the selection of the type of modulation to be used. Modulation may be generally defined as the process whereby a message is transformed from its original form into a signal that is more suitable for transmission and processing to meet needs imposed by specific circumstances. Mathematically, modulation may be described as the process of mapping from a message space to a signal space, and in its more conventional interpretation, modulation is often understood to signify a continuous reversible mapping with a limitation on memory, in which a small change in the message leads only to a small change in the signal. In this way modulation and coding can be distinguished. In the last analysis, coding is a method of message or signal characterization, and modulation is the final transformation of the message, coded or uncoded, into the desired signal space.

The transformation from message space to signal space fundamentally amounts to a translation of the spectrum. In systems like AM, the translation is effected without any attendant change in the relative energy distribution with frequency of the spectral components that carry the message specifications. In the case of frequency-or phase-modulation systems, the message spectrum reappears in a different frequency region with a spectral distribution for the energy in the message-carrying components that is different from the original distribution. The requirement for distortionless reversibility of the transformation rules out nonlinear dependence of the modulated parameter of the carrier signal upon the message fluctuations.

In this chapter we shall discuss some of the important considerations that affect the choice of the type of modulation in the design of a communication system. The discussion will start with a brief survey of modulation methods and their evolution. This is followed by a discussion of some basic types of modulation and of some special aspects of the analysis of linear-system response to modulated signals, including the conditions for low-distortion transmission of modulated sinusoids through linear, frequency-selective systems. The major emphasis shifts thereafter to the effect of the receiver signal-processing techniques upon the sensitivity of AM and FM systems to interference from undesired signals, to random thermal-type noise, and to impulsive disturbances. No discussion of the effects of multiplicative disturbances that cause fading rates comparable with or faster than the message modulation rates will be attempted. This subject is not sufficiently well understood at the present time, not only because of the analytical complexities of the situation but also because of the lack of sufficient experimental data, particularly on the characteristics of the phase fluctuations.

II. GENERAL DISCUSSION

2.1 Preparation of Message for Transmission

The original message is frequently in a form that is not suitable for transmission over a desired medium. At the transmitting end, the fundamental problem is to translate the message into a form that is more suitable for transmission over the desired medium, and at the same time is relatively immune to the effects of intervening sources of disturbances. The process of preparing the signal for transmission often involves

(a) A message representation procedure (such as coding) that recognizes the identifying characteristics of the message and translates these characteristics into a language that is known to the intended receiver. The purpose of this operation is
    1) to capitalize on the ability of transmitter and receiver to contrive in advance to minimize the effects of anticipated sources of disturbance upon the quality or accuracy of the received message; and
    2) to meet basic information transmission requirements for improved efficiency and reliability in the use of the available communication channel in the presence of anticipated forms of noise.

(b) Modulation processes for converting the message from its original form (or any coded or uncoded representation of it) into a new form that is more suitable for processing in transit between the message source and the message destination or ultimate user.

What we have been calling "messages" is usually referred to as "baseband signals" to distinguish them from their derived frequency translates, the modulated signals.

The need for modulation arises for a variety of reasons. Among these, we note the following:

(i) The message-carrying disturbance often must be transformed from one form of energy into another. Usually, the conversion is from some nonelectrical phenomenon into an electrical signal at the sending end, and the reverse may or may not be necessary at the receiving end. Some examples are sound to electrical fluctuations; light to a waveform whose spectrum is centered about much lower frequencies (and therefore can be processed by available circuitry); mechanical movement or stress or pressure, etc., into electric current fluctuations.

(ii) Important portions of the message spectrum, (often the whole spectrum) usually involve frequencies that are too low for efficient radiation with antennas of reasonable and practical sizes. By translating the spectrum into high-frequency regions, the process of modulation enables efficient radiation of message-bearing signals whose wavelengths require radiators of reasonable dimensions for efficient radiation. Other equipment design problems are simplified and greater uniformity of transmission characteristics is assured by the attendant reduction in fractional bandwidth occupancy of the message.

(iii) The need for simultaneous transmission of several different messages having overlapping spectra, over the same transmission medium, without serious impairment of the transmitted messages, and without making it impossible to separate the transmitted messages, can be satisfied only through modulation processes. For example, simultaneous transmission of different messages with overlapping spectra is often achieved by assigning different high-frequency spaces for the different messages, and the modulation process then serves to displace the spectrum that carries the message into a preassigned high-frequency channel.

A fundamental requirement for the generation of the desired type of modulation is the use of a *carrier*. A carrier is a waveform whose principal attributes are (1) that it be distinguishable and separable from other carriers; (2) that it possess significant parameters that could be varied to carry informative fluctuations; and (3) that it be transmittable with adequate economy and efficiency. In some systems the carrier is retained partially or fully as a constituent of the final signal, in others it is completely suppressed. Multiple modulation operations are also widely used, especially in telemetry, in which various messages modulate corresponding carriers in some suitable fashion, and the sum of these in turn modulates an ultimate carrier. The carriers used in the intermediate modulation steps are usually called *subcarriers*.

The choice of carrier waveform and type of modulation is usually based upon the choice of transmission medium, type of multiplexing, imposed constraints on bandwidth or power, as well as considerations of system simplicity, compatibility with other systems, and performance in the presence of noise and interference introduced in the transmission medium. A carrier must be characterized by some property or event that makes it distinguishable from other carriers of the same or different class that may be present simultaneously. For example, a sinusoidal carrier may be distinguished by its frequency f, its phase ϕ, or its amplitude A. A pulsed carrier may be distinguished by the time of occurrence of its leading edge, trailing edge, center of the time interval in which the pulse occurs, the amplitude of the pulse, etc.

2.2 Multiplexing

The simultaneous transmission of a multiplicity of signals over the same transmission facility is spoken of as multiplexing. In the multiplexing process, a composite signal that is appropriate for transmission over the designated facility is synthesized from the various message-bearing waveforms and a suitable carrier or carriers, in such a way that the several message-carrying waveforms can still be recovered with some degree of accuracy.

Sinusoidal high-frequency carriers having different and easily separable frequencies may be used. Each carrier may be modulated by only one of the messages, and the separation of the messages may be achieved by selective filters that are tunable to one modulated carrier at a time. This is called *frequency-division multiplexing.* Indeed the use of sinusoidal carriers permits multiplexing by frequency division, by phase discrimination, by amplitude discrimination, as well as by independent modulation of the positive half and negative half of a sine wave.

Alternatively, one may use several pulse carriers that are so timed that their individual pulses can be adequately discerned. Each pulse carrier may then be modulated in some way by only one of the messages. The proper separation of the carriers at the receiving end may then be achieved by proper gating. This is called *time-division multiplexing*.

More generally, we may interpret the fundamental principle of multiplexing as being the deliberate creation of fundamental differences, either between the carriers or between the modulations impressed on the same carrier, which will enable circuits that can distinguish these differences to separate the desired from the simultaneously transmitted undesired messages. The successful separation of the transmitted messages involves, fundamentally, the solution of an interference problem. Carriers can be made easily distinguishable, and hence separable, on the basis of carrier frequency or phase, or on the basis of the time of occurrence of an event that characterizes the carrier. Modulations can be made distinguishable either through the use of subcarriers, if all of the messages are to modulate the same parameter of the ultimate carrier, or through the modulation of separate distinguishable parameters of the carrier by separate messages, or by a combination of both.

The possibility of assigning limited frequency bands for the various types of messages and the corresponding modulated signals has made it feasible to transmit simultaneously a multiplicity of messages by frequency-division multiplexing. The fact that band-limited waveforms are specifiable completely and unambiguously by a set of properly timed or (spaced) samples (or instantaneous measurements) has made it feasible to transmit a multiplicity of messages through the same communication facility by time-division multiplexing. The most general class of carriers that are suitable for multiplex transmission is a set of orthogonal functions.

2.3 Evolution of Modulation Systems

The various stages of evolution in modulation techniques have been motivated by corresponding evolutions in the performance criteria of communication systems. The desire to devise systems of real-time telecommunication led to the introduction of the electrical signal carrier. With the availability of workable systems of code and voice transmission, the need to communicate with minimum distortion of signal arose. Subsequent developments led to increased demands on accuracy, and the evolution of other sophisticated needs, such as greater efficiency in processing and transmission of information, better use of frequency space, better use of time available for transmission, etc.

Early in the communication art, the sinusoidal carrier was found easy to generate, modulate, and transmit. In particular, amplitude modulation became widely used because of the simplicity of instrumenting AM systems. With the evolution of the vacuum tube and the techniques of filtering and electronic processing of signals, the potentialities of AM systems were quickly exploited, and serious limitations on the overall system performance were discovered to lie with the great sensitivity to noise, interference, and distortion. It was soon realized that these disturbances modulated the amplitude of the signal carrier in much the same way that the desired messages did. Consequently, no simple ways were available in which the receiving circuits that were designed to extract the desired message could be made to ignore the accompanying noise effects. Only impulsive interference resulted in clearly distinguishable sharp spikes and it was combatted with reasonable success by ''noise-silencing'' spike-clipping schemes.

It thus became clear that a cure for susceptibility to the natural disturbances lay in the adoption of a modulation process that could not be readily imitated by the random natural disturbances. E. H. Armstrong[1] reasoned that the randomness of natural phenomena set a limitation on the coordination with which the various random noise components could act to produce consistently large deviations of the frequency of a signal carrier. Thus, if the desired message was made to produce instantaneous deviations in the frequency of the carrier which greatly exceeded those that the random noise components could cause, material improvement in fidelity of transmission should result. Wideband FM was thus invented, and the possibility of improving system performance in the presence of noise by widening, rather than narrowing, the frequency-space occupancy of the modulated carrier was thus demonstrated. The penalty for this appeared to be in the form of a relatively high threshold that the signal must exceed in order to overcome the noise.

Meanwhile, the discovery that a continuous message waveform that has a spectrum of finite extent could be completely and uniquely recovered from a set of properly timed samples pointed out that discrete and not only continuous specifications of the message waveform were permissible. Immediately a new type of carrier was utilized which offered at least three important parameters for modulation by discrete samples. A series of periodically recurring pulses may be modulated in amplitude, each pulse having its height stretched or compressed by one sample of the message waveform. This is called *pulse-amplitude modulation* (PAM). Alternately, the time of occurrence of either the leading or the trailing edge of each pulse, or both, may be varied from the position of exact periodicity by the samples to produce *pulse-duration modulation* (PDM). One can even modulate by introducing or eliminating a pulse (presence or absence of a pulse). Finally, one may choose to vary the position of each of the pulses on the time scale in accordance with the values of the samples. This is called *pulse-position modulation* (PPM).

Pulse-amplitude modulation did not offer any important advantages over AM or FM. On the other hand, the pulse-time (PDM and PPM) systems exhibited the feature of trading bandwidth for signal-to-noise ratio characteristic of FM, again with the provision that the peak signal exceed the peak noise which imposed a sharp threshold for acceptable performance.

Finally, the realization that in practice it is not possible to transmit the exact value of a sample, neither as a pulse height, nor as a pulse position or duration sparked the search for better message representation or "signal selection". Noise and interference intervene to introduce changes in modulated-carrier parameters that make it impossible to guess the exact intended value of the message sample with certainty at the receiving end. Consequently, it soon became realized that as long as the errors were introduced by phenomena beyond the control of the operator, uncontrollable errors would always be present. The transmission of sample values which could vary continuously over some range would always be susceptible to uncontrollable and unpredictable errors. On the other hand, if it is agreed beforehand, between transmitter and receiver, that within a specified range of expected sample values only certain discrete (or quantized) levels would be allowed, then at the transmitter the allowed value nearest the true value of a sample is sent, while at the receiver, the allowed value nearest the actual received value is guessed as the value intended by the transmitter. If the uncontrollable error introduced by the noise is not allowed to exceed one-half the difference between any two successive allowed levels then the guess of the receiver will always be correct. Clearly, quantizing the sampled values of a signal will introduce a maximum error of one-half a quantum step in the value of each transmitted sample. But this is an error which the designer can control within the limitations of the necessary instrumentation and the noise contribution of the transmission medium. Thus, the quantization scheme enables the replacement of uncontrollable noise that contaminates the signal during its transmission (and thus prevents the receiver from guessing the true sample value sent by the transmitter) by deliberate but controllable noise (called quantization noise) that contaminates the message waveform before modulating the carrier and enables the receiver to guess correctly the actual modulating wave.

Furthermore, with only a certain finite number of allowed discrete values for the samples, the message representation process could be made so elaborate that the random natural phenomena would be unable to imitate it. A code group of pulses could be devised to describe uniquely each of the discrete levels and the information conveyed by each of the samples could then be transmitted with almost complete immunity to noise, interference, and distortion. If the code group is made up of on or off pulses, no particular parameter of the pulse is of importance as long as there is a sufficient indication of the presence or absence of a pulse. Once the presence of a pulse is recognized it could be reconstructed in exactly the same form as it was first generated at the transmitter, and the code groups may therefore either be decoded to extract the message or re-transmitted over the next lap of the transmission path. This type of message representation is called *pulse-code modulation* (PCM).[2] It is important for repeated regeneration and retransmission without significant accumulation of distortion.

2.4 Compound Modulation Systems

Multiple-modulation methods combining two or more of the individual modulation techniques that we have just surveyed are in common use, especially in telemetry. For example, there are situations in which each of several different baseband signals (or messages) is first made to modulate the frequency of a corresponding sinusoidal carrier (usually called a subcarrier), and then the sum of the resulting FM signals is made to modulate the frequency of a sinusoid of much higher frequency than the subcarriers. This two-step compound modulation is known as FM/FM. In radio applications, pulse carriers are usually used as subcarriers (for time-division multiplexing) that eventually modulate the frequency or amplitude of a sinusoidal radio-frequency carrier. The outcome may be PPM/FM, PCM/FM, etc. Even three (and more) modulation steps are sometimes used with designations such as PAM/FM/FM, etc.

III. PROPERTIES OF SINUSOIDAL-CARRIER SIGNALS

In radio communication the ultimate carrier is inevitably a radio-frequency sinusoid. Such a carrier is used to generate a suitable radio-frequency signal that carries the desired information. To do this, the carrier may be modulated in amplitude, frequency, or phase either by one message only, or by a composite of frequency-or time-division multiplexed messages, or the carrier may simply serve as a tool for translating the desired spectrum upward in frequency. The discussion in this chapter will henceforth be restricted to modulations that result from operations on a sinusoidal carrier at the transmitter and to the corresponding demodulation operation at the receiver. On the basis of the functional dependence of the final spectrum upon the spectrum of the modulating waveform we classify the modulations that originate with direct operations on a radio-frequency sinusoidal carrier into *linear* and *nonlinear*. If every component in the final spectrum (with the possible exclusion of the carrier component) is the frequency translate of a component that is present in the spectrum of the modulating waveform, then the modulation process involved will be called *linear;* otherwise it is *nonlinear*. In a linear modulation process, the real time function that describes the modulating waveform and the real time function that describes the carrier are effectively multiplied together and no higher powers of either are involved. In nonlinear modulation, products of the carrier with powers of the message time function that are higher than the first are included in the structure of the resulting modulated signal.

3.1 Linear Modulation

Fundamentally, linear modulation is a process whereby the time function that describes the message specifications is multiplied by the time function that describes the carrier. If the message time function is $g(t)$ and the carrier is described by $A_c \cos(\omega_c t + \phi_c)$ then the product of the two is

$$e(t) = A_c g(t) \cos(\omega_c t + \phi_c). \tag{1}$$

In order to appreciate the spectral significance of this operation, consider the Fourier transform of each side. The Fourier transform of the product of two time functions is given by the convolution of their Fourier transforms (or spectra). Denote the Fourier transform of $g(t)$ by $G(\omega)$. The Fourier transform of cos $[\omega_c t + \phi_c]$ is $\pi[e^{j\phi_c}\delta(\omega - \omega_c) + e^{-j\phi_c}\delta(\omega + \omega_c)]$, where $\delta(x)$ is a unit impulse at $x = 0$. The Fourier transform of $e(t)$ is therefore

$$E(\omega) = \frac{1}{2}A_c\left\{e^{j\phi_c}G(\omega - \omega_c) + e^{-j\phi_c}G(\omega + \omega_c)\right\}. \tag{2}$$

This shows that the multiplication of the time functions is equivalent to a translation of the baseband spectrum through a distance of ω_c to the right and to the left on the frequency axis. (See Fig. 1).

Several types of linear modulation are derived by auxiliary operations on the product in Eq. (1). For example, amplitude (or envelope) modulation (AM) results in

$$e_{AM}(t) = A_c[1 + k_a g(t)] \cos(\omega_c t + \phi_c) \tag{3}$$

which differs from $e(t)$ in Eq. (1) by the addition of a carrier component of sufficient magnitude so that

$$A_c[1 + k_a g(t)] \geqslant 0 \text{ for all } t\,. \tag{4}$$

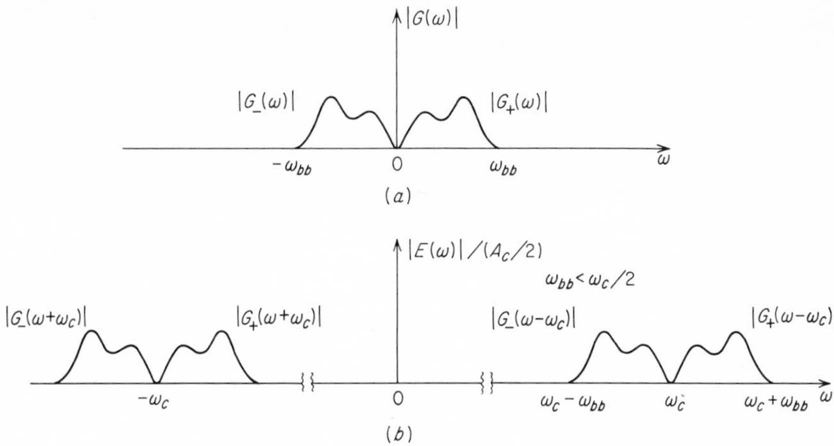

Fig. 1. Result of fundamental operation in linear modulation. (a) Magnitude function of baseband spectrum; (b) Magnitude function of translated spectrum.

If less carrier is added than the minimum necessary to satisfy this condition, then a type of *reduced-carrier* AM results.

Single-sideband modulation (SSB) results from the elimination of one-half of the translated spectrum. The desired elimination may of course be achieved through a linear filter of appropriate selectivity. But it is instructive to consider two other methods of SSB generation which we shall call the *phasing method* and the *double-translation* method.[3] Block diagrams of these methods are shown in Fig. 2. The Fourier transforms of the signals at the various key points are indicated on the figures. The notation $G(\omega) = G_+(\omega) + G_-(\omega)$ was introduced in Fig. 1. The reader is urged to check the correctness of the expressions marked on Figs. 2(*a*) and 2(*b*). The "rules of the game" are:

(a) Shifting the phase of the entire spectrum of $g(t)$ an amount ϕ_m means specifically that the phase of the positive-frequency half, $G_+(\omega)$, of $G(\omega)$ is shifted ϕ_m, and the phase of the negative-frequency half is shifted $-\phi_m$.

(b) Shifting the phase of the carrier an amount ϕ_c shifts the phase of $G(\omega - \omega_c) = G_+(\omega - \omega_c) + G_-(\omega - \omega_c)$ an amount ϕ_c and the phase of $G(\omega + \omega_c)$ an amount $-\phi_c$. [See Eq. (2)].

Sketches of the type illustrated in Fig. 1 should be made while studying the spectral analysis on the double-translation block diagram in order to visualize the interesting and simple principle of the method.

In terms of the analytic-signal representation introduced in section II of Chapter 12, only the positive-frequency half of the Fourier transform of a time function need be retained to represent the spectrum, and the corresponding complex time function can represent the real

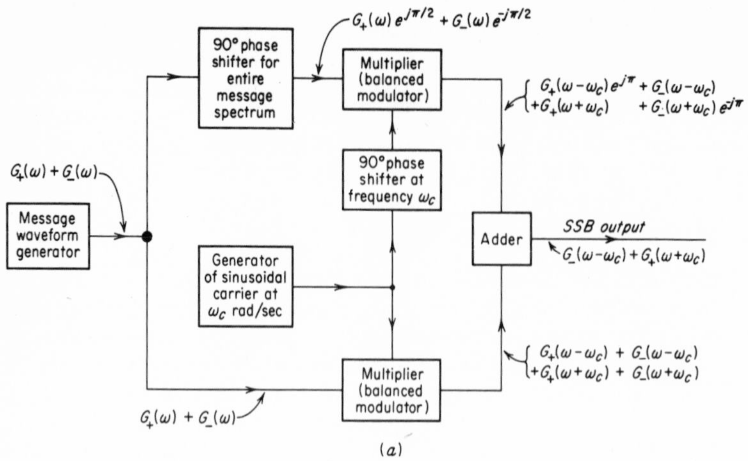

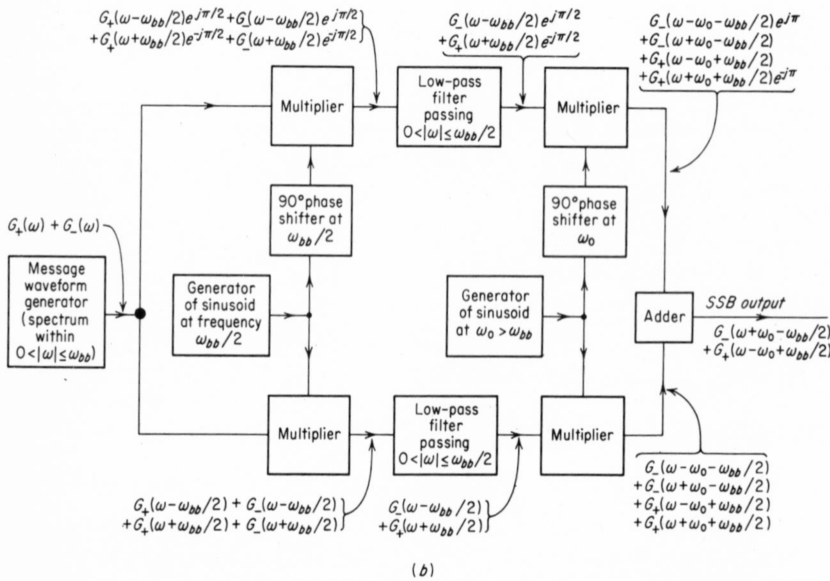

Fig. 2. Two methods for SSB generation. (a) Phasing method. (b) Double-translation method.

signal in all manipulations that are commutative with the operation of taking the real part of a complex function. Accordingly, a sinusoidal carrier can be represented by

$$c(t) = A_c e^{j(\omega_c t + \phi_c)} \tag{5}$$

and linear modulation results if this expression is multiplied by a *real* time function that depends *linearly* upon the message function $g(t)$.

In linear modulation systems, the ideal inverse-modulation (or demodulation) process at the receiver is a multiplication by a sinusoid (whose frequency and phase are identical to those of the real or virtual carrier component of the incoming signal) followed by low-pass filtering. Such an operation is often called synchronous detection, or *product demodulation.* For example, if $e(t)$ in Eq. (1) is multiplied by $\cos(\omega_c t + \phi_c)$, the result is

$$(A_c/2)[g(t) + g(t)\cos(2\omega_c + 2\phi_c)]$$

from which $g(t)$ can be extracted by a low-pass filter.

But in practice, linear-modulation signals are often demodulated in other ways. For example, "envelope detectors" are almost always used to demodulate AM signals. There are also square-law detectors, etc. The principal merit of the alternative methods of demodulation is usually their relative simplicity and operational reliability. But a price is paid in system performance, which can be heavy under unfavorable conditions of reception, as we shall illustrate in a later section.

3.2 Exponential (or Transcendental) Modulation

In a nonlinear modulation process, the structure of the final signal includes products of the carrier time function and $[g(t)]^n$, n any number (positive, negative, integral, fractional, etc.). One may visualize $g(t)$ as being subjected to a nonlinear transformation before multiplication by the carrier. The most outstanding transformation is an exponential one and, in practice, it is by far the most interesting one because we know how to invert back to $g(t)$ with as little residual distortion as is desired. Accordingly, *exponential modulation* is an operation whereby the carrier function in Eq. (5) is multiplied by

$$e^{jk_p g(t)} \quad \text{or} \quad e^{jk_f \int^t g(\xi)\, d\xi} \tag{6}$$

in order to derive an exponential signal function whose exponent depends *linearly* upon $g(t)$ or upon the outcome of a linear operation on $g(t)$.

Before we explore the consequences of the exponential modulations that correspond to each of the forms in (6), it is appropriate to state general definitions of some fundamental terms.

Definitions. If the real time function $f(t)$ that describes the signal is reducible to the forms $A(t)\cos\phi(t)$ or $A(t)\sin\phi(t)$, both of which are clearly included in the complex function

$$F(t) = A(t)e^{j\phi(t)} \tag{7}$$

where $A(t)$ and $\phi(t)$ are *real* functions of time [and $f(t)$ is the real or imaginary part of $F(t)$], and furthermore, if $A(t)$ contains none of the zero crossings of $f(t)$, then $\phi(t)$ is by definition the "instantaneous phase angle" of $f(t)$ and $\omega_i(t) = d\phi(t)/dt$ is by definition the "instantaneous frequency." The amplitude function $A(t)$ is the "instantaneous amplitude," and its magnitude is the "envelope".

The definitions of instantaneous phase and instantaneous frequency are unique and unambiguous in all situations in which $A(t)$ is bounded and does not contribute to the zero crossings of the signal. Zero crossings contributed by $A(t)$ modify the definition of phase and frequency by adding corresponding instantaneous-phase steps and instantaneous-frequency impulses. Proper demodulation of $A(t)$, $\phi(t)$, or $\omega_i(t)$ also requires that the unmodulated carrier frequency be much larger than the extent of the significant spectra of the modulating functions in $A(t)$, $\phi(t)$ or $\omega_i(t)$; and the extent of the frequency swings about the mean unmodulated carrier frequency must amount to a small fraction of that frequency.

A second definition of instantaneous frequency essentially counts the density of zero crossings per unit interval of time. In a period of $2\pi/\omega_0$ seconds, for instance, the sinusoidal signal $\cos\, \omega_0 t$ has two zeros. Therefore, in every second, this sinusoid has ω_0/π zeros, and the (angular) frequency can be said to be equivalent to the number of zeros in a time interval of π seconds. When these notions are extended to the case of a time function $f(t)$, the definition[4] becomes:

The instantaneous frequency of $f(t)$ is defined at the time t as the ratio of the number of zeros of $f(t)$ in the interval of time between $t - \tau/2$ and $t + \tau/2$ to τ/π, or as the mean density of zero crossings averaged over τ/π seconds.

The two definitions of instantaneous frequency yield the same result for an ordinary sinusoidal-carrier frequency-modulated signal whose amplitude contributes no zero crossings, but the first one is the more common and it will be applied in our discussions. The second one is more suitable for use in the analysis of frequency-modulated signals whose amplitudes contribute zero crossings, but the mechanism of its application is more difficult.

Most modulation studies can be carried out in terms of signals that consist of a superposition of several sinusoidally varying time functions that have different frequencies and amplitudes. The quickest, as well as the most elegant, way of achieving the reduction of the sum to the form indicated in the first statement of the definition of instantaneous frequency is as follows:

1. Replace each sinusoidal component of amplitude $A_n(t)$ and phase $\phi_n(t)$ by the corresponding complex function indicated in Eq. (7), with the understanding that only the real or the imaginary part of this function is the quantity of physical significance.

2. Represent each complex function $F_n(t) = A_n(t) \exp [j\phi_n(t)]$ thus obtained by a directed rotating line (henceforth called "phasor") in a complex plane, using an arbitrary reference axis (labeled the "axis of reals") for the measurement of the phase angle $\phi_n(t)$. The rotation of the phasors is conventionally positive if it is counterclockwise.

3. Add the representative component phasors vectorially to obtain their resultant. The amplitude and phase functions of this resultant will then be those of the resultant signal.

Analytically, the addition indicated in step 3 leads to

$$F(t) = \sum_{n=1}^{k} A_n(t)\, e^{j\phi_n(t)}$$
$$= A(t)\, e^{j\phi(t)}$$

where

$$A(t) = \sqrt{[\mathrm{Re}\, F(t)]^2 + [\mathrm{Im}\, F(t)]^2} \qquad (8)$$
$$\phi(t) = \mathrm{Im}\,[\ln F(t)].$$

Let us now consider the nature of the exponent modulations that result from multiplying the carrier signal function of Eq. (5) by each of the choices in (6). These products lead to

$$e_{\mathrm{PM}}(t) = \mathrm{Re}\left\{A_c e^{j[\omega_c t + \phi_c]}\, e^{jk_p g(t)}\right\}$$
$$= A_c \cos[\omega_c t + \phi_c + k_p g(t)] \qquad (9)$$

and

$$e_{\mathrm{FM}}(t) = A_c \cos[\omega_c t + \phi_c + k_f \int^t g(\xi)d\xi\,]. \qquad (10)$$

The instantaneous phase of $e_{\mathrm{PM}}(t)$, Eq. (9), depends linearly upon $g(t)$. For this reason $e_{\mathrm{PM}}(t)$ is called a *phase-modulated* signal. In the case of $e_{\mathrm{FM}}(t)$, Eq. (10), the instantaneous frequency depends linearly upon $g(t)$,

$$\omega_i(t) = d\phi(t)/dt = \omega_c + k_f g(t), \qquad (11)$$

and $e_{\mathrm{FM}}(t)$ is a frequency-modulated signal. As far as their properties as signals are concerned $e_{\mathrm{PM}}(t)$ and $e_{\mathrm{FM}}(t)$ differ in a trivial way; namely, the phase of one depends upon $g(t)$ whereas the phase of the other depends upon the integral of $g(t)$. But at the receiver, the corresponding trivial difference in demodulation techniques leads to nontrivial differences in the way in which disturbances added in transmission affect the received message, as we shall find out later on. In the remainder of the present section, we explore the properties of the signal

$$e_{\exp}(t) = A_c \cos[\omega_c t + \phi_c + \psi(t)] \qquad (12)$$

in which $\psi(t)$ may be understood to be either of the two phase-modulating functions in (9) and (10).

Equation (12) can be rewritten as

$$e_{\exp}(t) = \mathrm{Re}\left\{A_c e^{j(\omega_c t + \phi_c)} \cdot e^{j\psi(t)}\right\}$$
$$= \mathrm{Re}\left\{A_c e^{j(\omega_c t + \phi_c)}\left[1 + j\psi(t) - \frac{1}{2}\psi^2(t) - \frac{1}{3!}\, j\psi^3(t) + \cdots\right]\right\} \qquad (13)$$

which shows that if $|\psi(t)|_{\max}$ is not small compared with unity, then products of the carrier signal function and the higher powers of $\psi(t)$

make important contributions to the structure of $e_{\text{exp}}(t)$. If, however, $|\psi(t)|_{\max} \ll 1$, then

$$e_{\text{exp}}(t) \cong \text{Re}\left\{A_c[1 + j\psi(t)]\, e^{j[\omega_c t + \phi_c]}\right\} . \tag{14}$$

From this we conclude that if the maximum value of phase deviation, $|\psi(t)|_{\max}$, is a sufficiently small fraction of a radian, then the exponential modulation described by Eq. (12) is approximately linear. Note, however, that there is an important difference between $e_{\text{exp}}(t)$ in Eq. (14) and its nearest kin in the family of linear-modulation signals, $e_{\text{AM}}(t)$ of Eq. (3). The difference is due to the presence of j in front of the message time function in Eq. (14). The effect of this j is brought out by rewriting (14) as

$$e_{\text{exp}}(t) = \text{Re}\, A_c \left\{e^{j(\omega_c t + \phi_c)} + \psi(t) e^{j(\omega_c t + \phi_c + \pi/2)}\right\} . \tag{15}$$

In contrast, $e_{\text{AM}}(t)$ of Eq. (3) is represented by

$$e_{\text{AM}}(t) = \text{Re}\, A_c \left\{e^{j(\omega_c t + \phi_c)} + k_a g(t) e^{j(\omega_c t + \phi_c)}\right\} . \tag{16}$$

The quantities in braces in Eqs. (15) and (16) are represented by phasor diagrams in Fig. 3. The exponential-modulation signal is

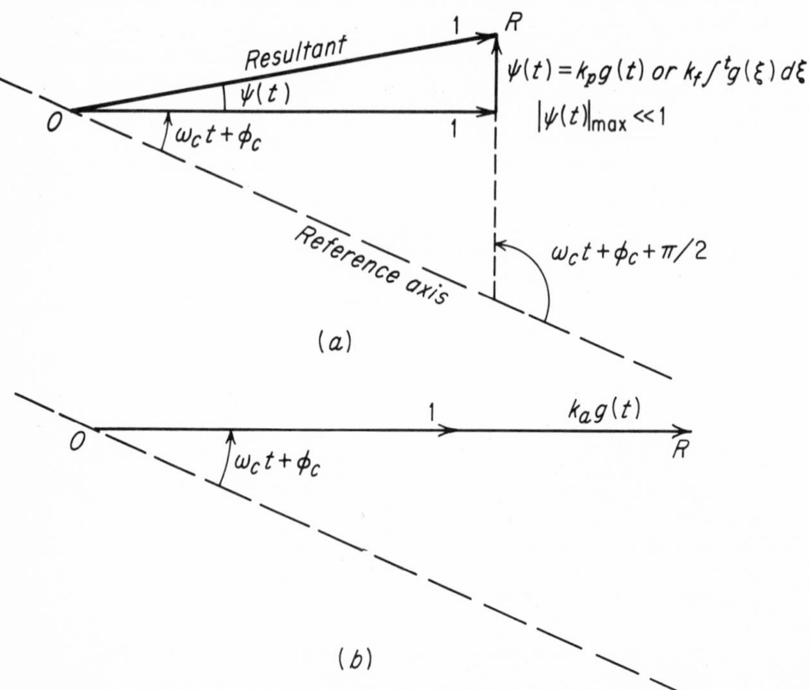

Fig. 3. Phasor diagrams for comparing low-deviation exponent modulation, (a), with amplitude modulation, (b).

closely approximated by two phasors *at right angles all the time*, one of which has an amplitude that varies with time according to the modulation waveform. As time goes on, the variable-amplitude phasor builds up to a maximum length that is small compared with unity and shrinks back, and may go through zero to build up in the opposite direction. This causes the resultant OR to "wobble" through small angular excursions about the instantaneous phase position of the carrier, without any change in amplitude

In comparison, the amplitude-modulation signal is represented exactly by two phasors that are *always in line*, the variable-amplitude phasor builds up to some (arbitrarily large) value *in phase* with the carrier phasor, and then wanes through zero and in the opposite direction to a value that is $\leqslant 1$, for full-carrier AM, and an unrestricted value for reduced-carrier AM. The instantaneous phase of the resultant is always identical with that of the carrier component.

The fact that $e_{\exp}(t)$ is closely approximated by Eq. (14) is extremely valuable in the analysis of the effect of random-fluctuation noise upon exponential-modulation signals when the noise level is low compared with the signal (see section VII). This approximation also led Armstrong[1] to the invention of the first method for generating FM signals without the use of reactance modulators. (FM signals can also be *demodulated* by a method that essentially reverses the operations of the Armstrong generating technique.)

In the general case in which the magnitude of $\psi(t)$ is not restricted to be small compared with unity, Eq. (13) shows that the second and higher powers of $\psi(t)$ become important in the structure of $e_{\exp}(t)$. The phasor representation of the quantity in braces in Eq. (13) is shown in Fig. 4. Odd powers of $\psi(t)$ contribute components that are

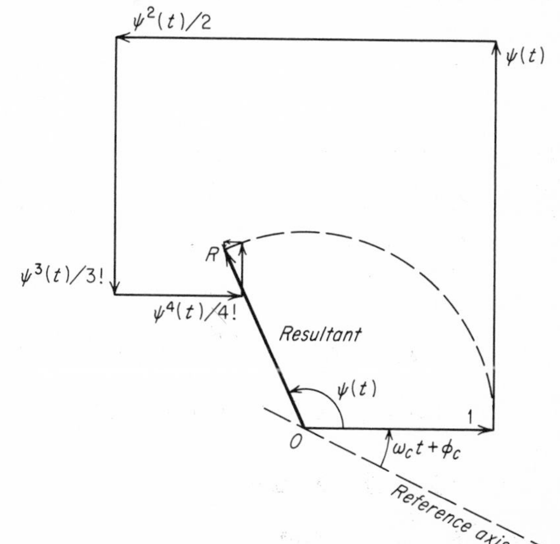

Fig. 4. Phasor representation of exponential-modulation signal described by Eq. (13) for large instantaneous phase deviations.

in quadrature with the carrier component while even powers contribute components in parallel with the carrier component.

The presence of the higher powers of $\psi(t)$ in Eq. (13) complicates the resulting spectrum. Recall, for example, that if $\psi(t)$ is the sum of several low-frequency tones, then $\psi^n(t)$ will contain the *nth* harmonic of each frequency present, in addition to components whose frequencies are sums and differences of various multiples of the frequencies in $\psi(t)$. If ω_m is the highest frequency in $\psi(t)$, the highest frequency in $\psi^n(t)$ is $n\omega_m$. The fact that all integer powers of $\psi(t)$ are present in exp $[j\,\psi(t)]$ therefore means that the spectrum of the exponential has an unlimited bandwidth despite the fact that $\psi(t)$ is assumed band-limited.

But exp $[j\,\psi(t)]$ can in general be approximated to any desired accuracy by a finite number of terms in its power expansion. Taylor's formula for e^x is

$$e^x = \sum_{n=0}^{N} \frac{x^n}{n!} + \frac{x^{N+1}}{(N+1)!}\, e^{\eta x},\ 0 < \eta < 1. \tag{17}$$

This shows that

$$e^{j\psi(t)} \cong \sum_{n=0}^{N} \frac{j^n}{n!}\, \psi^n(t) \tag{18}$$

with an error whose magnitude is less than or equal to

$$\epsilon_{\max} = \frac{1}{(N+1)!}\, |\psi(t)|_{\max}^{N+1} \ . \tag{19}$$

A finite bandwidth can therefore be defined for $e_{\exp}(t)$ depending upon some specified tolerance on the error incurred in truncating the expansion as in (18).

Let us now consider some specific examples of $\psi(t)$. The simplest example is

$$\psi(t) = \delta \sin(\omega_m t + \phi_m),\ \omega_m \ll \omega_c . \tag{20}$$

The amplitude factor δ is usually called the *phase deviation* if it is independent of ω_m, and it is called the *modulation index* if $\delta = \Delta\Omega/\omega_m$, where $\Delta\Omega$ is the frequency deviation in rad/sec. Substitution from (20) into (13) yields

$$\begin{aligned} e_{\exp}(t) &= \text{Re}\, A_c \left\{ e^{j(\omega_c t + \phi_c)} \cdot e^{j\delta \sin(\omega_m t + \phi_m)} \right\} \\ &= \text{Re}\, A_c \left\{ e^{j(\omega_c t + \phi_c)} \sum_{n=-\infty}^{\infty} J_n(\delta)\, e^{jn(\omega_m t + \phi_m)} \right\} \\ &= A_c \sum_{n=-\infty}^{\infty} J_n(\delta) \cos\left[(\omega_c + n\omega_m)t + \phi_c + n\phi_m\right] \end{aligned} \tag{21}$$

where we used the identity

$$e^{j\delta \sin\theta} = \sum_{n=-\infty}^{\infty} J_n(\delta)\, e^{jn\theta} \ . \tag{22}$$

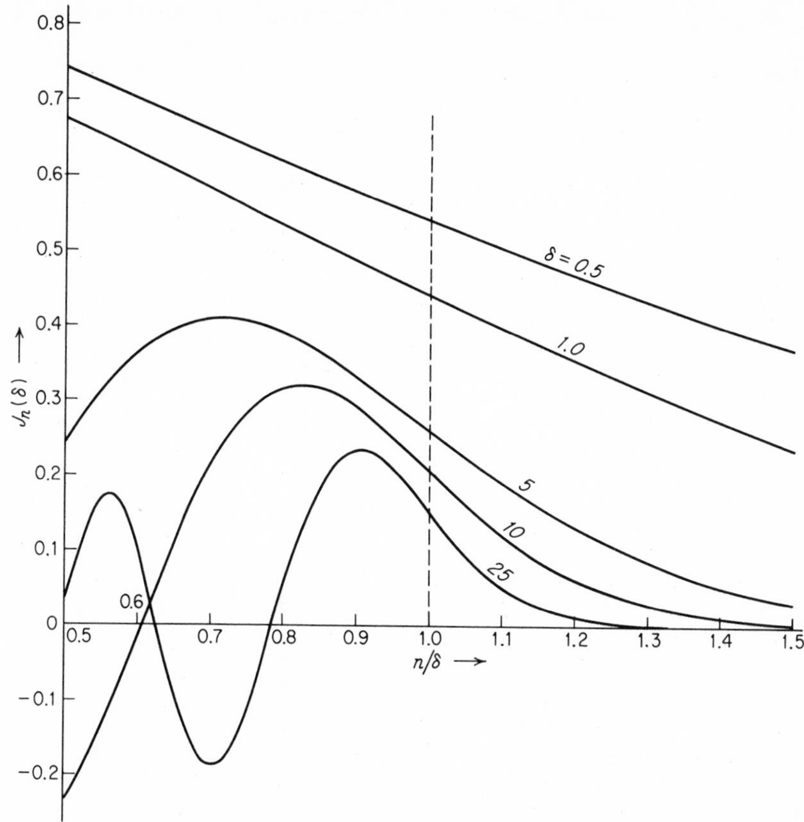

Fig. 5. Variation of $J_n(\delta)$ with n/δ for values of n/δ around unity.

The variation with n of the coefficient of the nth component in the Fourier expansion of exp $[j\,\psi(t)]$ for periodic $\psi(t)$ is best brought out by plots in which n is treated as a continuous independent variable. In Fig. 5 we present plots of $J_n(\delta)$ as a function of n/δ, in which δ is treated as an independent parameter. For any value of δ, $J_n(\delta)$ has its largest magnitude at a value of $n/\delta < 1$ after which it decays monotonically toward zero at a rate that increases with δ. Note that for an FM signal, $n/\delta = n\omega_m/\Delta\Omega$. Therefore, if δ is changed by changing ω_m and holding $\Delta\Omega$ constant, the horizontal scale in Fig. 5 can be multiplied by $\Delta\Omega$ to show how the shape of the spectrum is affected by decreasing ω_m relative to $\Delta\Omega$. Figure 5 then indicates clearly how the spectrum of the signal of Eq. (21) tends to have a more clearly defined bandwidth (that is not much wider than $2\Delta\Omega$) as δ becomes large. In the limit as $\delta \to \infty$, the spectrum becomes exactly confined within $\omega_c - \Delta\Omega \leqslant |\omega| \leqslant \omega_c + \Delta\Omega$.

As another example, let

$$\psi(t) = \sum_{k=1}^{M} \delta_k \sin(\omega_k t + \phi_k), \quad \omega_k \ll \omega_c . \tag{23}$$

We distinguish two cases. In the first case, the ω_k are *not commenmensurable;* in the second, they are (as, for example, when $\psi(t)$ is some general periodic waveform). The first case is easily handled by noting that $\exp[j\psi(t)]$ is a product of M factors of the form $\exp[j\delta \sin\theta]$ and therefore repeated application of Eq. (22) quickly yields the spectrum of $e_{\text{exp}}(t)$. But in the second case, another route must be taken. Specifically, let $\psi(t)$ be some periodic waveform. The analysis starts with

$$\begin{aligned} e_{\text{exp}}(t) &= A_c \cos[\omega_c t + \phi_c + \psi(t)] \\ &= A_c \{\cos(\omega_c t + \phi_c) \cos\psi(t) - \sin(\omega_c t + \phi_c) \sin\psi(t)\} . \end{aligned} \tag{24}$$

It is then noted that $\sin\psi(t)$ and $\cos\psi(t)$ are periodic with the same fundamental period as $\psi(t)$. A Fourier representation of each can thus be introduced into Eq. (24), and the result simplified into a useful form.

Some general observations about the shape of FM spectra can be made. First, the shape of the spectral amplitude distribution is symmetrical about the center frequency of the signal only if the frequency-modulating time function is symmetrical about the value of the center frequency. Second, there often is a clear correspondence between the relative amplitudes of spectral components and the fraction of time during which the instantaneous frequency of the resultant signal falls near the frequencies of those components.

IV. SIGNAL PROCESSING WITH LINEAR TIME-INVARIANT SYSTEMS

The analysis of linear frequency-discriminatory processing of sinusoidal-carrier signals can be carried out by the standard frequency-analysis and time-domain convolution techniques discussed in Chapter 3 and elsewhere in this volume. Modulated sinusoids being a special type of signal, and bandpass filters a special type of linear system, it is possible to carry out some of the ground work in advance, and derive some useful results that can in turn be specialized to the needs of more specific situations. Knowledge of such results also suggests new signal as well as filter design approaches, and imparts a clearer appreciation of the nature of the low-distortion transmission problem.

4.1 Response of Linear Systems to Linear-Modulation Signals

The principal result that we shall derive here is the method of analyzing high-frequency problems by means of low-frequency analogs.

Consider a bandpass filter with a system function $H_{BP}(s)$, and let the excitation be represented by

$$i(t) = x(t)e^{j\omega_c t} \tag{25}$$

(in which the carrier frequency ω_c is usually assumed not to differ much from the center frequency of the filter passband). The response, according to Eq. (22) of Chapter 3, can be written as

$$e(t) = \frac{1}{2\pi j} \int_{\sigma_0 - j\infty}^{\sigma_0 + j\infty} I(s)\, H_{BP}(s) e^{st} ds$$

subject to the conditions outlined in connection with that equation. Since $I(s) = X(s - j\omega_c)$, we have

$$e(t) = \frac{1}{2\pi j} \int_{\sigma_0 - j\infty}^{\sigma_0 + j\infty} X(s - j\omega_c)\, H_{BP}(s)\, e^{st}\, ds$$

$$= \left\{ \frac{1}{2\pi j} \int_{\sigma_0 - j\infty}^{\sigma_0 + j\infty} X(\zeta) H_{BP}(\zeta + j\omega_c)\, e^{\zeta t}\, d\zeta \right\} e^{j\omega_c t}$$

by an obvious change of variables. Notice that $H_{BP}(\zeta + j\omega_c)$ is $H_{BP}(\zeta)$ translated in frequency *downward* an amount $j\omega_c$. $H_{BP}(\zeta + j\omega_c)$ is therefore a low-frequency analog of $H_{BP}(\zeta)$. If we denote this low-frequency analog $H_{LP}(\zeta)$, we can write

$$e(t) = y(t)e^{j\omega_c t} \tag{26}$$

where

$$y(t) = \frac{1}{2\pi j} \int_{\sigma_0 - j\infty}^{\sigma_0 + j\infty} X(s) H_{LP}(s)\, e^{st}\, ds\ . \tag{27}$$

Thus, by a trivial manipulation, we learn that the response of the bandpass filter to the high-frequency excitation [Eq. (25)] can be expressed in the form of Eq. (26) in which $y(t)$ is the response of a low-frequency analog of the bandpass filter to the time function $x(t)$ which describes the instantaneous amplitude of the excitation. The appropriate low-frequency analog of the filter is obtained by translating $H_{BP}(s)$ downward in frequency an amount that equals the carrier frequency of the excitation.

The preceding result applies independently of the exact nature of $x(t)$. That is to say, $x(t)$ may be complex (indicating combined amplitude and phase modulation) or real. Moreover, $y(t)$ will in general be a complex time function. But the result is especially useful when

$x(t)$ is real, $H_{BP}(j\omega)$ exhibits bandpass symmetry (even for magnitude and odd for phase) about some $\omega = \omega_0$, and the carrier frequency ω_c equals the center frequency of the filter ω_0. In that case, $y(t)$ is real (indicating absence of phase fluctuations in the response), and $H_{LP}(s)$ is the system function of a simple low-pass analog circuit that can frequently be determined *by inspection** from the bandpass circuit. (It is also common practice in the synthesis of bandpass networks, with characteristics that are symmetrical about some center frequency, to synthesize first a low-pass analog centered about zero frequency, from which the bandpass circuit can always be determined by inspection.)[5]

*The procedure stems from the fact that an exact, reversible, lowpass to bandpass transformation can generally be achieved by letting

$$s \rightarrow k\left(\frac{s}{\omega_0} + \frac{\omega_0}{s}\right)$$

in which ω_0 fixes the center of the high-frequency band, and k fixes the relationship between the lowpass and bandpass bandwidths. For our purposes, k is chosen equal to $\omega_0/2$, and ω_0 is so high relative to the filter bandwidth that the response will be substantial only for frequencies that satisfy $|s - j\omega_0| \ll \omega_0$. Under these conditions, the transformation becomes

$$s \rightarrow \frac{\omega_0}{2}\left(\frac{s}{\omega_0} + \frac{\omega_0}{s}\right) \cong s - j\omega_0, \text{ as desired.}$$

The corresponding transformation of circuit elements is:

every

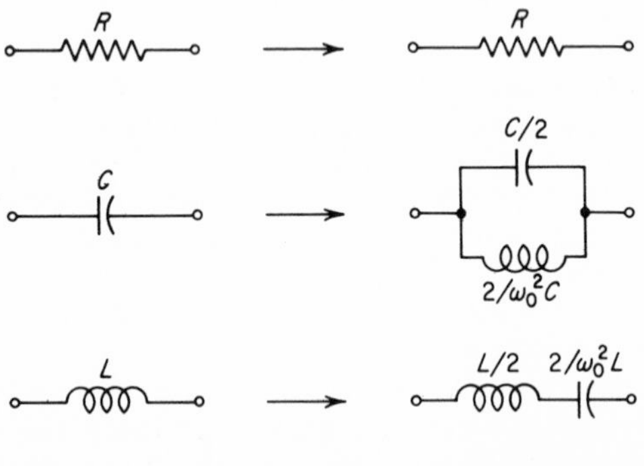

The reverse transformation from bandpass to lowpass can be determined by inspection only when the necessary identifications are obvious. A simple situation in which this is not possible arises when $H_{BP}(s)$ pertains to a pair of coupled single-tuned circuits or to a cascade of stagger-tuned circuits. For this situation, a lowpass analog is usually determined to have the form

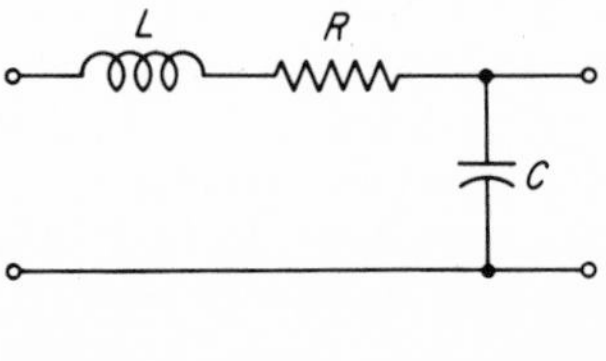

The relation between the impulse response of the high-frequency filter and its low-frequency analog is obtained by writing

$$H_{BP}(j\omega) = H_{LP}(j\omega - j\omega_0) + H_{LP}(-j\omega - j\omega_0)$$

whence

$$\begin{aligned} h_{BP}(t) &= h_{LP}(t)e^{j\omega_0 t} + h^*_{LP}(t)\, e^{-j\omega_0 t} \\ &= 2\, \mathrm{Re}\{h_{LP}(t)e^{j\omega_0 t}\}. \end{aligned} \tag{28}$$

If the magnitude and phase functions of $H_{BP}(j\omega)$ do not possess even and odd symmetry, respectively, about $j\omega_0$, then $h_{LP}(t)$ is complex. In general,

$$h_{LP}(t) = h_{\ell c}(t) + j\, h_{\ell s}(t)$$

and

$$h_{BP}(t) = 2h_{\ell c}(t)\cos\omega_0 t - 2h_{\ell s}(t)\sin\omega_0 t. \tag{29a}$$

If the magnitude and phase characteristics of $H_{BP}(j\omega)$ are even and odd, respectively, about $j\omega_0$, then $h_{LP}(t)$ is real, and

$$h_{BP}(t) = 2\, h_{LP}(t)\cos\omega_0 t. \tag{29b}$$

From Eq. (27), it is clear that the instantaneous amplitude $y(t)$ of the bandpass filter response to the excitation represented by Eq. (25) is obtained by convolving $x(t)$ and $h_{LP}(t)$.

4.2 Response of Linear Systems to Exponential-Modulation Signals

In the analysis of linear-system response to exponential-modulation signals, it is helpful, where possible, to anticipate the character of the problem by guessing roughly into which of three possible categories the frequency modulation falls. An excellent basis for this classification is offered by the maximum rate of change of the instantaneous frequency of the excitation, when compared with the square of the duration (or a few time constants) of the impulse response of the filter. On this basis, three types of possible frequency changes can be recognized:

(a) Those that are so fast (on the time scale of the system) that they are essentially *abrupt*. This constitutes one easily recognizable extreme.

(b) Those that occur at a rate that is comparable to the speed with which the system response can build up and decay.

(c) Those that are so *slow* in comparison with the speed of natural response of the system that the frequency change during a few time constants does not amount to a substantial fraction of the filter bandwidth. This is another easily recognizable extreme.

Fortunately, the first and third situations are of more frequent interest than the second in the design of frequency-selective filters for FM communication systems, and they can be handled with relative ease in comparison with most of the cases that fall into the second category. There are very "neat" (and peculiar) ways for obtaining results that satisfy the most critical judgments in cases (a) and (c), but the same is seldom true of case (b).

4.2A Analysis of Response to Abrupt Frequency Changes

When the frequency change of the excitation is essentially abrupt, we have a situation in which the analysis can often be reduced to a greatly simplified pictorial form. We shall illustrate this situation by considering the response of a single-tuned high-Q circuit to a frequency step.

With reference to Fig. 6, assume that the excitation is described by

$$i(t) = \exp j\left\{\int^{t} [\omega_i + u_{-1}(\tau)(\omega_f - \omega_i)]\, d\tau + \phi_0\right\} \tag{30}$$

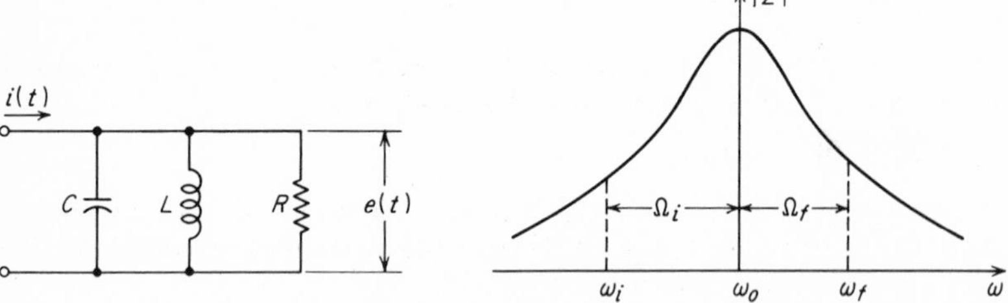

Fig. 6. High-Q resonant circuit and definition of symbols.

where $u_{-1}(t)$ is the unit-step function. (The subscripts i and f stand for "initial" and "final".) The impedance of the high-Q single-tuned circuit can be written as

$$Z(j\Omega) = \frac{R}{1 + j\dfrac{\Omega}{\alpha}}, \quad \Omega = \omega - \omega_0 \tag{31}$$

where $\alpha = 1/(2RC)$, and ω_0 is the frequency of resonance. Before $t = 0$, the filter response is assumed to be in a steady-state condition. After $t = 0$, the response is made up of two sinusoids—one at center frequency and one at $\omega = \omega_f$. The sinusoid at the center frequency dies out with time, whereas the sinusoid at $\omega = \omega_f$ represents the steady-state component that corresponds to the new excitation at $\omega = \omega_f$. If $e(t)$ is the filter response, then

$$e(t) = \begin{cases} Z(j\Omega_i)e^{j\omega_i t}, & \text{for } t \leqslant 0 \\ A_T' e^{-\alpha t} e^{j\omega_0 t} + Z(j\Omega_f)\, e^{j\omega_f t}, & \text{for } t \geqslant 0 \,. \end{cases} \tag{32}$$

Since the two expressions must be idential at $t = 0$, we have

$$A_T' = Z(j\Omega_i) - Z(j\,\Omega_f).$$

If we take $\exp(j\omega_f t)$ as a reference, then at $t = 0+$ the response is completely described by the phasor diagram shown in Fig. 7.

Usually, the frequency deviations from the final frequency ω_f are of interest. Therefore, the analysis is best carried out by taking

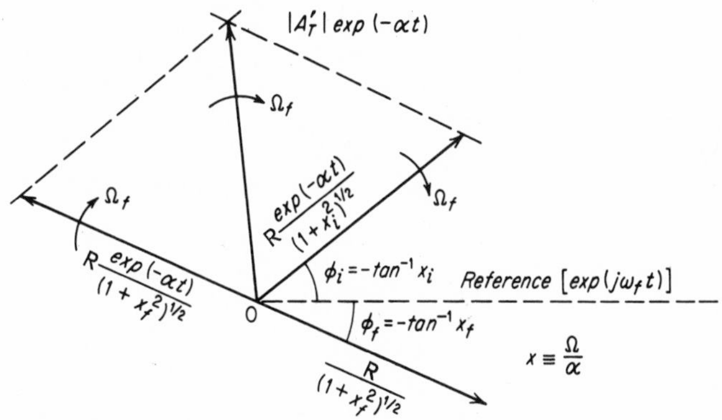

Fig. 7. Phasor representation of response at $t = 0+$.

the final steady-state response as reference and normalizing with respect to $Z(j\Omega_f)e^{j\omega_f t}$. The result of this operation is the simplified representation

$$
\begin{aligned}
e_1(t) &= \frac{e(t)}{Z(j\Omega_f)}\, e^{-j\omega_f t} \\
&= 1 + A_T\, e^{-\alpha t} \cdot e^{j(\phi_T - \Omega_f t)}
\end{aligned}
\tag{33}
$$

which is illustrated by the phasor diagram of Fig. 8, where the symbols are also defined.

The phasor model of Fig. 8 can be used to explain all of the amplitude and frequency transient phenomena that are observed in the laboratory. Moreover, all of the significant information (for example, the magnitudes and times of occurrence of overshoots and under-

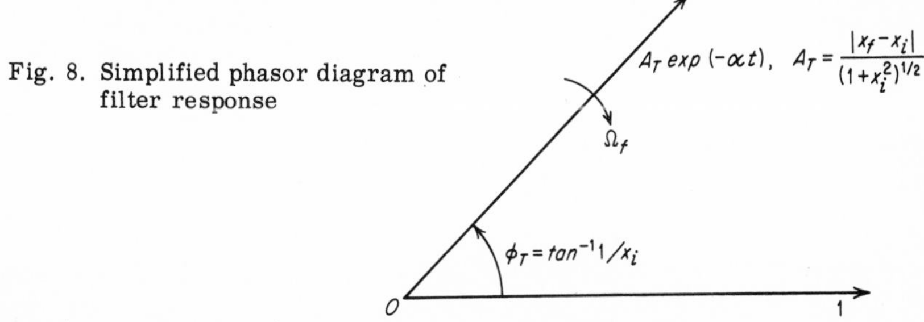

Fig. 8. Simplified phasor diagram of filter response

shoots, rise times, and the conditions that give rise to amplitude nulls) can be quickly obtained from this diagram by inspection.

Let us first illustrate the nature of the response observed in the laboratory.[6] Oscillograms of the instantaneous frequency of the response of a single-tuned circuit to a series of frequency steps are shown in Fig. 9. In oscillograms 9 (a) through 9(k), the input fre-

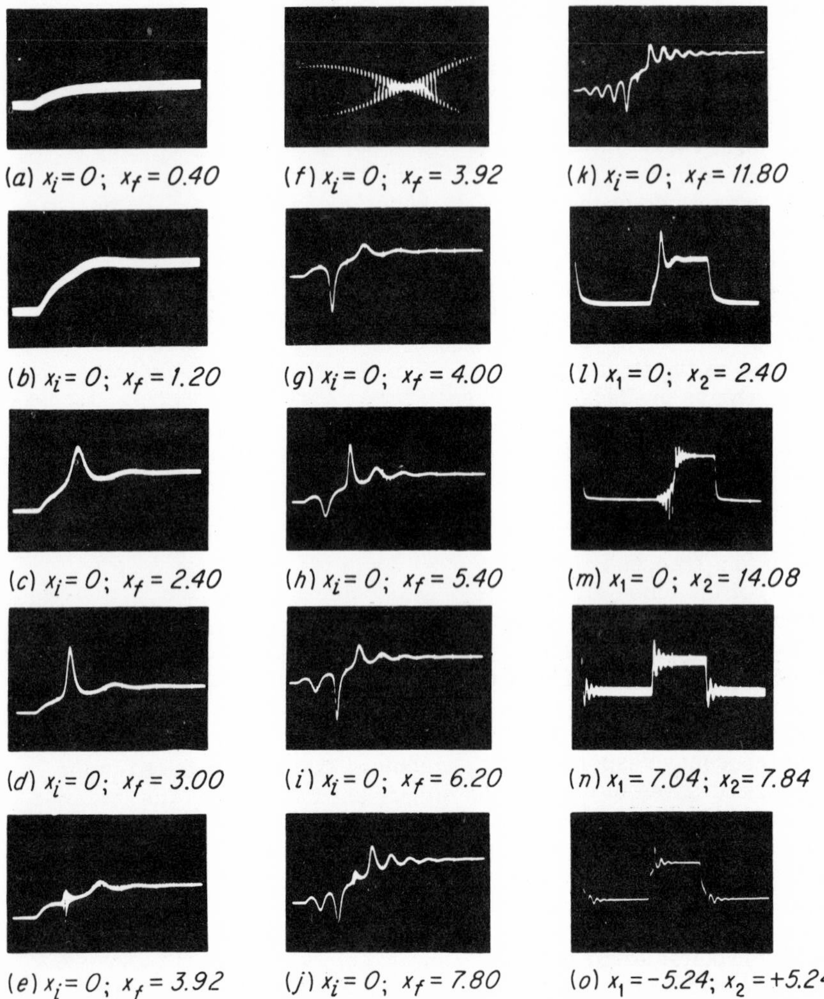

Fig. 9. Oscillograms of response of a single-tuned circuit to a sinusoid whose frequency has a step modulation. All but (f) show the instantaneous frequency of the response. Oscillogram (f) shows that an amplitude null accompanies the transitional phenomenon in (e). The variable $x = (\omega - \omega_0)/\alpha$; the subscripts i and f denote "initial" and "final" while subscripts 1 and 2 in (*l*), (*m*), (*n*) and (*o*) denote the extremes of the square-wave modulation.

quency steps start at the resonance frequency of the filter. For x_f less than 0.80, the response resembles a rising exponential whose rise time is approximately independent of x_f [see Fig. 9(a)]. A small overshoot is first noticeable (not shown here) for $x_f = 0.80$. As x_f becomes greater than 0.80, the magnitude of the overshoot increases with a corresponding decrease in the rise time of the response and the time of maximum overshoot. An inflection point is also apparent on the leading edge of the transient [see Fig. 9(b), (c), (d)]. For $x_f = 3.92$, the overshoot is caught in the act of turning into an undershoot, and, at the instant of transition, the instantaneous amplitude of the response drops to zero. These two effects are shown in Fig. 9(e) and (f), respectively. For $x_f = 4.00$, the "overshoot" has definitely become an undershoot [see (g) of the figure]. With a further increase in x_f, the magnitude of the first undershoot decreases in value, whereas the magnitude of the second overshoot increases [see (g) and (h)]. For $x_f = 6.00$, the second overshoot becomes an undershoot [see (i)], and the instantaneous amplitude of the response again drops to zero. For larger values of x_f, the magnitude of the second undershoot decreases in value. The third, fourth, and successive overshoots behave exactly the same as the first and second. Note that the undershoots, when they occur, always precede the overshoots and that, for a given x_f, successive undershoots are always larger than the preceding ones, whereas successive overshoots are always smaller. Note also that the frequency of ringing in all cases (approximately) equals Ω_f [see (j) and (k)].

In Figs. 9(l) and (m), the leading edge of the square wave corresponds to a frequency deviation away from the center frequency ($x_i = 0$) of the tuned circuit; the trailing edge corresponds to a deviation towards the center frequency ($x_f = 0$). When $x_f = 0$, the response is always exponential and has no overshoot, regardless of the values of x_i. Figure 9(n) shows a response in which the inflection point in the leading and trailing edges is almost unnoticeable. Figure 9(o) indicates that when $x_i = x_f$ the leading and trailing edges of the square-wave frequency response have identical rise times, percentage overshoots, and times of maximum overshoot.

Let us now show how these effects can be predicted from the phasor model of Fig. 8. Consider, for example, the situation shown in Fig. 10. As the phasor $A_T e^{-at}$ decays exponentially, the phasor $e_1(t)$ wobbles back and forth with a period that is equal to $2\pi/\Omega_f$. At point A, $e_1(t)$ is at rest, and the instantaneous frequency of $e(t)$ equals ω_f. As $e_1(t)$ rotates towards B, the time rate of change of the phase angle, θ, increases and an overshoot in the instantaneous frequency of $e(t)$ results. The maximum overshoot occurs at point B. The time rate of change of θ decreases as $e_1(t)$ rotates from B. At point C, $e_1(t)$ is again at rest. As $e_1(t)$ rotates toward D, $d\theta/dt$ continues to decrease and the instantaneous frequency of $e(t)$ falls below ω_f. The instantaneous frequency reaches its minimum value at point D. As $e_1(t)$ rotates from D, $d\theta/dt$ begins to increase once again. At point E $d\theta/dt = 0$, and one cycle of ringing in the instantaneous frequency of

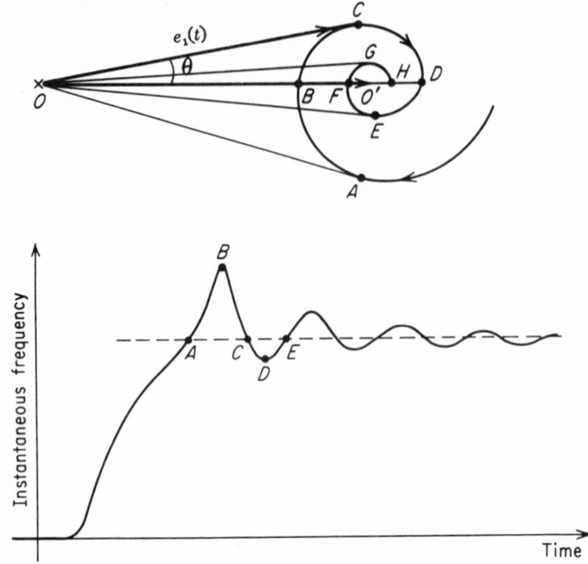

Fig. 10. Behavior of $e_1(t)$ that results in occurrence of instantaneous-frequency and instantaneous-amplitude transients in the tuned-circuit response. Note that 0-0′ is the unit phasor representing the filter steady-state response at the final frequency, which is chosen for reference in the computations.

the response $e(t)$ is completed. The cycle is repeated for points, E, F, G, and H and continues to repeat until $A_T e^{-\alpha t}$ is negligible compared to the unit vector. Since such points as B and F occur at increasingly greater distances from 0, overshoots in the frequency of the response $e(t)$ occur with successively smaller magnitudes.

The occurrence of undershoots in the instantaneous frequency of the response is explained with the use of Fig. 11. For the case shown, the phasor $A_T e^{-\alpha t}$ is sufficiently large with respect to the unit phasor at $t = 0$, and the frequency Ω_f is sufficiently high to enable the tip of the $e_1(t)$ phasor to encircle the origin, 0, twice as $A_T e^{-\alpha t}$ revolves at the angular frequency, Ω_f. Since the instantaneous frequency of the resultant of two signals of different frequencies always overshoots in the direction of the frequency of the stronger signal (see Fig. 14, below), the instantaneous frequency of $e_1(t)$ undershoots at such points as A and B, which occur to the left of 0, and overshoots at such points as C and D, which occur to the right of 0. Note that the undershoots, if they occur, must always precede the overshoots; also, successive undershoots have magnitudes that increase in value, whereas successive overshoots have magnitudes that decrease in value. When the tip of the $e_1(t)$ phasor passes through the origin, the magnitude of $e_1(t)$

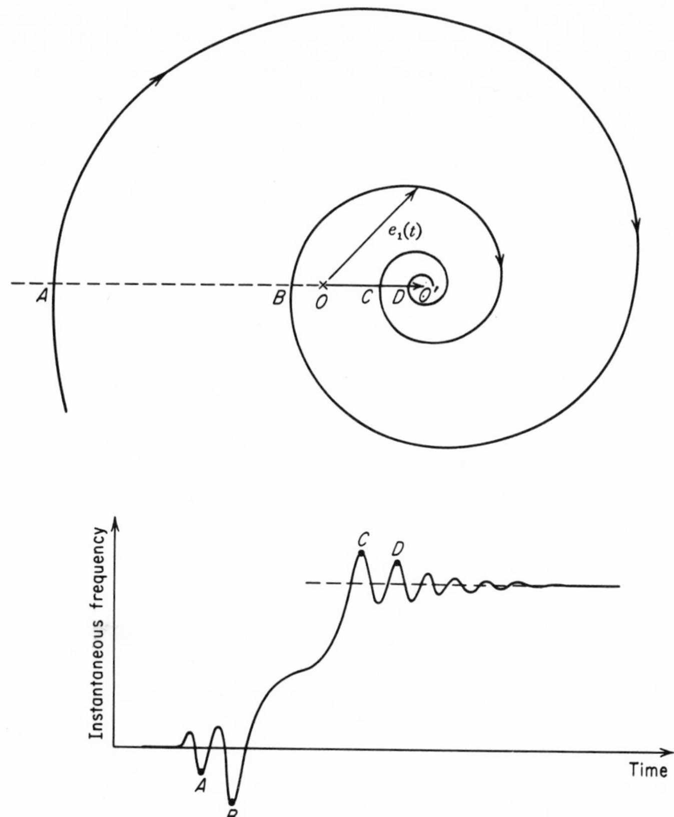

Fig. 11. Behavior of $e_1(t)$ that results in occurrence of both undershoots and overshoots in the instantaneous-frequency of $e_1(t)$. Note that 0-0′ is the unit phasor representing the final steady-state response of the filter and chosen for reference in the computations.

equals zero, and the instantaneous frequency of the response is transitional between an overshoot and an undershoot.

When $\omega_f = \omega_0$, $\Omega_f = 0$ and the phasor $A_T e^{-\alpha t}$ is stationary with respect to the unit phasor. Thus, the response to a frequency jump that terminates at ω_0 consists of a smooth exponential rise caused by the exponential decay of $A_T e^{-\alpha t}$. (See Fig. 9(l) and (m). When ω_f approximately equals ω_0, Ω_f is very small. Thus, $\phi = \phi_T - \Omega_f t$ is approximately constant as $A_T e^{-\alpha t}$ decays, and the response is close to an exponential rise. (See Fig 9 (a)).

The inflection point that occurs, for certain values of Ω_f, in the leading edge of the instantaneous-frequency response is caused by the fact that the transients in the frequency-step response of the single-tuned circuit are the result of the exponential decay of $A_T e^{-\alpha t}$, and the angular rotation of $A_T e^{-\alpha t}$. When first one effect predominates and then the other, an inflection point is seen on the leading edge of the response. If Ω_f is small, only the first effect predominates, and no inflection point is observed. If Ω_f is very large, only the second effect predominates, and again, no inflection point occurs.

With a more complicated filter, any initial energy that might be stored in the system before $t = 0$ will be dissipated at the natural frequencies (normal modes) of the system after $t = 0$. At $t = 0+$, the term that represents the final steady-state response will be cancelled out by a term whose components die out with time at the natural frequencies of the system. Once the component solutions have been determined, the determination of the instantaneous-amplitude and instantaneous-frequency behavior of the total response is best carried out by solving a multisignal interference problem. The situation in general becomes much more complicated than is indicated by the example of the single tuned circuit worked out above. However, in the case of bandpass filters whose pole patterns display symmetry about some frequency, significant additional simplifications are possible.

4.2B General Analysis for Arbitrary Frequency Modulations

The general analysis for arbitrary frequency modulations most often is hopelessly involved. The derivation of an expression for the instantaneous frequency of the response of a general linear filter to a general FM excitation is next to impossible. Existing general theory stops almost at the limit of analytical tractability, which is far from the end result, and signals the reader to proceed on his own thereafter. The stopping point of the general analysis is an expression for the response itself, not its instantaneous frequency.

Two general approaches of fundamental value are known. For periodic frequency modulations, the *Fourier spectral approach* has been employed most frequently. Here, as in other problems, the signal is represented by its Fourier spectrum and the filter is regarded as a frequency selector and is represented by its response to a general sine wave. Unfortunately, the usefulness of this approach is often severely hampered by the complexity of the required computations, particularly when it is used as a design basis for low-distortion FM systems and when no estimates of the penalties involved in the incorrect processing of certain portions of the input spectrum are readily obtainable.* This has led various investigators to seek new approaches, which we have chosen to describe as "dynamic" as opposed to "spectral".

In the "dynamic" approach, the filter is considered essentially as a dynamic system which, by virtue of its energy-storage elements,

*When the modulation is periodic and has a fundamental frequency that is comparable to or greater than one-half of the filter bandwidth (between half-power points), the spectral approach is much simpler for computations than the other methods because the number of components that must be included in the computation is generally manageable.

exercises an inertia or sluggishness that sets a limit on the speed with which its response can build up or decay. This outlook does not require a frequency analysis of the FM excitation. In fact, the more general forms of "dynamic" analysis allow the frequency modulation to be completely general (and not necessarily periodic). A paper by Carson and Fry[7] appears to be the earliest publication of a detailed mathematical analysis of the dynamic response of a linear system to a variable-frequency excitation. Various other important contributions have since been published.[8-11]

The basic viewpoint taken by Carson and Fry is that the dynamic response can be broken up into two components—the quasi-stationary component and the distortion component. The quasi-stationary component represents the part of the response that can be obtained formally from conventional sinusoidal steady-state circuit theory by substituting the variable instantaneous frequency for the assumed constant frequency. The validity of this substitution depends on the assumption that the speed with which the system can respond is such that its system function can be considered to change instantaneously with the changing frequency of the excitation. In general, however, the system response cannot build up or decay so quickly, and the complete solution requires a second so-called correction term. This correction term embodies the effect of the system sluggishness upon its response to a given FM signal. The quasi-stationary component of the total response represents essentially the total response only when the maximum rate of variation in the frequency of the excitation is slow compared with the speed of response of the system.

Carson and Fry derived the correction term as an *infinite series* whose convergence properties were obscured by the complexity of the analysis. The basic expansion that they derived and used in adducing the desired form for the final expression has since carried their name. Van der Pol and Stumpers followed up with a more direct expansion of the filter response into the desired form of expression. Stumpers restricted his analysis to periodic frequency modulations and demonstrated an asymptotic character for his own form of the expansion, as well as for the basic expansion of Carson and Fry.

In what follows, we derive two expansions that are similar to the Carson-and-Fry and the van der Pol-Stumpers expansions, but which are more general and complete and have well-defined convergence properties.

Let $h(t)$ represent the impulse response of a realizable and stable linear system. An excitation

$$\begin{aligned} i(t) &= f(t), \qquad t \geqslant 0 \\ &= 0, \qquad t \leqslant 0 \end{aligned}$$

causes a response

$$e(t) = \int_0^t h(\tau) f(t-\tau)\, d\tau \tag{34}$$

where $f(t)$ describes some signal. In particular, let

$$f(t) = e^{j[\omega_c t + \theta(t)]} \tag{35}$$

where ω_c is a constant and $\theta(t)$ is some function of time. If $e(t)$ is expressed in the form

$$e(t) = E(t)e^{j[\omega_c t + \theta(t)]}$$

the function $E(t)$ can, by simple rearrangements, be described by either of the two expressions

$$E(t) = \int_0^t h(\tau)e^{-j\omega_c\tau}\{e^{j[\theta(t-\tau) - \theta(t)]}\}d\tau \tag{36}$$

$$= \int_0^t h(\tau)e^{-j\omega_i\tau}\{e^{j[\theta(t-\tau) - \theta(t) + \tau\theta'(t)]}\}d\tau \tag{37}$$

where $\omega_i \equiv \omega_c + d\theta/dt$. The integration of each of these expressions is facilitated by expanding the corresponding function in braces into a series in powers of $(-\tau)$. To this end, let the function in braces in either expression be denoted $g(t,\tau)$. If $\theta(t)$ is analytic for all $|t| < 2T$, say, then $g(t, \tau)$ will be analytic for all $|t| < T$ and $|\tau| < T$. This means that $g(t,\tau)$ can be expressed in the form

$$g(t,\tau) = \sum_{n=0}^{\infty} a_n(t)\,(-\tau)^n \tag{38}$$

where the series converges uniformly and absolutely for every value of $|t| < T$ and τ in any interval $a \leqslant \tau \leqslant b$ which is interior to the interval $(-T, T)$. Thus, if $h(\tau)$ is bounded for all $|\tau| < T$, the series

$$\sum_{n=0}^{\infty} a_n(t)(-\tau)^n\,h(\tau)e^{-j\omega\tau} \tag{39}$$

will also be uniformly convergent for all $|t| < T$ and τ in any interval $a \leqslant \tau \leqslant b$ which is interior to the interval $(-T, T)$. Series (39) can therefore be integrated term by term in any closed interval (*e.g.*, 0 to t) that lies entirely within its region of convergence ($|t| < T$), to yield

$$E(t) = \sum_{n=0}^{\infty} a_n(t)\left[\int_0^t (-\tau)^n\,h(\tau)e^{-j\omega\tau}d\tau\right]. \tag{40}$$

This series, in turn, will converge uniformly for every value of t in any interval that is interior to the interval $(0, T)$. If we now write

$$E_{\text{cis}}(j\omega, t) = \int_0^t h(\tau)e^{-j\omega\tau}d\tau, \tag{41}$$

then the quantity in brackets in (40) is recognized as being $\partial^n E_{\text{cis}}(j\omega,t)/\partial(j\omega)^n$, and we can write

$$E(t) = \sum_{n=0}^{\infty} a_n(t)\frac{\partial^n E_{\text{cis}}(j\omega,t)}{\partial(j\omega)^n}\;. \tag{42}$$

For the arrangement of terms in (36), $\omega = \omega_c$, and, for convenience, we set

$$a_n(t) \equiv \frac{1}{n!} B_n(t). \tag{43}$$

For the arrangement of terms in (37), $\omega = \omega_i$, and

$$a_n(t) \equiv \frac{1}{n!} C_n(t). \tag{44}$$

The coefficients as defined in Eqs. (43) and (44) are presented in Table I.

In order to appreciate the significance of $E_{\text{cis}}(j\omega, t)$, note that if the excitation is given by

$$\begin{aligned} i(t) &= e^{j\omega t}, \text{ for } 0 \leqslant t < \infty \\ &= 0, \text{ for } t < 0, \end{aligned}$$

TABLE I

The Functions $B_n(t)$ and $C_n(t)$ of Eqs. (43) and (44)

n	$B_n(t) \equiv e^{-j\theta(t)} \dfrac{d^n}{dt^n} e^{j\theta(t)}$	$\dfrac{1}{n!} C_n(t)$
0	1	1
1	$j\, d\theta/dt$	0
2	$-\left[\dfrac{d\theta}{dt}\right]^2 + j\dfrac{d^2\theta}{dt^2}$	$j\dfrac{\theta''(t)}{2!}$
3	---	$j\dfrac{\theta'''(t)}{3!}$
4	$B_{n+1} = \left[j\dfrac{d\theta}{dt} + \dfrac{d}{dt}\right] B_n$	$j\dfrac{\theta^{iv}}{4!} + \dfrac{1}{2!}\left[j\dfrac{\theta''}{2!}\right]^2$
5		$j\dfrac{\theta^{v}}{5!} + \left[j\dfrac{\theta''}{2!}\right]\left[j\dfrac{\theta'''}{3!}\right]$
6		$j\dfrac{\theta^{vi}}{6!} + \left[j\dfrac{\theta''}{2!}\right]\left[j\dfrac{\theta^{iv}}{4!}\right] + \dfrac{1}{2!}\left[j\dfrac{\theta'''}{3!}\right]^2 + \dfrac{1}{3!}\left[j\dfrac{\theta''}{2!}\right]^3$
--		------------------

then the response will be

$$e_{cis}(t) = e^{j\omega t} \int_0^t h(\tau) e^{-j\omega\tau} d\tau$$

$$= E_{cis}(j\omega, t)\, e^{j\omega t}, \quad 0 \leqslant t < \infty. \tag{45}$$

The subscript "cis" stands for "cissoid," a convenient name for $e^{j\omega t}$

If $\theta(t)$ is an entire function (*i.e.*, singular only in the point at infinity), then $T = \infty$, and the termwise integration in (40) can be carried out to any finite (but otherwise arbitrarily large) value of t. The final expression for $E(t)$ in (42) will then converge uniformly for every value of t in any finite interval that is interior to the interval $0 \leqslant t < \infty$.

The Carson and Fry and van der Pol-Stumpers expansions follow from the preceding analysis if the upper limit of integration, t, is extended to infinity. This simplifies the results by replacing

$$E_{cis}(j\omega, t) \text{ by } E_{cis}(j\omega, \infty) = H(j\omega)$$

which is the well-known system function of the filter. But a heavy price is paid for this apparent simplification. There are several advantages that can be cited for working with the expression given in Eq. (34) for the system response, rather than with expressions that involve infinity in either (or both) of the limits of integration. First, uniform convergence of a series whose radius of convergence is infinite guarantees the validity of term-by-term integration only over every *finite* interval, but not over any interval that includes the point at infinity. Second, (disregarding the questionability of the series convergence) if $h(t)$ is of infinite duration, and if the range of integration includes the point at infinity, the individual terms in (39) must be guaranteed to be integrable over this range. This requires that all moments of $h(t)$ exist, which constitutes an added restriction on $h(t)$ that is not implied in the attributes "realizable" and "stable". Note that $h(t)$ has moments of all orders if it is composed of terms that decay exponentially as t approaches infinity. But the class of realizable and stable $h(t)$ functions includes impulse responses whose envelopes are not decaying exponentials.

A third reason can be added for not desiring to extend the upper limit of integration to infinity. Let us note that Eq. (34) can be written in the form

$$e(t) = \int_0^\infty h(\tau)\, f(t-\tau) d\tau - \int_t^\infty h(\tau) f(t-\tau)\, d\tau. \tag{46}$$

In this expression it is obvious that as $t \to \infty$,

$$\int_t^\infty h(\tau) f(t-\tau)\, d\tau \to 0.$$

Strictly speaking, this "transient component" must be taken into account as long as t is finite. It is therefore an approximation (which can be beyond the power of resolution of any existing measuring instrument) to assume that

$$e(t) = \int_0^\infty h(\tau) f(t-\tau) d\tau$$

for values of t that come much later than the longest time constant in $h(\tau)$. Similarly, it may be an excellent approximation to state that although

$$\begin{aligned} E_{\text{cis}}(j\omega, t) &= \int_0^\infty h(\tau) e^{-j\omega\tau}\, d\tau - \int_t^\infty h(\tau)\, e^{-j\omega\tau}\, d\tau \\ &= H(j\omega) - H(j\omega, t), \end{aligned} \tag{47}$$

one can write

$$E_{\text{cis}}(j\omega, t) = H(j\omega)$$

as long as the value of t exceeds many times the longest time constant in $h(t)$. Here, $H(j\omega)$ is the system function (see section IV, Chapter 3), and $H(j\omega, t)$ has been termed the "transient system function."

But *approximations*, or parts of the whole, these generally are. Working with a part of the whole, or with an approximate expression, is justifiable only if there are some analytical advantages to be gained from it. The opposite is true here.

Thus, if $h(\tau)$ is of infinite duration and if the excitation is maintained for all positive t, the extension of the upper limit of integration to infinity in Eq. (40) is justified only if $h(\tau)$ is considered to vanish *before* the upper limit of integration is reached. However, one must guard against substituting the system function, which is computed as the transform of the untruncated impulse response, into the final expansions (as is strictly done in the Carson and Fry and the van der Pol-Stumpers expansions) and expecting the resulting series to converge. The truncation of $h(\tau)$ that results from setting it equal to zero after some conveniently large value of τ must be strictly observed in the evaluation of E_{cis} in Eq. (41) if the convergence properties stated for the expansion (42) are to hold.

Since the point at infinity *is included* in the integrations that lead to the Carson and Fry and the van der Pol-Stumpers expansions, with no truncation of $h(\tau)$, our analysis uncovers the convergence properties of these expansions only for the situations in which $h(t)$ is of finite duration, or the FM excitation is applied during a finite time interval. For the class of linear, lumped, finite and stable networks, Stumpers[9] considers only a periodic frequency modulation, $s(rt)$, of fundamental repetition frequency r rad/sec, and establishes that the Carson and

Fry and the van der Pol-Stumpers expansions are expressible in the form*

$$E(rt) = \sum_{n=0}^{\infty} G_n(rt)r^n. \tag{48}$$

In this form, the two expansions are divergent, but asymptotic as the fundamental repetition frequency of the modulation goes to zero. Such expansions have the peculiar property that their terms diminish in magnitude with increasing n, until a minimum is reached, after which the terms increase with n beyond limits. This behavior of the terms in an asymptotic expansion does not impair the usefulness of such expansions. Indeed, asymptotic expansions possess some remarkably useful properties.[12] The following facts are of interest. First, the error incurred in approximating the expanded function by the sum of only the first n terms of the series is less than the first rejected term. The best approximation is obtained, therefore, when n is so chosen that the $(n + 1)$ term is the smallest term in the expansion. Thus, while a convergent series can be used to approximate the expanded function within an arbitrarily small tolerance, an asymptotic series cannot. But it is not uncommon for an asymptotic series to yield a better numerical approximation with a given number of terms than a convergent series.

If the general expansions derived above are used as computational tools, only a finite number of terms can usually be considered. Therefore, it is not necessary to expand into an infinite series: A direct application of Taylor's formula can be made to yield an expansion into the desired number of terms plus a remainder. If the appropriate number of moments exist for $h(t)$ (with integration from 0 to ∞), only $H(j\omega)$ and its derivatives need be considered in the expansion when events long after $t = 0$ are of interest. This will be illustrated, next, in the treatment of an extremely important situation.

4.2C Analysis of Response to Slow Frequency Modulations

We now seek the conditions that a general, linear system function must satisfy in order to insure an acceptable reproduction of a specified frequency modulation (when this function pertains to a selective filter) or an appropriate FM-to-AM conversion of this modulation (when the system function characterizes a discriminator circuit). As a basic requirement, the system must respond in a quasi-static manner; *i.e.*, its "dynamic" response must be closely described by its "static" response as predicted by *ac* steady-state circuit theory. This would enable us to view the FM excitation in terms of the resultant of all of its constituent spectral components, and to visualize it

*This form of expansion is readily obtainable from the more standard forms by substituting

$$\theta^{(n)}(t) = r^{n-1}s^{(n-1)}(rt)$$

in the standard forms and then grouping the result in terms of ascending powers of r. (See ref. 10.)

on the plots of the filter characteristics (*vs* frequency) as a sinusoid (or one spectral line) whose instantaneous position on the frequency scale varies in accordance with the dictates of the modulation. To be sure, this quasi-static response condition is not sufficient for either of the two aforementioned purposes. We must require also that the swept portion of the amplitude characteristic be linear for undistorted FM-to-AM conversion, and that the swept portion of the phase characteristic be linear for low-distortion transmission of the frequency modulation.

Thus, the desired response is

$$e(t) = H(j\omega_i(t))\, e^{j\int^t \omega_i(\xi)\, d\xi} \tag{49}$$

which is formally the same as the expression for the steady-state response to a constant-frequency excitation. But the actual response is given by

$$e(t) = E(t)\, e^{j\int^t \omega_i(\xi)\, d\xi} \tag{50}$$

where, according to the arrangement of the terms in the exponent as shown in Eq. (37),

$$E(t) = \int_0^\infty g(t,\tau)h(\tau)e^{-j\omega_i\tau}\, d\tau \tag{51}$$

$$\omega_i(t) = \text{instantaneous frequency of excitation}$$
$$= \omega_c + \theta'(t)$$

and

$$g(t,\tau) = e^{j[\theta(t-\tau) - \theta(t) + \tau\theta'(t)]} \tag{52}$$

Our main objective in the analysis that follows is to express $E(t)$ in the form

$$E(t) = H(j\omega_i) + R_{1E}(t) \tag{53}$$

and to determine a "useful" upper bound on the correction term $R_{1E}(t)$.

If we assume that $\theta(t)$ and $\theta'(t)$ are continuous for all t, and that $\theta''(t)$ exists for all finite t, then by Taylor's formula

$$\theta(t-\tau) = \theta(t) - \tau\theta'(t) + R_{2\theta} \tag{54}$$

in which the remainder is

$$R_{2\theta} = \frac{1}{2}\theta''(t-\eta\tau)(-\tau)^2,\ \eta = \eta(t,\tau) \text{ and } 0 < \eta < 1. \tag{55}$$

Substitution from Eq. (54) into Eq. (52) and application of Taylor's formula to $g(t,\tau)$ yields

$$g(t,\tau) = e^{jR_{2\theta}} = 1 + R_{1g}, \tag{56}$$

where the remainder

$$R_{1g} = jR_{2\theta}\, e^{j\mu R_{2\theta}}, \ \mu = \mu\,(t\,,\,\tau), \text{ and } 0 < \mu < 1. \tag{57}$$

Note that

$$|R_{1g}| = |R_{2\theta}| \leq \frac{1}{2}\,|\,\theta''(t)|_{\max}(-\tau)^2 \tag{58}$$

since $|\theta''(t-\eta\tau)| \leq |\theta''(t)|_{\max}$.

Finally, substitution from Eq. (56) into (51) yields

$$E(t) = H(j\omega_i) + R_{1E}(t)$$

where

$$R_{1E}(t) = \int_0^\infty R_{1g} h(\tau) e^{-j\omega_i\tau}\, d\tau \tag{59}$$

provided that the integral converges.

As a "first crack" at an upper bound on $R_{1E}(t)$, we note that

$$|R_{1E}(t)| \leq \int_0^\infty |R_{1g}|\cdot|\,h(\tau)\,|\,d\tau$$

$$\leq \frac{1}{2}\,|\,\theta''(t)|_{\max} \int_0^\infty \tau^2\,|h(\tau)|\,d\tau \tag{60}$$

where we have made use of (58). This leads to two important conclusions:

(a) The most important aspect of a frequency modulation, as far as low-distortion transmission through a linear filter is con-concerned, is the maximum slope of the frequency-modulation waveform.

(b) The validity of the expression (59) for $R_{1E}(t)$ is assured if the second moment (or moment of inertia about $t = 0$) of the magnitude (or "envelope") of the impulse response of the filter exists.

It is extremely interesting to point out that for almost any satisfactory definition of a "finite duration" for $h(t)$,

(second moment of $|h(t)|$) $\propto$ (area under $|h(t)|$) [duration of $h(t)$]^2.

The constant of proportionality depends upon the definition of "duration". For a simple illustration, try $e^{-\alpha t}$, $t \geq 0$, and define the duration as some multiple of $1/\alpha$, the time constant.

Another interesting interpretation of the second moment in (60) can be derived from an examination of $|h(t)|$. Since $h(t)$ is implicitly assumed to be the impulse response of a high-frequency selective circuit, let us denote some representative frequency (usually conveniently chosen to be the central frequency) in its passband by ω_0. In the notation of section 4.1, the high-frequency $h(t)$ can be represented as in Eq. (29a), and

$$|h_{BP}(t)| = 2\,|h_{LP}(t)|. \tag{61}$$

The function $|h_{\mathrm{LP}}(t)|$ may be considered as the impulse response of a hypothetical low-frequency filter whose system function is denoted $\mathcal{H}_{\ell f}(j\omega)$. The function $\mathcal{H}_{\ell f}(j\omega)$ is identical with $H_{\mathrm{LP}}(j\omega)$ only if $h_{\mathrm{LP}}(t)$ is real and of one sign for all t (as for a single-tuned circuit, for example). Thus we can write

$$\int_0^\infty |h_{\mathrm{BP}}(\tau)|\, e^{-j\omega\tau} d\tau = 2\,\mathcal{H}_{\ell f}(j\omega) \tag{62}$$

and

$$\int_0^\infty \tau^2 |h_{\mathrm{BP}}(\tau)|\, d\tau = 2\left[\frac{d^2}{d(j\omega)^2}\,\mathcal{H}_{\ell f}(j\omega)\right]_{j\omega=0} \tag{63}$$

We now return to Eq. (60), and recall that our interest here centers on the conditions under which $E(t)$ can be closely approximated by $H(j\omega_i)$. Since ω_i is a function of t so is $H(j\omega_i)$. Certainly, if the upper bound on $|R_{1E}(t)|$ in (60) is negligible compared with the smallest value that is attained by $|H(j\omega_i)|$ in the time interval of interest then the desired approximation holds. Such a statement however suffers from two handicaps: First, taking the integral of the absolute value of the integrand as the upper bound on the absolute value of the integral seldom provides a "tight" upper bound; second, the integration that is necessary for computing the second moment in (60) is most often analytically unmanageable.

We therefore seek a tighter and more manageable bound, with the emphasis on "manageable." Such a bound can be seen from the situation in which the function $\theta(t)$ is periodic (with a fundamental frequency of r rad/sec, say). For this situation (recall Eq. (48) and the discussion related to it), Stumpers has shown that $E(t)$ can be expanded in a divergent infinite series in powers of r,

$$E(t) = H(j\omega_i) + j\,\frac{1}{2}\, s'(rt)\, H''(j\omega_i)\, r + \cdots \tag{64}$$

which is asymptotic for $r \to 0$. In this equation (see footnote, p. 472),

$$rs'(rt) = \theta''(t).$$

From the properties of this expansion, we can state that if the second term is negligible in comparison with the first for all t in a complete modulation cycle, then

$$E(t) \cong H(j\omega_i) \tag{65}$$

with an error that is bounded by the maximum value attained by the magnitude of the second term during a modulation cycle. In the notation of Eq. (53), we have, in the case of a periodic modulation,

$$|R_{1E}(t)| \leqslant \left|\frac{1}{2}\,\theta''(t) H''(j\omega_i)\right|_{\max} \tag{66}$$

and the approximation (65) holds as long as

$$\left|\frac{1}{2}\,\theta''(t)\frac{H''(j\omega_i)}{H(j\omega_i)}\right| \ll 1. \tag{67}$$

The same conclusions can be extended to the case of a non-periodic modulation by first constructing a periodic function that coincides with the non-periodic modulation function over the entire (finite) time interval of interest and continues outside of this interval in a manner that meets the requirements of periodicity. Since the preceding conclusions apply in any time interval within one period of the auxiliary periodic function, they apply in particular over the interval that encompasses the desired non-periodic waveform.

Accordingly, the general fundamental condition for the validity of a quasi-static argument [approximation (65)] in analyzing the response of a linear system to an FM signal (the so-called instantaneous-frequency approach) is summed up by demanding that the maximum relative error

$$\epsilon_m \equiv \frac{1}{2}\left[\left|\theta''(t)\right| \cdot \left|\frac{H''(j\omega_i)}{H(j\omega_i)}\right|\right]_{\max} \ll 1. \tag{68}$$

With a given FM excitation and a given filter, the value of ϵ_m will vary with the position of the unmodulated carrier frequency, ω_c, relative to the center of the pass-band. For certain values of ω_c, the maximum slope of $\omega_i(t)$ will occur at precisely those instants of time when $\omega_i(t)$ equals the frequency at which $|H''(j\omega)/H(j\omega)|$ is maximum (note absence of subscripts i). In applications in which this situation is likely to arise, condition (68) can be taken in the form

$$\epsilon_{\max} = \frac{1}{2}\left|\theta''(t)\right|_{\max} \cdot \left|\frac{H''(j\omega)}{H(j\omega)}\right|_{\max} \ll 1. \tag{69}$$

Situations in which this form of condition (68) (which is the most restrictive but most manageable) must be used become easily distinguishable once the functional behavior of the ratio $|H''(j\omega)/H(j\omega)|$ has been determined and the expected frequency range that will be covered by $\omega_i(t)$ has been specified.

The ratio $|H''(j\omega)/H(j\omega)|$ is all that represents a filter characterized by $H(j\omega)$ in condition (68) for quasi-stationary response to a given FM excitation. The sluggishness of the filter as a dynamic system, therefore, is characterized completely by $|H''(j\omega)/H(j\omega)|$. Consequently, this quantity has been called the "sluggishness ratio" of the filter. Sluggishness-ratio plots of Butterworth bandpass filters* of

*A Butterworth filter usually is characterized by a pole pattern in which the poles fall on a semicircle whose center lies on the $j\omega$ axis and whose radius equals one-half the overall bandwidth of the filter between half-power points. The exact positions of the poles of an nth-order Butterworth filter are at the locations of the $2n$th roots of $(-1)^{n+1}$ that lie in the left half-plane.

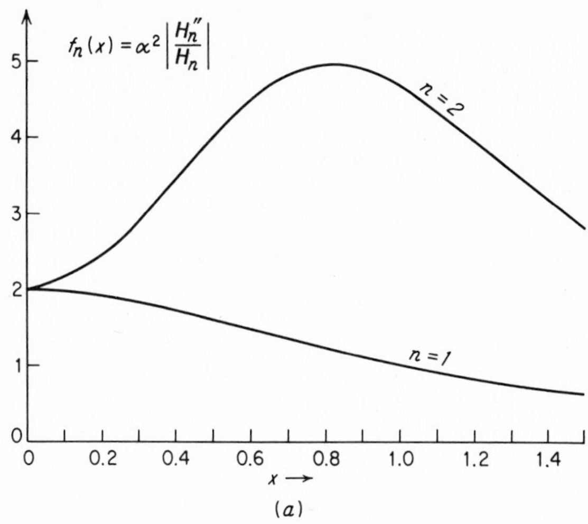

(a)

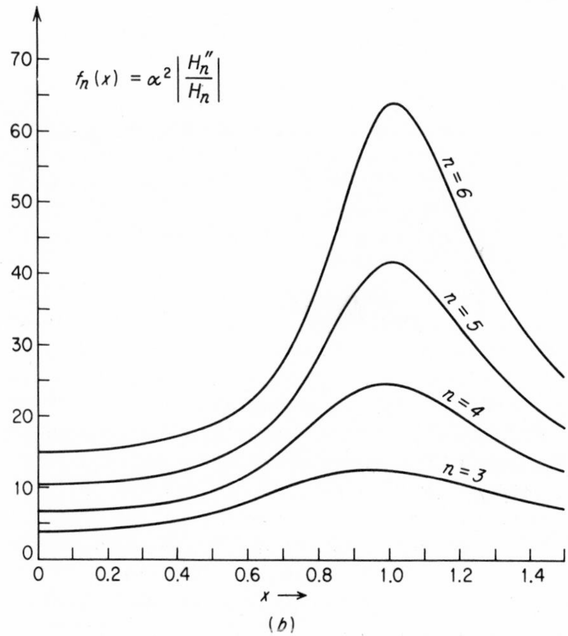

(b)

Fig. 12. Normalized sluggishness-ratio plots for nth-order Butterworth filters. The sluggishness ratio is $|H''(j\omega)/H(j\omega)|$; α is one-half the overall bandwidth (in rad/sec.) between half-power points; x measures the deviation from the center frequency in units of one α.

orders up to the sixth are presented in Fig. 12. The curve marked $n = 1$ pertains to a single-tuned high-Q circuit.

The appearance of the curves in Fig. 12 brings out the fact that the form (69) of condition (68) is more conservative than it need be for many applications in which $|H''(j\omega)/H(j\omega)|$ attains its maximum outside the range of expected instantaneous-frequency values. When the computations promise to be too involved, plots such as those of Fig. 12, in conjunction with condition (68), should provide a quick, safe estimate.

The use of condition (69), however, insures that the error will always be smaller than that which we may be willing to tolerate. The filter will then respond in a quasi-static manner, regardless of which part of the response characteristics is swept by the variable instantaneous frequency of the excitation.

As a simple example, let

$$\theta(t) = \delta \sin(\omega_m t + \phi_m), \tag{70}$$

wherin δ may be interpreted as either a phase deviation independent of ω_m or as the ratio of frequency deviation, $\Delta\Omega$, to the modulating frequency ω_m. Thus

$$|\theta''(t)|_{\max} = \omega_m{}^2\,\delta = \omega_m \cdot \Delta\Omega.$$

If the filter is a single-tuned, high-Q circuit, and ω_c is equal to the frequency of resonance, ω_0, then condition (68) reverts to condition (69), which yields

$$\epsilon_m = \frac{\omega_m}{(BW)/2} \cdot \frac{\Delta\Omega}{(BW)/2} \ll 1, \tag{71}$$

where (BW) is the bandwidth (in rad/sec) between the half-power points. This condition states that the product of the modulation frequency and the maximum frequency deviation, when each is measured in units of one-half the filter bandwidth, must be negligible compared with unity in order for a computation of the steady-state response of the tuned circuit on the instantaneous-frequency basis to approximate closely the true response.

As an alternative starting point for the analysis of the present subsection, we could have chosen the arrangement (36) for the expression for $E(t)$. The resulting expansion, when carried to two terms plus a remainder, bears directly upon the theory of FM-to-AM conversion. Thus, if the network is intended to perform FM-to-AM conversion and the envelope of its response is detected by a peak detector of unit detection efficiency, the result will be

$$|E(t)| = |H(j\omega_c)| \cdot \left|1 + j\,\frac{H'(j\omega_c)}{H(j\omega_c)} \cdot \frac{d\theta}{dt} + \frac{R_{2E}(t)}{H(j\omega_c)}\right|. \tag{72}$$

in which $R_{2E}(t)$ is the remainder. For good discriminator sensitivity and low distortion, we require that $jH'(j\omega_c)/H(j\omega_c)$ be real (as for a pure reactance), $H'(j\omega_c)$ be high, and that the relative error be

$$\epsilon = \frac{1}{2}\left[\sqrt{\left(\frac{d\theta}{dt}\right)^4 + \left(\frac{d^2\theta}{dt^2}\right)^2}\right]_{\max} \cdot \left|\frac{H''(j\omega_c)}{H(j\omega_c)}\right| \ll 1. \tag{73}$$

As an illustration, let $\theta(t)$ be given by Eq. (70) and let the system be a high-Q parallel-resonant circuit whose half-bandwidth between half-power points is α rad/sec. If x_c represents the deviation of ω_c from the resonance frequency in units of α, then

$$\epsilon = \begin{cases} \left(\frac{\Delta\Omega}{\alpha}\right)^2\left(1 + x_c^2\right)^{-1} < \left(\frac{\Delta\Omega}{\alpha}\right)^2 & \text{for } \delta > 1 \\ \frac{\omega_m \Delta\Omega}{\alpha^2}\left(1 + x_c^2\right)^{-1} < \left(\frac{\omega_m}{\alpha}\right)\left(\frac{\Delta\Omega}{\alpha}\right) & \text{for } \delta < 1. \end{cases}$$

Equation (49) also clearly shows that, under conditions of quasi-stationary response, the amplitude characteristic of the filter describes the envelope of the response. If $|H(j\omega_i)|$ varies with ω_i over the range of instantaneous-frequency variations, then discriminator action, or FM-to-AM conversion, results. For undistorted conversion, the time variations in the resultant envelope should be related linearly to the time variations of the instantaneous frequency. This requirement, evidently, can be met only if $|H(j\omega_i)|$ is a linear function of ω over the entire range of the desired undistorted conversion.

4.2D FM Bandwidth Requirements and Residual Distortion

The so-called dynamic and static responses of transmission filters and of discriminators become essentially one and the same when the condition for quasi-stationary response is satisfied. This condition, therefore, must form the basis for prescribing system bandwidths for low-distortion processing of FM signals. Because the frequency excursions of the FM signal must be contained within the filter passband in order to minimize the distortion, the appropriate formula for a transmission filter is derived by first setting

$$\epsilon = \frac{1}{2}\left|\theta''(t)\right|_{\max} \cdot \rho \left|\frac{H''(j\omega)}{H(j\omega)}\right|_{\max} \tag{74}$$

in which $\rho \leq 1$, with the requirement that $\epsilon \leq 1/10$. We then note that

$$\left|\frac{H''(j\omega)}{H(j\omega)}\right|_{\max} = k/(BW)^2 \tag{75}$$

where (BW) is the filter bandwidth between half-power points and k is a constant that has been called the "sluggishness index" or the "index of stiffness'' of the filter. Substitution in (74) and solution for (BW) leads to

$$(BW) = K\sqrt{|\theta''(t)|_{\max}}, \quad K = \sqrt{\frac{\rho k}{2\epsilon}}, \ \epsilon \leqslant 1/10. \tag{76}$$

From our previous discussions it is evident that if the peaks of $|H''(j\omega)/H(j\omega)|$ lie within the nominal pass-band (or within the range of expected frequency sweep), then ρ is best chosen equal to unity. Otherwise, values of $\rho < 1$ may be permissible, but no smaller values than 1/2 are generally advisable for low-distortion transmission filters. For most practical purposes, a satisfactory choice of (BW) is of the order of the value given in (76) with $K = \sqrt{5k}$.

For discriminator filters, it is often permissible to choose smaller values of (BW). In practice, FM-to-AM conversion usually is achieved with single-tuned circuits whose responses are combined in appropriate ways. The fact that the signal is always placed intentionally on the sloping sides of the amplitude characteristics of the tuned circuits enables us to recommend the formula

$$(BW) \geqslant 5\sqrt{|\theta''(t)|_{\max}} \tag{77}$$

for each single-tuned circuit.

The choice of (BW), therefore, generally must be made on the basis of the maximum rate at which the instantaneous frequency of the excitation is varied, and not on the basis of the maximum amount by which it is deviated. The type of desired filter, and often the portion of the filter characteristics that will be swept, must also be considered.

It is now of interest to examine the accuracy of a generally accepted rule of thumb whereby the significant bandwidth occupied by the spectrum of a frequency-modulated sinusoid is estimated to be twice the sum of the maximum frequency deviation and the fundamental modulation frequency. It has been common practice to use this rule in specifying filter bandwidths in order to achieve an acceptable compromise between the desire to minimize the distortion of the modulation by the filter and the desire to minimize the noise bandwidth.

Assume that the average frequency of the FM signal is expected to fall at or near the center of the filter pass-band, and denote the frequency modulation by

$$\frac{d\theta}{dt} = \Delta\Omega \cdot g(\omega_m t), \tag{78}$$

where $\Delta\Omega$ is the frequency deviation, $|g(\omega_m t)_{\max}| = 1$, and ω_m is the fundamental repetition frequency of the modulation. If in accordance with the aforementioned rule of thumb we choose $(BW) = 2(\Delta\Omega + \omega_m)$, and substitute from (78) in (74), we obtain

$$\epsilon = \kappa \frac{\delta}{(1+\delta)^2}, \quad \kappa \equiv \frac{1}{8}\rho k |g'(\omega_m t)|_{\max}.$$

Recall that ϵ is the upper bound on the magnitude of the relative error incurred in assuming that the dynamic response of the filter is at every instant identical with its sinusoidal steady-state response. For $\delta < 1/10$, $\epsilon \cong \kappa\delta$ and for $\delta > 10$, $\epsilon \cong \kappa/\delta$. When $\delta = 1$, ϵ takes on its maximum value $\kappa/4$. For a single-tuned circuit and a sinusoidal modulation, $\kappa = 1$, and $\epsilon_{max} = 1/4$, which does not indicate a negligible error. With most of the widely used filters in FM systems and with modulations for which $|g'(\omega_m t)|_{max} > 1$, ϵ_{max} can assume much larger values.

We may conclude, therefore, that the aforementioned rule of thumb involves errors that lie within tolerable limits only for very large ($\delta > 10\kappa$) or very small ($\delta < 1/10\kappa$) values of the modulation index, δ. In these cases, we may say that the bandwidth is approximately twice the frequency deviation or twice the modulation frequency, whichever is predominantly larger. Intolerable errors, however, are introduced in the range $10\kappa > \delta > 1/10\kappa$.

As a generally more satisfactory substitute, we propose the formula

$$(BW) = 2\,[\Delta\Omega + \nu\omega_m], \tag{79a}$$

which leads to $\epsilon = \epsilon_{max} = \kappa/4\nu$ when $\delta = \nu$. If we want $\epsilon \leqslant \epsilon_{max} < 1/10$ for all δ, we must choose

$$\nu > 5\,\kappa/2. \tag{79b}$$

These results show that a high modulation index (ratio of maximum frequency deviation to modulation frequency) does not necessarily imply that the significant spectrum of the FM wave will be contained within a bandwidth of nearly twice the frequency deviation. Moreover, the usual practice of estimating filter bandwidths on this basis (and without due regard to the specific filter) can lead to serious errors. A good example is not difficult to formulate in the light of the results of this section. One example of practical importance is provided by the frequency disturbance pattern caused by co-channel interference in FM reception (see section 5.3).

We next investigate the nature of the residual distortion in the instantaneous frequency of the response of a filter whose bandwidth is chosen in accordance with (76). For this purpose, we need an approximate expansion for the instantaneous frequency of the response, when the response is approximately quasi-static. We first substitute

$$H(j\omega_i) = A(\omega_i)\,e^{j\phi(\omega_i)}$$

into

$$E(t) \cong H(j\omega_i)\,[1 + j\epsilon(t)],\quad \epsilon(t) \equiv \frac{1}{2}\,\theta''(t)\frac{H''(j\omega_i)}{H(j\omega_i)} \tag{80}$$

where $|\epsilon(t)| \leq \epsilon_m$, and reduce the result to the form

$$E(t) = [E_r + jE_i]\, e^{j\phi(\omega_i)},$$

$$= |E(t)| \exp j\,[\phi(\omega_i) + \tan^{-1} E_i/E_r] \tag{81}$$

where E_r and E_i are real and imaginary parts. If ω_{io} denotes the instantaneous frequency of the response, then for $\epsilon_m \ll 1$, $\omega_{io}(t)$ is closely approximated by

$$\begin{aligned}\omega_{io}(t) = \omega_i + \phi'(\omega_i)\theta''(t) + \frac{1}{2}\left(\phi'^2 - \frac{A''}{A}\right)\Bigg[\theta'''(t) \\ - \frac{1}{2}\theta''^3\left(\phi''' + 2\frac{AA'' - A'^2}{A^2}\phi' + 2\frac{A'}{A}\phi''\right) - \frac{1}{2}\theta''\theta'''\left(\phi'' + 2\frac{A'}{A}\phi'\right)\Bigg] \\ + \frac{1}{2}\theta''^2\left[2\phi'\phi'' + \frac{A'A'' - AA'''}{A^2}\right].\end{aligned} \tag{82}$$

If in Eq. (80) we drop $\epsilon(t)$ and write $E(t) = H(j\omega_i)$, the instantaneous frequency of the response becomes

$$\omega_{io}(t) = \omega_c + \frac{d\theta}{dt} + \phi'(\omega_i)\frac{d^2\theta}{dt^2}. \tag{83}$$

It is clear from this expression that, even under conditions of quasi-static response, the filter will introduce some distortion into the instantaneous-frequency waveform. This distortion is a function only of the slope of the phase characteristic of the filter and the rate at which the instantaneous frequency of the excitation is varied. The nature of this distortion is brought out by rewriting Eq. (83) in the form

$$\begin{aligned}\omega_{io}(t) &= \omega_c + \theta'(t) + \phi'(\omega_c)\theta''(t) + \theta''(t)\sum_{\nu=1}^{\infty}\frac{1}{\nu!}\phi^{(\nu+1)}(\omega_c)[\theta'(t)]^\nu \\ &= \omega_c + \theta'(t + \phi'(\omega_c)) - \sum_{q=2}^{m-1}\frac{1}{q!}\theta^{(q+1)}(t)[\phi'(\omega_c)]^q - R_{m\theta'} \\ &\quad + \theta''(t)\sum_{\nu=1}^{n-1}\frac{1}{\nu!}\phi^{(\nu+1)}(\omega_c)[\theta'(t)]^\nu + \theta''(t)R_{n\phi'},\end{aligned} \tag{84}$$

in which $R_{m\theta'}$ and $R_{n\phi'}$ are remainders after the indicated number of terms in the Taylor formulas used. In this expression, the constituents of the residual distortion are explicitly separated into a part that isolates the unavoidable delay and a part that brings out the effect of nonlinearities in $\phi(\omega)$. Curiously, there is also a third part that depends upon the slope, $\phi'(\omega_c)$, of the phase characteristic, which must certainly be an error because uniform delay cannot cause waveform distortion.

The waveform distortion terms in powers of $\phi'(\omega_c)$ in Eq. (84) represent an inherent "truncation" error that is caused by the restriction of the expression for the dynamic response of the filter to the quasi-stationary term [as in Eq. (49)], and this fact must be kept in mind in any computations of distortion products that start from Eq. (83). The terms that make up this truncation error constitute the first two terms in a power series expansion of $\theta'(t + \phi'(\omega_i))$. It is interesting to note that a "quasi-stationary" argument that is based on visualizing the FM signal as a sinusoid that slides up and down the plot of $\phi(\omega)$ vs. ω would require a quasi-static approximation of $\omega_{io}(t)$ by $\omega_i(t + \phi'(\omega_i))$, or

$$\omega_{io}(t) = \omega_c + \theta'(t + \phi'(\omega_i)),$$

where $\phi'(\omega_i)$ is an "instantaneous time delay." If this instantaneous time delay varies with ω_i, then $\theta'(t + \phi'(\omega_i))$ will carry a waveform distortion as well as a time delay. However, if $\phi'(\omega_i)$ is a linear function of ω_i over the range of frequencies covered by ω_i, then $\phi'(\omega_i) = \phi'(\omega_c) =$ constant, and $\theta'(t + \phi'(\omega_c))$ is merely a delayed replica of the modulation, $\theta'(t)$.

V. RECEPTION IN THE PRESENCE OF ADDITIVE DISTURBANCES —COHERENT-SIGNAL INTERFERENCE

Additive disturbances encountered in radio communications can be identified with one, or a combination, of three distinct types:

(a) Interference from one or more spurious signals whose general characteristics are similar to those of the desired signal. The source of the interfering signals may be radio equipment that does not belong to the communication system proper, although there are important situations (for example, two-way communication systems using the same frequency channel, or partially overlapping channels, for outgoing and incoming signals) in which the interfering signals originate in the same system. The interference may represent intentional jamming from unfriendly sources, unintentional jamming resulting from inadequate geographic spacing of systems operating in neighboring frequency channels (with no compensating control of radiated power levels), multipath transmission, or deliberate superposition of different carriers or subcarriers for multiplex transmission. For convenience, we shall call this type of disturbance *coherent-signal interference*.

(b) *Impulse noise*, or interference from bursts of radiation whose duration is short in comparison with the duration of a message element or with the period of the fastest message fluctuations. This type of noise usually originates from electric discharges between charged bodies or between separating surfaces in the process of breaking a circuit (or interrupting a current). Notable sources are lightning discharges, car-ignition systems, arcing commutators and telephone switches. Corona discharges and precipitation static are also distinguished members of this family.

(c) *Random-fluctuation noise,* or noise originating in the ultimate *unsmoothness* of current flow in solids and electronic emission from cathodes. This type of noise may also be imitated by the random superposition of a large number of different sinusoids or other waveforms. Other sources (such as colliding galaxies, or so-called "radio stars") have been discussed in Chapter 15.

The manner in which each of these types of disturbance may affect the reception of the various kinds of modulated signals is of vital concern in the planning and evaluation of communication systems. In the final analysis, the design of a reliable radio communication system hinges upon the choice of the modulation method that shows the greatest promise of reliable message recovery (within some desired geographic or spacial range) in the presence of one or more of the types of additive disturbance listed above, consistent with unavoidable regulatory constraints on transmitted power and bandwidth occupany. There are also important situations in which the most decisive factor in the design of a system is the relative *simplicity* of the receiver instrumentation that would be required with each type of modulation for securing the desired quality of reception in the presence of specified disturbances.

In the remainder of this chapter, we discuss the effect of the various types of additive disturbances upon reception. The most important aspect of this discussion is the emphasis that we shall place upon the role of the signal-processing operations after the front-end of the receiver in shaping the outcome of the demodulation process. It is these operations that usually set the limitations on the noise performance of a modulation system. Throughout our discussions, we shall continually seek the distinctions that can be made between the characteristic properties of the signal and those of the disturbance. The basis of any effective technique for suppressing extraneous disturbances is the ability to distinguish between the disturbance and the desired signal and to utilize this distinction automatically. Interference can be suppressed if it can be distinguished from the desired signal before demodulation, or if its disturbance after demodulation is fundamentally distinguishable from the type of fluctuations that carry the message. The basis for distinction can be any definable and useable property of the radio-frequency signals, such as their relative amplitudes or frequencies, or of the message and disturbance waveforms, such as their spectra, etc. A successful scheme for interference or noise suppression will be capable of discriminating against the characteristic features of the disturbance that are not normally expected in proper message modulation, without seriously affecting the message modulation itself.

But although we shall concentrate on signal-processing methods at the receiver, it is difficult to dissociate developments in techniques for suppressing additive noises from developments of overall system concepts. Indeed, the discovery of new effective methods of separating signals and suppressing disturbances inevitably suggests new signaling and multiplexing methods.

5.1 Interference in Linear-Modulation Systems

In section 3.1, it was stated that a generic representation for a linear-modulation signal is given by

$$e_s(t) = E_s g_s(t) \cos(\omega_s t + \phi_s). \tag{85}$$

The interference is assumed to arise from the presence of another signal that could not be adequately suppressed by standard intermediate-frequency (i-f) filtering in the receiver. If the desired signal is represented by $e_s(t)$ at the input of the demodulator, let the undesired signal at that point be described by

$$e_n(t) = E_n g_n(t) \cos(\omega_n t + \phi_n). \tag{86}$$

In a product demodulator, the resultant of $e_s(t)$ and $e_n(t)$ is multiplied by a locally generated oscillation

$$e_{osc}(t) = E_{osc} \cos(\omega_{osc} t + \phi_{osc}) \tag{87}$$

and the product is usually applied to a filter whose passband is assumed to extend only over the range of frequencies (0 + to $B_{\ell p}$ cps, say) that are expected in the class of message waveforms represented by $g_s(t)$. The low-frequency components of the product $2e_{osc}(t)\left[e_s(t) + e_n(t)\right]$, *before any filtering is applied,* are

$$E_{osc} E_s g_s(t) \cos\left[(\omega_s - \omega_{osc})t + \phi_s - \phi_{osc}\right] \tag{88}$$

and

$$E_{osc} E_n g_n(t) \cos\left[(\omega_n - \omega_{osc})t + \phi_n - \phi_{osc}\right]. \tag{89}$$

We assume that the high-frequency components have sufficiently well-removed spectra to be completely separable from (88) and (89). The desired outcome of the demodulation is a waveform whose time dependence is completely defined by $g_s(t)$. There are several ways in which this outcome could be secured, with varying degrees of disturbance in the output. Let us illustrate by examining some of these possibilities.

Conventional product demodulation—Suppose we adjust the local oscillation so that $\omega_s = \omega_{osc}$. This transforms (88) into

$$E_{osc} E_s g_s(t) \cos(\phi_s - \phi_{osc}) \tag{90}$$

and (89) into

$$E_{osc} E_n g_n(t) \cos\left[(\omega_n - \omega_s)t + \phi_n - \phi_{osc}\right]. \tag{91}$$

The signal component in (90) is maximized if $\phi_{osc} = \phi_s$. The noise component is given by (91). If the multiplication is assumed to be followed by a filter that passes (uniformly) only those frequencies that fall between 0+ and B_{ℓ_p} cps (which is the range of frequencies expected in $g_s(t)$, the output of the filter will certainly contain the desired signal component

$$\kappa_d E_{osc} E_s g_s(t) \cos(\phi_s - \phi_{osc}) \tag{92}$$

in which κ_d is a constant of the demodulator. Whether or not a noise component will also be present in the output depends upon the spectrum of the component described by (91). This spectrum is (to within a constant magnitude factor) given by

$$G_n(\omega - \omega_n + \omega_s)e^{j(\phi_n - \phi_{osc})} + G_n(\omega + \omega_n - \omega_s)e^{-j(\phi_n + \phi_{osc})} \tag{93}$$

in which $G_n(\omega)$ is the Fourier transform of $g_n(t)$. If (93) is identically equal to zero within $0 < \omega/2\pi \leq B_{\ell_p}$, then no disturbance will be present in the output of the low-pass filter. With the aid of a sketch that is similar to Fig. 1, it will be seen that if ω_{nh} is the highest frequency in $G_n(\omega)$ then (93) will be identically zero in $0 < \omega/2\pi \leq B_{\ell_p}$ provided that $|(|\omega_n - \omega_s| - \omega_{nh})| > 2\pi B_{\ell_p}$. Consequently, no disturbance will be present in the output when the beat frequency $|(\omega_n - \omega_s)| > \omega_{nh} + 2\pi B_{\ell_p}$, and this constitutes one possible extreme. Another extreme occurs when $|(|\omega_n - \omega_s| + \omega_{nh})| < 2\pi B_{\ell_p}$: for then the entire noise component

$$\kappa_d E_{osc} E_s g_n(t) \cos[(\omega_n - \omega_s)t + \phi_n - \phi_{osc}] \tag{94}$$

will be present in the output, along with the signal component. An examination of (94) relative to (92) and comparison with (86) relative to (85) shows a degradation in the signal relative to the noise by a factor of $|\cos(\phi_s - \phi_{osc})| \leq 1$.

Intermediate between the extremes just described is the situation in which

$$|(|\omega_n - \omega_s| - \omega_{nh})| < 2\pi B_{\ell_p} < |(|\omega_n - \omega_s| + \omega_{nh})|.$$

Here the expression for the noise component in the output is not easily described but it can be computed from a knowledge of $G_n(\omega)$ by standard Fourier techniques.

The preceding discussion can be adapted (with trivial elaborations or modifications) to conventional product demodulation of all linear-modulation systems (AM and related systems). It can be concluded that if the spectrum of the undesired signal, $e_n(t)$, overlaps the spectrum of the desired signal, $e_s(t)$, then a disturbance will be present in the output whose properties depend upon the degree of overlap between the spectra of $e_n(t)$ and $e_s(t)$.

Linear interference-suppression techniques— Some interesting interference-suppression or immunization operations can be developed from a reexamination of (88) and (89), this time concentrating on the noise component first. For example, suppose we adjust the oscillation so that

$$\omega_{\text{osc}} = \omega_n$$

and

$$\phi_n - \phi_{\text{osc}} = \text{an odd multiple of } \pi/2. \tag{95}$$

This reduces the noise component to zero, and leaves a low-frequency signal component given by

$$E_{\text{osc}} E_s g_s(t) \cos [(\omega_s - \omega_n)t + \psi] \tag{96}$$

in which ψ is a constant phase angle. If $\omega_s = \omega_n$ (cochannel interference), a filter with a passband from 0+ to B_{ℓ_p} cps delivers

$$\kappa_d E_{\text{osc}} E_s g_s(t) \cos \psi \tag{97}$$

in which it is quite unlikely that $\cos \psi = 0$. However, if $\omega_s \neq \omega_n$, several possibilities can be considered. First, if $|\omega_s - \omega_n| > 2\pi B_{\ell_p}/2$, then it is possible to use a bandpass filter with an adjustable lower-cut-off frequency that can be set equal to $|\omega_s - \omega_n|$ in order to isolate $e^{j\psi} G_{s+}(\omega - |\omega_s - \omega_n|) + e^{-j\psi} G_{s-}(\omega + |\omega_s - \omega_n|)$ from the spectrum of (96) (where we have used a notation that was defined in Fig. 1). The outcome is an undisturbed single-sideband signal that carries the desired message. This signal can then be multiplied by $\cos [(\omega_s - \omega_n)t + \psi]$ and applied to a filter with passband from 0+ to B_{ℓ_p} in order to deliver the desired message undisturbed.

If, however, $|\omega_s - \omega_n| < 2\pi B_{\ell_p}/2$, the positive-and negative-frequency halves of the spectrum of (96) overlap, with distortion consequences that depend upon the beat frequency $|\omega_n - \omega_s|$, and no linear "spectral shuffling" and filtering will yield $g_s(t)$ without considerable distortion.

We conclude from these results that it is possible to suppress interference in linear-modulation systems by linear-modulation operations under either of two conditions: (a) $\omega_n = \omega_s$ and $\phi_n \neq \phi_s$; and (b) $|\omega_n - \omega_s| > 2\pi B_{\ell_p}/2$, in which B_{ℓ_p} is assumed to bound the highest-frequency expected in the spectrum of $g_s(t)$. Otherwise, even though the noise component *per se* can be suppressed, the output signal will as a result "jam itself" to a degree that depends upon $|\omega_n - \omega_s|$ and the shape of $|G_s(\omega)|$ (*i.e.*, its functional dependence upon ω, or the manner in which the energy content of $g_s(t)$ is distributed among its spectral components). The dependence of the unavoidable self-jamming upon $|G_s(\omega)|$ provides interesting opportunities for signal design that minimizes this effect. These conclusions hold for arbitrary relative strengths for $e_s(t)$ and $e_n(t)$.

5.2 Interference in AM with Envelope Detection

Envelope detectors are almost universally employed in AM receivers because of their relative simplicity and low cost. Such a detector ideally delivers an output voltage that is directly proportional to the magnitude of the instantaneous amplitude of the resultant signal at its input. Thus, if the sum of two sinusoids,

$$e_{\text{if}}(t) = E_s \cos pt + a\,E_s \cos(p + r)t, \tag{98}$$

where E_s = constant, $a < 1$, and $r \ll p$, is applied at the input of an envelope detector, the output, $e_{\text{out}}(t)$, is determined by first rewriting (98) in the form

$$e_{\text{if}}(t) = E_s A(t) \cos\left[pt + \theta(t)\right] \tag{99}$$

$$A(t) = \sqrt{1 + 2\,a \cos rt + a^2}$$

$$\theta(t) = \tan^{-1} \frac{a \sin rt}{1 + a \cos rt},$$

and then claiming that

$$e_{\text{out}}(t) \propto E_s \sqrt{1 + 2a \cos rt + a^2}. \tag{100}$$

If, in practice, the envelope detector is realized in the form shown in Fig. 13, the validity of the claim (100) requires that the time constant

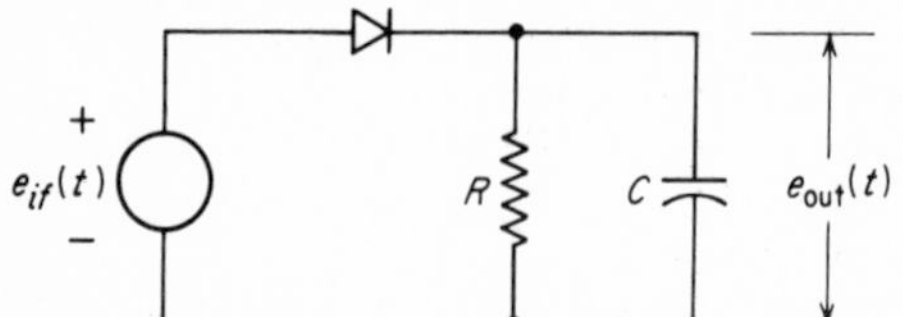

Fig. 13. A simple envelope-detector circuit.

RC be sufficiently small to enable voltage fluctuations proportional to $A(t)$ to appear across the RC combination. Stated more explicitly, the condition is that the magnitude of the rate ($|E_s A(t)/RC|$) at which the capacitor can charge (or discharge) at any instant of time must be greater than (or, at worst, equal to) the magnitude of the rate ($|E_s A'(t)|$) at which $A(t)$ is increasing (or decreasing) at that instant of time. For this condition to be satisfied at all instants of time, RC must be chosen so that

$$RC \leqslant \left|\frac{A(t)}{A'(t)}\right|_{\min}. \tag{101}$$

For $A(t)$ of Eq. (99), we must have

$$RC \leqslant \frac{1 - a^2}{ar}. \tag{102}$$

For simplicity, we assume here that one of two circumstances applies: In the envelope-detector circuit, the switching element is buffered from the associated low-frequency circuit, or, if it is not, condition (102) (or its equivalent for the actual circuit) is satisfied. In either case, the effect of the interference upon the output can be determined as follows.

We start with the sum of two sinusoids as described in Eq. (98). A Fourier analysis of $A(t)$ yields

$$A(t) = \sum_{n=0}^{\infty} A_{nr}(a) \cos nrt \tag{103}$$

in which

$$A_0(a) = 1 + (a/2)^2 + \frac{1}{4}(a/2)^4 + \cdots = \text{average value of } A(t) \tag{104}$$

$$A_r(a) = a\left[1 - \frac{1}{2}(a/2)^2 - \frac{1}{4}(a/2)^4 - \cdots\right] \equiv af_r(a), \text{ say} \tag{105}$$

$$A_{2r}(a) = -(a/2)^2\,[1 - (a/2)^2 - \cdots]$$

- - - -

$$A_{nr}(a) \propto (a/2)^n. \tag{106}$$

The structure of the envelope of $e_{\text{if}}(t)$ [as described by Eq. (98)] is thus seen to contain a zero-frequency component whose amplitude $E_sA_0(a)$ depends principally upon E_s, the amplitude of the stronger sinusoid, a beat-frequency component whose amplitude $E_sA_r(a) = E_wf_r(a)$, say, depends principally upon the amplitude, E_w, of the weaker sinusoid; and components at harmonics of the beat frequency, r, the nth harmonic having an amplitude that depends principally upon $(a/2)^nE_s$. An envelope detector with a low-pass filter that passes frequencies from zero to $B_{\ell p}$ cps would therefore deliver all components whose frequencies are contained in this range. In contrast, a product demodulator that multiplies $e_{\text{if}}(t)$ by $\cos pt$, when followed by the same low-pass filter, would yield only a zero-frequency component whose amplitude depends upon E_s and a beat-frequency component whose amplitude depends upon E_w. Not only would harmonics of r be (ideally) absent, but also the amplitudes of the two components that are present would be independent of the amplitude ratio $a = E_w/E_s$.

If E_s and E_w are now allowed to carry fluctuations that are slow in comparison with fluctuations at r rad/sec, the preceding analysis remains applicable on a quasi-static basis. The zero-frequency term then delivers the message of the stronger signal with distortion and "cross-talk" from the weaker signal that can be estimated with the aid of Eq. (104). If the low-pass filter is intended to pass only the fluctuations expected in E_s, then the quasi-static argument requires that the beat frequency r, fall well beyond the upper cutoff frequency. This is essentially the situation under conditions of off-channel interference. We can therefore conclude that when the two signals are *widely spaced in frequency* relative to the spectral bandwidths of their modulations, the message of the stronger of the two will dominate in the output provided, of course, that the instantaneous amplitude ratio

$$a(t) = \frac{E_{w0}[1 + k_w g_w(t)]}{E_{s0}[1 + k_s g_s(t)]} \tag{107}$$

remains consistently less than one. More generally, $a(t)$ may fluctuate between values on both sides of unity. In any time interval that extends over many times $2\pi/r$ sec, the signal whose amplitude is at the higher level will dominate in the output. The effect of the weaker signal upon the output can be estimated from

$$E_s A_0(a) = E_s + (a/2)^2 E_s = E_s + \frac{1}{4} aE_w \tag{108}$$

essentially for all $a < 1$. The amplitude ratio is reduced from a by a factor of $a/4$.

The phenomenon whereby one of several input signals dominates in the output is known as "capture". According to the preceding results, a stronger-signal capture effect is exhibited by an AM receiver utilizing an envelope detector when two signals whose frequency separation exceeds the low-pass bandwidth of the receiver are present at the input of the envelope detector. If a product demodulator is used instead, a more complete capture of *either signal* can be secured by an appropriate setting of the oscillator frequency and phase.

There is virtually no capture effect in AM with an envelope detector in the presence of *cochannel interference* ($r < 2\pi B_{\ell p}$). However, there are ways for securing a useful degree of capture of a desired AM (or other linear-modulation) signal. An example (whose circumstances can be extended by special signal design) has already been given in the preceding section.

5.3 Interference in FM Systems

Characteristics of FM interference—Consider the situation in which the interference is caused by one signal, whose frequency and intensity are such that it could not be attenuated sufficiently by the i-f filter. Thus the i-f amplifier delivers two carriers with amplitudes E_s and $aE_s(a < 1)$ and frequencies p and $p + r$ rad/sec ($r \ll p$). The signals are assumed to be unmodulated in amplitude and frequency, or, at worst, to have modulations that are so slow relative to the frequency difference r that the signal frequencies or amplitudes are not appreciably changed during several cycles of the variations that recur at the beat frequency. The severity of the interference increases as the frequency difference r is increased and is greatest, therefore, when r assumes values that exceed the highest frequency of importance in the message spectrum. This situation exists all the time under conditions of adjacent-channel interference, most of the time with abutting-channel interference, and often enough to be important with cochannel interference in wideband FM systems. Note that if the intruding signal is frequency modulated, and it falls on a sloping side of the i-f amplitude-vs-frequency response characteristic, the intruding signal will acquire an amplitude modulation that is synchronous with its frequency modulation. If the instantaneous frequency difference, r, exceeds the highest frequency of importance in the modulation of the intruding signal, all amplitude and frequency changes that carry this modulation can be ignored during intervals extending over several cycles of the beat frequency.

The resultant signal at the output of the i-f amplifier can then be expressed as in Eqs. (98) and (99), namely

$$\begin{aligned} e_{\text{if}}(t) &= E_s \cos pt + aE_s \cos (p + r)t, \\ &= A(t) \cos [pt + \theta(t)] \end{aligned} \tag{109}$$

with $a < 1$ and $r \ll p$. The instantaneous frequency of this signal is

$$\begin{aligned} \omega_i(t) &= p + \frac{d\theta}{dt} \\ &= p + \frac{1}{2} r \left[1 - \frac{1 - a^2}{1 + 2a \cos rt + a^2} \right]. \end{aligned} \tag{110}$$

Clearly, $d\theta/dt$ represents the instantaneous deviation of the frequency of the resultant signal from that of the stronger signal. It therefore represents the extraneous instantaneous-frequency perturbations caused by the superposition of the weaker signal upon the stronger signal. Plots of $d\theta/dt$ are shown in Fig. 14, for $a = 0.8$

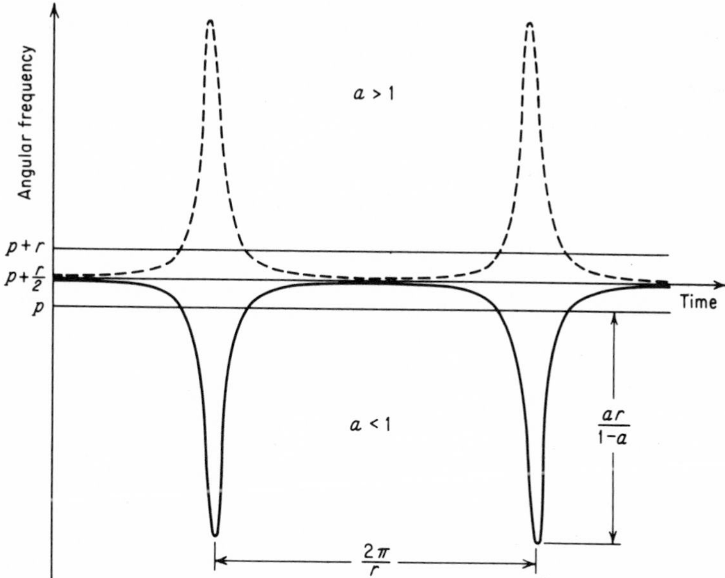

Fig. 14. FM disturbance pattern caused by two-carrier interference, plotted for $a = 0.8$ and $a = 1/0.8$.

(solid curve) and $a = 1/0.8$ (dashed curve). The spike pattern will reverse polarities if $r \to -r$, or if a becomes greater than 1.

It is important to observe that the net change in the phase of the resultant signal in any complete cycle of the disturbance is equal to the phase change acquired by the stronger signal in that time. Consequently, *the average frequency of the resultant signal over a period of* $2\pi/r$ *second is precisely the frequency of the stronger signal.* Thus, if the FM demodulator can eliminate the amplitude changes and deliver a rectified output voltage that is linearly related to the instantaneous-frequency variations of the input signal, the output of this demodulator, before any audio (or video) filtering, is equal to some constant multiplied by $E_0(p) + d\theta/dt$, where $E_0(p)$ is a direct-voltage level dictated by the frequency p. Since $d\theta/dt$ averages to zero over a period of $2\pi/r$ second, the average value of the detected voltage will correspond to the direct-voltage level dictated by the frequency p of the stronger signal. A slow message modulation carried by p will be delivered by the direct-voltage level corresponding to p at the output The rectified output voltage will also contain sinusoidal components at frequency r rad/sec and at harmonics of r.

From the viewpoint of audio filtering after proper demodulation, if a disturbance of the type shown in Fig. 14 is delivered at the output of the discriminator, the amplitudes of its Fourier components, as well as the number of these components that go through the low-pass filter, will vary with r. The rate, r, at which the disturbance pattern recurs is, therefore, an important distinguishing feature of the disturbance. For, if $r/2\pi$ lies outside the expected audio (or video) band, the disturbance will be completely wiped out by the low-frequency filtering after the discriminator. If $r/2\pi$ lies within the audio band, then several factors combine to reduce the effectiveness of the disturbance that leaks through to a small fraction of full message modulation. These factors (discussed on page 506) relate to the dependence of the amplitudes of the Fourier components of the disturbance waveform upon r, the properties of wide-band FM signals, and the possible use of a de-emphasis filter.

Let us now determine the requirements for reproducing a reasonable approximation to the disturbance pattern of (110) in the response of a filter (that follows an ideal limiter) and for converting the FM to AM by a discriminator circuit.

We recall from subsection 4.2C that the most important feature of an FM disturbance, as far as the reproduction of this disturbance is concerned, is the maximum slope of its waveform. In our problem this is

$$|\theta''(t)|_{\max} = B^2_{\lim}\left(\frac{1+a}{1-a}r\right)^2 \tag{111}$$

where $B_{\lim}$ is as plotted in Fig. 15.

If we combine (111) and (76) (with $\rho = 1$), we find that the filter that

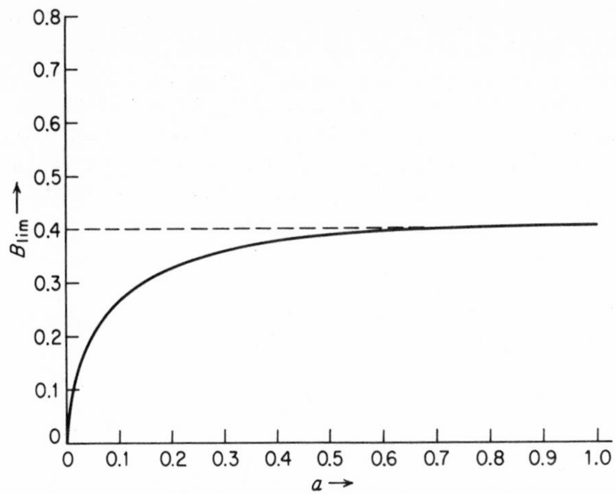

Fig. 15. Variation of B_{lim}, of Eqs. (111) and (112), with a.

follows the first ideal limiter must have a bandwidth given by

$$(BW)_{lim} = KB_{lim} \cdot \frac{1+a}{1-a} r \tag{112}$$

where

$$K = \sqrt{\frac{k}{2\varepsilon}} \text{ and } \varepsilon \leqslant 1/10,$$

in order to follow the amplitude-limited resultant of the two input carriers through quasi-stationary states. For a between 0.4 and 1, $B_{lim} \cong 0.4$, and if $\varepsilon \leqslant 1/10$, we have

$$KB_{lim} \geqslant \begin{cases} 2.5 \text{ for a single-tuned circuit} \\ 4 \text{ for a maximally flat double-tuned circuit.} \end{cases}$$

For a value of $a = 0.95$, (112) indicates that a single-tuned circuit will reproduce an acceptable approximation to the disturbance pattern if $(BW)_{lim} \geqslant 100\, r$. For a maximally flat double-tuned circuit, $(BW)_{lim} \geqslant 160 r$. Since r may be as high as one i-f bandwidth, $(BW)_{if}$, in cochannel interference, and a few times $(BW)_{if}$ in off-channel interference, the indicated values for $(BW)_{lim}$ are often quite impracticable.

Next, let us assume that the discriminator FM-to-AM conversion filter is excited by the amplitude-limited resultant of the two signal carriers. Such a filter is best represented by a pair of high-Q, stagger-tuned, parallel-resonant circuits. The rectified output of the discriminator often is (or is equivalent to) a superposition of the envelope of one resonant-circuit response upon the envelope of the other resonant-circuit response reversed in polarity. If the damping factor of each circuit is taken as α rad/sec, then best linearity in the discriminator characteristic is achieved if the resonance frequencies of the circuits are 2.45 α rad/sec apart. With this separation, the extent of the linearity of the discriminator characteristic will be (nearly) α radians per second centered about the center frequency of operation. A prerequisite for proper operation is quasi-static response by each of the parallel-resonant circuits. According to (77) we need

$$\alpha \geqslant 2.5\sqrt{|\theta''(t)|}_{max}.$$

For a between 0.4 and 1, this means that

$$\alpha \geqslant \frac{1+a}{1-a}r.$$

This condition states that α, which also equals the extent of the discriminator linearity, must be equal to the frequency range that the largest spikes can cover. Consequently, the peak-to-peak separation of the discriminator characteristic must be approximately

$$2.5\frac{1+a}{1-a}r.$$

For $a = 0.95$, this separation is of the order of $100r$. Since 100 per cent message modulation is less than $\pm(BW)_{if}/2$, a discriminator characteristic of this width provides no tangible detection sensitivity and is, indeed, useless, not to mention the prospect of its construction.

Properties of the spectrum that results from amplitude limiting— In view of the difficulty of meeting the FM demodulator design requirements for faithful reproduction of the FM disturbance, an attempt should be made to suppress, or at least minimize, this disturbance *before* (rather than *after*) it is detected. Various methods have resulted from this new emphasis on *predetection* (as opposed to postdetection) suppression of signals that cannot be eliminated by conventional i-f filtering. The amplitude limiter, among a few other nonlinear devices, has been found to be an extremely effective tool for this purpose. We shall discuss here only the simplest amplitude-limiter techniques. But first we need to consider the properties of the spectrum of the amplitude-limited resultant of the two input sinusoids.

The amplitude limiter is, by definition, a device that will operate upon $e_{if}(t)$ of Eq. (109) and deliver an output signal given by

$$e_\ell(t) = k_\ell \cos[pt + \theta(t)] \tag{113}$$

where k_ℓ is a constant of the limiter, and

$$\theta(t) = \tan^{-1}\frac{a \sin rt}{1 + a\cos rt}.$$

A Fourier analysis lead to

$$e_\ell(t) = k_\ell \sum_{n=-\infty}^{\infty} A_n(a)\cos(p - nr)t\,. \tag{114}$$

The detailed properties of this spectrum have been fully explored.[13-15]

The most important components in the spectrum of $e_\ell(t)$ are those whose frequencies correspond to the frequencies of the two input sinusoids. The amplitude of the spectral component that has the frequency of the stronger of the two input signals is $k_\ell A_0(a)$. The component with amplitude $k_\ell A_{-1}(a)$ has the frequency of the weaker signal. The functions $A_0(a)$ and $A_{-1}(a)$ are plotted in Fig. 16 and they can be approximated by

$$A_0(a) \cong 1 - a^2/4, \text{ for } a < 0.7$$

and

$$A_{-1}(a) \cong a/2, \text{ for } a < 0.6.$$

If we set

$$R(a) = \frac{A_{-1}(a)/A_0(a)}{a} \tag{115}$$

then, from Fig. 16, it is obvious that $R(a) \cong 1/2$ for all $a < 1/2$, and $R(a) \to 1$ only as $a \to 1$. This signifies that the amplitude-limiting operation reduces the weaker-to-stronger signal amplitude ratio by a factor $R(a)$ that is essentially 1/2 for small a.

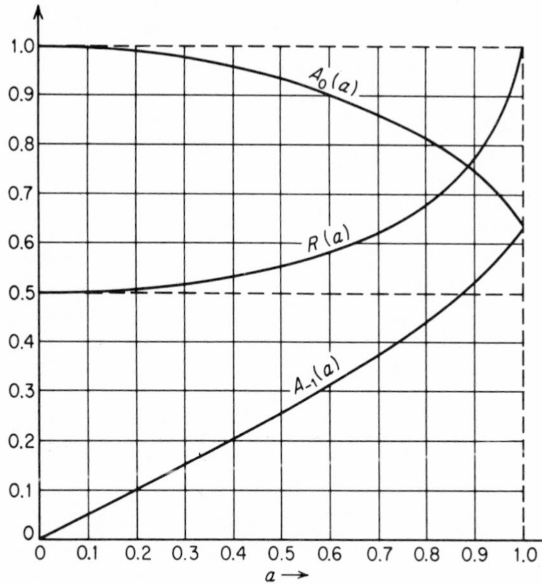

Fig. 16. Plots of the functions $A_0(a)$, $A_{-1}(a)$ and $R(a) = [A_{-1}(a)/A_0(a)]/a$.

The amplitudes of the side-frequency components in (114) are not symmetrically distributed about the center-frequency component A_0. This lack of symmetry conforms to physical expectations. On an instantaneous-frequency basis, the instantaneous frequency of the resultant signal (see Fig. 14) keeps this signal much longer on one side of the center frequency than on the other. This means that the power in the composite signal will not be equally shared by the two sidebands. Since the instantaneous frequency of the composite signal lingers in the vicinity of the mean of the two carrier frequencies (that is, $p + (1/2)r$ rad/sec) during the greater part of the frequency-difference cycle, more signal power should reside in each of the two components that have frequencies closest to the average frequency (namely, A_0 and A_{-1}) than in any of the other components. This is confirmed by the computed values for the amplitudes. Figure 16 shows that the magnitude of A_0 is larger than that of A_{-1}, and this may be appreciated by noting that the instantaneous frequency of the composite signal always puts it on the A_0 side of the mean frequency $(p + (1/2)r)$ rad/sec. Inasmuch as the spectral components are basically the "building blocks" of the resultant signal, the components that tend to pull the instantaneous frequency of the resultant signal toward the frequency of the weaker signal must logically be those that lie on the same side relative to the frequency p (of the stronger signal) as the frequency of the weaker signal. The components in the opposite sideband provide the necessary balancing for preserving the desired average value, p, of the frequency of the resultant signal.

The extent of the significant spectrum of $e_\ell(t)$ can be determined

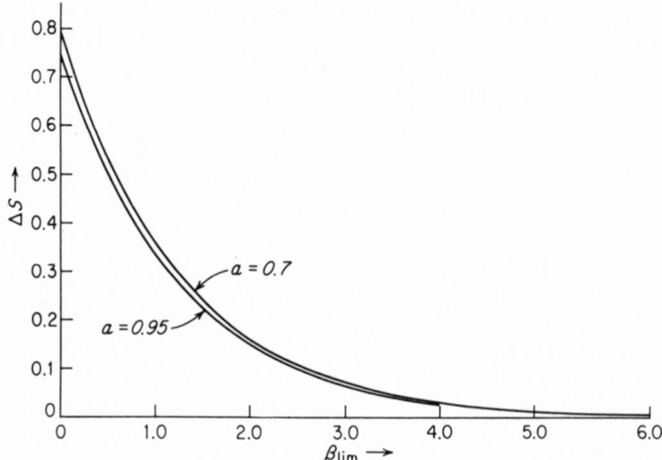

Fig. 17. Degree of reduction in intensity of FM disturbance as a function of the normalized bandwidth of the ideal narrow-band limiter. $100\Delta S$ represents the percentage of reduction in the magnitude of the FM disturbance spike (*i.e.*, the value of the FM disturbance when the two input sinusoids go through instantaneous phase opposition).

from Fig. 17. In a process whereby the amplitude-limited resultant of the two signals is resynthesized from its spectral components, ΔS in Fig. 17 gives the fractional amount by which the original frequency spike magnitude has been decreased by rejecting those portions of the spectrum that fall outside a bandwidth of

$$\beta_{\text{lim}} \frac{1 + a}{1 - a} r.$$

The value of β_{lim} that will result in a 10 per cent decrease in the frequency spike magnitude is approximately 2.6. For a decrease of 1 per cent, $\beta_{\text{lim}} = 5.5$.

The effect brought out in Fig. 16 can be utilized in various ways to achieve stronger-signal, as well as weaker-signal, enhancement. Of principal importance are the techniques of cascading narrowband limiters, and applying feedback or feedforward across the limiter.

Cascaded narrow-band limiters[15, 16]—Cascading narrow-band limiters whose bandwidths do not exceed a few times the i-f bandwidth is an effective stronger-signal enhancement technique. The basic mechanism of weaker-signal suppression is based on the fact that each limiter spreads out the significant spectrum (which is necessary for the reproduction of the FM disturbance caused by the weaker signal) over a frequency range that exceeds many times the bandwidth of the i-f amplifier. The more severe the interference, the greater will be the spread of the spectrum through amplitude limiting. It follows that by filtering after amplitude limiting, sizeable portions of the interference spectrum can be excluded, without substantially affecting the spectrum that carries the message on the stronger signal. After one stage of limiting and filtering, residual interference will pass in the unfilterable parts of the spectrum, but successive limiters will again spread out the interference spectrum, which can be further reduced by additional filtering

The first step in the development of this cascading scheme for interference suppression is to determine the minimum permissible limiter bandwidths. This has been done using the Fourier spectral method of analysis (see subsection 4.2B) in terms of an ideal limiter followed by an ideal filter.[14, 15] The limiter bandwidth must be so chosen that it will always pass configurations of sideband components that will add up to a resultant signal whose average frequency is equal to the frequency of the stronger of the two input carriers. The results of the analysis show that the minimum permissible bandwidth for the idealized filter associated with an amplitude limiter is, theoretically, one i-f bandwidth for all values of $a \leqslant 0.863$. This requirement on the bandwidth of any limiter stage is independent of the number and of the bandwidths of the limiter-filter units in a cascaded chain which may precede that stage. A bandwidth of $3(BW)_{\text{if}}$ is sufficient for all $a \leqslant 0.98$.

If a system of cascaded ideal narrow-band limiters, each of bandwidth $(BW)_{\text{if}}$, is incorporated in an FM receiver, then the most adverse condition of two-signal interference will occur at both input and output of the scheme when the two signals differ in frequency by $r = (BW)_{if}$, provided that the input interference ratio, a, is less than 0.84. The spectrum at the output of the scheme will then consist of only two sinusoids which correspond to the input sinusoids, with the ratio of weaker-to-stronger signal amplitude reduced from its input value of $a < 0.84$ to a value that can be made as small as desired by cascading the necessary number of narrow-band limiters.

From Fig. 16 it is clear that the greatest achievable reduction in the relative amplitude of the weaker signal in one stage of narrow-band limiting amounts to a factor of 1/2 (or 6 db) when $a < 0.5$. It turns out, however, that this performance can be improved by applying feedback or feedforward across the limiter.

The disturbance added by the weaker signal on the frequency of the stronger signal will be diminished by a bandpass filter only if the significant spectrum of the resultant impressed signal is spread out beyond the extent of the filter pass band. If the bandpass filter following an idealized limiter is capable of following the instantaneous-frequency variations of the amplitude-limited resultant of two carriers through quasi-stationary states—or, equivalently, if the filter pass band is sufficiently wide to accommodate the entire significant first-zonal spectrum [Eq. (114)] caused by the ideal limiting action—then the disturbance caused by the weaker signal will not be affected by the bandpass limiting action. Thus, for a given value $(BW)_{lim}$ of the limiter-filter bandwidth, the effect of narrow-band limiting upon the disturbance becomes more pronounced with increasing values of the frequency difference r and the interference ratio a. For fixed values of a and $(BW)_{lim}$, the degree of disturbance suppression achieved through narrow-band limiting is greatest when the two carriers are farthest apart in frequency. As the frequency difference between the two carriers decreases, the intensity of the disturbance will decrease, and so will the degree of improvement in the capture conditions achievable with each stage of narrow-band limiting. When the frequency difference decreases to a value r_{min} that is specifiable as a small fraction of the limiter-filter bandwidth, the extraneous modulation caused by the interference becomes sufficiently slow for

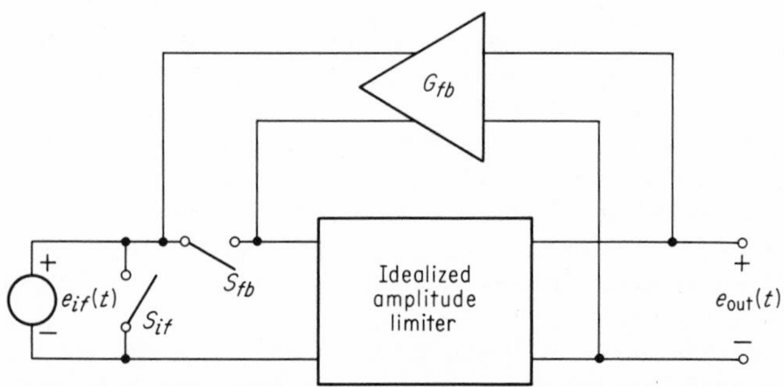

Fig. 18. Limiter and amplifier in feedback connection.

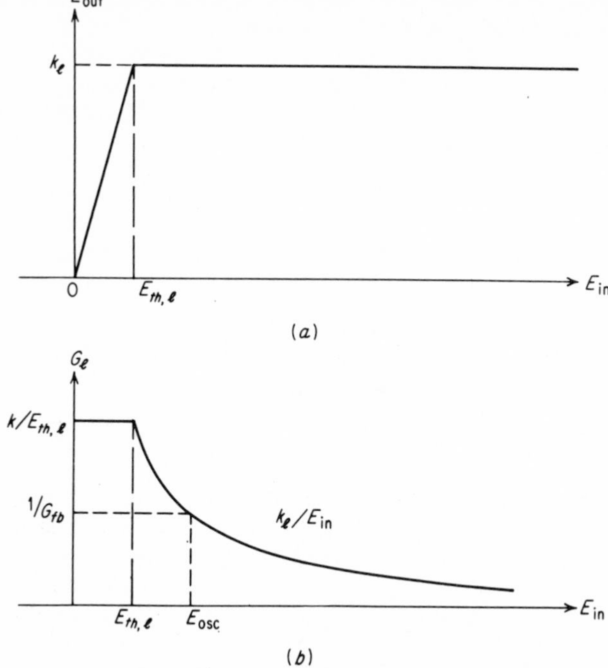

Fig. 19. Definition of limiting and amplification characteristics of amplitude limiter.

the filter to follow it through quasi-stationary states, and the disturbance will pass through unabated. The closer the interference amplitude ratio approaches unity, the smaller the value of r_{min} which marks the limit of noticeable improvement in the capture. An expression for r_{min} which follows from (112) is

$$r_{min} = \lambda \frac{1 - a}{1 + a}(BW)_{lim},$$

where $\lambda = 1/KB_{lim}$. In the range $0.4 < a < 1$, λ may be taken as 2/5 for a single-tuned circuit, and 1/4 for a maximally flat double-tuned circuit.

Feedback around the limiter[17, 18]—The application of positive feedback through a bandwidth of the order of the i-f bandwidth, from the output of the limiter to its input, can result in pronounced improvement in the stronger-signal capture performance of the receiver. The positive feedback increases the amplitudes of both signal and interference at the input of the limiter, but it adds more to the stronger signal than to the weaker signal. In this way, the predominance of the stronger signal is improved at the input of the limiter, and further improvement is effected by narrow-band limiting in the same limiter

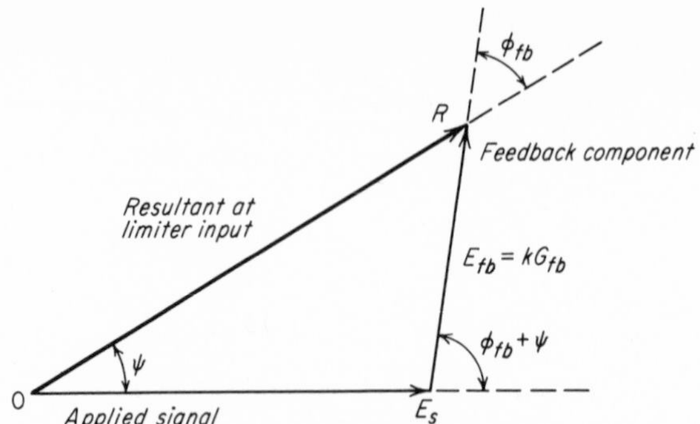

Fig. 20. Signal-phasor relationships at the input of the limiter in Fig. 18 in the feedback steady state in which only one sinusoid of the same frequency as the applied signal appears at the output of the limiter.

stage. The overall improvement in one stage with bandlimited positive feedback can be made equivalent to the improvement that would result from several stages that do not use feedback.

The stronger-signal capture improvement achieved with regenerative band-limited feedback around the limiter is greater the greater the amplitude E_{fb} (of the signal fed back) is relative to the amplitude E_s of the applied signal.

The basic limiter-with-feedback scheme is shown in Fig. 18. The idealized amplitude limiter is a device with associated frequency selectivity which transforms a sinusoid of amplitude E_{in}, whose frequency lies in the passband, into a sinusoid of the same frequency, whose amplitude E_{out} is described in Fig. 19(a) as a function of E_{in}. The ratio $E_{\text{out}}/E_{\text{in}} = G_{\ell}$ is a voltage "amplification" that varies with E_{in} as shown in Fig. 19(b). The amplitude-limiting threshold is denoted $E_{\text{th},\ell}$. For $E_{\text{in}} < E_{\text{th},\ell}$, the idealized limiter performs as a linear amplifier with a voltage amplification of $G_{\ell,\max} = k_{\ell}/E_{\text{th},\ell}$.

It is clear from Fig 19(b) that because of non-zero $E_{\text{th},\ell}$, the system of Fig. 18 with S_{if} closed and S_{fb} open will oscillate if $E_{\text{fb}} = kG_{\text{fb}} \geqslant E_{\text{th},\ell}$, and will not oscillate if $E_{\text{fb}} < E_{\text{th},\ell}$. In either case, if a signal of amplitude E_s is applied by opening S_{if}, then, with reference to Fig. 20, the condition under which the signal will be transmitted without distortion through the system is

$$\frac{E_{\text{fb}}}{E_s} \sin|\phi_{\text{fb}}(\omega_s)| < 1 \tag{116}$$

where $\phi_{\text{fb}}(\omega_s)$ is the phase shift around the feedback loop at the frequency ω_s of the input sinusoid, and the limiter is assumed to be saturated.

If $E_{\text{fb}} < E_{\text{th},\ell}$, condition (116) is the condition for a feedback steady state. The amplitude limiter will then be saturated only if OR (in Fig.

20) $> E_{th,\ell}$. For small values of ϕ_{fb}, the condition for limiter saturation is

$$E_s \geq E_{th,\ell} - E_{fb}\,. \tag{117}$$

This shows that regenerative feedback decreases the threhold that the incoming signal amplitude must exceed in order to saturate the limiter. But as long as $E_{fb} < E_{th,\ell}$, the new saturation threshold will be nonzero, and this imposes an upper bound on the ratio E_{fb}/E_s. In the absence of interference, condition (117) requires that

$$K_s = \frac{E_{fb}}{E_s} \leq \frac{E_{fb}}{E_{th,\ell} - E_{fb}}\,. \tag{118}$$

The right-hand side is guaranteed positive by the condition for no oscillation, $E_{fb} < E_{th,\ell}$. In the presence of interference, the upper bound on K_s becomes

$$K_s \leq \frac{(1-a)E_{fb}}{E_{th,\ell} - E_{fb}}\,. \tag{119}$$

The restrictions and consequent performance limitations imposed by the requirement for limiter saturation when $E_{fb} < E_{th,\ell}$ are removed by letting $E_{fb} \geq E_{th,\ell}$. Although this causes a self-sustained oscillation in the absence of input signal, the application of a signal that satisfies condition (116) suppresses the oscillation and reestablishes non-oscillatory regenerative feedback limiter operation. In addition, the amount of feedback can be adjusted so that substantial interstation noise squelch is caused by the oscillation.

In order to understand the mechanism whereby a signal that satisfies condition (116) is able to suppress the oscillation and fully control the output of the scheme, let us note that the open-loop transfer function of the system shown in Fig. 18 is essentially the transfer function of a fixed-parameter filter, scaled by the magnitude factor $G_\ell = k_\ell/E_{in}$ which is contributed by the saturated limiter. The phase shift around the loop will generally be a function of frequency. At some frequency, say the center of the passband, the signal that is fed back will arrive in phase with the input signal. In the absence of an applied signal, and, if $k_\ell G_{fb}(\omega_0) \geq E_{th}$, the system will oscillate at the frequency of exact in-phase feedback, with an amplitude that equals $E_{in} = E_{osc} = k_\ell G_{fb}(\omega_0)$. With the assumed idealizations, $k_\ell |G_{fb}|$ is independent of frequency over a well-defined passband (of one i-f bandwidth for best improvement of the stronger of two applied signals), and the frequency ω_0 of exact in-phase feedback is fixed. The presence of an applied signal can only change the value of the magnitude factor G_ℓ which is contributed by the idealized limiter. An "oscillating limiter" will "lock" to an applied signal by *ceasing to oscillate* and by operating as a stable system with regenerative feedback if the presence of the applied signal causes the amplitude E_{in} of the resultant signal at the input of the limiter to increase beyond the value $E_{in} = E_{osc} = k_\ell G_{fb}$ which is necessary for a feedback-loop gain of unity.

In contrast, there are oscillating systems that will lock to an applied signal if this signal is able to change the frequency of exact in-phase feedback so that it coincides with the signal frequency. In such systems, the applied signal can be said to introduce, or change the value of, a simulated reactance that changes the frequency of the resonator. If the feedback-loop gain remains fixed (or is maintained at the value of unity) the oscillator can be said to lock to the applied signal by being forced to oscillate at the frequency of the applied signal.

It is also possible for the applied signal to reduce the feedback-loop gain, as well as to change the frequency of exact in-phase feedback of an oscillating system. Such a system belongs fundamentally to the class of oscillating limiters and, with appropriate design, it represents an oscillating limiter in which one possible measure has been taken to widen the locking range and lower the locking threshold.

Thus we are distinguishing here between two fundamentally different locking mechanisms. A "locked oscillating limiter" does not oscillate while it is locked to the frequency of an applied signal. But when this signal is removed, it will oscillate. A locked oscillator oscillates all the time, but its frequency of oscillation is shifted by the controlling applied signal without destroying the gain condition for oscillation.

With reference to Fig. 20, it is easy to see that if the applied sinusoid has amplitude E_s and a frequency ω_i at which $\phi_{\text{fb}} \neq 0$, a feedback steady state will exist only if condition (116) is satisfied, namely

$$(E_{\text{osc}}/E_s)\sin|\phi_{\text{fb}}(\omega_i)| < 1 \tag{116}$$

is satisfied. It is interesting to note that if we seek the condition for the amplitude of the resultant signal (at the input of the limiter in the feedback steady state) to exceed the value $E_{\text{in}} = kG_{\text{fb}} = E_{\text{osc}}$, which is necessary for unit feedback loop gain, this condition turns out to be

$$2K_s \sin(\phi_{\text{fb}}/2) < 1, \quad K_s = E_{\text{osc}}/E_s\,. \tag{120}$$

If condition (116) is rewritten in the form

$$2K_s \sin(\phi_{\text{fb}}/2)\cos(\phi_{\text{fb}}/2) < 1 \tag{121}$$

it becomes obvious that the satisfaction of condition (120) guarantees the satisfaction of condition (116); but the reverse is not true. Since $\cos(\phi_{\text{fb}}/2) \geqslant 0.99$ for $|\phi_{\text{fb}}| \leqslant 16.33°$, and $\cos(\phi_{\text{fb}}/2) \geqslant 0.94$ for $|\phi_{\text{fb}}| \leqslant 36.33°$, the two conditions are substantially equivalent over a wider range of feedback phase shifts than should normally be encountered within the desired passband in a well-designed system.

Since condition (120) is more stringent than condition (116), we might inquire how condition (116) can rule out the existence of a self-sustained oscillation when, under circumstances in which it is satisfied, the limiter operates at a point which enables the feedback loop gain to exceed or equal unity. The answer to this is that a feedback steady state is really possible only after the self-oscillation has died out. The resultant signal phasor acquires amplitudes that exceed the steady-state amplitude OR before it settles down to OR. The system operates in a condition of "stable equilibrium," once the steady-state condition has been reached. Any attempt by a self-oscillation to regenerate will raise the amplitude level at the limiter input, and thereby undermine the loop-gain condition that is necessary for the existence of a self-sustained oscillation.

When $K_s = E_{fb}/E_s > 1$, condition (116) restricts the permissible values of $\phi_{fb}(\omega_s)$ for given values of K_s (thereby imposing a locking range), and it restricts K_s for a given maximum value of $\phi_{fb}(\omega_s)$ (thereby imposing a locking threshold). The phase shift around the loop should ideally be close to zero within the desired passband, and should rise sharply outside the passband. In view of the limitations that are imposed by nonzero feedback phase shift upon the signals that can pass through the oscillating limiter, it is evident that the ideal phase characteristic would enable the oscillating limiter to simulate an ideal dynamic filter for FM signals. Such a filter would discriminate against incoming signals on the basis of the feedback phase shift at their frequencies, and on the basis of their amplitudes as compared with the amplitude of the self-oscillation. Unfortunately, the amplitude characteristic that accompanies the desired phase characteristic has two extremely sharp peaks at the edges of the band, and dips to uncomfortably low levels within the passband. The effect of the amplitude peaking at the edges of the band is drastically cut down by the attendant high phase shift in those regions, but the low level of the passband transmission sets a limitation on the feedback signal level which must be offset by appropriate amplifier design.

By appropriate design, the application of regenerative feedback around the limiter will enable FM signals to be received well below the conventional random-noise threshold (see pp. 540-546). For this reason, the circuit has been termed the "regenerative weak-signal booster."

Feedforward across the limiter[19, 20]—In Fig. 21, an amplitude limiter is bridged by a linear amplifier that enables the resultant signal at the limiter input to be subtracted from the resultant signal at the limiter output. This subtraction can be easily arranged to result in the suppression of the undesired signal over a significant fraction of a modulation cycle, when the two signals occupy the same frequency

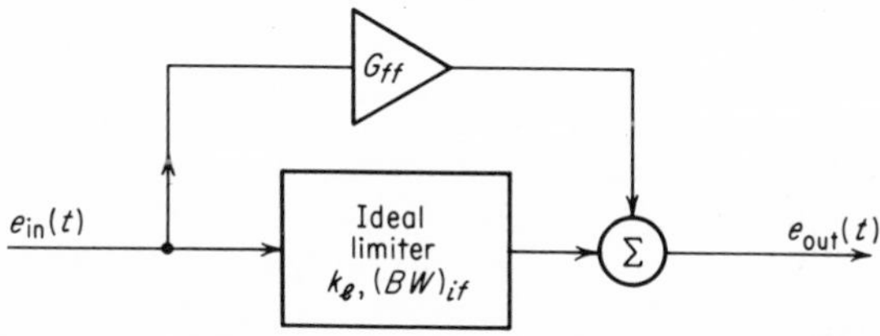

Fig. 21. Limiter and amplifier in feedforward connection.

channel all the time. The fraction of the time during which the undesired signal can be suppressed completely increases rapidly when the separation of the center frequencies of the two signals is increased. The basic theory of operation will be briefly reviewed.

Let us assume that the outputs of the amplifier and the ideal limiter are superimposed at the input terminals of a common filter that defines the passband of each. This passband is, for simplicity, assumed to be that of a filter whose characteristics are similar to those of the i-f filter. Under these conditions, and in the absence of spurious differences in the phase shifts in the amplifier and the limiter paths, the output signal is

$$e_{\text{out}}(t) = \text{Re}\left\{\sum_n H(j(p - nr))B_n(a)\, e^{j(p-nr)t}\right\} \tag{122}$$

where

$$B_0(a) = G_{\text{ff}}E_s + k_\ell A_0(a) \tag{123}$$

$$= \text{amplitude of component at } p \text{ rad/sec}$$

$$B_{-1}(a) = aG_{\text{ff}}E_s + k_\ell A_{-1}(a) \tag{124}$$

$$= \text{amplitude of component at } p + r \text{ rad/sec}$$

$$B_n(a) = k_\ell A_n(a),\ n = 1, \pm 2, \pm 3, \ldots \tag{125}$$

and $H(j\omega)$ is the system function of the filter. From Eqs. (123) and (124) it is obvious that by an appropriate adjustment of either G_{ff}, or k_ℓ, or both, the component at p rad/sec, or the component at $p + r$ rad/sec, can be cancelled out, whichever is undesired.

Under conditions of abutting- or adjacent-channel interference, the desired signal can always be assumed to fall within the uniform passband of the i-f filter. If the interfering signal, with its amplitude modified by the out-of-band attenuation of the i-f amplifier, appears stronger than the inband (desired) signal at the input of the feedforward arrangement, then the extraneous components at $p - r$, $p + 2r$, $p + 3r$, etc., are all negligible. Under these conditions, cancellation of the undesired component at p rad/sec essentially eliminates the interference. A similar conclusion can be reached if the in-band (desired) signal is the stronger of the two at the input of the feedforward arrangement.

With cochannel interference, it can be shown that if the reception of the weaker signal is desired, there is no adjustment that will enable the average frequency of $e_{\text{out}}(t)$ to be consistently equal to the frequency of the weaker signal for all possible values of the frequency difference. When the frequency difference r exceeds one-half the i-f bandwidth, an adjustment can be made to enable the component at the frequency of the weaker signal to dominate in $e_{\text{out}}(t)$. But when r falls below $(BW)_{\text{if}}/2$, the reception of the weaker signal should be marred, first, by a burst of capture-transition distortion, after which the average frequency of $e_{\text{out}}(t)$ quickly approaches the frequency of the stronger signal. The capture transition will take place within a range of frequency differences that are centered about a value r_{crit}

that is intermediate between $(BW)_{\text{if}}/2$ and zero. The value of r_{crit} changes with changes in the instantaneous frequency locations of the signals within the passband, as well as with the ratio $K = G_{\text{ff}} E_s / k_{\ell}$. In general, the optimal choice for K is the one that results in a minimum mean value for r_{crit} for specified frequency modulations or for specified classes of such modulations.

The performance of the system of Fig. 21 depends critically upon the ratio $K = G_{\text{ff}} E_s / k_{\ell}$ of the outputs of the amplifier and the limiter. This ratio varies with the input signal level. Consequently, for certain signal levels, the system will suppress the stronger signal; for others, it will suppress the weaker signal. The quality of the reception of either signal will also depend upon the behavior of the signal amplitudes at the input.

The parameter K can be made a constant (that can be fixed by the operator for a specified range and type of input signal amplitude variations) by using appropriate means for regulating either the signal level at the feedforward input, or the gain of the feedforward amplifier path. The use of amplitude limiters to achieve each of these results appears to be the simplest and most reliable means. If the system of Fig. 21 is preceded by a limiter, the bandwidth of this limiter must be of the order of one i-f bandwidth, and it is best chosen equal to the i-f bandwidth.

The feedforward operation indicated in Fig. 21 can be extended so that the amplifier bridges two or more cascaded narrow-band limiters, one (or more) limiters with feedback, or even a limiter with another feedforward amplifier. Either of these possibilities, in particular the last named, can outperform the system of Fig. 21 for weaker-signal capture because of the higher degree of weaker-signal suppression that can be achieved in the signal path that is bridged by the "main" feedforward amplifier. However, only the double feedforward across one limiter presents no important difficulties in achieving proper phasing of the combined outputs over a wide frequency band.

The capture-transition distortion, which appears whenever the two signals approach a condition of frequency crossover, constitutes a performance limitation on the simpler (and more practical) forms of the feedforward technique in applications that require close reproduction of the weaker-signal message. If the two signals are cochannel, they may often pass through zero frequency difference, with consequent severe distortion in the weaker-signal reception at the receiver output. However, if the center frequencies of the signals are separated so that their instantaneous frequencies seldom, or never, coincide, the distortion will not be present. Effectively, then, the feedforward system of Fig. 21 is an extremely simple realization of a simulated ideal bandpass filter with extremely sharp cutoff characteristics for FM signals that can be expected to sweep over nonoverlapping (or only slightly overlapping) frequency channels.

In the wake of the reductions in the effectiveness of the interference are some valuable relaxations in the design requirements on limiters and discriminators that are intended for handling high-level interference. Reduction in the intensity of the disturbance leads to important reductions in the minimum permissible discriminator bandwidth and to important increases in the upper bounds on the discriminator and limiter low-frequency time constants.[21]

Post-detection filtering of disturbance—In general, after a proper detection of the instantaneous-frequency variations of the signal that drives the discriminator, the output voltage variations caused by the disturbance are modified by the action of the de-emphasis and audio filters that follow the discriminator circuit. If the frequency difference between the two input carriers lies beyond the range of audibility, the Fourier components of the detected frequency disturbance will all be filtered out. However, if the frequency difference between the two signals is audible, the component with the fundamental frequency of recurrence, plus a number of harmonics, depending upon the position of this frequency in the audible spectrum, will pass through the low-pass filters and will, therefore, disturb the output signal.

Two factors play more or less obvious roles in minimizing the importance of the unfilterable disturbance:

1) The de-emphasis filter attenuates most of the harmonic components, and
2) the magnitude of the FM disturbance (hence the amplitude of each of its constituent Fourier components) varies directly with r.

Thus, with r well within the audio band, the increased number of unfilterable harmonics does not imply a proportionately increased disturbance because the amplitudes of the harmonics decrease with r.

A third factor that tends to minimize the audible disturbance is introduced by the partial suppression of the interference before it is detected. Computations, made with the assumption that the interference suppressor is a narrow-band limiter, show that the Fourier components of the modified FM disturbance have smaller amplitudes than their counterparts in the undistorted disturbance. Also, the fundamental component (of frequency r) becomes increasingly predominant in amplitude over the components at harmonics of r.

Summary of capture performance of FM receivers—Consider a simple experiment in which an FM receiver is excited by two signals that have different constant amplitudes and carry identifiable frequency modulations. Assume that the frequencies of the two signals are such that if either of the two signals is switched off, the output from the receiver will be an undistorted replica of the message carried by the other signal. Set the amplitude of one signal at some constant suitable value E_s and slowly increase the amplitude aE_s of the other from zero. The observed performance of a conventional (limiter-discriminator) FM receiver is typically as follows: At $a = 0$ one signal is completely off and the receiver output consists of the detected frequency modulation of the other signal. As a is increased from zero, the output will continue to be essentially an undistorted replica of the stronger-signal message until some value of $a = a_{cap} < 1$

is reached at which noticeable distortion in the output begins to set in. As a is increased from a_{cap} to unity (equality of input signal amplitudes) the observed distortion rises to a very disturbing level with unmistakable evidence of the presence of the aE_s signal. As a acquires values increasingly greater than one, the output sounds more like the program of the aE_s signal with heavy distortion and cross-talk from the E signal. For $a > 1/a_{cap}$, the output is essentially an undistorted replica of the modulation of the aE_s signal.

In the laboratory, it is convenient to modulate the signals with single tones whose frequencies are sufficiently well spaced to enable the observer to isolate them and measure them separately in the output. If the observed strength of each tone at the output is plotted (in percent of its would-be value in the absence of the signal carrying the other tone) against the ratio of amplitudes, a, the result is called a "capture characteristic."

Typical stronger-signal and weaker-signal capture characteristics are shown in Fig. 22. A medium-quality FM receiver, operating

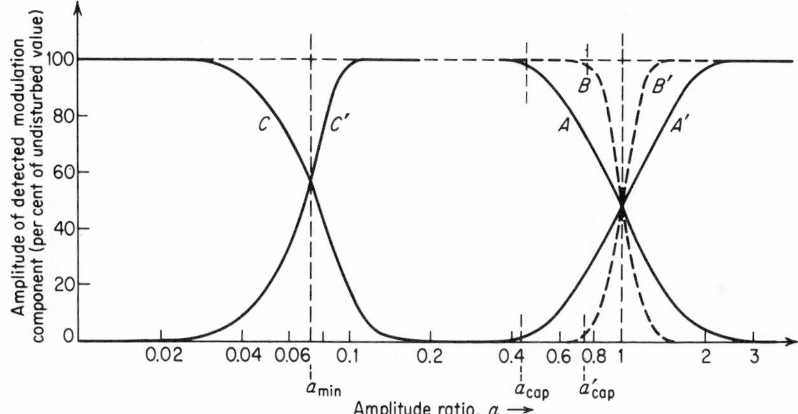

Fig. 22. Typical capture characteristics for an FM receiver.
A and A' describe likely stronger-signal capture performance.
B and B' describe performance of same receiver with a stronger-signal-capture-improvement operation added to its circuit.
C and C' result from addition of a weaker-signal capture device.

in the presence of cochannel interference, is likely to have the capture characteristics marked A and A'. The amplitude ratio a_{cap} is called the *capture ratio* of the receiver and it is a function of the receiver design as well as the type of interference (cochannel or otherwise) for which it is measured. If a stronger-signal enhancement circuit (for example one or more narrow-band limiters, or a feed-forward circuit, etc.) is switched into the signal path in the receiver, the A curves are transformed into curves such as the B curves. The A and B curves, of course, continue at the 100 per cent level outside the region shown, although they are stopped in the figure below $a = a_{cap}$. The introduction of a weaker-signal capture circuit leads to characteristics such as C and C'. The C and C' curves usually merge into curves such as the A or B curves around $a = 1$.

It is clear from Fig. 22 that improvements in the stronger-signal capture ability of the receiver result in a narrowing of the capture transition range ($a_{cap} < a < 1/a_{cap}$), or the range of values of the amplitude difference between two competing signals in which the receiver is unable to deliver the message of either signal without harmful disturbance from the other.

The ability to receive a desired signal even in the presence of a much stronger cochannel or neighboring-channel interference has interesting implications in efficient utilization of assigned frequency channels. The necessary modifications in the receiver circuits may range from the very simple and economical feedforward circuit to the moderately more complicated trapping techniques.[19, 20] The economy and effectiveness of these techniques makes power-division (at the transmitter) amplitude-discrimination (at the receiver) duplexing a feasible operation—even for commercial applications.[19, 20]

VI. IMPULSE NOISE AND ITS SUPPRESSION

6.1 Preliminary Survey

The most important distinguishing property of impulse noise is the fact that the noise energy is initially delivered in *very intense bursts of very short duration.* Of these two attributes, the short duration is the defining property, the length of the duration being gauged relative to the duration of a typical message element. Consequently, the spectrum of each noise pulse is essentially flat over the entire frequency band occupied by the signal spectrum, the relative phasing of the spectral components being such that their resultant is zero at all times except for a short interval in which they combine to yield the noise pulse. In a given noise environment with more than one source emanating the impulsive radiations, the noise pulses will recur at randomly spaced instants of time and will possess randomly distributed energy content. For this reason, the term "random noise" usually applies to both impulse noise and fluctuation noise (and not only the latter). Usually the impulse-noise pulses occur widely spaced in time (relative to the duration of the disturbances that they set up in receiving circuits) although it is not infrequent to encounter sudden bursts of closely spaced or overlapping pulses.

For the preceding reasons, the fraction-of-time envelope distribution of the noise energy of impulsive disturbances is strongly affected by the frequency characteristics of the medium or filter through which it reaches the observer. The interval of time over which the impulsive noise is observed (or the noise power is averaged) has a marked effect upon the percentage-of-time distribution of the noise power received.

At the point of observation and comparison with the signal, two important situations may therefore be distinguished—the distinction depending upon whether the impulse noise has been transmitted through a bandwidth that is much wider than the bandwidth of the message elements (as is frequently the case in radio reception), or has unavoidably been processed through a bandwidth that is comparable with the bandwidth of the message elements (as is the case in conventional telephone circuits, for example). If "impulsiveness" is defined to stress the attribute of *short duration* (in comparison with the duration of a message element) rather than the high intensity, then in the second-named situation the character of the noise has departed from impulsiveness, and the unavoidable filtering has reduced the disturbance to an interference from a signal that resembles the desired one.

At the present time, known techniques for suppressing the effects of impulsive disturbances can be identified with one of four general approaches:

(a) The use of nonlinear saturating elements or noise clippers;
(b) Disturbance-triggered, gating-out schemes, whereby the receiver signal path is interrupted at some suitable stage that may fall anywhere from the front end to the input of the back-end transducer;
(c) The use of special signal design such as special coding, or linear premodulation waveform alteration and postdemodulation correction of the message (for example, pre-emphasis and de-emphasis, presmearing and restoration, and so forth); and
(d) The use of linear receiver diversification of the disturbance followed by subtractive combining of the diversified noisy signals.

In a typical noise-clipping [Class (a)] scheme, the pre-clipping bandwidth may be widened as much as is permissible under the prevailing circumstances, and a clipper with a fixed or a (signal-controlled) "floating" clipping threshold is arranged to slip off as much of the noise as possible without running into the danger of clipping the signal between the (assumed widely spaced) noise impulses.

In a typical noise-gating-out [Class (b)] scheme, the input noise plus signal may be applied at the common input of two receiver signal paths, one of which is essentially a noise-detecting circuit, the other, a circuit whose operation is controlled by the first. Operating under the influence of the incoming impulse noise, the noise-detecting branch gates-out the "controlled" branch completely, as long as the amplitude of the disturbance exceeds a preset threshold. The desired signal emerges from the controlled-branch output with "holes" that may be smoothed out by later filtering.

Techniques that fall under the classifications (a) and (b) are effective as long as it is possible to operate on the sum of signal plus impulse noise:

(i) While the duration of the impulsive disturbance is still short compared with the duration of the shortest message element, and

(ii) While the noise peak is appreciably higher than the highest expected signal amplitude.

Both of these conditions are met by the impulse response of a linear wideband transmission filter (see sub-section 6.2). If either, or both, of these two conditions is seriously violated, the received message may be severely disturbed as a result of too long a "scar" [or too long an interruption], or of no noise clipping [or no gating-out]. In most circumstances in radio communication, both conditions hold at the front end of the receiver, and techniques (a) and (b) have been profitably used. The ultimate performance of each of these approaches can be shown to be a function of the ratio of the preclipping [or pre-gating-out] bandwidth to the postclipping [or postgating-out] bandwidth.

Techniques (a) and (b) inevitably leave harmful traces, or "scars," on the message waveform, as well as intermodulation products among the message components and crossmodulation between the desired signal and other signals that may be present. Moreover, these techniques are helpful only when the impulses recur at intervals that are so widely spaced that the disturbance of each impulse dies out before the advent of the next one. Otherwise, the scars in (a) may extend over substantial portions of the message waveform and distort it beyong recognition, or the reception in (b) may be interrupted for extended periods of time.

Under circumstances in which the duration of the impulse-noise disturbance may not differ, to a useful extent, from the duration of a typical message element (as is the case in telephone circuits carrying digital data, for example), approaches (a) and (b) are out of the question. A different approach must be sought, preferably one that anticipates the trouble and designs the signals accordingly. The point of the signal design is to build into the structure of the transmitted waveform an adequate measure of distinguishability from the expected impulse noise. One way to do this is to decide upon some linear operation that would effectively abate the noise if applied at the receiver, and to subject the signal or message to the inverse of this linear operation at the transmitter. It is usually possible to predistort the signal in reversible ways, the reverse of which could greatly reduce the impulse-noise disturbance by smoothing it out This technique is old, and it has been used with remarkable results in the form of pre-emphasis of the message waveform at the transmitter and de-emphasis at the receiver The need for de-emphasis in order to restore the desired form of the message provides the ability to cut down the post-demodulation (and hence postclipping or postgating-out) bandwidth (if an (a) or a (b) technique is employed) against the noise without, at the same time, hurting the message waveform. In digital-transmission systems, design of signals may involve more "sophisticated" or elaborate operations on the message, such as an error-correction coding operation.

An interesting signal design technique has recently been borrowed from radar. (See section VI of Chapter 11.) This technique appears promising, especially for use in digital transmission in the presence of narrowband-filtered impulse noise. The basic idea stems from the fact that it is possible to presmear (in time) the message elements at the transmitting end and restore them to their original form at the receiving end by means of complementary smearing filters. The smearing time may be much larger than the duration of a message element. At the receiver, the signal de-smearing (restoring) filter operates on the sum of impulsive disturbance and presmeared signal, and reassembles the signal in its original waveform while it smears out the disturbance. The smearing operation essentially redistributes the energy of an impulse over a "smearing-time" interval that is large compared with the "duration" of the disturbance before smearing and thus reduces the noise intensity in any time interval that equals the duration of a message element. If the impulses recur so rapidly that a large number of them occur during a smearing interval, the statistics of the resulting smeared noise that rides over the restored message elements will approach those of a gaussian-noise process, regardless of the original percentage-of-time distributions of the incoming noise. This suggests a method whereby the non-gaussian impulse noise can be transformed into a gaussian noise against which matched-filter detection methods are optimal. The resulting smeared-noise level is greatly abated by standard clipping before the smearing operation. The major drawback of this technique, at the present time, lies in the complexity of the available smearing methods. Also, this technique is ineffective against non-impulsive disturbances that resemble the presmeared forms of the message characters and it is quite susceptible to circuit nonlinearities when the smearing time is so large relative to the data pulse duration that considerable overlapping occurs among the presmeared data pulses.

Technique (d) is new, fundamentally simple, and linear. It is effective even when the i-f filter responses to the various impulses overlap, as long as the number of overlapping responses is not great. As we shall illustrate in sub-section 6.3, the diversification of the noise is possible because of an important property of the impulse response of a linear filter—that its maximum value is directly proportional to the filter bandwidth. The technique is applicable to the reception of all types of modulation, even to pulsed transmissions, subject to the fundamental assumption that the individual bursts have durations that are substantially shorter than the duration of the shortest important message element.

6.2 Some Properties of the Impulse Response of Bandpass Filters

We shall review some properties of the impulse response of a linear filter which are of fundamental importance to the present discussion. We shall derive these properties in a very general manner for linear filters of finite bandwidth, and then point out how they can be used to construct an effective linear suppressor of impulse noise.

We start with the general relation

$$h(t) = \frac{1}{2\pi}\int_{-\infty}^{\infty} H(j\omega)\, e^{j\omega t}\, d\omega \tag{126}$$

which relates the impulse response $h(t)$ of a linear filter to the system function $H(j\omega)$ of the filter. Using the subscripts BP and LP to denote bandpass and lowpass, we write

$$H_{\text{BP}}(j\omega) = \begin{cases} H_{\text{LP}}(j\omega + j\omega_0) + H_{\text{LP}}(j\omega - j\omega_0), & \omega_1 \leqslant |\omega| \leqslant \omega_2, \\ & \omega_0 = (\omega_2 + \omega_1)/2 \\ 0 & \text{, elsewhere.} \end{cases} \tag{127}$$

Then

$$\begin{aligned} h_{\text{BP}}(t) &= \frac{1}{2\pi}\left[\int_{-\omega_2}^{-\omega_1} H_{\text{LP}}(j\omega + j\omega_0)\, e^{j\omega t}\, d\omega \right. \\ &\quad \left. + \int_{\omega_1}^{\omega_2} H_{\text{LP}}(j\omega - j\omega_0)\, e^{j\omega t}\, d\omega\right] \\ &= \frac{1}{\pi}\int_{\omega_1}^{\omega_2} \text{Re}\left\{H_{\text{LP}}(j\omega - j\omega_0)\, e^{j\omega t}\right\} d\omega. \end{aligned}$$

Now, if we let $x = (\omega - \omega_0)/(\omega_2 - \omega_1)/2$, then x measures the frequency deviation $(\omega - \omega_0)$ from the center frequency ω_0 in units of one-half the bandwidth $(BW) = (\omega_2 - \omega_1)$, $\omega = \omega_1$ goes to $x = -1$, $\omega = \omega_2$ goes to $x = 1$, and if we set $H_{\text{LP}}(jx(BW)/2) = A_{\text{LP}}(x)\, e^{-j\phi_{\text{LP}}(x)}$, we can write

$$\begin{aligned} h_{\text{BP}}(t) &= \frac{(BW)}{2\pi}\int_{-1}^{1} A_{\text{LP}}(x) \cos\left[x\frac{(BW)}{2}t - \phi_{\text{LP}}(x) + \omega_0 t\right] dx \\ &= a_c(t) \cos \omega_0 t - a_s(t) \sin \omega_0 t \\ &= \sqrt{a_c^2(t) + a_s^2(t)} \cos\left[\omega_0 t - \tan^{-1}\frac{a_s(t)}{a_c(t)}\right] \end{aligned} \tag{128}$$

where

$$a_c(t) = \frac{(BW)}{2\pi}\int_{-1}^{1} A_{\text{LP}}(x) \cos\left[x\frac{(BW)}{2}t - \phi_{\text{LP}}(x)\right] dx \tag{129}$$

and

$$a_s(t) = \frac{(BW)}{2\pi}\int_{-1}^{1} A_{\text{LP}}(x) \sin\left[x\frac{(BW)}{2}t - \phi_{\text{LP}}(x)\right] dx.$$

For the special case in which $A_{LP}(x)$ is an even function of x and $\phi_{LP}(x)$ is an odd function, $a_s(t) = 0$, and Eq. (128) reduces to

$$h_{BP}(t) = 2h_{LP}(t) \cos \omega_0 t \tag{130}$$

in which we have set $a_c(t) = 2h_{LP}(t)$.

Let us now examine the preceding expressions. The restriction of the system function of the filter as stated in Eq. (127) is a tolerable idealization for practical receiver filters. The purpose of Eq. (127) is to emphasize the frequency-selective character of the filter response; therefore ω_2 and ω_1 are to be interpreted as limits outside of which the filter amplitude-response characteristic is negligible for all practical purposes. The frequency ω_0 is, by definition, the midband frequency, and according to Eqs. (128) and (130) it has the significance of a carrier frequency for the impulse response of the filter. The assumption of even and odd symmetry for $A_{LP}(x)$ and $\phi_{LP}(x)$ is realistic when the natural frequencies of the filter are symmetrically disposed with respect to the line $s = j\omega_0$ and $(\omega_2 - \omega_1) \ll \omega_0$ (the so-called high-Q approximation). When this assumption can be made without serious error, as is most often the case, the impulse response of the filter can be interpreted as being a constant-frequency amplitude-modulated sinusoid whose instantaneous amplitude is given by two times the impulse response of a lowpass filter whose system function is

$$H_{LP}(j\omega) = \int_{-\infty}^{\infty} h_{LP}(t)\, e^{-j\omega t}\, dt\,. \tag{131}$$

The most important properties of the instantaneous amplitude of the impulse response can be seen from Eqs. (129) and (130). According to the expression in Eq. (129), the time variable t in any final expression for $h_{LP}(t)$ will always be multiplied by a scaling factor that equals some constant times any convenient measure of filter bandwidth (be it the separation between the half-power points, or the separation between the frequencies ω_1 and ω_2 which were described above). One consequence of this time scaling is that if the filter bandwidth is scaled *up* by some factor, the time scale of the impulse response will be scaled *down* by the same factor. Also, since $A_{LP}(x)$ is positive for all x, the absolute maximum of $h_{LP}(t)$ occurs when the cosine factor attains its first maximum value of unity; that is, when

$$t = t_m = \frac{\phi_{LP}(x)}{x} \Big/ (BW)/2. \tag{132}$$

Accordingly, the maximum value of $h_{LP}(t)$ is

$$h_{LP}(t_m) = \frac{(BW)/2}{2\pi} \int_{-1}^{1} A_{LP}(x)\, dx. \tag{133}$$

Equations (133) and (132) show that the maximum value of the envelope of the impulse response is directly proportional to the filter bandwidth, and the instant of time at which the maximum occurs is inversely proportional to the filter bandwidth. This statement holds independently of whether or not $A_{LP}(x)$ and $\phi_{LP}(x)$ have the appropriate symmetries about $x = 0$, and the stated types of proportionality hold for any convenient choice of bandwidth-measurement criterion.

Finally, we note from Eq. (131) that

$$\int_{-\infty}^{\infty} h_{LP}(t)\,dt = H_{LP}(0) \; ,$$

which shows that the area under the instantaneous amplitude of the impulse response is a constant that is fixed by the center-frequency value of the filter amplitude response.

The preceding results apply directly to the impulse-noise problem. If the impulsive input is of such a short duration that its spectrum is substantially flat over the range $\omega_1 \leqslant |\omega| \leqslant \omega_2$, then the response of the linear filter will differ from $h(t)$ only by a constant multiplier. We can therefore draw the following conclusions:

(a) The impulsive disturbance causes a response that is generally a combined amplitude and frequency-modulated sinusoid with a carrier frequency that equals the center frequency of the filter passband. If the filter amplitude and phase characteristics are closely approximated by even and odd functions, respectively, of frequency deviation from the center frequency, then the frequency modulation is negligible, and the envelope of the response is given by two times the impulse response of a physical lowpass analog filter.

(b) The maximum value of this envelope is directly proportional to the filter bandwidth, and the duration of its important part is inversely proportional to this bandwidth—the criteria of bandwidth and duration measurements being dictated entirely by arbitrary considerations related to the practical situation at hand. Thus, if the nominal bandwidth of the filter is multiplied by a factor k, the maximum value of the impulse response is multiplied by k, and the nominal duration of this response by $1/k$. The area under the impulse response is a constant independent of this scaling.

6.3 The Linear Impulse-Noise Suppression Technique[22, 23]

The preceding results can be applied directly, as illustrated in Fig. 23, to suppress impulse noise. The indicated operation can be performed either in the r-f section or in the i-f section of a receiver, even though for practical reasons, as well as for reasons of receiver sensitivity to fluctuation noise, the i-f section may be preferable. The design of each of the paralleled amplifiers is assumed to satisfy the linearity and bandwidth requirements for low-distortion transmission of the desired signal $e_s(t)$. If the minimum bandwidth re-

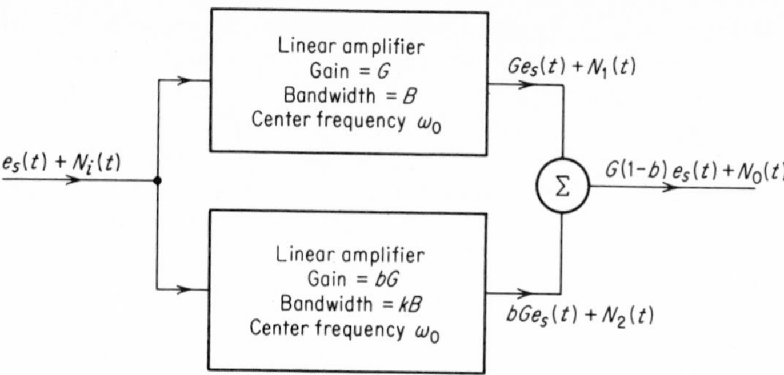

Fig. 23. Fundamental block diagram of the linear-cancellation technique for suppressing impulse noise.

quired to accommodate the signal $e_s(t)$ is B cps, then one amplifier is designed to have this bandwidth and a gain of G, the other is designed to have a bandwidth kB, $k > 1$, and gain bG. Direct subtraction of the amplifier responses leads to an output-signal component given by $G(1 - b)e_s(t)$ and an impulsive-noise component given by $N_0(t) = N_1(t) - N_2(t)$. The maxima of $N_1(t)$ and $N_2(t)$ will attain equal values if $b = 1/k$, but they will occur at instants whose spacing depends on k. An appropriate choice of b should therefore enable the subtraction to result in an $N_0(t)$ that is substantially milder than $N_1(t)$ when compared with the desired signal. Bandwidth restriction to the minimum necessary value of B in circuits that follow the arrangement shown in Fig. 23 is expected to result in the removal of any added random noise or interference that may pass through the excess bandwidth of the lower amplifier branch. The circuits that precede the arrangement of Fig. 23 should preferably have a bandwidth that is considerably wider than kB, in order to preserve the impulsive character of the input disturbance until it reaches the input terminals of the paralleled amplifiers.

Let us examine the effectiveness of some specific circuit embodiments of this technique. The ultimate criterion for judging the effectiveness of specific circuits is, of course, some measure of the reduction of the noise effects upon the receiver output. For example, with an FM receiver the ultimate performance criterion may be the percentage of reduction in the capture time (or the time interval during which the response of the filter to the impulsive disturbance exceeds the signal amplitude) because the probability that the disturbance will cause a "pop" noise (a phase step of 2π and a corresponding frequency impulse) in the output is directly proportional to the capture time. It will be found, however, that the improvement in the ratio of signal amplitude to the peak value of the noise amplitude as a result of the subtraction is a much easier quantity to compute, as well as a criterion that is more generally applicable to FM and to systems other than FM.

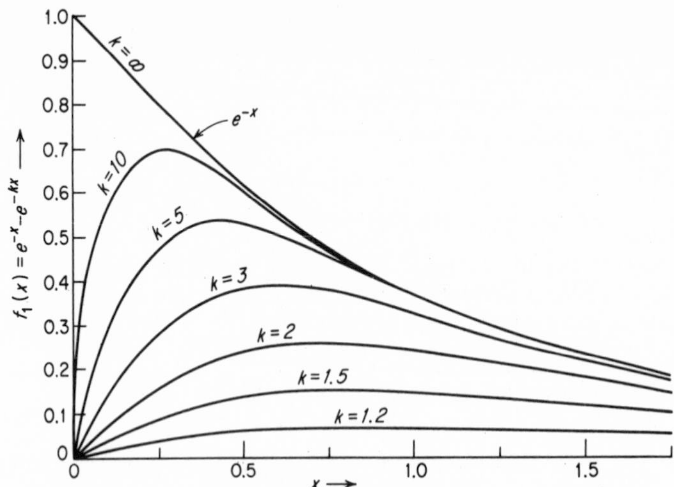

Fig. 24. Normalized impulse response of the arrangement of Fig. 23 when the paralleled amplifiers have single-tuned, high-Q loads.

Consider the situation in which each of the parallel branches in Fig. 23 is made up of an amplifier with a high-Q single-tuned circuit as the load. The instantaneous amplitude of the unit-impulse response of such an amplifier can be written as

$$2h_{LP}(t) = 2\alpha Ge^{-\alpha t} \tag{134}$$

where α is one-half the bandwidth of the circuit measured between the half-power points, and G is the gain of the amplifier at its center frequency. Thus, if the duration of the input disturbance $N_i(t)$ in Fig. 23 is so short relative to the time constants of the paralleled amplifiers that the spectrum of $N_i(t)$ is essentially flat over the significant passband of the lower-Q circuit, and if the magnitude of the Fourier transform of $N_i(t)$ within this passband is A_N, then $N_i(t)$ simulates an impulse of strength A_N, and the instantaneous amplitudes of $N_1(t)$ and $N_2(t)$ are $2\alpha A_N Ge^{-\alpha t}$ and $2\alpha A_N bkGe^{-k\alpha t}$, respectively. Since both of these responses attain their maximum values at the same instant of time, we choose $b = 1/k$ for a perfect cancellation at $t = 0$.

The instantaneous amplitude of $N_0(t)$ with $b = 1/k$ is

$$E_N(t) = 2\alpha A_N G[e^{-\alpha t} - e^{-k\alpha t}]. \tag{135}$$

The function

$$f_1(x) = e^{-x} - e^{-kx} \tag{136}$$

is plotted in Fig. 24 for various choices of k. The peak value of $f_1(x)$

occurs when

$$x = x_m = \ln k^{1/(k-1)}$$

and

$$f_1(x)]_{\max} = (k-1)k^{-k/(k-1)}. \tag{137}$$

Therefore, the maximum value of the output noise envelope, $E_N(t)$, is

$$E_N(t)]_{\max} = 2\alpha A_N G(k-1)k^{-k/(k-1)}. \tag{138}$$

In contrast, if the input signal is a sinusoid of amplitude E_s, the output signal amplitude is $GE_s(k-1)/k$. The ratio of output signal amplitude to peak noise amplitude is then

$$\left[\frac{S_{\text{peak}}}{N_{\text{peak}}}\right]_{\text{out}} = \left[\frac{E_s}{2\alpha A_N}\right] k^{1/(k-1)}. \tag{139}$$

The quantity in brackets on the right is recognized as the ratio of signal amplitude to peak noise at the output of the upper branch in Fig. 23. The factor $k^{1/(k-1)}$ represents the improvement achieved through subtracting the output of the lower amplifier from the output of the upper amplifier. This improvement factor is a monotonically decreasing function of k for $k > 1$. The maximum value, which is approached as $k \to 1$ from above, can be found by setting $k = 1 + \epsilon$, and letting $\epsilon \to 0$. This results in

$$\lim_{\epsilon \to 0} (1+\epsilon)^{1/\epsilon} = e = 2.718 \ldots$$
$$= \text{base of natural logarithms.}$$

We therefore conclude that since k is, by hypothesis, always chosen greater than one ($k = 1$ results in complete cancellation of signal as well as disturbance), the improvement factor will be less than 8.686 db. For $k = 1.2$, it is 8 db, and for $k = 1.1$ it is 8.28 db.

Note that it is possible, by appropriate preclipping of the incoming noise peaks, to keep $(E_s/2\alpha A_N)$ sufficiently low that the ratio of peak signal to peak noise (Eq. 139) after the cancellation in Fig. 23 always exceeds unity by a comfortable margin. This would effectively eliminate all pops in FM and all confusion (in gates with preset thresholds) between impulsive noise pulses and the desired pulses in pulse transmission, and it should improve other types of reception well beyond the limits on improvement with noise clipping alone.

As a second example, we consider the situation in which each of the parallel branches in Fig. 23 is made up of n synchronously tuned stages in cascade, each having a single-tuned high-Q circuit with a damping factor α for the upper branch, and $k\alpha$ for the lower branch. Let the overall gains be G_n for the upper branch, and G_n/k for the lower branch. If (according to section 4.1) we take the expression in Eq. (134) for the envelope of the impulse response of the first stage in the upper branch and convolve it with $h_{\text{LP}}(t)$ of the second stage, the outcome will be the envelope of the impulse response of the first two stages in cascade. Repetition of this procedure leads to

$$a_{nu}(t) = \frac{2\alpha G_n A_N}{(n-1)!}(\alpha t)^{n-1} e^{-\alpha t} \tag{140}$$

for the envelope of the overall response of the upper branch. The peak of this envelope is

$$2\alpha G A_N \frac{1}{(n-1)!}\left(\frac{n-1}{e}\right)^{n-1} \tag{141}$$

and it occurs at $t = (n-1)/\alpha$. Thus, the ratio of signal amplitude to peak noise amplitude at the output of the upper branch is

$$\begin{aligned} \rho_n &= \frac{E_s}{2\alpha A_N}\left(\frac{e}{n-1}\right)^{n-1}(n-1)! \\ &= \frac{E_s}{(BW)A_N}\psi(n) \end{aligned} \tag{142}$$

where (BW) is the overall bandwidth in rad/sec, and

$$\psi(n) = (n-1)!\left(\frac{e}{n-1}\right)^{n-1}\sqrt{2^{1/n}-1}. \tag{143}$$

The function $\psi(n)$ represents an improvement factor [relative to the output of one stage of bandwidth (BW)] that is characteristic of cascading synchronous, single-tuned, high-Q amplifiers. Some values of $\psi(n)$ are: $\psi(1) = 1$, $\psi(2) = 1.75$, $\psi(3) = 1.88$, $\psi(n) \cong 2.1\sqrt{1-(1/n)}$ for $n > 3$.

The envelope of the impulse response of the scheme illustrated in Fig. 23, in the present example, is therefore

$$E_N(t) = \frac{2\alpha G A_N}{(n-1)!}\left[(\alpha t)^{n-1} e^{-\alpha t} - (k\alpha t)^{n-1} e^{-k\alpha t}\right]. \tag{144}$$

The determination of the peak value of $E_N(t)$ is not a simple task here. But our major interest at this point is only in the upper bound on the improvement (that is attributable to the subtraction) in the ratio of signal amplitude to peak value of $E_N(t)$. This upper bound is the limit as $k \to 1$ from above, of the measure of improvement for any $k > 1$. The desired upper bound is therefore most expeditiously obtained by setting $k = 1 + \epsilon$ in Eq. (144) and then operating on an approximation to $E_N(t)$ that holds for $0 < \epsilon \ll 1$. If we set

$$f_n(x) = x^{n-1}e^{-x} - (kx)^{n-1}e^{-kx}, \tag{145}$$

then the desired approximation for $E_N(t)$ is

$$E_N(t) = \frac{2\alpha G A_N}{(n-1)!}\,\epsilon\{x^{n-1}e^{-x}[x-(n-1)]\}. \tag{146}$$

Let the function in braces be denoted $g(x)$. The upper bound on the ratio of signal amplitude to peak-noise amplitude after subtraction is then

$$\frac{E_s}{\dfrac{2\alpha A_N}{(n-1)!}} \bigg/ [g(x)]_{\max}\,. \tag{147}$$

In contrast, the ratio of signal amplitude to peak-noise amplitude at the output of the upper branch is

$$\frac{E_s}{\dfrac{2\alpha A_N}{(n-1)!}} \bigg/ \left(\frac{n-1}{e}\right)^{n-1}. \tag{148}$$

The improvement factor attributable to subtraction is therefore bounded by $|I_n|$, where

$$\begin{aligned} I_n &= \left(\frac{n-1}{e}\right)^{n-1} \bigg/ [g(x)]_{\max} \\ &= \frac{4(n-1)^{n-1}\, e^{\frac{1}{2}[1 \pm \sqrt{4n-3}]}}{6n - 4 \pm 2n\sqrt{4n-3}} \end{aligned} \tag{149}$$

in which the sign that yields the *smaller* of the two values of $|I_n|$ is chosen (minus for $n \geqslant 3$). Illustrative values of $|I_n|$ are: $I_1 = e$, which checks the result of the first example (Eq. (139) *et seq.*), $I_2 = 1.2$, $|I_3| = 4/e = 1.47$, $|I_4| = 3.33$, $|I_5| = 14.2$, $|I_7| \cong 790$. The improvement builds up very rapidly with increasing n for $n > 3$. The overall improvement factor relative to the output of one stage of bandwidth (BW) is obtained by multiplying $|I_n|$ by the cascading improvement factor, $\psi(n)$, of Eq. (143).

We now illustrate the effect of timing the peak values of the envelopes of the impulse responses of the paralleled amplifiers so that they occur at the same instant of time. We take the case in which $n = 2$ in the preceding example. Here, the instantaneous amplitude of $N_0(t)$ depends upon αt according to the function

$$f_2(x) = xe^{-x} - kxe^{-kx} \tag{150}$$

which is plotted in Fig. 25(a) for various values of k. The peak values of xe^{-x} and kxe^{-kx} are attained at $x = 1$ and $x = 1/k$, respectively. Through the use of appropriate delay, kxe^{-kx} can be made to attain its peak value at $x = 1$, in order to null the peak value of xe^{-x}. If such delay is introduced into the lower branch then $f_2(x)$ is replaced by

$$f_{2d}(x) = xe^{-x} - [kx - (k-1)]\, e^{-[kx-(k-1)]} \tag{151}$$

which is plotted in Fig. 25(b). Comparison of Fig. 25(a) and 25(b) shows clearly that the peak values that are attained by the residual disturbance in Fig. 25(b) exceed the peak values attained in Fig. 25(a).

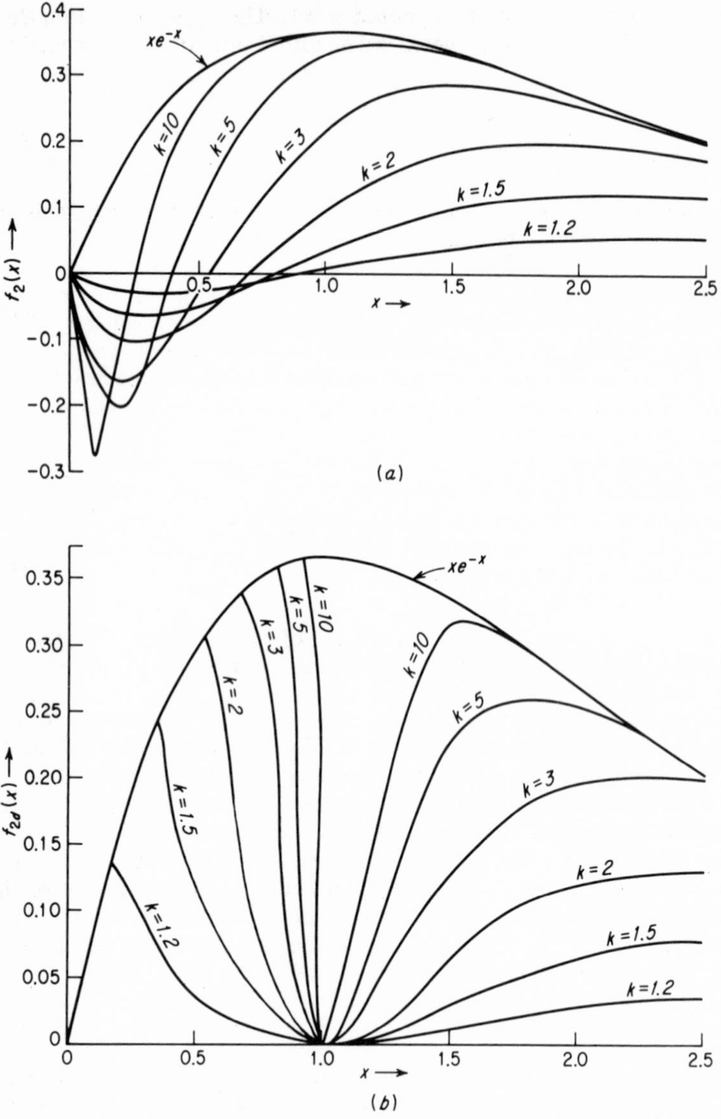

Fig. 25. Impulse noise envelopes described by:
(a) $f_2(x)$ of Eq. (150);
(b) $f_{2d}(x)$ of Eq. (151).

Accordingly, we conclude that the introduction of time delay in one of the signal paths, in order to enable the peaks of the impulse responses of the parallel paths to occur at the same time, may cause a deterioration in the impulse-noise-suppression performance of the scheme.

The preceding examples show that it is possible to achieve substantial reductions in the relative strength of impulsive disturbances by means of simple linear-cancellation circuits. This technique can be combined with a preclipping operation of appropriately chosen threshold to effect almost complete elimination of the harmful effects of impulse noise, although some forms of the linear-cancellation technique will achieve such a result without the use of preclipping. The subtraction that results in these reductions is effective against a moderate number of impulses whose effects overlap completely or partially; it is not effective against very large numbers of randomly superimposed impulses (such as shot noise for example) because of the large number of residual overlapping disturbances caused by the input noise pulses. In this second situation, the coherent nature of the signal and the large number of the random residual noise disturbances combine to cause a decided deterioration in the mean signal to mean random-noise power ratio.

Some interesting ramifications of this technique, as well as specializations of it for specific modulation systems, such as cascading of simple linear-cancellation blocks, postdetection subtraction, and so forth, can be derived from the fundamental principles presented above, but this will not be attempted here.

VII. RANDOM FLUCTUATION NOISE

In the absence of the two types of disturbance discussed in sections V and VI, random fluctuation noise sets the limit on signal detectability or message extractability, and on the accuracy with which measurements can be made. This type of noise is often characterized by an irreducible average power density and it therefore sets a lower limit on the level of useable signals at the receiver

Consequently, range and reliability of communication systems are frequently discussed from the viewpoint of their limitation by random fluctuation noise. Although the desire to extend range and reliability has always been in the background spurring investigators to seek newer and better signaling and signal-processing techniques, the advent of space communications and of earth satellites as possible transmission media (see Chapter 22) has intensified the need for more reliable extraction of messages from signals imbedded in high-level fluctuation noise. In Chapters 15, 16, and 17 the effect of front-end receiver design upon receiver sensitivity was stressed. In the present section we discuss the effect of signal-processing after the front end upon the demodulation of a signal in the presence of fluctuation noise passed by the i-f amplifier.

We first need a suitable model of the noise. We shall employ an empirical model that has intuitive appeal as well as ample theoretical justification.

Suppose we attempt to make measurements on the noise with the aid of a tunable narrow-band filter. Let the filter have a nearly rectangular bandpass amplitude characteristic of width Δf, and center frequency f_n adjustable in Δf steps such that $f_0 - f_n = n\Delta f$ where f_0 is some reference frequency such as the center of the i-f passband. Also, assume that the mean-square value of the filter output is measured by a meter that averages over a period much longer than $1/\Delta f$. When the filter is connected to the noise source and tuned to f_n, the meter reading will be proportional to some quantity $w(f_n)\Delta f$, where $w(f)$ is effectively constant over the interval Δf centered about f_n. The function $w(f)$ has the significance of a density function, and we shall refer to it as the mean-square spectral density function of the noise. If Δf is sufficiently small, the band of noise passed by the filter cannot be distinguished from a sinusoid of constant amplitude and constant frequency,

$$\sqrt{2w(f_n)\Delta f}\, \cos(2\pi f_n t - \phi_n), \tag{152}$$

whose mean square value is equal to that of the noise within the frequency band of width Δf about f_n (see Fig. 26). The phase ϕ_n is

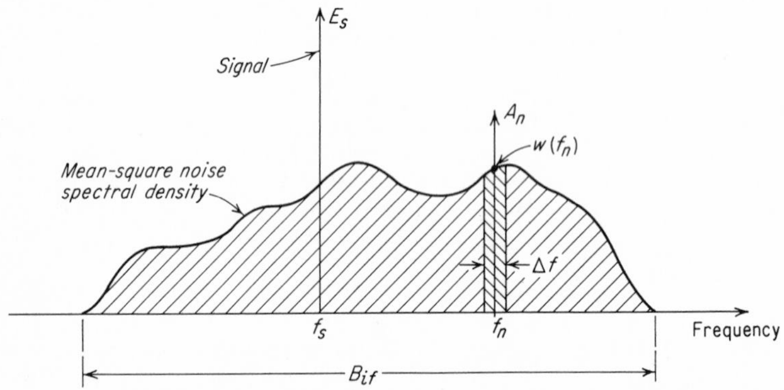

Fig. 26. Decomposition of the noise into a sum of random-phased sinusoids. Shaded area under the curve for $w(f)$ is proportional to the total noise power. Noise in incremental bandwith Δf centered about f_n is represented by equivalent sinusoid described by (152).

chosen at random to have some value between 0 and 2π, all possible choices in this interval having equal probability weighting. The meter reading gives no information about ϕ_n and the character of the noise being modeled is such that one cannot justify any other assumptions about ϕ_n.

Accordingly, a band of width B_{if}, say, may be divided into narrow slots of width Δf, and the total noise, $e_n(t)$, occupying B_{if} with a mean-square spectral density $w(f)$ can be represented as the limit, as Δf becomes infinitesimally small, of

$$\sum_{n\Delta f=-B_{\text{if}}/2}^{B_{\text{if}}/2} A_n \cos\,[\omega_n t + \phi_n], \quad A_n \equiv \sqrt{2w(f_n)\Delta f}$$

$$\omega_n = 2\pi f_n = \omega_0 + 2\pi n \Delta f \tag{153}$$

in which ϕ_n is a random variable that is uniformly distributed over $0 \leq \phi_n \leq 2\pi$, and ϕ_n and ϕ_m, $m \neq n$, are statistically independent. According to the Central Limit Theorem (section 2.5 of Chapter 2), this choice of phasing of the sinusoids restricts the representation (153) to gaussian noise of mean-square spectral density $w(f)$.

We shall occasionally find it convenient to consider the resultant of all the sinusoidal components in (153) as one sinusoid

$$V(t) \cos\,[\omega_c t + \phi(t)]$$

whose envelope $V(t)$ and phase $\phi(t)$ are time functions that vary slowly (relative to $\cos \omega_c t$) for a narrowband noise process (*i.e.* a noise process whose spectrum occupies a bandwidth that constitutes a small fraction of any frequency contained in this spectrum). For a narrow-band gaussian noise process, $V(t)$ is Rayleigh distributed, and $\phi(t)$ is uniformly distributed over $0 \leq \phi \leq 2\pi$.

For modulation systems, the criterion of performance in the presence of fluctuation noise is usually the signal-to-noise mean-power ratio, even when the interest is ultimately not in waveform reproduction but rather in the correct identification of received symbols. This is especially the case if a demodulation precedes the decision operations. In such cases, the error probability is evaluated as a function of S/N ratio out of the demodulator proper and into the decision circuits.

7.1 Fluctuation Noise in Linear-Modulation Systems

As in section V, we consider only product demodulation for a general linear-modulation signal, and envelope detection for an AM signal.

Product demodulation—Let the signal be described by

$$e_s(t) = E_s g_s(t) \cos\,(\omega_s t + \phi_s).$$

It is convenient to choose the reference frequency, ω_0, in the representation of the noise to be equal to ω_s, the carrier frequency of the signal. Multiplication of the sum of the signal and noise by

$$e_{\text{osc}}(t) = E_{\text{osc}} \cos\,(\omega_s t + \phi_{\text{osc}})$$

followed by low-pass filtering that retains only components in the range 0+ to $B_{\ell p}$ [which encompasses the range of frequencies expected in $g_s(t)$] yields

$$\kappa_d E_{\text{osc}} E_s\, g_s(t) \cos\,(\phi_s - \phi_{\text{osc}}) \tag{154}$$

for the signal component, where κ_d is a constant of the demodulator. The corresponding noise component is given by the limit, as Δf becomes infinitesimally small, of

$$\kappa_d E_{osc} \sum_{n\Delta f=-B_{\ell p}}^{B_{\ell p}} A_n \cos(2\pi n \Delta f t + \phi_n - \phi_{osc}) \tag{155}$$

with A_n as defined in Eq. (153). The mean-square value of the signal component is

$$\kappa_d^2 E_{osc}^2 E_s^2 \overline{g_s^2(t)} \cos^2(\phi_s - \phi_{osc}) \tag{156}$$

where the bar indicates time averaging. On account of the assumed random character of the ϕ_n's, and their statistical independence, the noise components add incoherently (*i.e.* the mean-square value of the sum equals the sum of the mean-square values of the components). The mean-square value of the output noise is, therefore,

$$\kappa_d^2 E_{osc}^2 \int_{-B_{\ell p}}^{B_{\ell p}} w(f_s + f)\, df. \tag{157}$$

Thus, the output S/N mean-power ratio is

$$(S/N)_{out} = \frac{\overline{g_s^2(t)} E_s^2 \cos^2(\phi_s - \phi_{osc})}{\int_{-B_{\ell p}}^{B_{\ell p}} w(f_s + f)\, df}. \tag{158}$$

Notice that only the noise components whose frequencies differ from the signal carrier frequency f_s by $f \leqslant B_{\ell p}$ contribute to the output. The output ratio (158) is a maximum when $\phi_s = \phi_{osc}$.

If, as a specific illustration, we assume the noise to be white and of mean-square density N_0 square volts per cps, (158) takes the form

$$(S/N)_{out} = 2\overline{g_s^2(t)} \left(\frac{E_s^2/2}{2B_{\ell p} N_0}\right) \cos^2(\phi_s - \phi_{osc}). \tag{159}$$

In double-sideband, suppressed-carrier (DSB) linear modulation, the signal is completely described by $e_s(t)$ as assumed above. If we assume that the i-f passband is sharply confined to a bandwidth $B_{if} = 2B_{\ell_p}$ cps, the S/N mean power ratio at the demodulator input is

$$(S/N)_{in} = \left(\frac{E_s^2/2}{2B_{\ell p} N_0}\right) \overline{g_s^2(t)}\,. \tag{160}$$

The ratio of (159) to (160) yields

$$\frac{(S/N)_{out}}{(S/N)_{in}} = 2\cos^2(\phi_s - \phi_{osc}) \tag{161}$$

which represents an improvement in the output ratio over the input ratio as long as $|\phi_s - \phi_{osc}| < \pi/4$. The maximum improvement is 3db and it holds when $\phi_s = \phi_{osc}$.

In AM, the signal is described by

$$e_{\mathrm{AM}}(t) = E_s[1 + k_a g(t)] \cos(\omega_s t + \phi_s) \tag{162}$$

where we assume that the maximum negative value of $g(t)$ is unity (in which case k_a is known as the modulation factor). For full or 100% modulation, $k_a = 1$. The mean-square value of $e_{\mathrm{AM}}(t)$ is

$$\begin{aligned}\overline{e^2_{\mathrm{AM}}(t)} &= \frac{1}{2}E_s^2 + E_s^2 k_a \overline{g(t)} + \frac{1}{2}E_s^2 k_a^2 \overline{g^2(t)} \\ &= \frac{1}{2}E_s^2 [1 + k_a^2 \overline{g^2(t)}], \text{ if } \overline{g(t)} = 0 .\end{aligned} \tag{163}$$

Thus, if the receiver passband is confined to a bandwidth $B_{\mathrm{if}} = 2B_{\ell p}$ cps, and if $g(t)$ has no d-c component, the S/N ratio at the demodulator input (for the case of white noise) is

$$(S/N)_{\mathrm{in}} = \left(\frac{E_s^2/2}{2B_{\ell p} N_0}\right)[1 + k_a^2 \overline{g^2(t)}] . \tag{164}$$

The low-frequency passband from 0+ to $B_{\ell p}$ cps excludes zero-frequency terms. Therefore

$$(S/N)_{\mathrm{out}} = 2\left[\frac{E_s^2/2}{2B_{\ell p}N_0}\right] \overline{g^2(t)}\, k_a^2 \cos^2(\phi_s - \phi_{\mathrm{osc}}). \tag{165}$$

The output ratio is directly proportional to the square of the modulation factor, k_a, and is a maximum when $k_a = 1$ and $\phi_{\mathrm{osc}} = \phi_s$. The factor in brackets on the right-hand side of Eq. (165) is the ratio of mean carrier power to mean noise power.

In a single-sideband receiver whose bandwidth is confined to the frequency range of the SSB signal, the S/N ratio at the output of the product demodulator is equal to the input ratio multiplied by $\cos^2(\phi_s - \phi_{\mathrm{osc}})$. This assumes that no carrier component is present in the SSB signal.

It should be emphasized that no assumptions were made in the preceding discussion concerning the relative strengths of signal and noise. Under ideal conditions of product demodulation, the expressions derived for output S/N ratios hold for all input S/N ratios.

Noise in AM with envelope detection—We shall discuss only the special cases in which the signal is either much stronger or much weaker than the noise. These cases can be handled by extremely simple and intuitive arguments that do not require complicated mathematical analysis. The more general methods of analysis of random fluctuation noise in non-linear devices, although conceptually simple, usually require extremely involved computations and lead to incomprehensible expansions and higher mathematical functions. Largely, and perhaps only, thanks to the well-developed state and the elegance of the theory of the gaussian process has it been possible thus far to execute the general solutions for various non-linear devices of wide interest. An excellent tutorial treatment of the general methods can be found in Davenport and Root,[24] particularly chapters 12 and 13.

When the signal is much stronger than the noise, the S/N mean-power ratio at the output of the detector can be computed as follows:

Step 1. Ignore the noise and compute the mean-square value of the output signal when the input consists only of the signal that carries the desired message modulation.

Step 2. Ignore the message modulation, and compute the mean-square value of the output noise when the input consists of an unmodulated carrier plus the noise.

The desired output S/N mean-power ratio is very closely approximated by the ratio of the result of Step 1 to that of Step 2. The justification for Step 1 stems from the fact that when the average signal amplitude is well above the noise level, the switching of the rectifying element is effectively controlled by the signal (except perhaps during intervals when the modulation drives the envelope down to very low levels). The justification for Step 2 arises from the fact that when the signal is much stronger than the noise, the effect of the interaction between the noise and the modulation is vastly dominated by the modulation of the carrier by the noise.

Thus, in accordance with Step 1, and assuming that the input signal is given by Eq. (162), we write

$$S_{\text{out}} = \kappa_d^2 k_a^2 E_s^2 \overline{g^2(t)} \tag{166}$$

for the mean-square value of the output signal component.

The computation for Step 2 proceeds as follows: The effect of the noise contained in an element of bandwidth Δf centered at f_n (= f_s + $n\Delta f$) can be evaluated by replacing the noise by the equivalent random-phased sinusoid (152). Since, by assumption,

$$A_n = \sqrt{2w(f_n)\,\Delta f} \ll E_s$$

this noise sinusoid combines as illustrated in Fig. 27 with the unmodulated carrier to yield a resultant whose envelope is given by

$$\begin{aligned} &E_s\sqrt{1 + 2(A_n/E_s)\cos[(\omega_n - \omega_s)t + \phi_n - \phi_s] + (A_n/E_s)^2} \\ &\quad \cong E_s + A_n \cos[(\omega_n - \omega_s)t + \phi_n - \phi_s]. \end{aligned} \tag{167}$$

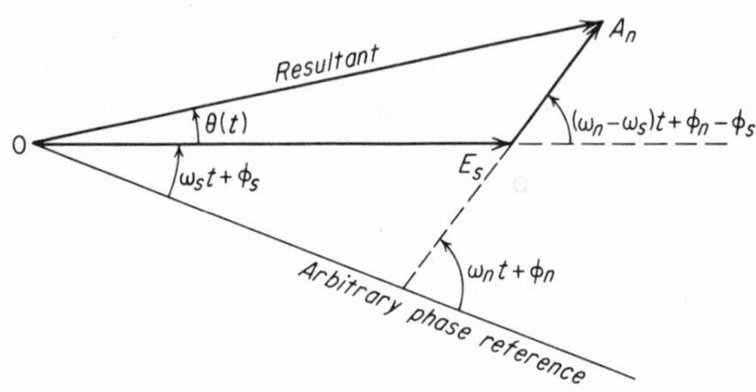

Fig. 27. Combination of signal carrier with a relatively weak noise component.

In the absence of the other noise components, the noise element considered would thus yield an output whose mean-square value is given by $\kappa_d^2 A_n^2/2$, provided that $|\omega_n - \omega_s| \leqslant 2\pi B_{\ell p}$. The contributions of individual noise components can be computed in this way as if none of the other components were present. Interactions among the noise components lead to a negligible contribution to the output noise power because they involve fourth and higher powers of (A_n/E_s). The various component-noise contributions combine incoherently because of their independent random phasing. Consequently, in the limit as Δf becomes infinitesimally small, the mean-square value of the total noise output becomes

$$N_{\text{out}} = \kappa_d^2 \int_{-B_{\ell p}}^{B_{\ell p}} w(f_s + f)\, df. \tag{168}$$

The output S/N mean-power ratio is therefore given by

$$(S/N)_{\text{out}} = \frac{S_{\text{out}}}{N_{\text{out}}} = \frac{k_a^2 E_s^2 \overline{g^2(t)}}{\int_{B_{\ell p}}^{B_{\ell p}} w(f_s + f)\, df} \tag{169}$$

which is identical with the result for product demodulation with $\phi_{\text{osc}} = \phi_s$. For white noise with $w(f_n) = \text{constant} = N_0$,

$$(S/N)_{\text{out}} = 2\left(\frac{E_s^2/2}{2B_{\ell p} N_0}\right) k_a^2\, \overline{g^2(t)}. \tag{170}$$

It is instructive to observe that the same result can be obtained by treating the total noise in the band $\omega_s - 2\pi B_{\ell p} \leqslant \omega \leqslant \omega_s + 2\pi B_{\ell p}$ as a resultant sinusoid

$$V(t) \cos\left[\omega_s t + \phi(t)\right] \tag{171}$$

whose envelope $V(t)$ is Rayleigh distributed and whose phase $\phi(t)$ has a uniform distribution over $0 \leqslant \phi \leqslant 2\pi$. On the assumption that $V(t) \ll E_s[1 + k_a g(t)]$, the resultant noise (171) combines with $e_s(t)$ of Eq. (162) to yield a sinusoid whose envelope is closely approximated by

$$E_s[1 + k_a g(t)] + V(t) \cos[\phi(t) - \phi_s]. \tag{172}$$

The low-pass filter passband associated with the envelope demodulator excludes the d-c term, and passes a signal component whose mean-square value is given by $\kappa_d^2 k_a^2 E_s^2 \overline{g^2(t)}$, and a total noise of mean-square value $\kappa_d^2 \overline{V^2(t)}/2$ where*

$$\overline{V^2(t)}/2 = \text{variance of noise process}$$
$$= \int_{-B_{\ell p}}^{B_{\ell p}} w(f_s + f)\, df. \tag{173}$$

*See Chapter 7, Eq. (5) *et seq.*

We now turn to the situation in which the noise is strong relative to the signal. Here, the representation of the total noise in the band $\omega_s - 2\pi B_{\ell p} \leq \omega \leq \omega_s + 2\pi B_{\ell p}$ by (171) is more appropriate than its representation as a sum of random-phased sinusoids. The total noise and the AM signal combine to yield a resultant sinusoid whose envelope is given by

$$\sqrt{V^2(t) + 2V(t)E_s[1 + k_a g(t)] \cos[\phi(t) - \phi_s] + E_s^2 [1 + k_a g(t)]^2}. \quad (174)$$

When $V(t) > E_s[1 + k_a g(t)]$, the noise is dominant in (174). This dominance of the noise is emphasized by writing (174) in the form

$$V(t)\sqrt{1 + 2\{E_s[1 + k_a g(t)]/V(t)\} \cos[\phi(t) - \phi_s] + E_s^2[1 + k_a g(t)]^2/V^2(t)}. \quad (175)$$

During any time interval in which $V(t) \gg E_s[1 + k_a g(t)]$, the expression (175) is closely approximated by

$$V(t) + E_s \cos[\phi(t) - \phi_s] + k_a E_s g(t) \cos[\phi(t) - \phi_s]. \quad (176)$$

The first two terms are noise, pure and simple. The message time function $g(t)$ appears in the third term multiplied by the cosine of a randomly fluctuating, uniformly distributed phase. In general, this may mean a complete loss of the message.

It is important to observe that as long as $V(t) > E_s[1 + k_a g(t)]$, a binomial expansion of (175) would result only in terms in which $g(t)$, or some power of it, is *multiplied* by a noise time function. This signifies that the noise effects upon the message are *multiplicative* as long as the noise envelope exceeds the instantaneous amplitude of the signal. This represents a severe degradation in the recoverability of the message.

The preceding results reveal an extremely important phenomenon —a *threshold effect*. When the signal amplitude exceeds the noise envelope, factorization of $E_s[1 + k_a g(t)]$ out of the square-root sign in (174), followed by a binomial expansion of the square-root factor leads to a *pure signal term* added to noise terms that result from interactions between signal and noise. The pure signal term becomes more and more dominant the more the signal amplitude exceeds the noise envelope, and the limit described by (172) is approached when $E_s[1 + k_a g(t)] \gg V(t)$. On the other hand, when $V(t) > E_s[1 + k_a g(t)]$, a binomial expansion of (175) shows that $V(t)$ is now dominant and $g(t)$ is burried multiplicatively in the noise. Indeed, when $V(t) \gg E_s[1 + k_a g(t)]$, the significance of "signal-to-noise mean power ratio" may be completely lost because it may be impossible to identify "signal."

The threshold effect is a phenomenon that is experienced with all nonlinear detection devices. It is usually illustrated by a plot of S/N mean-power ratio at the output of the nonlinear detector against S/N mean-power ratio at the input of the detector, in which the curve relating the two approaches one asymptote for large input S/N and another asymptote for small input S/N. This method of illustration is of questionable validity when none of the terms in the time representation of the detector output can be identified as the undisturbed message time function, because S/N mean-power ratio has no meaning when no signal component *per se* is present in the time-functional description of the detector output. Note for example that the usual mean-power computations of noise theory would mistake the term $k_a E_s g(t)\cos[\phi(t) - \phi_s]$ in (176) for a pure signal term because in the mean-square-value computation it would be represented by $k_a^2 E_s^2 g^2(t)/2$.

7.2 Fluctuation Noise in Exponential-Modulation Systems

According to Eq. (12) a general exponential-modulation signal can be described by

$$e_{\exp}(t) = E_s \cos[\omega_s t + \psi(t)] \tag{177}$$

where $\psi(t)$ is directly proportional to $g(t)$ for phase modulation, and to the integral of $g(t)$ for frequency modulation. Let the total noise contained within the i-f passband be represented by

$$V(t)\cos[\omega_s t + \phi(t)]. \tag{178}$$

The resultant of signal and noise at the output of the i-f amplifier is

$$e_{\text{if}}(t) = E_s \cos[\omega_s t + \psi(t)] + V(t)\cos[\omega_s t + \phi(t)]. \tag{179}$$

An exponent demodulator is now defined as being a device whose output is a voltage that varies linearly with the instantaneous phase deviation from $\omega_s t$ of $e_{\text{if}}(t)$, for phase modulation, or with the derivative of that phase deviation for FM, and this output is independent of the instantaneous value of the envelope of $e_{\text{if}}(t)$ as long as this envelope exceeds some circuit operational threshold, $E_{d,\text{th}}$. We assume that the low-pass filter associated with this demodulator has an ideal characteristic that passes only frequencies between 0+ and $B_{\ell p}$ cps (*i.e.* it rejects d-c components). The definition of the FM demodulator is illustrated in Fig. 28.

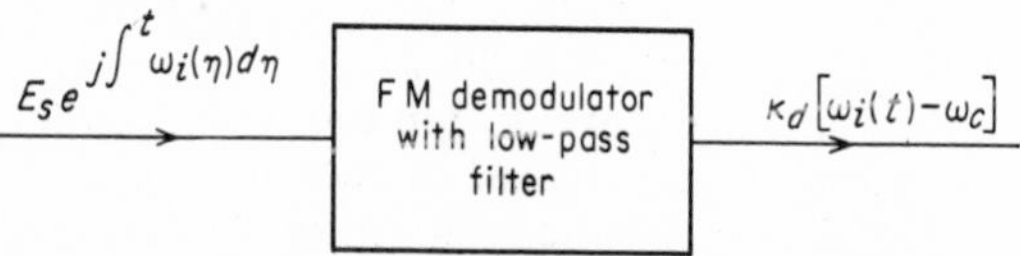

Fig. 28. Definition of FM demodulator. Associated low-pass filter is assumed to have a uniform passband that cuts off abruptly at $f = 0+$ and $f = B_{\ell p}+$ cps.

The instantaneous phase of $e_{\text{if}}(t)$ can be expressed in two equivalent ways as

$$\omega_s t + \psi(t) - \tan^{-1} \frac{V(t) \sin[\psi(t) - \phi(t)]}{E_s + V(t) \cos[\psi(t) - \phi(t)]} \tag{180}$$

or as

$$\omega_s t + \phi(t) + \tan^{-1} \frac{E_s \sin[\psi(t) - \phi(t)]}{V(t) + E_s \cos[\psi(t) - \phi(t)]} \; . \tag{181}$$

The choice of the form of expression is a matter of analytical convenience. In (180), the instantaneous phase of the signal is taken as the reference, and the inverse-tangent term represents the phase disturbance caused by the noise. In (181) the instantaneous phase of the noise is taken as the reference.

If the signal is stronger than the noise so that $E_s > V(t)$ essentially all of the time, the choice (180) is definitely the more convenient of the two. If however $V(t) > E_s$ almost all of the time, then (181) is the more convenient choice.

Two extreme situations are of special interest. In the first, the signal is much stronger than the noise, and one can assert that $E_s \gg V(t)$ almost all the time. In this case, the instantaneous phase of $e_{\text{if}}(t)$ is closely approximated by

$$\omega_s t + \psi(t) - \frac{V(t)}{E_s} \sin[\psi(t) - \phi(t)]. \tag{182}$$

In the second situation, the noise is much stronger than the signal, and here the instantaneous phase of $e_{\text{if}}(t)$ is closely approximated by

$$\omega_s t + \phi(t) + \frac{E_s}{V(t)} \sin[\psi(t) - \phi(t)]. \tag{183}$$

From (182) it is clear that when the signal is much stronger than the noise, the effect of the noise upon the phase of the carrier is to introduce a random phase perturbation whose peak value almost never exceeds a small fraction of a radian. But when the noise is much stronger than the signal, (183) shows that the desired phase information, $\psi(t)$, is inextricably burried in the noise.

A *threshold effect* is therefore to be expected in exponent-modulation detection. A capture phenomenon enables the signal to suppress the noise when the signal is well above the noise, and it enables the noise to suppress the signal when the noise is stronger. As we shall note shortly, this threshold will occur at different signal levels at the input of the receiver, for the same input noise level, depending upon the nature of the signal processing that precedes the demodulator *per se*, or upon the mechanism of the demodulation, or upon the combination of both. It is of course the signal and noise conditions at the input of the demodulator proper that determine the ultimate threshold as observed from measurements at the receiver input. This seemingly trivial observation proves helpful in understanding the basis for the threshold reduction methods that we shall discuss in section 7.3.

Expression (182) is not well suited for a computation of output signal-to-noise ratio because there is no provision in the noise representation that led to it for a simple account of the effect of low-pass filtering when the i-f bandwidth exceeds twice the low-pass bandwidth, $B_{\ell p}$. The analysis is greatly simplified if we adopt the alternative representation in which the noise is considered to consist of an infinite number of random-phased sinusoids. The method of computation follows the one outlined in Steps 1 and 2 of section 7.1, p. 526

Thus, in accordance with Step 1, we first ignore the noise, apply the message modulation, and note that if

$$e_{\exp}(t) = E_s \cos\left[\omega_s t + \Delta\Phi \cdot g(t) + \phi_c\right] \tag{184}$$

then a phase demodulator, whose circuit-operation threshold* $E_{d,\,\mathrm{th}} < E_s$, yields (after low-pass filtering)

$$e_{\mathrm{out}}(t) = \kappa_d \Delta\Phi \cdot g(t); \tag{185}$$

and if

$$e_{\exp}(t) = E_s \cos\left[\omega_s t + 2\pi\Delta F \int^{t} g(\eta)\,d\eta + \phi_c\right] \tag{186}$$

then a frequency demodulator, whose circuit-operation threshold $E_{d,\,\mathrm{th}} < E_s$, yields (after low-pass filtering)

$$e_{\mathrm{out}}(t) = \kappa_d \Delta F \cdot g(t). \tag{187}$$

If $|g(t)|_{\max}$ is assumed to be unity, then $\Delta\Phi$ in (184) is the peak phase deviation, and ΔF in (186) is the peak frequency deviation.

Next, in accordance with Step 2, we compute the mean-square value of the output noise when the input of the demodulator is an unmodulated carrier plus low-level random noise. The effect of the noise contained within a narrow bandwidth Δf can be determined by replacing this noise by the random-phased sinusoid described by (152). With reference to Fig. 27, we note that the instantaneous phase deviation caused by the noise is

$$\begin{aligned}\theta(t) &= \tan^{-1}\frac{A_n \sin[(\omega_n - \omega_s)t + \phi_n - \phi_s]}{E_s + A_n \cos[(\omega_n - \omega_s)t + \phi_n - \phi_s]}\\ &\cong (A_n/E_s)\sin[(\omega_n - \omega_s)t + \phi_n - \phi_s]\end{aligned} \tag{188}$$

since, by assumption, $A_n \ll E_s$. The instantaneous frequency perturbation caused by the incremental noise element is

$$d\theta(t)/dt \cong (\omega_n - \omega_s)(A_n/E_s)\cos[(\omega_n - \omega_s)t + \phi_n - \phi_s]. \tag{189}$$

*This driving threshold is to be distinguished from the threshold of signal detectability in the presence of noise (or signal suppression by the noise) discussed in connection with the properties of (180) and (181). Throughout this discussion, the driving threshold is assumed to fall well below the threshold of signal detectability in the presence of noise.

Therefore, in the absence of the other noise components, the noise element considered would cause an output whose mean-square value is

$$\kappa_d^2 A_n^2/2E_s^2 \text{ in phase modulation ,} \tag{190}$$

and

$$\kappa_d^2 (f_n - f_s)^2 A_n^2/2E_s^2 \text{ in frequency modulation ,} \tag{191}$$

provided that in each case $0 < |f_n - f_s| \leq B_{\ell p}$. As in the parallel computation for AM demodulation with an envelope detector, we again note that the contributions of individual noise components can be computed separately as if none of the other components were present. Interactions among the noise components lead to a negligible contribution to the output noise power because they involve fourth and higher powers of (A_n/E_s). The various component-noise contributions combine incoherently because of their independent random phasing. Consequently, in the limit as Δf becomes infinitesimally small, the mean-square value of the total noise output becomes

$$N_{\text{out}} = \kappa_d^2(1/E_s^2) \int_{-B_{\ell p}}^{B_{\ell p}} w(f_s + f)\, df \qquad \text{for PM} \tag{192}$$

and

$$N_{\text{out}} = \kappa_d^2(1/E_s^2) \int_{-B_{\ell p}}^{B_{\ell p}} f^2 w(f_s + f)\, df \qquad \text{for FM} \tag{193}$$

It is clear from (192) and (193) that the mean-square output noise density is $\kappa_d^2\, w(f_s + f)/E_s^2$ for PM and $\kappa_d^2 f^2 w(f_s + f)/E_s^2$ for FM, when the signal is sufficiently stronger than the noise to validate our reasoning. Notice that whereas the shape of the mean-square noise density function is preserved in going through the phase demodulator, it is multiplied by f^2 in going through the FM demodulator. This is the result of the fact that the output of a frequency demodulator is the time derivative of the output of a phase demodulator. The multiplication by f^2 modifies the shape of the frequency dependence of the noise density as illustrated in Fig. 29. The contribution of each noise component to the output of the FM demodulator is directly proportional to the square of its frequency difference from the signal carrier frequency. Since each input random-phased noise sinusoid interacts with the signal carrier to give rise to an output noise sinusoid whose frequency equals the difference between the frequency of the input noise sinusoid and the frequency of the carrier, only those input noise components whose frequencies fall within $\pm B_{\ell p}$ cps of the carrier frequency contribute to the noise output. The introduction of a relatively slow frequency modulation of the carrier should therefore not affect the total noise output, unless the frequency deviation of the carrier brings the instantaneous frequency of the carrier within less than $B_{\ell p}$ cps from either edge of the i-f passband. The message modulation should therefore not affect the total output noise

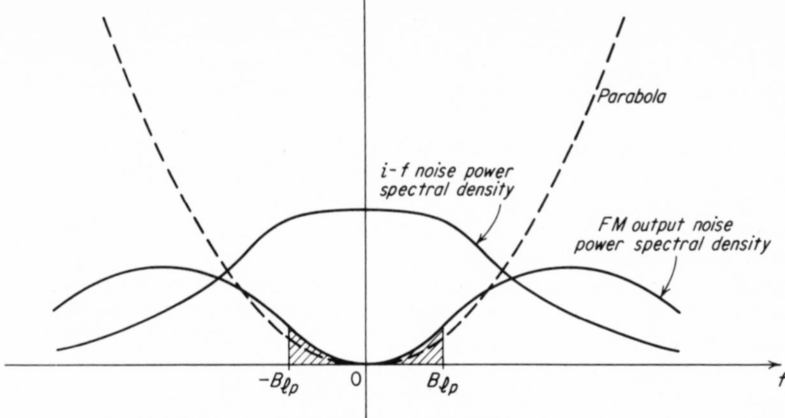

Fig. 29. Illustration of the shape of the power spectral density of the noise at the output of an FM demodulator, for a specified i-f noise power spectral density, when the signal is much stronger than the noise. Total FM noise power passed by an ideal low-pass filter is represented by the shaded area between $-B_{\ell_p}$ and B_{ℓ_p}.

if the i-f filter amplitude characteristic maintains its uniformity over a frequency range that extends at least B_{ℓ_p} cps beyond the extremes of the signal frequency excursions; otherwise, message modulation should decrease the output noise an amount that depends upon the cut-off characteristics of the i-f filter beyond the limits of the signal frequency excursions. However, this effect of the message modulation upon the output noise will henceforth be ignored.

Using the results (185), (187), (192) and (193), we have, finally,

$$(S/N)_{\text{out}} = (\Delta\Phi)^2 E_s^2 \overline{g^2(t)} \Big/ \int_{-B_{\ell_p}}^{B_{\ell_p}} w(f_s + f)\, df \qquad \text{for PM} \tag{194}$$

and

$$(S/N)_{\text{out}} = (\Delta F)^2 E_s^2 \overline{g^2(t)} \Big/ \int_{-B_{\ell_p}}^{B_{\ell_p}} f^2 w(f_s + f)\, df \qquad \text{for FM.} \tag{195}$$

It is interesting to compare the results (194) and (195) with (158), with $\phi_s = \phi_{\text{osc}}$, or with (169), with $k_a = 1$, assuming the same E_s, $g(t)$, and total noise power in a bandwidth of $2B_{\ell_p}$ cps. If we drop the subscript "out" and use subscripts FM, PM, and LM, to denote frequency, phase and linear modulation, respectively, we have

$$\frac{(S/N)_{\text{PM}}}{(S/N)_{\text{LM}}} = (\Delta\Phi)^2 \tag{196}$$

and

$$\frac{(S/N)_{\text{FM}}}{(S/N)_{\text{LM}}} = (\Delta F/R)^2 \tag{197}$$

where

$$R^2 = \int_{-B_{\ell p}}^{B_{\ell p}} f^2 w(f_s + f)\, df \Big/ \int_{-B_{\ell p}}^{B_{\ell p}} w(f_s + f)\, df \tag{198}$$

and R has the significance of a radius of gyration. Thus, under strong-signal conditions, phase modulation with a peak phase deviation $\Delta\Phi > 1$ results in better S/N ratio at the output than is achievable under equivalent conditions with linear modulation, and the improvement factor is independent of the variation of the mean-square noise density with frequency. The corresponding performance of frequency modulation is, however, dependent upon the radius of gyration of the portion of $w(f_s + f)$ that is enclosed within $-B_{\ell p} \leqslant f \leqslant B_{\ell p}$. If the i-f filter delivers white noise with $w(f_s + f) = N_0$ to the FM demodulator, then $R^2 = B_{\ell p}^2/3$, and

$$\frac{(S/N)_{\text{FM}}}{(S/N)_{\text{LM}}} = 3\left(\frac{\Delta F}{B_{\ell p}}\right)^2 \tag{199}$$

and the output S/N mean power ratio for FM is

$$(S/N)_{\text{FM}} = 3\left(\frac{\Delta F}{B_{\ell p}}\right)^2 \cdot \left[\frac{E_s^2 \overline{g^2(t)}}{2B_{\ell p} N_0}\right]. \tag{200}$$

Summary of performance of FM and PM receivers in presence of fluctuation noise—Laboratory measurement of output S/N ratio is facilitated by the choice of a sine wave (or a test tone) as the message function $g(t)$. Thus, with $g(t) = \cos(\omega_m t + \phi_m)$, where ω_m gives the frequency of the test tone, $\overline{g^2(t)} = 1/2$ and (200) becomes

$$(S/N)_{\text{FM}} = 3\left(\frac{\Delta F}{B_{\ell p}}\right)^2 \left[\frac{E_s^2/2}{2B_{\ell p} N_0}\right]. \tag{201}$$

This output is usually presented graphically as a function of

$$(S/N)_{\text{in, AM}} = \frac{E_s^2/2}{2B_{\ell p} N_0} \tag{202}$$

which is recognized as a factor in Eq. (201) and as the carrier-to-noise average power ratio of a reference AM receiver designed for the same class of messages as the FM receiver. The ratio in (202) has two additional interpretations: First, it represents the best (S/N) ratio that can be achieved at the output of the AM receiver under appropriate conditions; second, it represents the ratio of average power of the input FM signal to the total average power of only those noise components whose disturbances appear at the output of the receiver. According to the first of these interpretations, the output

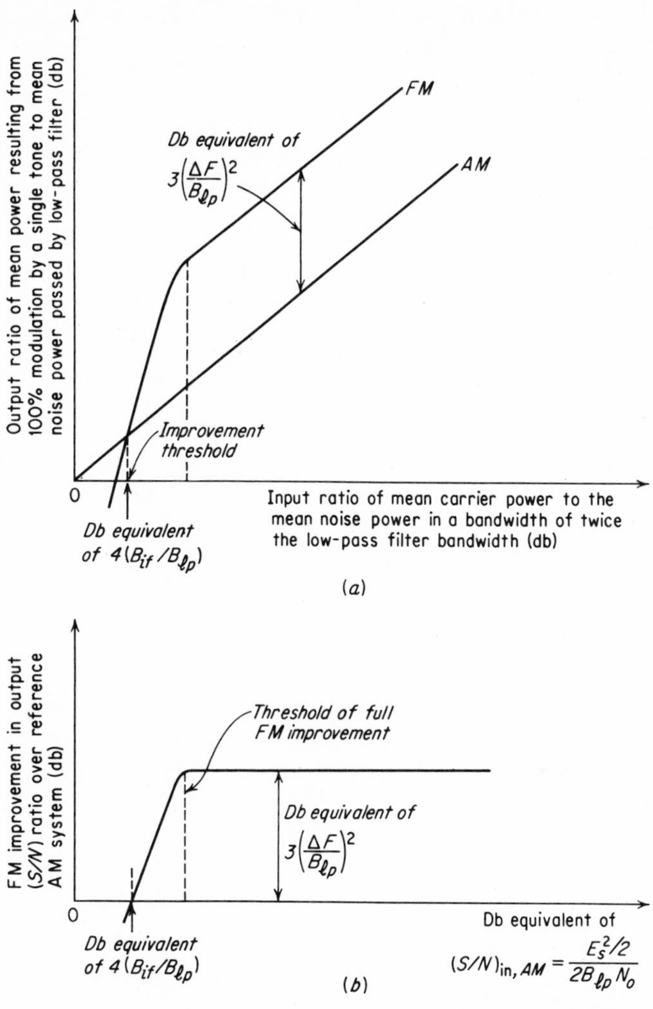

Fig. 30. Noise performance of conventional FM receiver.

ratio for FM as given by Eq. (201) falls 10 $\log_{10}[3(\Delta F/B_{\ell p})^2]$ db above the best corresponding output ratio for AM, when both are plotted in db against the ratio in Eq. (202), expressed also in db (see Fig. 30). According to the second interpretation, the output S/N ratio for FM depends only upon the noise components that fall within $\pm B_{\ell p}$ cps of the instantaneous frequency of the FM sinusoid, as long as the resultant of all of the noise components passed by the i-f amplifier does not exceed or equal the desired signal in amplitude (except perhaps during a negligible fraction of the observation time).

Consider now an experiment in which we start with random noise with a uniform mean-square spectral density of N_0 volts²/cps in a band of width B_{if} cps which equals the i-f bandwidth. The demodulator is assumed to be driven by the noise above its operational threshold. With no signal present at the input, the output of the demodulator is pure noise. A sinusoid is now introduced whose amplitude E_s is increased progressively. The effect of the sinusoid upon the receiver output can be deduced from Eq. (183) and it will be unnoticeable until E_s begins to approach some capture threshold value $E_{n,\text{th}}$ within an order of magnitude. As the value of E_s approaches $E_{n,\text{th}}$, the noise at the output of the receiver takes on a crackling impulsive character, as opposed to the gentler "shot noise" produced by the noise alone. Further increase in E_s through and beyond $E_{n,\text{th}}$ brings about rapid quieting of the noise at the output. When E_s is a few decibels above $E_{n,\text{th}}$ another threshold is reached, which we shall call the threshold of full FM improvement (see Fig. 30). For all values of E_s in excess of this second threshold, the output signal-to-noise average power ratio is given by Eq. (201). The first threshold $E_{n,\text{th}}$ marks the signal level above which the performance of the FM receiver will be superior to that of the corresponding reference AM receiver when the deviation ratio $\Delta F/B_{\ell_p} > 1/\sqrt{3}$.

The value of the threshold $E_{n,\text{th}}$ is determined by the rms value of the noise present at the input of the demodulator. This so-called "noise threshold" is therefore directly proportional to the square root of

$$N_{\text{rms}}^2 = \int_{B_{\text{if}}} w(f)\,df \tag{203}$$

in which the integration is carried out over the entire significant passband (assumed here to be well-defined by B_{if}) of the i-f amplifier. The ratio $E_{n,\text{th}}/N_{\text{rms}}$ is termed the equivalent *crest* or *peak factor* of the noise because $E_{n,\text{th}}$ has the significance of a crest value of the noise envelope. The equivalent crest factor of noise of the type generated in the front end of the receiver has been found experimentally to have a value of approximately 4, the exact value depending upon the design of the circuits used in the measurements.

The concept of a finite "crest factor" assumes that the envelope of the noise waveform considered has a well-defined crest or peak value. This is often not reconcilable with the theoretical models of fluctuation noise. The probability distribution functions of the model noise processes usually assumed in theoretical studies do not place a finite bound on the likely peak value of the envelope. But it is always possible to exercise judgement based on practical considerations to limit the crest value of the model noise process without seriously handicapping the usefulness of the theoretical model. For example, the envelope of a narrow-band gaussian noise process can assume any value between zero and infinity. Strictly speaking, this means that the crest factor of narrow-band gaussian noise is infinite. But the probability that the envelope V of the noise will exceed c times the rms value N_{rms} of the noise is given by $e^{-c^2/2}$. Thus, the probability that V will exceed $4N_{\text{rms}}$ is e^{-8}, or $V > 4N_{\text{rms}}$ only 0.034 per cent of the time. Similarly, V can be expected to exceed $3N_{\text{rms}}$ during 1.111 per cent of the time.

For practical purposes, we can therefore assume that in the case of white gaussian noise at the input of the demodulator,

$$E_{n,\,\text{th}} = 4\sqrt{N_0 B_{\text{if}}}\ . \tag{204}$$

When the signal amplitude E_s has this value, the ratio of mean signal power to *total* mean noise power at the input of the demodulator is 8 (or a little over 9 db). The corresponding value of $(S/N)_{\text{in, AM}}$ (Eq. 202) is

$$\text{Threshold } (S/N)_{\text{in, AM}} = 4(B_{\text{if}}/B_{\ell_p}). \tag{205}$$

For example, if $B_{\text{if}} = 75$ kc and $B_{\ell_p} = 15$ kc, the threshold value in Eq. (205) is a little over 13 db!

One good reason for the high value of the threshold in exponential-modulation detection is, of course, the fact that the full i-f bandwidth, B_{if}, is there to pass noise power. This value of bandwidth is provided in order to accommodate the desired signal at any instant in its modulation cycle. But the curious fact is that the exponential-modulation signal *does not* occupy this bandwidth all of the time; it can only be expected to fall somewhere within that bandwidth at any instant of time. This is evident if the signal is visualized as a sinusoid whose position on the frequency scale is changed according to the pattern required by the message modulation. Ideally, a system that could automatically sense the instantaneous frequency position of the signal and greatly attenuate all frequencies that differ from it would greatly decrease the noise threshold that the signal must exceed. Such a system would realize a very pleasant dream that can be entertained only because of the unique nature of the FM signal. This view of the FM signal also brings out the important fact that the ultimate threshold of detectability of an FM signal need only be set by the noise *power density* and *not* by the total noise power.

7.3 Techniques for Improving the Detectability of FM Signals[25, 26]

In the remainder of this chapter, we discuss signal-processing techniques for enhancing an exponential-modulation signal, or improving the conditions for its demodulation, in the presence of additive random-fluctuation noise. Improvement in S/N ratio can result either

(a) from a net increase in the ratio of mean signal power to mean noise power density without any change in the effective noise bandwidth; or

(b) from a reduction in the effective noise bandwidth without any change in the ratio $E_s^2/2w(f)$; or

(c) from a combination of improved relative signal power and reduced noise bandwidth [combination of (a) and (b)].

It is usually possible to distinguish between the signal and the noise on the basis of the high degree of coherence of the former and the low degree of coherence of the latter. Predetection operations that utilize this difference can then be applied in order to achieve a net increase in the ratio of mean signal power to noise power density. Examples of these techniques are *narrow-band limiting, regenerative feedback around the limiter,* and *delay diversification followed by linear combination.*

It is also possible to operate on the signal plus noise in a manner that eliminates the effect of the noise components whose frequencies differ from the instantaneous frequency of the signal by some predetermined amount, without at the same time changing the ratio of mean signal power to noise power density. The fundamental mechanism here is one of signal tracking or its direct equivalent. The desired effect can be achieved by a *dynamic selector,* by *signal-tracking oscillators,* or by signal bandwidth compression by *frequency division.*

Other techniques, such as narrowing the bandwidth when the signal strength is low, thus accepting a high degree of distortion by narrow-band filtering in order to survive the noise, will not be discussed here.

A. **Narrow-band limiters**—In analyzing the effect of amplitude limiting upon the sum of a sinusoid plus random noise it is convenient to conceive of the limiter as being made up of a clipper and a bandpass filter in cascade with no interaction between the two (that is, neither of them influences the operation of the other). This concept of the amplitude limiter is illustrated in Fig. 31, in which the clipper is characterized by an ideal symmetrical clipping charac-

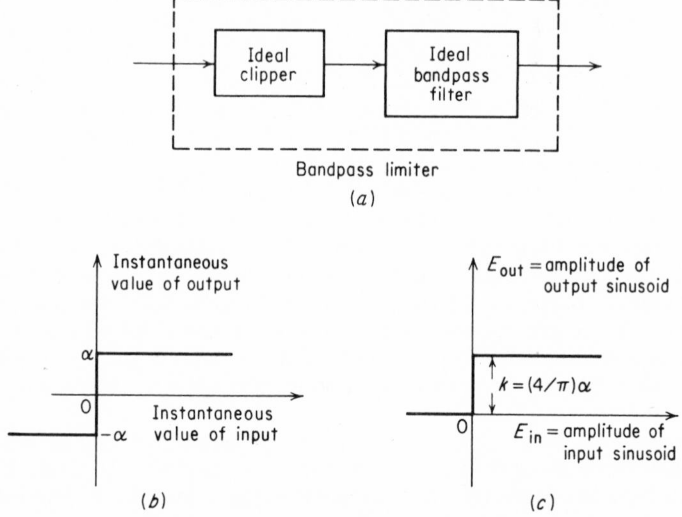

Fig. 31. Characterization of amplitude limiter assumed in Davenport's noise analysis.

teristic with a zero threshold. Evidently, if a single sinusoid whose frequency falls within the passband of the filter is applied at the input of the cascade, then a single sinusoid of the same frequency will appear at the output of the cascade, provided that the filter bandwidth is much smaller than its center frequency. The amplitude-limiting operation is assumed to cause no perceivable phase distortion. The amplitudes of the input and output sinusoids are related as shown in Fig. 31(c), which differs from Fig. 19(a) only in that $E_{\mathrm{th},\ell}$ is completely neglected.

The problem of relating the input and output signal-to-noise average power ratios at the terminals of the bandpass limiter when the input is made up of the sum of a sinusoid and a narrow-band gaussian random noise has been solved by Davenport.[27] He assumed the filter passband to be sufficiently wide to pass the entire spectrum that falls around the frequency of the sinusoid, but not so wide that it passes any parts of the spectral zones that fall around harmonics of that frequency. If, however, the passband of the filter is restricted to cover only one i-f bandwidth, then the output noise will be confined to the same bandwidth as the input noise, and the total average noise power at the output will be less than the value computed by Davenport, the difference being significant only at the lower values of $(S/N)_{\mathrm{in}}$. With this added restriction on the filter bandwidth, the output (S/N) average power ratio is related to the input ratio as shown in Fig. 32. It is important to note from this curve that $(S/N)_{\mathrm{out}} > (S/N)_{\mathrm{in}}$ for all $(S/N)_{\mathrm{in}}$ in excess of approximately 0.35 and that $(S/N)_{\mathrm{out}} \to 2(S/N)_{\mathrm{in}}$ as $(S/N)_{\mathrm{in}}$ grows very large.

Davenport's results also show that for the higher values (above about 3) of $(S/N)_{\mathrm{in}}$ the average power in the signal component at the limiter output is essentially a constant that equals $k^2/2$, whereas the noise power is very closely given by $(k^2/4)/(S/N)_{\mathrm{in}}$, where k is defined in Fig. 31(c). For values of $(S/N)_{\mathrm{in}} > 3$, the bandpass limiter is therefore seen to increase the signal-to-noise mean power ratio by depressing the total mean noise power. In the range $0.35 < (S/N)_{\mathrm{in}} < 3$, the signal is intensified relative to the noise, but the net increase results from a combined increase of the mean signal power and a depression of the mean noise power. From the point of view of carrier-to-noise mean power, the bandpass limiter makes matters worse for the signal only when the mean carrier power is less than approximately 0.35 (less than −4.5 db) of the total mean noise power. If we recall that $(S/N)_{\mathrm{in}} = 0.35$ is about 14 db below the FM improvement threshold, we realize that it would not be correct to accuse the limiter of causing, or having any adverse effect on, the conventional FM threshold.

The problem of what happens when the output of the first narrow-band limiter is subjected to a second round of bandpass limiting has not been solved analytically. But an interesting experiment has been carried out, the results of which indicate that rapidly decreasing additional improvements accrue as more narrow-band limiters are cascaded.

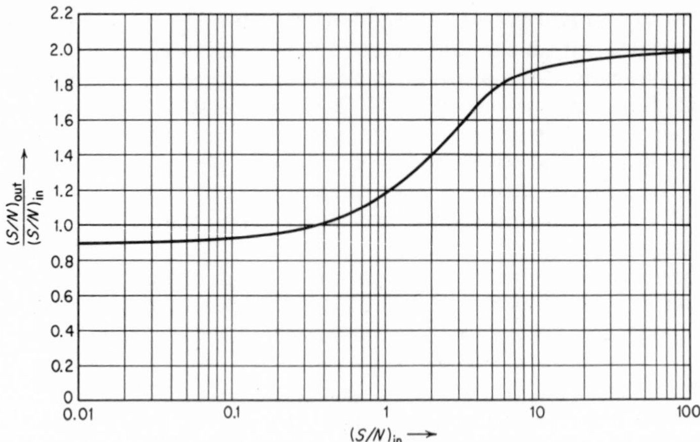

Fig. 32. Relation between output and input signal-to-noise mean power ratios for a bandpass limiter whose output noise bandwidth equals the input noise bandwidth. The input noise is assumed to be narrow-band gaussian and the signal is an unmodulated sinusoidal carrier.

B. Limiters with regenerative feedback—Let us refer back to Fig. 18 and consider the situation in which the input $e_{if}(t)$ is made up of a sinusoid of constant amplitude E_s and instantaneous frequency ω_i, plus an independent random-fluctuation noise of total mean-square value N_{if}. If we start with the i-f switch open and the feedback switch closed, then from Fig. 32 we noted earlier that (if gaussian noise is assumed) the signal power is enhanced relative to the noise power in going through the bandpass limiter as long as $(S/N)_{in} > 0.35$. Therefore, for all such input ratios, we would expect that upon opening the feedback switch, more signal than noise will be fed back to the input, and (under appropriate regenerative feedback conditions) a net improvement in the output S/N ratio should result over and above what is achievable with bandpass limiting and no feedback. In fact we would generally expect the noise fed back to be not as well correlated with the input noise as the signal component is with the input signal, and therefore the relative incoherence of the noise should result in S/N improvements even at S/N ratios (from the i-f) that are less than 0.35. In order to substantiate these expectations, we shall now derive a general expression for the output S/N mean power ratio, and explore the significance of the result.

For convenience, the block diagram of Fig. 18 is redrawn in Fig. 33 with S and N symbols to indicate the mean-square values of signal and of noise at the principal locations. To start with, if $n_{if}(t)$ denotes the i-f sample noise time function and $n_{fb}(t)$ the noise fed back, then, with the bar denoting time averaging over a suitably long interval,

$$N_{in} = \overline{[n_{if}(t) + n_{fb}(t)]^2} = N_{if} + N_{fb} + 2\rho\sqrt{N_{if}N_{fb}} \tag{206}$$

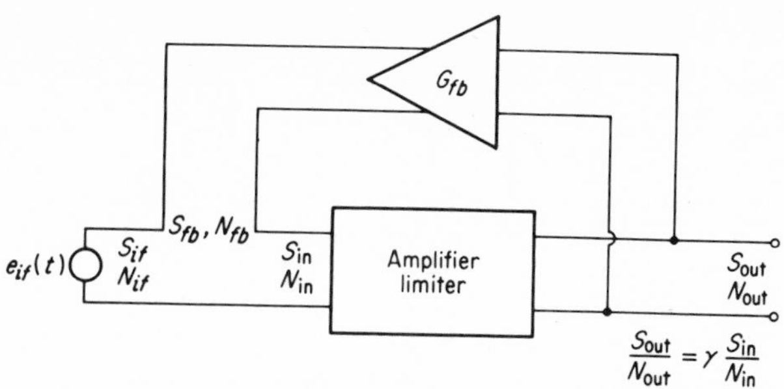

Fig. 33. Limiter with regenerative feedback. The S and N symbols represent the mean-square values of signal component and noise component at the points indicated by the subscripts.

where ρ is the correlation coefficient of i-f and feedback noises. Similarly, if we assume the feedback phase shift $\phi_{\text{fb}}(\omega_i)$ at the instantaneous frequency of the signal to be negligible,

$$S_{\text{in}} = S_{\text{if}} + G_{\text{fb}}^2 S_{\text{out}} + 2G_{\text{fb}}\sqrt{S_{\text{if}}S_{\text{out}}}\,. \tag{207}$$

The S/N mean power ratio at the limiter input is given by $S_{\text{in}}/N_{\text{in}}$.

If we now write

$$\frac{S_{\text{out}}}{N_{\text{out}}} = \gamma\frac{S_{\text{in}}}{N_{\text{in}}}, \tag{208}$$

then substitution from (206) and (207) into (208) followed by a rearrangement of the terms leads to a quadratic equation in $\sqrt{S_{\text{out}}/N_{\text{out}}}$. Since the square-root quantity in the third term of Eq. (207) is strictly intended to be positive, so is $\sqrt{S_{\text{out}}/N_{\text{out}}}$, and of the two roots of the quadratic equation only the positive one is acceptable. This leads to

$$\sqrt{\frac{S_{\text{out}}}{N_{\text{out}}}}\bigg/\sqrt{\frac{S_{\text{if}}}{N_{\text{if}}}} = -\rho\sqrt{S_{\text{fb}}/S_{\text{if}}} + \sqrt{\gamma(1+\sqrt{S_{\text{fb}}/S_{\text{if}}})^2 - (1-\rho^2)(S_{\text{fb}}/S_{\text{if}})}\,. \tag{209}$$

The right-hand side of Eq. (209) gives the factor by which the ratio of rms signal to rms noise has been altered in going from the input to the output of the limiter with regenerative feedback, on the assumption (to be examined later on) that a feedback quasi-stationary state exists in which signal and noise having mean-square values S_{out} and N_{out} appear at the output. In the discussion of the significance of this result, it is helpful to have an expression for the mean-square value of the noise fed back. Such an expression follows from $N_{\text{fb}} = G_{\text{fb}}^2 N_{\text{out}}$, $N_{\text{out}} = S_{\text{out}}/(S_{\text{out}}/N_{\text{out}})$ and Eq. (209). The result is

$$N_{\text{fb}} = \frac{N_{\text{if}}}{[-\rho + \sqrt{\gamma(1+\sqrt{S_{\text{if}}/S_{\text{fb}}})^2 - (1-\rho^2)}]^2} \tag{210}$$

$$\cong N_{\text{if}}/[-\rho + \sqrt{\gamma + \rho^2 - 1}]^2 \quad \text{for large values of } \sqrt{S_{\text{fb}}/S_{\text{if}}} \tag{211}$$

$$\cong (S_{\text{fb}}/\gamma S_{\text{if}})N_{\text{if}} \quad \text{for small values of } \sqrt{S_{\text{fb}}/S_{\text{if}}}\,. \tag{212}$$

The expression on the right in Eq. (209) involves three quantities that we must examine closely.

First, there is the quantity γ that relates the signal-to-noise mean power ratios at the input and output of the limiter in accordance with Eq. (208). This quantity, γ, is a complicated function of $S_{\text{in}}/N_{\text{in}}$. For the case of *gaussian noise at the input of the limiter*, γ was computed by Davenport[27] and it is substantially* given by the curve in Fig. 32. But, in the present problem, the limiter action alters the statistics of the noise so that it is no longer gaussian. Consequently, the noise at the input of the limiter is the sum of gaussian noise from the i-f amplifier and non-gaussian noise from the feedback terminals, and the two add up to non-gaussian noise. Therefore γ for the limiter in the feedback steady state cannot be expected to be exactly the same as the one plotted in Fig. 32. But it can be expected to behave in a similar manner as a function of $(S/N)_{\text{in}}$—in particular, exceeding unity for the larger values of $(S/N)_{\text{in}}$ and becoming less than unity for very low $(S/N)_{\text{in}}$. Note from (212) that when the signal component fed back is weak relative to the signal coming from the i-f amplifier, the noise fed back is small compared with the noise from the i-f. Under this condition, the resultant noise at the limiter input is largely made up of the i-f noise, and its statistics are therefore approximately gaussian if the i-f noise is gaussian. Consequently, under conditions of strong input signal relative to the amount of feedback present, γ is given very closely by the curve in Fig. 32. The problem of determining γ analytically in the feedback steady state when S_{fb} is not small compared with S_{if} is formidable and it remains unsolved.

It is important to observe that the right-hand side of Eq. (209) will exceed unity provided that

$$\gamma > \frac{1 + 2\rho\sqrt{\dfrac{S_{\text{fb}}}{S_{\text{if}}}} + \dfrac{S_{\text{fb}}}{S_{\text{if}}}}{\left[1 + \sqrt{\dfrac{S_{\text{fb}}}{S_{\text{if}}}}\right]^2}\,. \tag{213}$$

Fortunately, the right-hand member of this inequality is $\leqslant 1$ for all $\rho \leqslant 1$.

Second, there is the correlation coefficient, ρ, of the noise coming from the i-f amplifier and the noise coming through the feedback amplifier to the input of the limiter. Decorrelation between the i-f and feedback noises is caused by two mechanisms that are present

*As we pointed out earlier, the curve of Fig. 32 excludes output noise outside the limits of the input noise bandwidth. Davenport's curve includes all the noise in the first zone. The difference between the two cases is noticeable only at low values of $(S/N)_{\text{in}}$. As $(S/N)_{\text{in}} \to 0$, the noise power that falls outside the limits of the input bandwidth, and in the first zone, becomes a little over 12% of the total noise in the first zone.

in the loop. First there is decorrelation by the memoriless amplitude limiting of the sum of signal plus noise. The amount of noise decorrelation that results from memoriless amplitude limiting of signal plus noise is a function of the S/N ratio at the limiter input. For *gaussian noise at the limiter input*, the correlation coefficient of input and output noise can be computed directly from expressions derived by Davenport.[27] The results show that the correlation coefficient is slightly below 0.95 for $(S/N)_{in} < 1/10$ and about 0.71 for $(S/N)_{in} > 10$, with a smooth transition in between. Second, there is decorrelation as a result of delay in transmission around the loop. The envelope of the autocorrelation function of filtered fluctuation noise falls off at a rate that depends upon the noise bandwidth, the exact shape of the curve being a function of the shape of the noise-power spectral density at the filter output. The mathematical reason for this of course lies in the fact that the autocorrelation function of the noise is the inverse Fourier transform of its power spectral density. But the physical reason can perhaps be seen by tracing the noise back to its source, where it is generated as a random superposition of short pulses, with a resultant power spectral density that is essentially uniform over the passband of the intervening concatenation of filters that precede the point of observation. At the point of observation, the noise is therefore a superposition of the impulse responses of the overall filter to the noise "impulses" from the source. The ability to extrapolate the noise waveform into the future therefore is essentially lost if the "future" comes one or more overall-filter time constants later.

Now, the resultant noise at the limiter input is the sum of the i-f noise and the noise fed back. Since the correlation coefficient of the i-f noise and the limiter input noise is given by

$$\rho_{\text{if, in}} = \sqrt{\frac{N_{\text{if}}}{N_{\text{in}}}} + \rho\sqrt{\frac{N_{\text{fb}}}{N_{\text{in}}}},$$

decorrelation by the limiter and by the delay in transmission around the loop ensures that the limiter input noise starts the cycle around the loop with only a partial correlation with the i-f noise. When the level of the voltage fed back is large in comparison with the level at the i-f terminals, approximation (210) shows that the resultant noise at the limiter input is to a large extent made up of the noise fed back. Therefore in the feedback steady state, the instantaneous behavior of the noise present across the feedback terminals tends to be little influenced by the instantaneous behavior of the i-f noise over a past that may stretch over intervals in excess of the decorrelation time of the i-f noise.

Thus even though no analytical solution as yet exists for the exact behavior of the correlation coefficient [ρ in Eq. (209)] of the i-f and feedback noises in the feedback steady state as a function of the relative i-f signal and noise conditions, ρ^2 can certainly be expected to be negligible compared with unity, and therefore it can be dropped in the second term in Eq. (209). It may even be assumed to be so low as not to influence materially the result in (209), even though it multiplies a quantity for which large values are desirable (as we shall indicate shortly). It is interesting to observe that negative values of ρ (which are not unlikely) are advantageous because the first term in (209) is thereby transformed into an asset. Note that nonzero ρ of either sign is an asset in the second term in (209).

Finally, there is the quantity S_{fb}/S_{if} on the right-hand side of Eq. (209). This quantity represents the ratio of mean-square values of the signal component fed back and the signal component introduced at the i-f terminals. The larger this ratio is, the greater the improvement in S/N ratio indicated in Eq. (209). Large values of this ratio also ensure smaller values of ρ, and should increase the value of γ. But there are bounds (imposed by the feedback phase shift at the instantaneous frequency of the signal) on how large we can allow S_{fb}/S_{if} to be before we begin to violate the assumption of feedback quasi-stationary state which underlies the validity of the argument leading to Eq. (209).

When the S/N mean power ratio at the input of the limiter is large, the mean-square value, S_{out}, of the signal component can be expected to be essentially $k^2/2$, where k is defined in Fig. 31(c). Using Eq. (208), we can then write

$$N_{out} = (k^2/2\gamma)/(S_{in}/N_{in}). \tag{214}$$

Under these conditions, the limiter operates on the sum of signal plus noise present at its input in a manner that enhances the signal relative to the noise by keeping the amplitude of the signal component substantially constant and depressing the relative mean-square value of the noise. The condition that leads to this can (setting $\rho = 0$ for simplicity) be expressed in the form

$$\frac{S_{in}}{N_{if}} > b + \frac{S_{fb}}{\gamma N_{if}}, \tag{215}$$

where b is a threshold value that can be determined from the curve that describes S_{out} as a function of $(S/N)_{in}$ by seeking the smallest value of $(S/N)_{in}$ for which $S_{out} \cong k^2/2$. For gaussian noise (plus a sinusoid) at the input of the limiter, b is around 3. If we set $S_{out} = k^2/2$ in (215) and write $E_{fb} = kG_{fb}$, we have

$$\frac{(E_s + E_{fb})^2/2}{N_{if}} > b + \frac{E_{fb}^2/2}{\gamma N_{if}}. \tag{216}$$

By straightforward manipulations, (216) can be reduced to

$$\sqrt{\frac{E_s^2/2}{N_{if}}} > \sqrt{b + \frac{E_{fb}^2/2}{\gamma N_{if}}} - \sqrt{\frac{E_{fb}^2/2}{N_{if}}}. \tag{217}$$

Inequality (217) defines the threshold that must be exceeded by the ratio of rms signal and rms noise at the i-f terminals in Fig. 33 in order that $(S/N)_{in} > b$ which in turn ensures that $S_{out} \cong k^2/2$. In deriving this condition, we have assumed that a feedback quasi-stationary state exists, and that $\rho = 0$.

It is clear from the preceding discussion that substantial signal enhancement in the presence of relatively strong random noise (and full limiter saturation) can be guaranteed only by choosing E_{fb} to be large compared to E_s (and greater than $E_{th,\ell}$). The regenerative signal-booster arrangement of Fig. 33 should therefore oscillate in the absence of a signal, and the oscillation should be sufficiently strong relative to the input noise to bring about an acceptable degree of FM noise quieting. By "FM noise quieting" is meant a compression of the instantaneous frequency excursions of the output from the scheme in the manner experienced when a sinusoid of adequate strength is added to the noise—which amounts to a narrowing of the probability density function of the instantaneous frequency of the output in the absence of an input signal. If, in the absence of signal, the amplitude of the oscillation is reduced below the adequate-quieting level relative to the total applied noise, the level of the noise disturbance on the oscillation frequency will rise. The output from the oscillator eventually loses all semblance of coherence when the noise takes effective control.

The improvement in S/N ratio that results from the regenerative feedback may or may not be sufficient to raise the signal from below to above a preassigned threshold of acceptable reception, depending upon the value of $\sqrt{S_{fb}/S_{if}}$. The theoretical upper limit on the permissible value of $\sqrt{S_{fb}/S_{if}}$ in a given circuit is set by the maximum value of feedback phase shift encountered by the signal around the loop. This limitation is imposed by the fact that—oscillation or no oscillation—a feedback quasi-stationary state (in the sense described earlier in conjunction with Fig. 20) must first be established around the loop. For example, suppose that the oscillation amplitude (as seen at the feedback terminals) must exceed a value $E_{osc,\,th}$ in order that the output S/N ratio in Eq. (209) exceed the threshold of acceptable noise performance of the FM demodulator used after the oscillating limiter. An input sinusoidal carrier whose frequency coincides with the frequency of in-phase feedback is indistinguishable from the oscillation at the output of the limiter. Therefore, the threshold that the input amplitude E_s of this sinusoid must exceed is zero if $E_{osc} \geqslant E_{osc,\,th}$. However, if the frequency of the applied sinusoid is changed to a value ω_i at which a phase-shift deviation $\phi_{fb}(\omega_i)$ from in-phase feedback is experienced, then as long as

$$(E_{osc}/E_s)\sin\left|\phi_{fb}(\omega_i)\right| < 1, \tag{218}$$

the signal should override the noise in the output when $E_{osc} \geqslant E_{osc,\,th}$. Satisfaction of this condition by the input sinusoid enables this sinusoid to shift the mean frequency about which the compressed fluctuations (in the instantaneous frequency of the output) occur to the desired value, ω_i. The regenerative action boosts the signal amplitude at the limiter input to a value which is effectively indicated by OR in Fig. 20. The magnitude of OR in Fig. 20 fluctuates with time in synchronism with a slow modulation in $\omega_i(t)$, but this magnitude will, at worst, very nearly equal E_{osc} at instants of time when $\phi_{fb}(\omega_i)$ attains its maximum permissible value.* Therefore, the relatively weak signal which (by itself) would have been suppressed by the total noise when applied to a conventional FM demodulator, is boosted by the regenerative action of the "locked" oscillating limiter to the higher level it must have in order to override the noise. If E_{osc} is adjusted so that it equals the threshold value $E_{osc,th}$, then E_s must satisfy the condition

$$E_s > E_{osc,\,th} \sin|\phi_{fb}(\omega_i)|_{max}\,. \tag{219}$$

In order to determine the amount of reduction in the threshold of satisfactory reception that is indicated by condition (219), we must first relate $E_{osc,\,th}$ to the noise threshold, $E_{n,\,th}$, of the FM demodulator. This can be done with the aid of Eq. (209). Thus, in terms of $E_{n,\,th}$, (219) can be written as

$$E_s > \left\{\frac{\rho + \sqrt{\rho^2 + \gamma(1 + \sin|\phi_{fb}(\omega_i)|_{max})^2 - 1}}{\gamma(1 + \sin|\phi_{fb}(\omega_i)|_{max})^2 - 1}\sin|\phi_{fb}(\omega_i)|_{max}\right\}E_{n,\,th} \tag{220}$$

If we assume that $\rho = 0$, and design the feedback loop so that $|\phi_{fb}(\omega_i)|_{max} \ll 1$, (220) can be simplified to the form

$$E_s > \left\{\frac{\sin|\phi_{fb}(\omega_i)|_{max}}{\sqrt{\gamma - 1}}\right\}E_{n,\,th}\,. \tag{221}$$

The noise threshold that E_s must exceed is thus reduced by the factor in braces in (220) and (221). If $|\phi_{fb}(\omega_i)|_{max} = 5°$ (or 0.087 rad), E_s can be nearly −20db below $E_{n,\,th}$.

From the definition of $E_{osc,\,th}$, it is clear that the signal need only override the noise components that fall in the immediate neighborhood of its instantaneous frequency in order to satisfy the "locking" condition. In a sense, this indicates that with the oscillating limiter the signal in effect combats "noise density" rather than "total noise."

C. Delay-diversification techniques—As we pointed out in the preceding subsection, the correlation between the instantaneous values assumed by a filtered noise waveform diminishes with the time separation between the two values at a rate that is proportional to the bandwidth of the filtered noise spectrum. The noise-decorrelation time constant has a value between 1/(2 times noise bandwidth) and 1/(noise bandwidth). By comparison, modulated sinusoidal carriers generally maintain a high degree of auto-correlation over time separations of the order of the decorrelation time of the noise. This difference in the degree of coherence of noise and of signal can be utilized in a number of ways of which we shall discuss two simple examples.

The first example is one in which the signal plus noise is passed through two amplifiers in parallel whose outputs are added. The two

*The magnitude of OR equals $E_s(1 + K_s)$, $K_s \equiv E_{osc}/E_s$, when $\phi_{fb}(\omega) = 0$, and is approximately given by $E_s(1 + K_s)(1 - \frac{1}{2}K_s\phi_{fb}^2)$ when ϕ_{fb} is nonzero but small.

signal paths differ in time delay an amount that is sufficient to reduce the correlation coefficient of the noise well below that of the signal. This can be achieved for example by allowing the noise applied to the paralleled amplifiers to have a bandwidth that is several times wider than the minimum bandwidth necessary for low-distortion reproduction of the signal modulation. Then one of the amplifiers is made wide enough to reproduce the signal without noticeable distortion while the bandwidth of the other is made several times wider than that. When the outputs are added together, the signal components can be expected to add up almost directly in phase throughout the range occupied by this signal, whereas the noises will add up essentially incoherently. After addition, reduction of the bandwidth to the minimum necessary value required by the signal results in a higher signal-to-noise ratio than would otherwise have been possible with straightforward filtering. Additional gains in S/N ratio may be achieved by starting with wider (but different) bandwidths in both amplifiers than the minimum required by the signal, and repeating the operation with progressively decreasing bandwidths until the minimum bandwidth required by the signal is reached.

Another simple operation involves feedback around an amplifier driven from a wideband noise plus signal source. The bandwidth of the feedback loop is made narrower than that of the input noise, the narrowest permissible loop bandwidth being equal to the minimum required for low-distortion signal transmission.

The shape of the noise power spectral density is sometimes such that the amplitude of its inverse Fourier transform, the autocorrelation function of the noise, assumes negative values for certain differential time delays. It is then possible to increase the gains achieved by each of the preceding schemes somewhat by seeking differential delays with which negative noise correlation coefficients will be experienced.

Complete analysis of any of the preceding schemes requires a knowledge of the power spectral density of the noise and the autocorrelation function of the modulated carrier. But the situation is often so simple that one can provide satisfactory rough estimates of the S/N ratio gains without serious computations. These gains, where possible, are usually of the order of a few decibels.

D. **Dynamic selectors**—A direct attempt at taking advantage of the fact that an FM signal can be considered as a variable-frequency sinusoid whose location on the frequency scale changes in accordance with the dictates of the message, is embodied in the scheme shown in Fig. 34. The effect of the sharp selector upon the overall noise performance depends upon the quality of guidance provided by the FM demodulator, as well as upon the bandwidth of the selector relative to the nominal i-f bandwidth. A noticeable reduction in the improvement threshold, as well as a sharpening of the transition from no improvement to full improvement, should be achievable with most FM demodulators. As long as the pattern of the message waveform

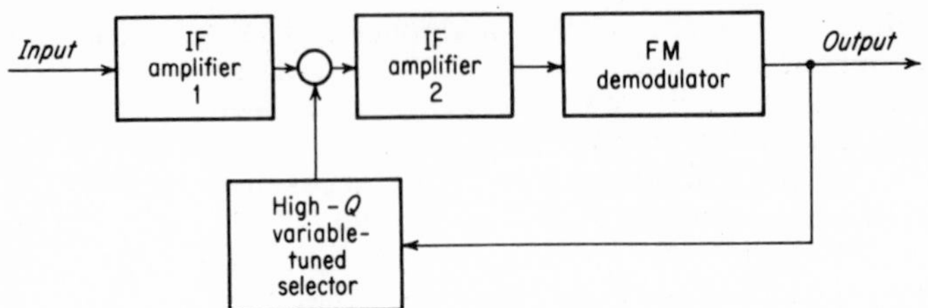

Fig. 34. Dynamic signal selector.

can be roughly delineated in the overriding noise fluctuations at the output of the receiver in the absence of the selector, the introduction of the selector should result in a clean output waveform. But if the message waveform is completely swamped by the noise in the absence of the selector, the introduction of the selector may not result in retrieval of the message.

E. Signal-tracking oscillators and related systems—We shall now consider two types of tracking oscillators that can be used for decreasing the threshold of detectability in the presence of noise for wideband FM signals. For convenience, we shall designate them as type I and type II. In type I tracking oscillators (Fig. 35), the frequency of a local oscillator is automatically and continuously adjusted to coincide with the instantaneous frequency of the incoming signal, in order to enable the phase of the local oscillation to be locked to the phase of the incoming signal. In type II tracking oscillators (Fig. 36), the frequency of a local oscillator is made to follow, but not coincide with, the instantaneous frequency of the incoming signal in such a way that the difference between the two instantaneous

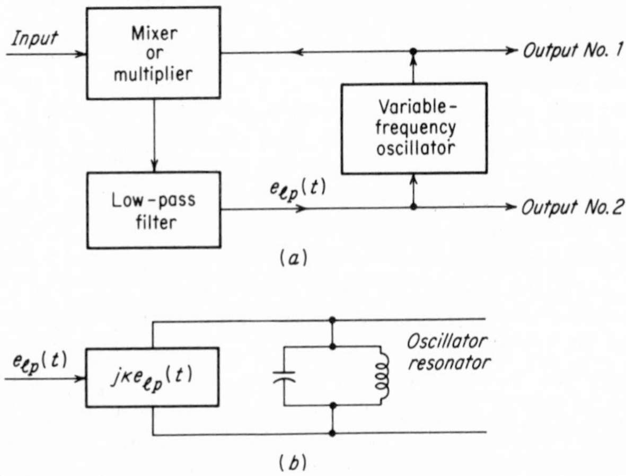

Fig. 35. Type I signal-tracking oscillator (phase-locked oscillator).

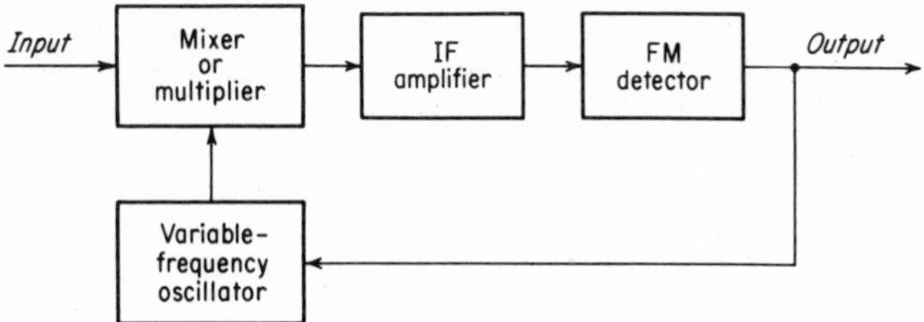

Fig. 36. Type II signal-tracking oscillator (compressive-feedback scheme).

frequencies still carries the desired message in linearly compressed frequency excursions. Although they were invented in attempts to avoid the use of the patented amplitude limiter, these two techniques are best performed in conjunction with amplitude limiters.

Phase-locked oscillators—In the type I signal-tracking system, the incoming signal, when it is combined with the local oscillation in the mixer, gives rise to a low-frequency voltage, $e_{\ell_p}(t)$. This low-frequency voltage changes the value of a simulated variable reactance that constitutes a part of the resonator in the oscillator circuit in such a way that the frequency of oscillation coincides with the frequency of the incoming signal.

The effectiveness of the type I tracking system as a detector of frequency or phase information on an incoming signal that is swamped by random noise stems from the fact that its mechanism is essentially that of a short-time crosscorrelator. The incoming signal plus noise is multiplied by the oscillator voltage at the mixer, and the short-time integration is carried out by the low-pass filter. The output of the low-pass filter should ideally be zero in order to indicate that the phase of the local oscillation is locked to the phase of the resultant incoming signal and differs from it only by some constant ϕ, say. The value of this constant phase difference is determined by the fact that $e_{\ell_p}(t)$ must be zero when the instantaneous phase difference between the oscillation and the resultant input signal is precisely ϕ, and that $e_{\ell_p}(t)$ must indicate the magnitude and the sign of any deviation from ϕ in the phase difference. Thus ϕ must be such that the short-time crosscorrelation $e_{\ell_p}(t)$ between the oscillation and the incoming sinusoid is an odd function of deviations from ϕ. Clearly, then, ϕ must be $\pi/2$ (or some odd multiple of it), and the local oscillation is said to be locked to the incoming sinusoid if the phase difference between the two is maintained near this value of ϕ.

The integration time is determined by the bandwidth of the low-pass filter. Since $e_{\ell_p}(t)$ modulates the frequency of the oscillator, $e_{\ell_p}(t)$ must carry the information in the frequency modulation of the resultant incoming signal. The low-pass filter must therefore pass this information with negligible distortion. Differences between the oscillation and the incoming waveform that can be averaged out over the interval of the integration by the low-pass filter will then be suppressed by the crosscorrelation operation. The error signal $e_{\ell_p}(t)$ will therefore retain noise fluctuations that are caused by the input noise components contained within a bandwidth of only twice the low-pass filter bandwidth centered about the instantaneous frequency of the signal-tracking oscillation. These residual noise fluctuations may be considered to result either from beating between input noise components and the oscillation, or from the combined amplitude and phase fluctuations inflicted on the desired carrier by the input noise. According to the latter view, the incoming signal and noise are considered combined into a resultant amplitude- and phase-disturbed carrier. Inasmuch as $e_{\ell_p}(t)$ must measure only phase-difference errors, best operation is ensured if the incoming noisy signal is amplitude limited before it is applied to the signal terminals of the multiplier. In a sense, then, an amplitude limiter ahead of the multiplier serves to prepare the incoming signal plus noise for maximum resemblance to the local oscillation by constraining the amplitude of the resultant of signal plus noise to be a constant, just as the amplitude of the oscillation is. Differences between the resultant incoming signal and the oscillation are thus constrained to be phase errors that are caused by the noise and by occasional transients arising from the inability of the low-pass filter to follow sudden changes in the phase of the resultant input.

Under the preceding conditions, it is interesting to note that, in the absence of noise, $e_{\ell_p}(t)$ will indeed be directly proportional to the frequency modulation of the incoming signal. For when the oscillation is locked to the incoming constant-amplitude frequency-modulated signal, the instantaneous phase of the local oscillation at time t can be written as

$$\omega_s t + \Delta\Omega \int^{t-\delta t} g(\eta)\,d\eta + \pi/2$$

if the instantaneous phase of the signal is

$$\omega_s t + \Delta\Omega \int^{t} g(\eta)\,d\eta,$$

where δt is a measure of the time it takes to readjust the oscillation frequency in accordance with an incremental smooth change in $g(t)$. Accordingly,

$$\begin{aligned} e_{\ell_p}(t) &= (\text{const}) \sin\left[\Delta\Omega \int^{t} g(\eta)\,d\eta - \Delta\Omega \int^{t-\delta t} g(\eta)\,d\eta\right] \\ &= (\text{const}) \sin\left[\Delta\Omega \int_{t-\delta t}^{t} g(\eta)\,d\eta\right] \\ &= (\text{const}) \sin\left[\Delta\Omega g(t)\delta t\right] \\ &\cong (\text{const})\, \Delta\Omega g(t)\delta t \end{aligned} \tag{222}$$

since $g(t)$ is assumed to vary so smoothly relative to the time of readjustment δt that the instantaneous phase difference between the oscillation and the signal departs from $\pi/2$ by a very small amount.

Inasmuch as δt is some fixed constant of the loop, (222) states that

$$e_{\ell_p}(t) \propto \Delta\Omega\, g(t). \tag{223}$$

The constant of proportionality that reduces (223) to an equality can be determined as follows. With reference to Fig. 35(b), note that at a frequency that deviates a small amount from the resonance frequency of the LC combination on the right, the susceptance of this combination is directly proportional to the frequency deviation. Thus if the instantaneous frequency of the input signal is $\omega_i(t) = \omega_0 + \Delta\Omega\, g(t)$, where $|g(t)|_{\max} = 1$, $\Delta\Omega \ll \omega_0$, and the spectrum of $g(t)$ occupies a bandwidth that is negligible compared with ω_0, then

$$Y_{LC}(j\omega_i) = j2C\Delta\Omega g(t).$$

Thus, the simulated susceptance on the left [in Fig. 35 (b)] must be readjusted by $e_{\ell_p}(t)$ to cancel out $Y_{LC}(j\omega_i)$. This requires that

$$j\kappa e_{\ell_p}(t) + j2C\Delta\Omega g(t) = 0$$

or

$$e_{\ell_p}(t) = -\frac{2C}{\kappa}\, \Delta\Omega g(t). \tag{224}$$

The signal from output No. 1 in Fig. 35 will be a relatively clean version of the desired FM signal, under proper conditions of operation. When viewed through this output, the scheme, with an amplitude limiter preceding it, simulates in effect a selective filter that tracks the signal and suppresses the FM effects of all noise components that fall outside a band $2B_{\ell_p}$ cps wide centered about the instantaneous frequency of the signal. Thus, assuming that the locking requirements of the scheme are satisfied, the use of a type I tracking oscillator may reduce the FM noise threshold only to the level that would be encountered with a conventional FM receiver whose i-f amplifier noise bandwidth is $2B_{\ell_p}$ cps.

Frequency-compressive feedback—In the type II signal-frequency tracking system, the frequency of the oscillator is forced by the filtered message waveform at the output of the FM detector to follow the frequency variations of the incoming signal, but the oscillator frequency is not deviated by the same amount as the incoming frequency. Two situations that depend upon whether or not an amplitude limiter is included in the frequency detector must be distinguished. Let us start by discussing the system, originally proposed by Chaffee,[28] which used an amplitude-sensitive FM detector.

Let the input signal be

$$e_{in}(t) = E_s \cos\left[\omega_{rf} t + \Delta\Omega \int^t g(\eta)\, d\eta + \phi_c\right] \tag{225}$$

and let the oscillator signal be

$$e_{osc}(t) = E_{osc} \cos\left[(\omega_{rf} + \omega_{if})t + \int^t f(\eta)\, d\eta\right]. \tag{226}$$

Then the signal delivered by the i-f amplifier to the FM detector is

$$e_{\text{if}}(t) = K_{\text{if}} E_s E_{\text{osc}} \cos\left[\omega_{\text{if}} t + \Delta\Omega \int^{t} g(\eta)\,d\eta - \int^{t} f(\eta)\,d\eta + \phi_c\right]. \quad (227)$$

The output of the amplitude-sensitive FM detector will therefore be

$$e_{\text{out}} = \kappa_d K_{\text{if}} E_s E_{\text{osc}}[\Delta\Omega g(t) - f(t)]. \quad (228)$$

Now let us set $f(t) = \beta_{\text{fb}} e_{\text{out}}(t)$. If we substitute for $f(t)$ and solve for $e_{\text{out}}(t)$, we find that

$$e_{\text{out}}(t) = \frac{(\kappa_d K_{\text{if}} E_s E_{\text{osc}})}{1 + \beta_{\text{fb}}(\kappa_d K_{\text{if}} E_s E_{\text{osc}})} \Delta\Omega g(t). \quad (229)$$

If $\beta_{\text{fb}}(\kappa_d K_{\text{if}} E_s E_{\text{osc}}) \gg 1$, then

$$e_{\text{out}}(t) \cong \frac{\Delta\Omega}{\beta_{\text{fb}}} g(t) . \quad (230)$$

This same result holds if E_s or E_{osc} varies with time, provided that such time variations are sufficiently slow. Therefore, very slow fluctuations in the input signal amplitude should have no noticeable effect upon $e_{\text{out}}(t)$. But rapid variations of E_s or E_{osc} would require a more involved analysis, and these variations can be quite visible in $e_{\text{out}}(t)$.* This trouble can be eliminated by using an amplitude limiter in the FM detector.

Another serious trouble with Chaffee's original proposal (which can also be removed by introducing an amplitude limiter in the FM detector) lies in the fact that the instantaneous frequency of $e_{\text{if}}(t)$ also depends upon the signal amplitude. Specifically, the instantaneous frequency of $e_{\text{if}}(t)$ is given by

$$\omega_{\text{if}} + \Delta\Omega g(t) - f(t) = \omega_{\text{if}} + \frac{\Delta\Omega}{1 + \beta_{\text{fb}}(\kappa_d K_{\text{if}} E_s E_{\text{osc}})} g(t). \quad (231)$$

Now, it is readily shown with the aid of Eq. (76) that the i-f filter bandwidth that is required for adequate reproduction of a frequency modulation varies as the square root of the maximum frequency deviation. It is therefore clear that the dependence of the frequency deviation in (231) upon E_s can cause serious distortion of the frequency modulation of $e_{\text{if}}(t)$ by the filter used to select $e_{\text{if}}(t)$, and this distortion will appear in $e_{\text{out}}(t)$.

The compression of the frequency deviation that results from making the oscillator frequency follow the signal frequency in the prescribed manner allows the i-f bandwidth (and hence the noise bandwidth) to be reduced. This allows an incoming wideband FM signal to be processed in relatively narrow-band circuits with a consequent reduction of the FM noise threshold. The limit of thresh-

*This observation was first made by P. F. Panter, and it is discussed in P. F. Panter and W. Dite, "Application of Negative Feedback to Frequency-Modulation Systems," *Electrical Communication*, vol. 26, pp. 173-178; June, 1949.

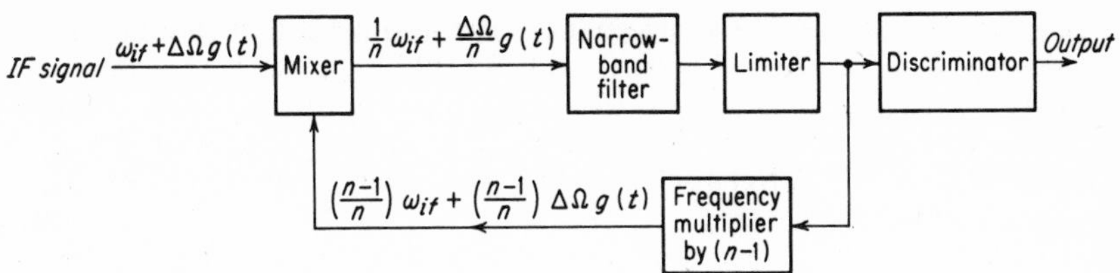

Fig. 37. Frequency-dividing band-compression system.

old reduction is reached when the bandwidth occupancy of the signal is compressed effectively to $2B_{\ell_p}$ cps.

A system in which the bandwidth occupancy of the incoming signal is compressed, by an operation that amounts to dividing the frequency by a factor n, is shown in Fig. 37. This system essentially carries out in separate boxes what the frequency-dividing, locked-in oscillator described by Beers[29] achieves in a much simpler circuit. In determining the bandwidth requirements of the compressed frequency excursions, it must be noted that if the same type of filter is to be used with compression as would have been used without it, and if the FM modulation waveform is to be reproduced with exactly the same quality, then compressing the frequency deviation $\Delta\Omega$ by a factor n compresses the required filter bandwidth by a factor of $\sqrt{n}$, *and not by n.*

REFERENCES

1. E. H. Armstrong, "A Method of Reducing Disturbances in Radio Signaling by a System of Frequency Modulation," *Proc. IRE,* vol. 24, pp. 689-740, May 1935.
2. B. M. Oliver, J. R. Pierce, and C. E. Shannon, "The Philosophy of PCM," *Proc. IRE,* New York, vol. 36, No. 11, pp. 1324-1331, November 1948.
3. D. K. Weaver, Jr., "A Third Method of Generation and Detection of Single-Sideband Signals," *Proc. IRE,* vol. 44, pp. 1703-1705, December 1956.
4. F. L. H. M. Stumpers, "Theory of Frequency-Modulation Noise," *Proc. IRE,* New York, vol. 36, pp. 1081-1902, September 1948.
5. E. A. Guillemin, *Synthesis of Passive Networks,* John Wiley and Sons, Inc., New York, 1957. Chapter 14.
6. D. D. Weiner, "Experimental Study of FM Transients and Quasi-Static Response," S. M. Thesis in the Department of Electrical Engineering, M.I.T., January 1958.
7. J. R. Carson and T. C. Fry, "Variable-Frequency Electric Circuit Theory," *Bell Sys. Tech. J.,* vol. 16, pp. 513-540, October 1937.

8. B. van der Pol, "The Fundamental Principles of Frequency Modulation," *J. IEE* (London), vol. 93, pt. 3, pp. 153-158, May 1946.
9. F. L. H. M. Stumpers, "Distortion of Frequency-Modulated Signals in Electrical Networks," *Commun. News,* vol. 9, pp. 82-92, April 1948.
10. E. J. Baghdady, "Theory of Low-Distortion Reproduction of FM Signals in Linear Systems," *Trans, IRE, PGCS,* vol. *CT-5,* pp. 202-214, September 1958.
11. E. J. Baghdady, "On the Response of a Linear System to an FM Signal," *Trans. IRE, PGCS,* vol. *CT-6,* pp. 387-388, December 1959.
12. T. I'a. Bromwich, *Theory of Infinite Series.* The Macmillan Co., London, Eng., 1908.
13. J. Granlund, "Interference in Frequency-Modulation Reception," *M. I. T., Res. Lab. Electronics, Cambridge, Mass., Tech. Rept.* 42, January 20, 1949.
14. E. J. Baghdady, "Frequency-Modulation Interference Rejection with Narrow-Band Limiters," *Proc. IRE,* vol. 43, pp. 51-61, January 1955.
15. E. J. Baghdady, "Interference Rejection in FM Receivers," *M. I. T., Res. Lab. Electronics, Cambridge, Mass., Tech. Rept.* 252, September 24, 1956.
16. E. J. Baghdady, "Theory of Stronger-Signal Capture in FM Recaption," *Proc. IRE,* vol. 46, pp. 728-738, April 1958.
17. E. J. Baghdady, "Theory of Feedback Around the Limiter," 1957 *IRE National Convention Record,* pt. 8, pp. 176-202.
18. E. J. Baghdady, "FM Interference and Noise Suppression Properties of the Oscillating Limiter," 1959 *IRE National Convention Record,* pt. 8, pp. 13-39; also *IRE Transactions on Vehicular Communications,* vol. *PGVC-13,* pp. 37-63, September, 1959.
19. E. J. Baghdady, "Signal Cancellation Techniques for Capturing the Weaker of Two Cochannel FM Signals," presented at the International Conference on Electromagnetic Wave Propagation, Liège, Belgium, Oct. 6-11, 1958, and published in M. Desirant and J. L. Michiels (ed.), *Electromagnetic Wave Propagation,* pp. 183-207, Academic Press, London and New York, 1960.
20. E. J. Baghdady, "New Developments in FM Reception and Their Application to the Realization of a System of 'Power-Division' Multiplexing," *IRE Transactions on Communications Systems,* vol. *CS-7,* pp. 147-161, September, 1959.
21. E. J. Baghdady, "FM Demodulator Time-Constant Requirements for Interference Rejection," *Proc. IRE,* vol. 46, pp. 432-440, February 1958.
22. E. J. Baghdady, "Linear Cancellation Technique for Supressing Impulse Noise," *IRE* 1960 *WESCON Convention Record,* pt. 7, pp. 27-35.
23. E. J. Baghdady and J. T. Boatwright, "Impulse Noise Supression with Linear Circuits" (to be published 1960).

24. W. B. Davenport, Jr., and W. L. Root, *Introduction to Random Signals and Noise*, McGraw-Hill Book Co., Inc., New York, 1958.
25. E. J. Baghdady, "Techniques for Enhancing an FM Signal in the Presence of Random Noise," presented at the 6th National Annual Meeting of the *American Astronautical Society* in New York, Jan. 18, 1960; to be published in the *Proceedings of the AAS*.
26. E. J. Baghdady, "A Survey of Some Recent Developments in Reliable FM Communications," presented at the National Aeronautical Electronics Conference in Dayton, Ohio, May 3, 1960; published in *NAECON 1960 National Conference Proceedings*, pp. 453-462.
27. W. B. Davenport, Jr., "Signal-to-Noise Ratios in Bandpass Limiters," *J. Appl. Phys.*, vol. 24, No. 6, pp. 720-727, June 1953.
28. J. G. Chaffee, "The Application of Negative Feedback to Frequency-Modulation Systems," *Proc. IRE*, vol. 27, pp. 317-331, May 1939.
29. G. L. Beers, "A Frequency-Dividing Locked-In Oscillator Frequency-Modulation Receiver," *Proc. IRE*, vol. 32, pp. 730-738, December 1944.

Chapter 20

Analysis Of Long-Term Variability

Donald G. Brennan

I. INTRODUCTION

The present chapter is devoted to the development of a method of analysis that has applicability to several problems in communication system engineering. The problems involved are those in which the phenomena in question may be usefully modeled as a "stationary" process multiplied by a "slowly varying" multiplier. In particular, conditions will be exhibited under which the multiplier and the process it multiplies may be treated as approximately independent. The analysis will develop quantitative bounds on the error introduced by the independence approximation, and these errors will be found to relate to quantitatively specifiable and experimentally measurable methods of defining "slowly varying" and "approximately stationary."

Problems for which this approach is suitable are fairly common; for example, certain problems analyzed in the following chapter may be cast in this framework. Other applications will be discussed in the final section of the present chapter. The analysis employed here (which depends on the use of model random variables whose structure "imitates" the structure of the phenomena to be modeled, as discussed in Chapter 2) is also applicable to statistical problems of similar type arising in other fields, such as meteorology.

It will be most convenient to develop the analysis in a relatively simple and familiar framework; this is done in the following section. Possible extentions to other and more complicated problems will then be indicated.

II. METHOD OF APPROACH

In fairly common circumstances, the envelope of a fading radio wave will exhibit a behavior that can be described as follows: The fraction-of-time distribution of the envelope V in each interval of suitable length will approximate a Rayleigh distribution. (We shall denote the "suitable length" T_{int}, following the notation of Chapter 7. Representative values of T_{int} would range from a few minutes to an hour.) However, the "scale" of the distribution will not usually be the same in different intervals; that is, any fixed average of the distribution, such as the mean or median, will usually differ from one T_{int}-interval to another, though only slightly in adjacent intervals. The situation would appear similar to that in Fig. 1, in which, for

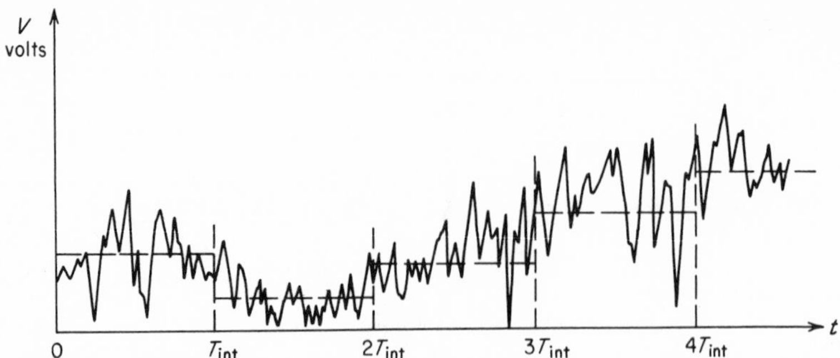

Fig. 1. Instantaneous envelope fluctuations about a "slowly varying" T_{int} median.

simplicity, only a few such intervals are drawn, and the change in (say) the median of V from one interval to the next has been exaggerated. It is to be noted that the fraction-of-time distribution of V in intervals of length one month or one year will *not* in general be approximately Rayleigh, in spite of the fact that it is in every interval of length T_{int}.

However, we can define a new variable U that will be better behaved. Let us put

$$W(t) \equiv \text{median of distribution of } V \text{ in the interval } (t - T_{int}, t), \tag{1}$$

i.e., W is the median of V in the "last" interval of length T_{int} before the "present" time t. We can then put

$$U(t) \equiv \frac{V(t)}{W(t)} . \tag{2}$$

Now, the fact that W changes very little in intervals of length T_{int} means that the distribution of U in such intervals will be of approximately the same form (here assumed to be Rayleigh) as that of V. However, the "scale" of the U distribution will now be *fixed;* in particular, the fraction-of-time distribution of U will have a unit median in every interval of length T_{int}. Moreover, it is easy to see that the fraction-of-time distribution of U in any collection of T_{int}-intervals—say, in an interval of length one year—will closely approximate the distribution of U in any single such interval. This situation is depicted in Fig. 2; W is a "slowly varying" multiplier of U such that the V of Fig. 1 factors into $V = UW$. This suggests a logarithmic change of variables. Let us put $v = 20 \log_{10} V$, $u = 20 \log_{10} U$, $w = 20 \log_{10} W$; then

$$v = u + w, \tag{3}$$

which provides an additive decomposition.

This procedure conforms to that followed in the engineering analysis of communication systems. The variable u is the logarithm of the Rayleigh variable U, *i.e.*, it is a "log-Rayleigh" variable; the scale of U was chosen so that the median of u is zero db in any T_{int}-interval.

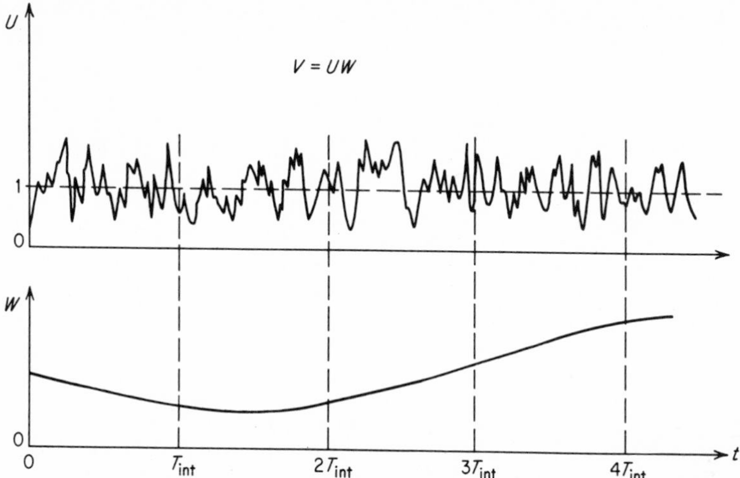

Fig. 2. Decomposition of V of Fig. 1 into the product of a rapidly fluctuating function U with constant unit median for arbitrarily long time intervals and a "slowly varying" function W.

It can be seen that most of the "Rayleigh" distributions plotted elsewhere in this volume are actually given as distribution functions of u in decibels. The "local median" w is still slowly varying because W is. Graphically, this would appear as in Fig. 3.

The following practical problem often arises in this setting. (Henceforth T_{int} is taken to be 1 hour for simplicity of language; thus, distributions of w will be distributions of "hourly medians.") Suppose the fraction-of-time distribution of w is fixed and known in intervals of length one year. (This yearly distribution of hourly medians is often approximated by a "log-normal" distribution.) As noted above, the distribution of u is closely approximated by the same fixed distribution in every hour and therefore the fraction-of-time distribu-

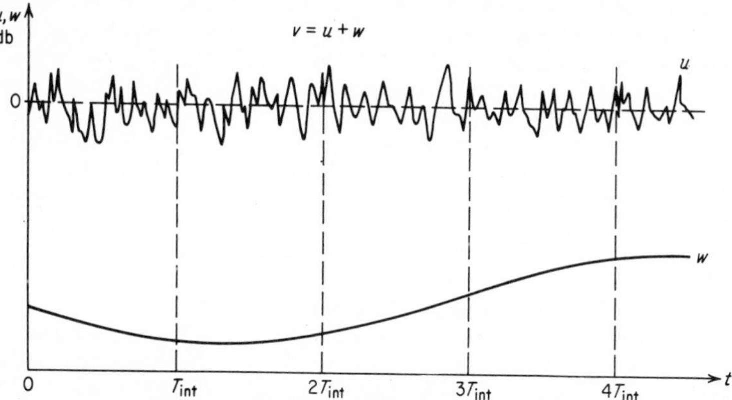

Fig. 3. Additive decomposition of V expressed in db.

tion of u in a year-long interval is also approximated by the same fixed distribution. (It is easy to see this; consider Fig. 1 of Chapter 2.) Let us write $F_u(x)$ and $F_w(x)$ for the distribution functions of u and w, respectively. What is the distribution of $v = u + w$?

Now, if u and w were strictly independent, the distribution function $F_v(x)$ of v would (according to Eq. (28) of Chapter 2) be given by the convolution of F_u and F_w, denoted $(F_u * F_w)(x)$,

$$F_v(x) \stackrel{?}{=} \int_{-\infty}^{\infty} F_u(x-t)dF_w(t) = \int_{-\infty}^{\infty} F_w(x-t)dF_u(t) \equiv (F_u * F_w)(x). \tag{4}$$

[A word on this notation may be in order. Convolutions in engineering literature are most often encountered as convolutions of density functions, as in Eq. (29) of Chapter 2, and are often written $p_1(x)*p_2(x)$. However, the integrated form used here (and in Eq. (28) of Chapter 2) for distribution functions is also a convolution; and the notation $(F_u * F_w)(x)$, though possibly less familiar, will be useful for the development below.] Now, it can actually be proved (though I shall not do so here) that two "smoothly varying" variables such as u and w in Fig. 3 *cannot* be strictly independent, and, therefore, Eq. (4) cannot be expected to give exactly the right result. However, we shall prove that u and w are "approximately independent" in the sense that (4) gives approximately the right result.

For this purpose, let us suppose the graphs of u and w to be given throughout an interval of a year. Let us replace w with an approximating step-function $\tilde{w}$ that is constant in one-hour intervals and approximates w within p decibels. ($\tilde{w}$ may and shall be so chosen that p is one-half the maximum change in w in any hour, which would be the smallest possible value of p.) Let $F_{\tilde{u}}$ be the approximating distribution function of u, which approximates the actual distribution function of u within q decibels in the sense that

$$F_{\tilde{u}}(x-q) \leqslant F_u(x) \leqslant F_{\tilde{u}}(x+q) \tag{5}$$

for all values of x. Let us replace u with an approximating variable $\tilde{u}$ with the property that the one-hour distribution function of $\tilde{u}$ in each of the intervals in which $\tilde{w}$ is constant is precisely $F_{\tilde{u}}$; it is easy to see that we can do this.* Let us put $\tilde{v} \equiv \tilde{u} + \tilde{w}$. We now have the situation depicted in Fig. 4, in which only a small fraction of the one-year interval is shown.

But this situation is reminescent of that in Fig. 4 of Chapter 2. The square-wave and pyramidal-wave variables of that illustration were found to be independent because the conditional distribution of either was the same as the complete distribution. In the present case, let $\tilde{w}_0$ be one of the possible values of $\tilde{w}$. What is the conditional distribution of $\tilde{u}$, given that $\tilde{w} = \tilde{w}_0$? This condition restricts $\tilde{u}$ to that collection of one or more one-hour intervals in which it is true that $\tilde{w} = \tilde{w}_0$. Within *each* of these intervals, the distribution function of $\tilde{u}$ is $F_{\tilde{u}}$ by construction; therefore, the fraction-of-time

*$\tilde{u}$ need not approximate u pointwise; it is sufficient that the d.f. of $\tilde{u}$ be $F_{\tilde{u}}$. E.g., $\tilde{u}$ may be taken to be periodic of period one.

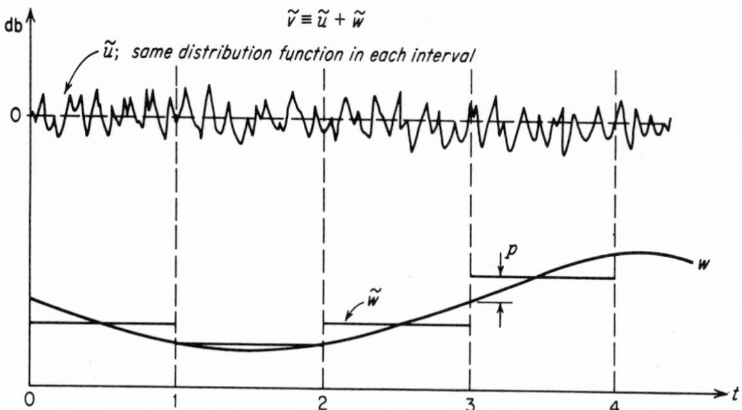

Fig. 4. Approximations $\tilde{u}$ and $\tilde{w}$ to the functions u and w of Fig. 3.

distribution of $\tilde{u}$ in the *collection* of intervals is also $F_{\tilde{u}}$—*i.e.*, the same as on the full one-year interval. This proves that $\tilde{u}$ and $\tilde{w}$ are independent; hence,

$$F_{\tilde{v}}(x) = \int_{-\infty}^{\infty} F_{\tilde{u}}(x-h)dF_{\tilde{w}}(h) = \int_{-\infty}^{\infty} F_{\tilde{w}}(x-h)dF_{\tilde{u}}(h) = (F_{\tilde{u}} * F_{\tilde{w}})(x). \tag{6}$$

Now, it is clear from the construction of $\tilde{w}$ that $F_{\tilde{w}}$ approximates F_w within p decibels in the same sense of (5), viz.,

$$F_{\tilde{w}}(x-p) \leqslant F_w(x) \leqslant F_{\tilde{w}}(x+p) \tag{7}$$

for all x, and similarly with F_w and $F_{\tilde{w}}$ interchanged. We shall now prove that $(F_u * F_w)$ approximates F_v within $2p + 2q$ decibels, which answers the question raised in (4). First, substituting the first and then the second inequality from (7) into (6) establishes that

$$F_{\tilde{v}}(x-p) \leqslant (F_{\tilde{u}} * F_w)(x) \leqslant F_{\tilde{v}}(x+p). \tag{8}$$

In the same way, the inequalities (5) substituted in the intergrals represented in (8) yield

$$F_{\tilde{v}}(x-p-q) \leqslant (F_u * F_w)(x) \leqslant F_{\tilde{v}}(x+p+q). \tag{9}$$

On the other hand, it follows directly from the definitions of $\tilde{u}$, $\tilde{w}$, and $\tilde{v}$ that

$$F_{\tilde{v}}(x-p-q) \leqslant F_v(x) \leqslant F_{\tilde{v}}(x+p+q). \tag{10}$$

Let $p + q = \alpha$. Then it follows from (9) and (10) that

$$F_v(x-2\alpha) \leqslant (F_u * F_w)(x) \leqslant F_v(x+2\alpha); \tag{11}$$

for if not, there is an x_0 such that one of these inequalities, say the second, fails, so that

$$F_v(x_0+2\alpha) < (F_u * F_w)(x_0). \tag{12}$$

But $(F_u * F_w)(x_0) \leqslant F_{\tilde{v}}(x_0+\alpha)$ by (9), while $F_{\tilde{v}}(x_0+\alpha) \leqslant F_v(x_0+2\alpha)$ by

(10), so $(F_u * F_w)(x_0) \leq F_v(x_0 + 2\alpha)$, which contradicts (12); similarly if the first inequality in (11) fails. Therefore (11) holds for all x, which was to be proved.

It is helpful to illustrate these results graphically, as is done in Fig. 5. Equations (9) and (10) indicate that both the distribution functions F_v and $(F_u * F_w)$ lie within the strip of *horizontal* width 2α centered on the distribution function $F_{\tilde{v}}$. It follows that the distribution functions F_v and $(F_u * F_w)$ cannot be displaced horizontally from each other by more than 2α, which is the result (11).

Let us recall that $2p = p'$ is the maximum change in the hourly median w in any hour. Let us also note that $2q = q'$ is the horizontal width of a strip centered on the distribution function F_u such that all the actual one-hour distribution functions of u fall within this strip. We may then state the foregoing results in words: *If the "hourly median" function* w *does not change more than* p′ *db in any hour, and if all the one-hour distributions of* u *can be included in a strip of width* q′ *db centered on the distribution function* F_u, *then the one-year distribution function of* $v = u + w$ *will be given with an error not exceeding* $p' + q'$ *decibels by the convolution* $F_u * F_w$.

III. DISCUSSION

The preceding result is of considerable importance. First, the long-term distribution of v is of importance for many applications, but it would be extremely difficult to obtain this distribution experimentally; to this author's knowledge, no year-long distribution of v has ever been thus obtained. On the other hand, year-long (or month-long) distributions of hourly medians are relatively common, as are one-hour distributions of u. These u and w distributions are often convolved (usually numerically) to obtain long-term distributions of v. The foregoing analysis shows that this procedure does in fact yield a good approximation, at least to the extent to which $p' + q'$ is negligible; moreover, experimental information on both p' and q' is often available.

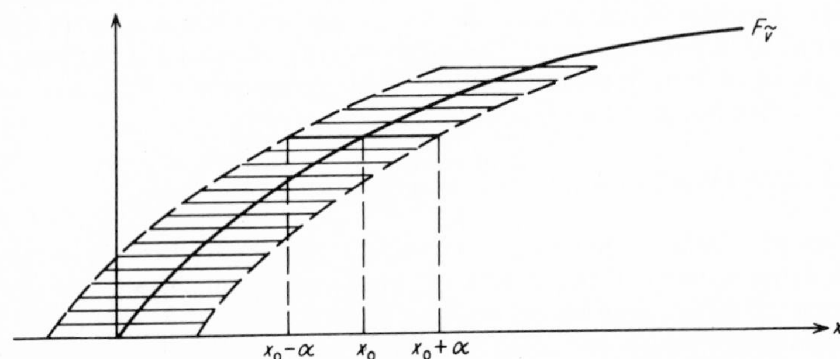

Fig. 5. Graphical illustration of the meaning of inequalities (9) and (10), and, in consequence, (11).

It is worth pointing out that this analysis depends on the explicit use of fraction-of-time distributions and model random variables whose structure "imitates" the quantities of interest. A more conventional approach would be to use *only* distribution functions, paying no attention to the detailed structure of the model random variables involved, and *assume* that the quantities u and w could be adequately represented by independent random variables. One would then compute the v distribution by convolving the u and w distributions. In principle, one would then have to verify the validity of this assumption by performing a new and extremely difficult year-long experiment. In contrast to this procedure, we have actually *proved, a priori,* that the assumption may be reasonable; moreover, we have obtained quantitative bounds on the accuracy of the approximation in terms of measurable quantities relating to the rate of change $[p']$ of the hourly medians and the dispersion $[q']$ of the one-hour distributions of v. Such estimates would be quite impossible to obtain with the use of less explicit and less structured model random variables.

It was shown above that the actual distribution function of v would be given within $p' + q'$ decibels by the convolution of the actual distribution functions of u and w. In the actual design of a communication system, the precise distribution function of u throughout a year (or any other period) would not be known in advance. What would be known would be the model or approximating distribution function $F_{\tilde{u}}$. However, it is easy to see that the error still does not exceed $p' + q'$ db if $F_{\tilde{u}}$ is used in the convolution instead of F_u.

The case of F_w is slightly different. Again, one would not know in advance the precise distribution function F_w; what would be known would be a fixed approximating distribution function F_a, and some information on the possible dispersion of the actual distribution functions F_w from the fixed model distribution F_a. (F_a might, for example, be taken to be a log-normal distribution.) If the actual distribution functions of w can be included in a strip of width r' db centered on F_a, as in the situation of Fig. 5, it is easy to see by the same analysis that the actual distribution functions of u will not differ by more than $p' + q' + r'$ db from the convolution $F_{\tilde{u}} * F_a$. This latter convolution then would use only known model distributions, and one would often have information available on p', q', and r'. For example, experimental data relating to r' (the year-to-year dispersion of yearly distributions of hourly medians) have been given by the National Bureau of Standards,[1-3] among others.

IV. APPLICATIONS

The most common application to date of long-term distributions such as F_v have been in the design of communication links in which the design criterion was based on maintaining the "local" signal strength v above some specified threshold level for more than some specified fraction of an interval such as a year. Very often in such cases, the model one-hour distribution $F_{\tilde{u}}$ would not be the Rayleigh distribution, but would instead be the distribution function appropriate to the output of a diversity combiner, such as a four-channel maximal ratio combiner, or other distributions of the type mentioned in Chapter 7. Long-term distributions of this type have been computed by Sichak,[4] among others.

The use of long-term distribution functions to set transmitter power levels and other parameters in communication link design on the basis of a simple threshold criterion may sometimes be subject to criticism, if the long-term distribution is not supplemented by other data. Notably, long-term distribution functions can obscure the question of whether the "outage time" consists of a relatively few but relatively long periods, or many very short periods. This problem has been discussed elsewhere in somewhat more detail.[5] However, if the long-term distributions of signal strength are supplemented by suitable additional data, they may be directly used for communication link design on a simple "threshold" basis.

However, a simple "threshold exceeded" design criterion for a communication link will lead to inefficient use of the system, in any event. It will usually mean that the system in question will not be working at the level it could or should be during the major part of the time, when more information could be transmitted. Long-term distributions are certain to be of much more importance in evaluating the performance of systems employing some kind of variable information rate. The economics of communication systems are very likely to require increasing attention to the possibility of, and the actual use of, variable-rate systems. These systems are especially likely to evolve in applications employing some form of informational feedback, of the type discussed in Chapter 14.

It is worth pointing out that the basic type of analysis employed above can be extended to many other and more complicated problems. For example, it is not at all difficult to see how to extend the analysis to cases in which the one-hour distributions of v are not all of approximately the same form, and different fading distributions must be used for different periods of time. Such "non-stationary" cases can be treated by a simple extension of the above techniques, whether the variations in the form of fading are or are not correlated with fluctuations in the hourly medians. Applications to statistical problems of a completely different type may involve the replacement of two or more model varying quantities with approximating step functions, as was done with the "hourly median" function above. As a general point, it is worth emphasizing that many statistical problems of the type arising in the analysis and design of communication systems can often be conceptually simplified, and made more susceptible of mathematical analysis, by the use of explicit model random variables of the type employed in this chapter.

REFERENCES

1. A. P. Barsis, K. A. Norton, and P. L. Rice, "Predicting the Per-

formance of Long Distance Tropospheric Communication Circuits," *Natl. Bur. Standards Rept.* No. 6032, December, 1958.
2. A. P. Barsis, P. L. Rice, and K. A. Norton, "The Use of Measurements in Predicting the Performance of Tropospheric Communication Circuits," *Natl. Bur. Standards Rept.* No. 6043, February, 1959.
3. P. L. Rice, A. G. Longley, and K. A. Norton, "Prediction of the Cumulative Distribution with Time of Ground Wave and Tropospheric Wave Transmission Loss. Part I: The Prediction Formula, *Natl. Bur. Standards Tech. Note* No. 15, July, 1959.
4. W. Sichak, *Federal Telecommunication Labs., Tech. Memo* No. 619, Nutley, N.J., December, 1956.
5. D. G. Brennan, "Linear Diversity Combining Techniques," *Proc. IRE,* vol. 47, pp. 1075-1102, June, 1959. See especially pp. 1094-1096.

CHAPTER 21

Communication Link Design

Walter E. Morrow, Jr.

I. INTRODUCTION

Communication link synthesis requires the bringing together of all the various topics described in previous chapters. The performance required of a communication link is established by the user in accordance with the criteria described in Chapter 18 and also in the following section of this chapter. These performance criteria may be stated either in terms of a fidelity criterion for analog signals or in terms of an error rate for digital links. The mathematical representation of the channel or possible channels to be used is described in Chapters 4, 5, 6, 7, and 15. Chapters 4, 15, and 17 cover the general representation of additive noise as well as the techniques of designing for minimum noise in the radio equipment itself. Chapters 4, 5, 6, 7, and 20 cover the representation of multiplicative channel disturbances, both long-term (Chapters 4 and 20) and the short-term variations caused by changing multipath in the channel (Chapters 5, 6, and 7). The selection of optimum transmission waveforms is only partially understood at this time. The cases for which optimum waveforms are known, namely, channels with additive gaussian noise and fixed or very slowly changing multipath are discussed in Chapter 11. Optimum demodulation and receiver decision techniques are covered in several chapters. Analog modulation and demodulation techniques are covered in Chapter 19. Digital signal detection techniques are covered in Chapters 8, 9, 11, and 12 for cases of additive gaussian noise and negligible or slowly changing multipath. Under some circumstances, it may be necessary to reduce the error rate of a digital system by means of techniques described in Chapters 7, 13, and 14. Chapter 13 covers the case of coding and decoding in the absence of any feedback of error information from the receiver to the transmitter; whereas Chapter 14 discusses the possible improvements obtainable with this feedback information.

II. PERFORMANCE CRITERIA

In order to design a communication system, it is necessary to specify the performance required. Such a specification should include the nominal capacity required, the quality of the transmissions, and the percentage of time, or reliability, with which the quality is to be maintained. The details of such a specification depend, of course, upon the particular system under design. However, it is possible to divide such specifications into two general classes: analog-transmission performance specifications and digital-transmission performance specifications.

A. Analog-Transmission Performance Specification

Analog channels are used to transmit such signals as speech, television, and telemetry signals. The specifications of such channels may include such factors as amplitude-vs-frequency response, time-delay-vs-frequency, and signal-to-noise ratio. The first two characteristics are usually specified in conventional terms such as the bandwidth within which the channel response is constant to within a certain tolerance. The numbers for these characteristics are usually chosen on the basis of fidelity of signal reproduction. In the last analysis the required performance is chosen on the basis of good engineering judgment.

Signal-to-noise performance criteria have been established over the years for various types of analog service. Here again, however, the standards have a certain degree of arbitrariness. One finds, for instance, that the Bell Telephone System in the United States has one signal-to-noise standard for long distance telephone circuits while the European telephone systems have agreed on a different signal-to-noise standard. The Bell System requires 44-db signal-to-noise ratio in a 3-kc bandwidth measured from zero level at the end of a 4000-mile long circuit. The Europeans require about 52-db signal-to-noise ratio at the end of a 1600-mile circuit or about 47-db signal-to-noise ratio for a 4000-mile circuit. Zero level in both standards corresponds to about 10 db above the average talker power.

The standards for analog circuit signal-to-noise ratios are usually set on the basis of experimental measurements. Figure 1 shows the per cent of monosyllable words understood by an average listener as a function of signal-to-noise ratio. From such measurements one can deduce that a 5- or 10-db average speech-to-noise ratio should be satisfactory for intelligibility. This corresponds to about 15-or 20-db

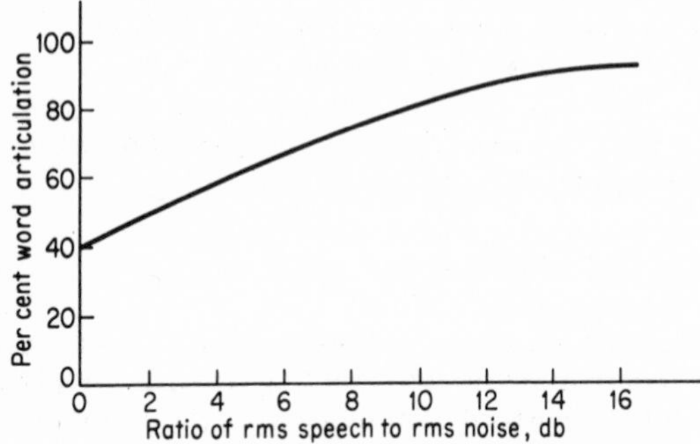

Fig. 1. Percent of monosyllable words understood by average listener as a function of signal-to-noise ratio.

signal-to-noise ratio measured from zero level. Telephone systems require much higher performance to account for variations in talker volume and losses in the lines connecting the subsets to the toll-board terminals. On the basis of such considerations, a minimum acceptable signal-to-noise ratio is selected.

For an actual circuit the variations in received signal strength give rise to variations in the circuit signal-to-noise ratio. Because of this variability in signal-to-noise performance, a statistical representation is useful. Similarly, the specification of the signal-to-noise performance may be made on a statistical basis. It is common, for instance, to specify that the signal-to-noise ratio be greater than a certain amount for a certain percentage of time. A typical specification might be that greater than 40-db signal-to-noise ratio be maintained for 99 per cent of the time. In some cases the average or median signal-to-noise ratio may also be specified.

In summary, the specification of analog circuit performance rests in the last analysis on engineering judgment. It is common to specify at least the signal-to-noise performance on a statistical basis.

B. Digital-Circuit Performance Specification

Digital-circuit performance is characterized in an entirely different manner from an analog circuit. The output of an analog circuit is permitted to take on *any* value between certain limits. A digital circuit is permitted to transmit only a sequence of *discrete symbols* taken from a *limited set*. Such a set might be the letters of the English alphabet, for instance. In this case it is not meaningful to speak of the signal-to-noise ratio at the circuit output. One can speak only of the probability of receiving correct symbols at the circuit output.

Thus a single number giving the probability of receiving correct symbols might be used. However, in many cases more details are desirable. For example, in a multi-symbol system, such as teletype, it becomes of interest to know the probabilities of different types of errors. These are specified by the transition-error probabilities giving the probability that a certain transmitted symbol, say the letter J, will be incorrectly received as the letter A, or B, or C, etc. Thus the complete specification of a 32-symbol system, such as teletype, involves 32^{31} numbers for the error probabilities and 32 numbers to give the probability of receiving correct symbols. The complete set can be represented by the conditional probabilities $P(y_i \mid x_j)$, which give the probability of receiving the y_ith output symbol when the x_jth input symbol is transmitted.

Usually the number of output symbols equals the number of input symbols, but in the case of an erasure circuit one of the outputs is an error symbol indicating that the receiver was unable to decide which symbol was transmitted.

Now the performance of a digital circuit may vary with time because of fluctuations in received signal strength, just as with an analog system. This gives rise to variations in error probabilities. In addition, variations in the additive noise statistics may lead to variability in the error probabilities. Thus it is not sufficient to specify simply a symbol error probability or a set of transition probabilities. Such a specification says nothing about the clumping of errors that may occur. For example, a symbol probability of error of 10^{-5} averaged over a year can permit 1 per cent of the year, or about eighty hours, to have error rates as poor as 10^{-3}. Thus it becomes necessary to describe the probability of error in a statistical fashion. In this regard there occurs a problem in specifying the time interval over which the probability of error is to be measured. Depending on the application, averages ranging from a fraction of a second up to an hour are often used. Having set an averaging interval, it is then possible to obtain a probability distribution function for the probability of error.

A very useful representation of the error performance is given by the distribution functions of the transition error probabilities averaged over some short time interval or intervals. In general, the distribution functions for the different transition probabilities will be similar except for scale factors. Thus a digital circuit performance may be specified by a set of error distribution functions taken for different time averages and a set of transition error probabilities that give the proper scale factors for the distributions.

III. LINK DESIGN

It is assumed that the designer of a communications link is given specifications on the required link performance of the type just described. It may well be that substantial reductions in the required link capacity can be achieved by proper processing of the incoming signals to remove redundant information. However, such techniques will not be considered in this book, and it is assumed that this type of processing, if any, has already been performed on the incoming signals.

The following is a brief resumé of the steps for designing a communication link to meet a specified performance. The designer must first *select a channel* between the two terminals of the link. Such a choice may be difficult to make initially, and it may be necessary to design systems for several different channels in order to decide which is optimum from some point of view such as reliability or cost. Having chosen a channel (or channels) it is necessary to *characterize the statistical properties of the channel* according to the techniques described in Chapter 4. Next it is necessary to *select a set of waveforms or analog signals* to be transmitted over the channel. These signals should be selected so as to minimize the probability of one signal being mistaken for another after corruption of the signals by the channel disturbances. It is then necessary to *design a receiver that is able to make the best possible decisions among the received signal waveforms.*

Having established the channel, the signals to be used, and the detection techniques, it should be possible to estimate the output signal-to-noise ratio or digital error rate for a given average received power. In the case of digital systems, if the error rate is not acceptable even for fairly large received signals, the use of error-correcting coding and decoding may be considered.

It should then be possible to match up the circuit performance with the specification and determine a minimum satisfactory received average signal power. Given this quantity and the long-term channel transmission-loss statistics, it is then possible to establish the transmitting power requirements for a given antenna system in order to meet the long-term reliability requirements.

Channels—Design of a communication link to meet a specified performance requires adequate information on channel properties. Depending on the channel, the following information may be required for characterization of the additive and multiplicative channel disturbances:

Probability distribution of additive noise disturbance.

Probability distribution of additive noise power averaged over various time intervals.

Spectral power density function of the additive disturbance.

Probability distribution of the long-term multiplicative channel variations.

Probability distribution of the short-term or rapid channel variations at a single frequency.

Autocorrelation function of the short-term or rapid channel variations at a fixed frequency.

Correlation coefficient of received envelopes of sinusoids at slightly different frequencies, or under any of the other conditions discussed in section IV of Chapter 7.

In the case of multi-terminal-pair channels, information is also required concerning the cross-correlation coefficients of the additive and multiplicative disturbances as measured between the various terminal pairs.

Signals—Given the channel characteristics and the required transmission performance, it is necessary to choose the signals to be transmitted and the detection techniques.

At the present time, a wide variety of different signaling techniques are available for transmission of analog and digital information. These techniques differ widely in their performance against various types of channel disturbances. No one of these techniques can be called "optimum" since the objectives of the various techniques are quite different. For example, signaling systems may be designed for such objectives as:

Maximum receiver output signal-to-noise ratio with fixed received power and fixed additive noise and no restrictions on the signaling bandwidth; or

Lowest digital error rate with fixed transmission rates, received power, additive noise, and bandwidth.

The design of optimum signaling techniques for various operating conditions is in its infancy. A few of the simpler cases have been worked out theoretically and equipment has been designed according to these principles. However, exact solutions remain to be discovered for most of the interesting cases found in real communication systems. It will not be possible to discuss all the various signaling techniques; however, the design and philosophy of at least one contemporary technique—the RAKE system—has been discussed in Chapter 12.

Performance functions—For any given signaling technique, the short-term performance may be determined for a specified channel as a function $f(\overline{P}_S, \overline{P}_N)$ of the average received signal power $\overline{P}_S$ and the average power $\overline{P}_N$ of the additive disturbance. In particular, the performance can be expressed as a function of the ratio of signal-to-noise mean power, $\overline{P}_S/\overline{P}_N$. Depending on the type of system, the short-term performance may be expressed either as an output signal-to-noise ratio or as a digital error rate.

For some of the simpler cases, such as single-sideband modulation, analog-signal transmission, and phase-reversal digital signaling through channels with flat amplitude and linear phase response in the presence of white gaussian noise, the performance can be calculated as illustrated in Chapter 11. Some of the more complicated cases, such as signaling with known waveforms through channels with slowly varying multipath and white gaussian-distributed noise have also been solved (Chapter 12). Exact solutions have not been obtained for some of the more complicated cases such as channels with multipath that changes in a time comparable with the multipath duration (that is, the reciprocal of the fading rate equals approximately the multipath duration). In these cases it may be necessary to obtain experimental measurements of the performance as a function of the ratio of average received signal power to average noise power.

In any case whether by calculation or experiment, the short-term performance function must be obtained. From such a function, it is possible to determine the minimum average received signal-to-noise ratio for satisfactory performance by setting the required short-term performance equal to the short-term performance function.

Now in order to insure that the long-term reliability of the system is met, it is necessary to obtain the long-term distribution of $\overline{P}_S/\overline{P}_N$, namely

$$\overline{P}(\overline{P}_S/\overline{P}_N) = \int_{-\infty}^{\overline{P}_S/\overline{P}_N} p(\overline{P}_S/\overline{P}_N)\, d(\overline{P}_S/\overline{P}_N)$$

For a radio circuit $\overline{P}_S/\overline{P}_N$ is given simply as

$$\overline{P}_S/\overline{P}_N = P_t G_t G_R \overline{K}_L/\overline{P}_N$$

where

P_t is the transmitted power
G_t is the transmitting antenna gain

G_R is the receiving antenna gain
$\overline{K}_L$ gives the transmission loss between isotropic antennas averaged over an interval of the order of a few seconds to a few hours (or of duration T_{int} in the notation of section III of Chapter 7).

Now some or all of the terms in the above expression may be functions of time which in most cases are statistically independent. Usually P_t may be considered constant. In some cases G_t and G_R suffer loss of plane-wave gain when used over certain types of propagation paths. $\overline{K}_L$ in almost all cases of radio paths is the most significant so far as fluctuations with time are concerned. $\overline{P}_N$ in many cases will be constant since it is primarily determined by receiver front-end noise. However, with the advent of low-noise front-end circuits such as parametric amplifiers (Chapter 16) and masers (Chapter 17), it is quite possible for $\overline{P}_N$ to vary with time because of galactic noise background variations due to the earth's rotation of the antenna beams past various parts of the sky (Chapter 15).

The determination of the probability density function of $\overline{P}_S/\overline{P}_N$ requires convolution of the probability density functions of the logarithms of the various terms that determine $\overline{P}_S/\overline{P}_N$. Thus, if we write

$$\log(\overline{P}_S/\overline{P}_N) = \log P_t + \log G_t + \log G_R + \log \overline{K}_L - \log \overline{P}_N$$

and assume that $\overline{K}_L$ and $\overline{P}_N$ are statistically independent and the other terms are constant, we have

$$p_3[\log(\overline{P}_S/\overline{P}_N)] = p_1[\log(P_t G_t G_R)\overline{K}_L] * p_2(-\log \overline{P}_N)$$

where $*$ denotes convolution. The probability density functions of $\log \overline{K}_L$ and $\log \overline{K}_N$ are known from the channel characteristics: therefore, the convolution can be carried out. If $p_1(\log \overline{K}_L)$ and $p_2(\log \overline{P}_N)$ are expressible as analytic functions, then it may be possible to obtain an exact solution. In many cases, the density functions are not simply represented and it may be necessary to perform a numerical integration.

Having obtained $p_3[\log(\overline{P}_S/\overline{P}_N)]$, the probability distribution of $\overline{P}_S/\overline{P}_N$ can be obtained by integrating this function. Here again it may be necessary to carry out a numerical integration. This final distribution function will of course have unknown terms in P_t, G_t, and G_R. The sum of the logs of these terms can be determined by setting the probability distribution function equal to the required long-term reliability, X, and using the minimum acceptable short-term signal-to-noise ratio as the limit of integration:

$$X = \int_{\log(\overline{P}_S/\overline{P}_N)_{min}}^{\infty} p_3(\eta)d\eta$$

The solution of this integral will yield the sum $\log P_t + \log G_t + \log G_R$.

The final design of the system depends upon a particular selection of P_t, G_t, and G_R.

Economics—Often it is possible to meet the performance requirements of a particular communication link by means of a number of different designs that employ different proportions of transmitter power, antenna size, and terminal apparatus complexity. For example, one may employ a very powerful transmitter but small antennas and simple terminal apparatus. Conversely, the same performance may be achieved by use of very complex terminal apparatus with small antennas and low-power transmitters.

Under these circumstances it is usually important to obtain the most economic arrangement of equipment. This involves the minimization of the link cost for a given link capacity. The cost may be expressed as either the initial investment or in terms of the annual operating expense. In this latter case the capacity may be stated in terms of the total number of bits transmitted during a year, in which case the optimization is one of obtaining the minimum cost per bit transmitted. The annual operating expense can be obtained by amortizing the initial cost over an appropriate number of years and adding to the resulting number the maintenance, operating, and other appropriate costs.

In the following discussion, optimization of initial costs will be considered. The total initial cost of a communication link is obviously the sum of its component parts:

$$C_T = C_1 + C_2 + C_3 + \dots C_n$$

where C_T is the total cost, and $C_1, C_2, \dots, C_n$ are the component costs. It is also necessary to obtain expressions that relate the performance of each component to its cost. Thus a set of functions can be obtained:

$$P_1 = f_1(C_1)$$
$$P_2 = f_2(C_2)$$
$$P_3 = f_3(C_3)$$

$$P_n = f_n(C_n)$$

where $P_1, P_2, P_3, \dots, P_n$ are component performance factors (such as transmitter power, antenna gain, etc.) that are related to link capacity. Now, if R is the link capacity in bits per second or some measure of the fidelity performance of an analog link (as, for instance, the rms percentage error between link input and output), then

$$R = f(P_1, P_2, P_3, \dots, P_n) .$$

R can also be expressed as a function of the component costs.

$$R = f'(C_1, C_2, C_3, \dots, C_n)$$

Substituting $C_n = C_T - C_1 - C_2 - C_3 - \dots - C_{n-1}$, we have

$$R = f''(C_1, C_2, C_3, \dots, C_{n-1}, C_T).$$

This expression can be differentiated with respect to the various costs and the various partial derivatives set equal to zero.

$$\left(\frac{\partial R}{\partial C_1}\right)_{C_2 C_3 \ldots C_T} = 0$$

$$\left(\frac{\partial R}{\partial C_2}\right)_{C_1 C_3 \ldots C_T} = 0$$

$$\left(\frac{\partial R}{\partial C_3}\right)_{C_1 C_2 \ldots C_T} = 0$$

and so on. These equations can be solved for

$$C_1 = f_1(C_T)$$

$$C_2 = f_2(C_T)$$

$$C_3 = f_3(C_T)$$

$$C_n = C_T - C_1 - C_2 - C_3 - \ldots - C_{n-1}$$

Thus the proper proportioning of the component costs can be determined for maximum link performance.

CHAPTER 22

Communication Using Earth Satellites

Jerome B. Wiesner

I. INTRODUCTION

The possibility of employing earth satellites to carry radio repeaters offers a new means of providing reliable long-range communications. Such communication systems would not be subject to the vagaries of the currently employed short-wave radio circuits and would be capable of transmitting much greater amounts of information than can be handled by the conventional systems. Satellite communication systems can be used for point-to-point radio relaying for military and civilian purposes and may ultimately be used to provide world-wide radio and television service as well. The electronic components required for these applications are not beyond present accomplishment, though considerable development work is necessary to provide the specialized equipment suitable for this purpose. A number of systems having restricted but useful capacities will be tried within the early sixties. Systems having greater capability but requiring the development of specialized radio and power equipment, satellites capable of carrying greater payloads, or both, are also feasible on a longer time scale.

Two types of relay satellites have been proposed and both are technically possible. The first is the passive satellite, a large light-weight metalized sphere that is used to reflect radio signals emanating from a transmitter at one point on the earth's surface to a distant point beyond the line-of-sight from the transmitter.

The second scheme involves the use of active repeaters in the satellite. In this system a radio receiver in the satellite intercepts the signal from a ground transmitter, amplifies it, and then retransmits it to a receiver somewhere on the earth's surface. In one variation of the active system the signals to be relayed are received as the satellite passes over the transmitting point, stored until the receiving site is within the range of the satellite, and then retransmitted. The passive satellite scheme has the advantage of simplicity of the airborne unit, and is available, without interference, for use by anyone who can provide his own ground equipment. Because it has no active parts, it is highly reliable. Unfortunately, passive systems have some disadvantages when compared with active relay systems. The transmission capacity of a passive relay is limited, as compared with possible active systems. The height at which the passive reflector can be placed in orbit to provide a useful communication circuit is restricted by signal-to-noise ratio limitations; consequently, the maximum range of a communication system using a single satellite reflection will be somewhat limited. Finally, a passive system requires the use of large tracking antennas and rather large transmitters—for which reasons it is not well suited for use as a mobile system. The need for very large receiving antennas also makes the use of a passive system unattractive for broadcast purposes.

II. FACTORS AFFECTING CHOICE OF ORBIT

The factors of orbit characteristics and satellite payload affect the design of both passive and active relay systems. These factors will therefore be examined before we consider specific relay configurations.

The orbit characteristics are important because they determine the period of time for which a single satellite can be observed from a given point on the ground, and hence the transmission time for a given satellite between two points. Consequently, the orbit characteristics will determine the number of satellites that are needed to provide continuous transmission between any two points. In a delayed-transmission system, the orbit characteristics will determine the anticipated time delays.

The period of an earth satellite is a function of the height. For a satellite in a circular orbit the period of revolution is given by

$$T = \frac{2\pi R^{3/2}}{rG} \tag{1}$$

where R is the orbit radius measured from the center of the earth, r is the radius of the earth, and G is the gravitational constant at the earth's surface.[1] For very low orbits (of the order of 100 miles above the earth's surface) the period is in the order of one and one-half hours; at a height of 22,200 miles, the orbit has a 24-hour period, which means that a satellite in an equatorial orbit could be made to remain stationary over a point on the earth's surface. While serious problems of orbital velocity control must be solved if such a satellite is to be employed, several schemes for accomplishing this control appear possible.

Orbits are conveniently classed into two categories: the stationary or 24-hour equatorial orbit, and the low orbits containing all non-stationary orbits regardless of orbit orientation. Generally, the low-orbit satellites will be employed at altitudes ranging from 1000 to 5000 miles above the surface of the earth.

A. Low Orbits

The orientation of the orbit with regard to the axis of the earth will be determined by the location of the points that the satellite relay is designed to link. For some purposes an equatorial orbit will be desirable; for others, a polar orbit—more accurately, a group of polar satellites if continuous communication is desired—may be advantageous. For example, Pierce and Kompfner[2] have chosen a polar orbit for a proposed relay link connecting the northern part of the United States with England.

There are a number of reasons for considering the use of satellites in low, nonequatorial orbits for communication purposes.

The stationary orbit requires a satellite at very high altitude (in excess of 22,000 miles). As we shall see, it is difficult and costly to design an adequate passive relay system with reflectors at so great a height; this distance may even be too great for some active satellite systems. Second, the fact that the 24-hour equatorial satellite cannot be seen within 8° of either pole eliminates the possibility of using it for communication to the Arctic or Antarctic regions. Finally, the low-altitude satellite may offer greater security from jamming than does the stationary satellite.

In order to provide continuous communication between two points on the earth's surface (whose antennas can see some part of the trajectory of a low satellite) a number of satellites will be needed. The exact number will depend upon the geometry of the situation and the station-keeping ability of the individual satellites. For a satellite

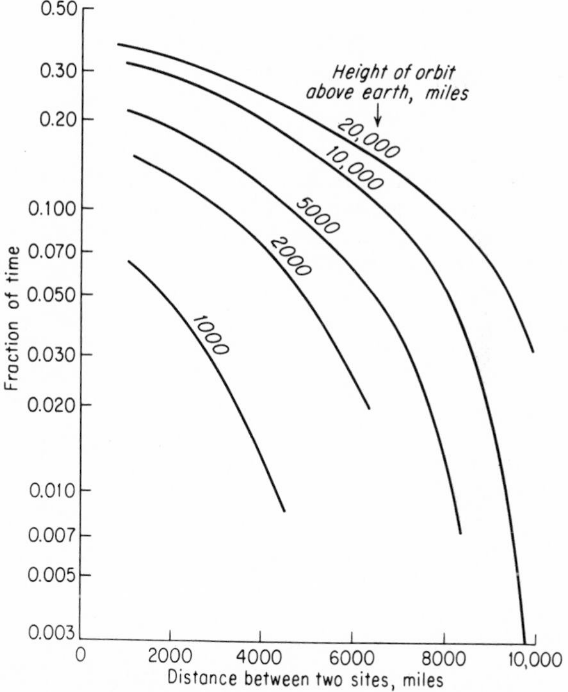

Fig. 1. Fraction of time that a satellite at a given height will provide service between two sites. (From Morrow.[1])

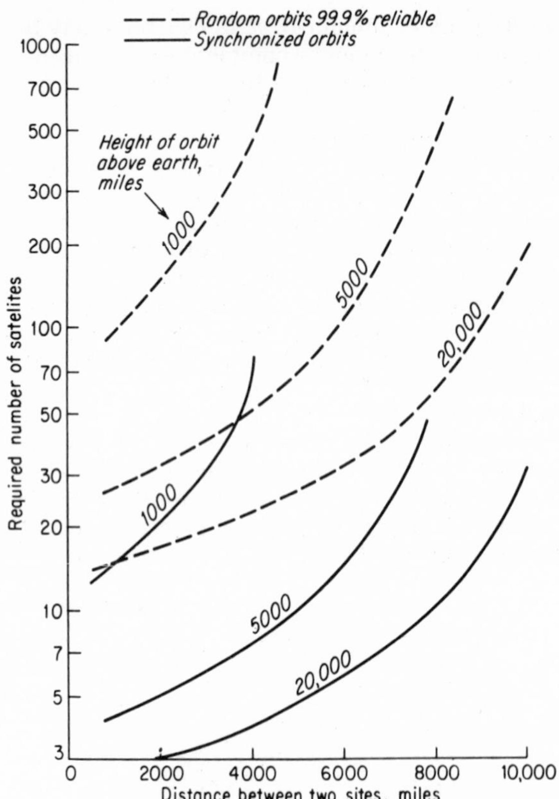

Fig. 2. Number of satellites required for synchronized and random orbits. (From Morrow.[2])

at height R, the fraction of the earth's surface over which a satellite is visible at one time is given[1] by

$$p = \frac{1.28}{2\pi}\left[\cos^{-1}\frac{r}{R\cos(L/2R)}\right]\left[\frac{\pi}{2} - \frac{L}{2r} - \sin^{-1}\frac{r}{R}\right] \tag{2}$$

where R and r have the same meaning as before and L is the distance between the two sites. Figure 1 is a plot of Eq. (2) for various heights and distances between sites.

From Eq. (2) it is possible to calculate the number of satellites in a circular orbit that will be required to provide communication for a given fraction of the time over a specified path of length L. The quantity p is the probability that a given satellite is visible to the two sites desiring to communicate. Thus $P = (1-p)^n$ gives the probability that of n satellites in random orbits none will be visible simultaneously from the two sites. Because of the statistical nature of the arrival of a satellite in the common volume between the transmitter and the receiver, a large number of satellites will be required to insure a high probability of having one satellite in this volume. But if the orbital position of each satellite is appropriately planned, and the period of the individual satellites is made the same so that they arrive uniformly spaced in time, a smaller number of satellites will provide essentially continuous service. In fact, approximately $1/p$ of them will then be adequate. The curves of Fig. 2 show the number of satellites in random orbits required to provide a circuit of 99.9 per cent reliability. Also shown are the number of satellites in synchronized orbits required to provide essentially continuous communication. It can be seen that a heavy penalty is paid for the inability to control the satellites in their orbits.

B. 24-Hour Orbit

The 24-hour satellite revolving in an equatorial plane is particularly attractive because it effectively hovers over a given point on the earth's surface and provides continuous coverage between any pair of points on the earth's surface from which it is simultaneously visible. Three such satellites would provide world-wide coverage (excluding the polar regions previously discussed). A single stationary satellite would suffice to span the Atlantic Ocean, a second could span the Pacific. We shall see later that it is possible to build for such a satellite a repeater having sufficient channel capacity to provide an effective world-wide communication system.

III. FACTORS AFFECTING SYSTEM PERFORMANCE

A. Passive Relay Systems

In the passive system a metalized balloon placed in orbit is used to reflect energy from a ground-based transmitter to a receiving station. Only a very small fraction of the initial radiated energy is intercepted by the sphere, and only a portion of the energy reflected by it is in the direction of the receiving station; consequently, a passive system requires large antennas and large transmitters.

The signal-to-noise ratio of a passive relay system is given by

$$\frac{S}{N} = \frac{P_t G_t A_R K_1 K_2 \sigma}{(4\pi)^2 R_1^2 R_2^2 (kTB)} \tag{3}$$

where

- A_R is the receiving cross-section of the ground antenna;
- P_t is the transmitted power;
- kTB is the effective receiver noise power in a bandwidth B at temperature T;
- G_t is the gain of the transmitting antenna;
- σ is the scattering cross-section of the passive satellite;
- R_1 is the distance from transmitter to satellite;
- R_2 is the distance from satellite to the receiver; and

K_1, K_2 are factors that account for atmospheric absorption of the radiowaves each way.

This result will be compared with that obtained for a satellite communication system employing an active repeater.

B. Active Relay Systems

In active systems the signal to be relayed is received and rebroadcast by the equipment in the satellite. In this situation two relay circuits are actually operated in cascade. The first circuit consists of a ground transmitter and its antenna system which beams a signal to be received by the satellite. The second channel consists of the satellite-borne transmitter and an antenna that radiates to a ground receiver system. Because of power supply limitations in the satellite, the latter circuit normally will limit the capacity of satellite relay systems and is the only circuit that we need to investigate.

Accordingly, the S/N ratio of an active relay will be

$$\frac{S}{N} = \frac{P_{ts} G_{ts} A_R K}{4\pi R_2^2 (kTB)} \tag{4}$$

where

- P_{ts} is the power output of the satellite transmitter;
- G_{ts} is the gain of the satellite antenna;
- kTB is the effective receiver noise power in a bandwidth B at a temperature T;
- R_2 is the distance from the satellite to the ground receiver; and
- K is a factor that accounts for atmospheric absorption of the radiowaves.

C. Comparison of Active and Passive Relay Systems

Since an active relay is probably more difficult to build and to place in a proper orbit, it should have clear-cut advantages if it is to be chosen in preference to a passive reflector. Assuming that the active satellite and the passive reflector are at the same height and the same distance from the receiver and that the same receiver and the same frequency are used in both cases, the performance of the active system relative to the passive one will be

$$\frac{S_{act}}{S_{pas}} = \frac{4\pi P_{ts} G_{ts} R_1^2}{P_t G_t K \sigma} = \frac{4\pi P_{ts} A_{ts} R_1^2}{P_t A_t K \sigma} \tag{5}$$

where A_{ts} is the effective cross-section of the transmitting antenna carried by the satellite. If we assume a stationary orbit and the following reasonable values for the factors in Eq. (5):

P_{ts} = 1 watt
A_{ts} = 1 square meter

R_1 = 24,000 miles
P_t = 10,000 watts
A_t = 100 square meters
σ = 100 square meters
K = 1

we find that

$$\frac{S_{\text{act}}}{S_{\text{pas}}} = 1.85 \times 10^8. \tag{6}$$

This comparison will be considered unfair by some people because satellites in a 24-hour orbit were compared. While it is true that the comparison would not have appeared so unfavorable if a lower orbit had been examined, there are reasons that make low orbits not as desirable as a stationary orbit.

For an active system, the signal-to-noise ratio in a one-megacycle bandwidth will be [from Eq. (4)] 26 db if $G_{ts} = 1$, $T = 30°K$, and $A_R = 3000$ square meters. This is sufficient circuit capacity for a substantial number of telephone or telegraph circuits. Obviously, the available power can be disposed of in other ways to give circuits with different bandwidths and other signal-to-noise ratios. The significant thing is that one watt of power radiated from a satellite is adequate to provide a very large amount of circuit capacity. In this example the satellite antenna was assumed to have a gain of one. If vertical stabilization can be achieved on the satellite—and this does not appear to be difficult—an antenna having approximately 20 db of gain can be employed on the satellite and still provide world-wide coverage. This would permit a circuit bandwidth of 100 mc with the same signal-to-noise ratio as was achieved in the unity-gain example.

D. Factors Affecting the Choice of Operating Frequency

The choice of operating frequency is affected by a large variety of considerations. Among the most important are the availability of components, the availability of adequate spectrum space for the service proposed, the sky noise that the ground receivers will intercept, and the primary power available in the satellite for operating the communication relay equipment. Let us examine these factors.

1. **Primary power sources**—The power available in the satellite for operating the relay equipment and the stabilization equipment sets the upper limit on the equipment that can be considered. In the near future—the next two to four years—the best source of power in the satellite for a continuous-duty service will be solar cells used in conjunction with a storage battery to supply energy when the satellite is in the earth's shadow. At the present time, solar cell-storage battery combinations weigh approximately four pounds per watt of available power. Since the presently available rockets can lift only a few hundred pounds into a 22,000-mile orbit, the total available power for relay operation will be limited to about 100 watts. Within a decade it

should be possible to place many tons into a stationary orbit and then the available primary power will not be a serious limitation on the design of these systems.

Other sources of power are being developed for satellite use. Among these are nuclear-powered units and solar engines that use solar energy in the form of heat. When larger satellites become available such energy sources will doubtless be used.

2. **Radio-frequency power sources**—Because of the limited amount of primary power available at the present time, the choice of transmitting devices for use in a satellite relay is severely limited. The scarcity of energy puts a premium on transmitter efficiency in relation to other factors and limits the total capacity of the relay system. The following devices appear to have some merit for use in relay systems.

a. *Transistors*—Transistors having a power output of approximately 1/4 watt at frequencies up to four or five hundred megacycles are now available. By using several of them in parallel a watt or two of power could be obtained. This performance is probably possible up to frequencies in the neighborhood of 1000 mc.

The transistor has the advantage of very high reliability and good efficiency. Unfortunately, there does not appear, in the near future, to be any reasonable hope of greatly increasing the power obtainable in the frequency range now achievable or of substantially increasing the frequency at which transistors can operate.

b. *Triodes*—Close-spaced triodes of the 416B, 2C39 types can be used to provide power outputs in the one-watt range. Below 1000 mc, as much as 1000 watts can be obtained from tubes of this general design.

Properly designed triode amplifiers can have good efficiencies at these frequencies.

If triode amplifiers are to be used in satellite applications, considerable care will have to be taken to provide proper cooling for the tubes so that they will have adequate life.

c. *Beam Tubes*—Klystron amplifiers and traveling-wave tubes are the most promising for use at frequencies above approximately 2000 mc and for power outputs in excess of a few watts.

Unfortunately, both the klystron amplifier and the traveling-wave tube are less efficient at low power levels than they are at high power levels.

It should be possible to make power amplifiers using beam tubes in the range from one watt to several hundred watts and with power gains of the order of 30 db at any frequency up to about 10,000 mc. At low power levels it may be difficult to obtain bandwidths that are adequate for communication purposes (*i.e.*, greater than 1 mc).

3. **Low-noise receivers**—The capacity of a radio-relay link is determined by the signal-to-noise ratio present at the output of the receiver. This in turn is determined by the total received signal power and the noise present at the output of the receiver. The received power, as we have already seen, is determined by the transmitter

power, the transmitting and receiving antennas, and the path geometry. Equations (3) and (4) also indicate that the signal-to-noise ratio varies inversely as the noise temperature, T, of the receiver. This temperature equals the temperature of a resistor that (a) has the same resistance as the output resistance of the receiver and (b) is capable of transferring the same noise power to a resistive load as would the actual receiver.

The noise output from the receiver originates from two principal components: the shot noise associated with the electron flow in the tubes and the external noise contributed by various sources of which the antenna noise and the sky noise are the most important.

Until quite recently, the shot noise contribution from the tubes was so large that it completely masked the external noise. Typical noise temperatures for amplifiers ranged from 600°K at 200 mc to 3000°K at 10,000 mc. Two new UHF developments have completely altered this situation: Parametric amplifiers[3] and masers[4] can have such low noise temperatures that noise from the "sky" is now often the limiting factor in determining receiver performance.

Parametric amplifiers having noise temperatures of less than 100°K can be operated at a few hundred mc. Comparable performance can be achieved up to frequencies in the neighborhood of 3000 mc. There is good reason to expect that similar performance can be obtained at very much higher frequencies.

Maser amplifiers can be made with noise temperatures in the range of 10°K–30°K over the frequency range of interest for satellite communications.

It is fortunate that the ground-to-satellite link is not power-limited, and that this makes ultimate receiver performance required only on the satellite-to-ground section of the link.

4. **Background noise**—The important sources of noise that must be taken into account in choosing the operating frequency for a satellite communication system are cosmic noise from space, thermal noise associated with atmospheric absorption, and noise from the sun.

Cosmic noise is strongest in the direction of the galactic center of our milky way. Figure 3, which is drawn for 250 mc, shows the manner in which the cosmic background noise varies in different positions of the sky. Measurements indicate that the cosmic noise decreases with increasing frequency. Figure 4 shows the variation of cosmic noise intensity as a function of frequency.

The absorption of microwave energy by constituents of the atmosphere implies a mutual coupling between these elements (principally oxygen and water vapor) and the receiving antenna. The exact effect of atmospheric absorption depends upon the direction of the signal from the earth; a ray departing along the horizon is affected the most. The curves of Fig. 5 show the absorption as a function of frequency for one set of conditions. By assuming a temperature for the atmospheric constituents, the noise that this effect will introduce into the receiver can be calculated. In general, it is well to stay below 10,000

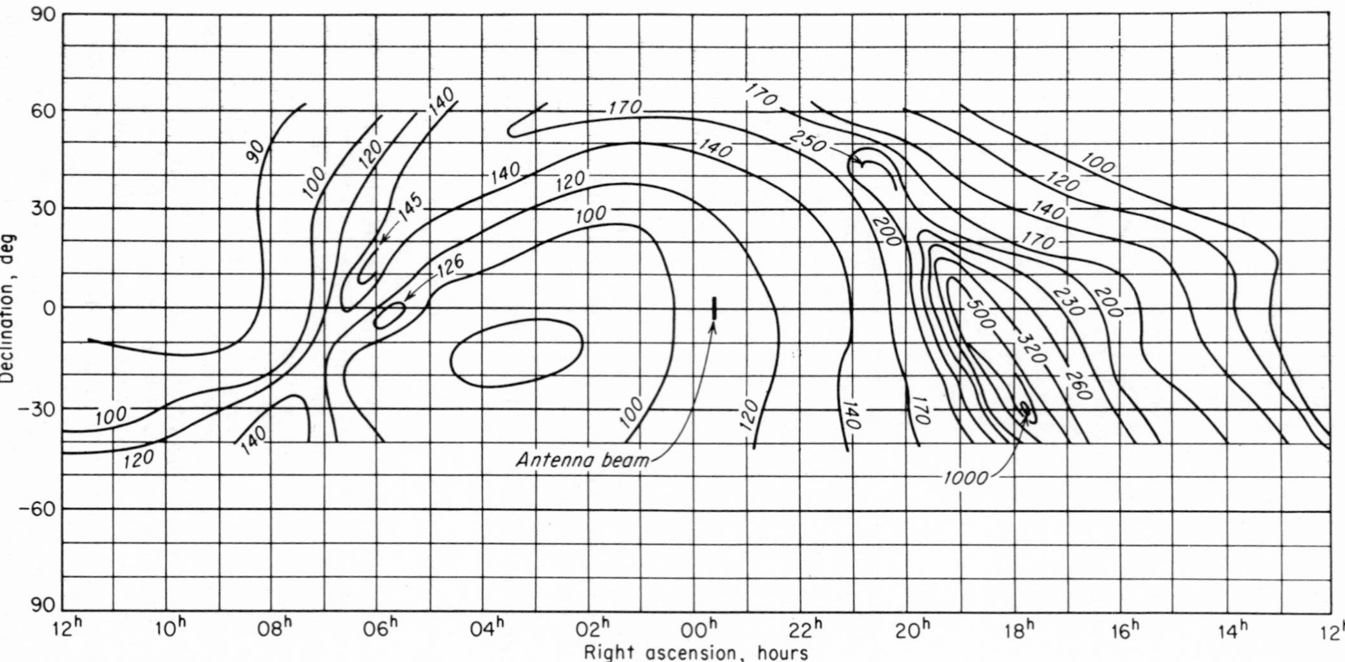

Fig. 3. Map of the radio sky background at 250 mc (after Ko and Kraus).

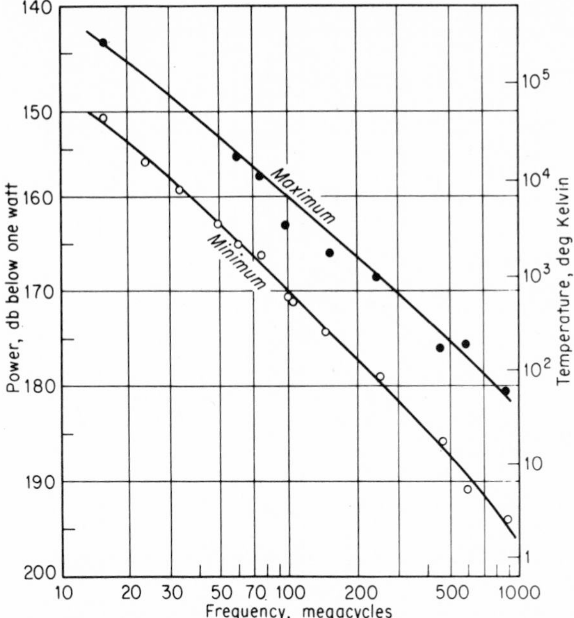

Fig. 4. Maximum and minimum cosmic noise in 1-kc bandwidth as a function of frequency.

mc if ultra-sensitive receivers are to be employed. Even at this frequency serious absorption may be encountered during heavy rains.

The sun is a prolific source of radio noise. In general, it is best to design the satellite system to avoid direct interception of the sun by the receiving beam. During those infrequent periods when this cannot be done, serious degradation of the system will be experienced.

IV. TYPICAL SYSTEMS

Several examples of active relay systems will now be worked out to illustrate a variety of applications and to show the performance that might be expected as the systems evolve. The properties of these systems are shown on Table 1.

A. Point-to-Point Relay

1. Low-power, lightweight—It would be possible within a time period of approximately one year to establish an experimental low-power active satellite relay system. Such a unit having a power output in the range of one watt could be made with a total weight of 50–100 pounds. Launching vehicles for such a payload will be available during this period. If the ground receiving system used a 60-foot antenna, and the satellite was at a height of 2500 miles, the system

TABLE I. SATELLITE COMMUNICATION SYSTEMS

	Power Aloft	Passive 100′ Diameter Balloon		Low Power – 1 Watt		
1	Function	Point-to-Point Relay [1]	Point-to-Point Relay [2]	Point-to-Point Relay [3]	Fixed Point to Mobile [4]	Point-to Point Relay [5]
2	Orbit	polar	equatorial	polar	polar	equatorial
3	Orbit Height	2,500 miles	22,000 miles	2,500 miles	2,500 miles	22,000 miles
4	Period	3 hours	24 hours	3 hours	3 hours	24 hours
5	Fraction of Time Available	0.15	1.0	~0.15	~0.15	1.0
6	Weight of Satellite	200#	200#	50-100#	50-100#	50-100#
7	Bandwidth	4 mc	1.0 kc	4 mc	10 kc	100 kc
8	Signal-to-Noise Ratio	20 db	20 db	24 db	20 db	24 db
9	Frequency	2,000 mc	2,000 mc	400 mc	400 mc	400 mc
10	Ground Trans. Antenna	250-foot diameter	250-foot diameter	28-foot diameter	28-foot diameter	28-foot diameter
11	Ground Trans. Power	10,000 watts	10,000 watts	100 watts	100 watts	500 watts
12	Ground Receiving Antenna	250-foot diameter	250-foot diameter	60-foot diameter	10 square feet	60-foot diameter
13	Ground Receiving Noise Temp.	30°K	30°K	100°K	300°K	100°K
14	Number of Sat. for 99% Avail.	10-20	1	10-20	10-20	1
15	Availibility of Exp. Model	1-2 yrs.	1-2 yrs.	1-2 yrs.	1-2 yrs.	1-2 yrs.

Note: Isotropic Antenna on satellite except for broadcast where

$$G_t = 20 \text{ db}$$

Table I. (Continued)

	Power Aloft		Medium Power – 100 Watts				
1	Function	Point-to-point Relay 6	Point-to-point Relay 7	Fixed point to Mobile 8	Fixed point to Mobile 9	Point-to-point Relay 10	FM Broad-cast 11
2	Orbit	equatorial	polar	polar	equatorial	equatorial	equa-torial
3	Orbit Height	22,000 miles	2,500 miles	2,500 miles	22,000 miles	22,000 miles	22,000 miles
4	Period	24 hours	3 hours	3 hours	24 hours	24 hours	24 hours
5	Fraction of Time Available	1.0	~0.15	~0.15	1.0	1.0	1.0
6	Weight of Satellite	50-100#	~1,000#	~1,000#	1,000#	1,000#	1,000#
7	Bandwidth	1.7 mc	~100 mc	400 kc	10 kc	8 mc	250 kc
8	Signal-to-Noise Ratio	24 db	24 db	20 db	20 db	24 db	24 db
9	Frequency	400 mc	400-2,000 mc	400-2,000 mc	400-2,000 mc	400-2,000 mc	100 mc
10	Ground Trans. Antenna	28-foot diameter	28-foot diameter	28-foot diameter	28-foot diameter	60-foot diameter	60-foot diameter
11	Ground Trans. Power	3,000 watts	100 watts	100 watts	~500 watts	500 to 1,000 watts	1,000 watts
12	Ground Receiving Antenna	250-foot diameter	28-foot diameter	4 square feet	4 square feet	60-foot diameter	10 square feet
13	Ground Receiving Noise Temp.	100°K	100°K	300°K	300°K	100°K	600°K
14	Number of Sat. for 99% Avail.	1	10-20	10-20	1	1	1
15	Availibility of Exp. Model	1-2 yrs.	2-4 yrs.	2-4 yrs.	2-4 yrs.	3-5 yrs.	3-5 yrs.

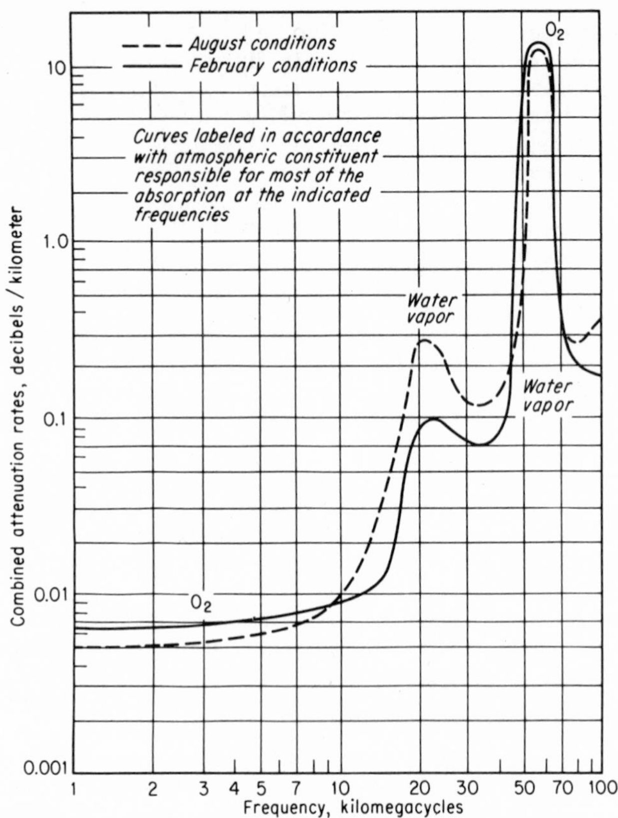

Fig. 5. Combined attenuation rates caused by oxygen plus water vapor at surface.

would have a signal-to-noise ratio of approximately 25 db and an intelligence bandwidth of 4 mc, enough for simultaneous telephone and television transmission.

Characteristics of this system are given in column 3, Table 1. The frequency and power levels of this system were chosen so that it would be feasible to build the airborne equipment now with existing transistors and solar-cell power supply. Column 4 shows the performance of the same airborne relay when used in conjunction with a 10-square-foot receiving antenna, such as might be available on a ship. The 10-kc bandwidth available would be entirely adequate for ship-to-shore communication. It is possible that it could be used with even smaller receiving antennas for communication with aircraft.

Columns 5 and 6 show the performance that could be achieved with this low-power relay in a 24-hour orbit. An intelligence bandwidth of 100 kc, entirely adequate for many communication purposes, can be achieved with a receiving antenna of 60-foot diameter. Comparable signal-to-noise performance can also be achieved with a 2-mc bandwidth if a receiving antenna 250 feet in diameter is used.

For comparison, column 2 shows the performance that could be achieved with a passive system if the satellite were placed in a 24-hour orbit at a height of approximately 22,000 miles. The achievable bandwidth is so narrow that this system is not likely to be very useful.

If the distance between transmitting and receiving sites were 3000 miles in the case of the low-altitude satellite, approximately ten such satellites would be required to provide a continuous service. The number required increases as the ground spacing is increased. Approximately twenty such satellites would be required if the distance between the sites were increased to 5000 miles. The number of balloons required could be reduced by increasing the height of the orbit, but unfortunately the strength of the signal falls off rapidly as the height is increased.

If continuous service is not required, a small number of satellites might give adequate service. For the 3000-mile path examined, and if we assume a balloon satellite at a height of 2500 miles, a single sphere in the proper orbit would provide a circuit for approximately 15 per cent of the time.

The passive satellite has one very attractive property: It is available to anyone who chooses to use it, and the only precaution that needs to be taken to avoid interference between different users is proper allocation of operational frequencies. Such a balloon is not frequency sensitive, and so a wide range of frequencies is available for this application. Active systems will probably not be able to operate over nearly as wide a frequency band. In addition, they must be used with care if they relay more than one signal, in order to avoid interchannel interference.

Designs exist for the balloons, and the first successful launching (Echo I) was made in August of 1960 by the U. S. National Aeronautics and Space Administration. This first 100-foot aluminum-coated plastic balloon circled the earth at altitudes between about 1000 and 1200 miles.

The spherical reflector appears to be the most satisfactory shape for a passive reflector. Various proposals for flat surfaces, corrugated surfaces, and specialized shapes have been made, but on critical examination they are found to have disadvantages when compared with the spherical balloon.

2. Medium power—As satellites capable of carrying larger payloads become available the performance of the active relay systems can be substantially improved. For example, if the power output of the satellite relay transmitter discussed in the previous section were increased to 100 watts, the system performance would be improved by 20 db. This improvement is particularly needed to make the mobile system fully effective. The performances of several such systems are given in columns 7, 8, 9 and 10. With the presently available power supplies, a 100-watt satellite would weigh approximately 1000 pounds. Most of this weight would be in the power system, so that improvements in power supply, particularly in the energy-storage-per-unit weight of storage batteries, would reduce the total satellite weight considerably.

A satisfactory transmitter tube for this application does not exist, but it does appear possible to achieve, at the present time, a tube that has the requisite efficiency and life expectancy.

3. Storage and rebroadcast systems—A system using storage equipment in a satellite has been proposed to extend the transmission range of a single satellite. Such a system would probably employ an equatorial orbit at a height of 1000 to 2000 miles and could be used in conjunction with a ground system similar to those discussed previously. The satellite would receive messages as it passed over the sending station, would store them on a magnetic-tape memory, and would retransmit them as it passed over the receiving site. This process would involve delays of 30 minutes to an hour; the exact value would depend on the location of the transmitting and receiving sites and the height of the orbit. For many purposes such delays would not be serious. Unfortunately, for foreseeable storage systems the information capacity of this system would be limited.

B. Broadcast Service

One of the most exciting advances made possible by the development of satellites is the possibility of establishing a world-wide broadcasting system in the standard frequency-modulation band with the employment of only a few medium-power transmitters. Column 11 shows the performance that would be obtained with a 100-watt transmitter in equatorial orbit. The signal on the surface of the earth is sufficiently strong that it would afford high-quality reception over most of the hemisphere illuminated by the satellite even with a modest outdoor receiving antenna on the ground. In fact, the signal is sufficiently strong that one might be tempted to provide this service with a lower-power satellite relay—for example, one radiatting only 10 watts instead of 100 watts. Such a system would probably give marginal performance under many conditions. In the example chosen, the standard 100-mc FM band was employed so that existing FM receivers would be able to receive programs from the satellite relay. If desired, the relay system could be equipped to provide subcarrier audio channels when voice messages were being broadcast so that messages could be broadcast simultaneously in several languages. In this case, the listener can select the desired language if appropriate selector circuitry is provided in the receiver.

The system whose characteristics are given in column 11 is not quite adequate for television broadcasting. A performance improvement of at least 10 db would be required for this purpose. This could be achieved by using a 1000-watt transmitter in the satellite or by employing a better receiving system. One thousand watts of radiated power would require a satellite system (including power supply) that is well beyond present achievement. The improvements in receivers and antenna systems, while they are now achievable, would probably make the individual television receiver too expensive for widespread use.

V. ECONOMIC FACTORS

Any estimate of the cost of creating and operating a satellite communication system will obviously be highly conjectural at this time. By far the most expensive item required for a satellite communication system is the large rocket required to lift the relay system into an orbit far above the surface of the earth. At the present time such rockets cost approximately five million dollars apiece. In addition, until the reliability of large rockets improves, one must count on failures which may greatly increase the cost of building a system.

Assuming that a satellite relay can be built and put into orbit for fifteen million dollars and that the associated ground equipment costs another five million dollars for connecting two points on the surface of the earth, the total cost of the relay system will be twenty million dollars. A circuit bandwidth of 100 mc can readily be achieved, so that the initial cost of the circuit will be approximately two hundred thousand dollars per megacycle. Further, assuming that a satellite will have a five-year life, the equipment cost amounts to approximately forty thousand dollars per year per megacycle. Compared with this sum, the operating cost will be insignificant.

The circuit cost is independent of distance for all distances within the line of sight of a single satellite; that is, for distances up to approximately 8000 miles. From this data, it can be seen that even for relatively short circuits the cost of a satellite relay system makes them competitive with other means of relaying wideband information.

REFERENCES

1. Much of the orbital data presented here is taken from a report prepared by W. E. Morrow for the Signal Corps Barnstable project.
2. J. R. Pierce and R. Kompfner, "Communication by Means of Satellites," *Proc. IRE,* vol. 47, no. 3, pp. 372-380, March 1959.
3. A. Uhlir, Jr., "The Potential of Semiconductor Diodes in High Frequency Communications," *Proc. IRE,* vol. 47, no. 6, pp. 1099-1115, Section VIII, June 1958.
4. G. Makhov, C. Kikuchi, J. Lambe, R. W. Terhune, "Maser Action in Ruby," *Phys. Rev.*, vol. 109, no. 4, pp. 1399-1400, February 15, 1958.

CHAPTER **23**

CONCLUSION

Present Trends

R. M. Fano

In concluding this series of lectures on recent developments in long-distance communications it seems appropriate to discuss some of the factors that are likely to shape the future in the same area. These factors can be grouped, for our purposes, under three headings: new requirements, new physical tools, new theoretical tools. We shall discuss briefly these three groups of factors, with particular emphasis on the last one with which this writer is most familiar.

I. NEW REQUIREMENTS

Technical developments in other areas are confronting society with a variety of critical problems that require much faster and more accurate reaction to events taking place over a large geographical area. The problem of air-traffic control, created by the increasing number of airplanes in flight, and by the greater speed and fuel consumption of jet aircrafts is one example. Stock and production control in large industries, and traffic routing and control in transportation industries are other examples. Many urgent military problems of a similar type have been created by the need for immediate reaction to a surprise attack, and by the increasingly complex character of military operations.

In most of these new problems, actions have to be taken at widely separated places on the basis of large volumes of data collected over equally extended areas. The information processing aspects of these problems require faster, larger, and more reliable digital computers, and, above all, more powerful and flexible programming techniques. The communication aspects of these problems are just as challenging. In the first place, the data to be transmitted over large distances are going to swell the already fast growing volume of communication of the traditional type, thereby placing a higher value on the efficient use of transmission facilities. In the second place, the nature of the information to be transmitted will place new, more stringent performance requirements, matching those of the digital computers by which the information is processed.

The traditional forms of communication, such as telephony and telegraphy, are characterized by the fact that humans are the original transmitters and the ultimate receivers. The transmission links used for these purposes perform in effect the function of extending the range of human senses, thereby allowing individuals to communicate when they are widely separated, in the same manner as when they are in each other's presence. Thus, in the overall communication system, two human brains are available for use as terminal equipment, and advantage is taken of a highly complex form of encoding, *i.e.* the language, developed through evolution to permit effective communication in the presence of random disturbances. It is well known that telegraphic messages are usually understandable with as much as one incorrect letter per word on the average, and that normal telephone conversation can take place when individual phonemes could not be recognized out of context with any degree of reliability. It is not as generally appreciated, however, that individuals automatically vary the speed of communication with the severity of existing disturbances, not only by reducing the number of words per minute, but also by changing the language they employ, and, particularly, by reducing their vocabulary.

It is clear that the features permitting accurate and efficient communication between men must somehow be introduced in machine-to-machine communication through the use of a suitable artificial language, and of terminal equipment capable of performing the corresponding encoding and decoding operations. The alternative to introducing such features is the use of transmission links that are inherently capable of transmitting individual binary digits with an accuracy consistent with that of the machines at their terminals. We shall compare these two approaches in connection with our discussion of the theoretical tools.

II. NEW PHYSICAL TOOLS

Two types of new physical tools are of primary interest to long-distance communications, namely tools providing new transmission paths, and tools that facilitate the processing of signals at the terminals of a link and at intermediate relay points. The characteristics of various modes of propagation have been discussed in previous chapters, and the last chapter has been devoted to the use of satellites as relay stations. I would like to add to the list of new transmission means the circular-waveguide links, and the digital cables developed at the Bell Telephone Laboratories during the last decade. The digital cable is of special historical interest because it departs from the traditional goal of providing a linear transmission medium. The repeaters along the cable are digital devices that generate pulses of fixed amplitude in response to incoming pulses. Thus the cable can be used only for digital transmission; this limitation is the price of greater simplicity, reliability and transmission accuracy.

The outstanding new tool of the second type is the stored-program digital computer. Computer technology has been progressing by leaps and bounds over the last decade, in terms of reliability, size of components, speed of operation, and ease of assembly. Furthermore, digital devices are inherently suitable for mass production—various promising techniques are under development. It seems reasonable to assume, therefore, that it will be feasible and economical in the near future to employ special-purpose digital computers as terminal equipment in long-distance communication systems.

Stored-program (externally programmable) computers have two main advantages over non-programmable circuitry, whether digital or analog. In the first place, they become relatively more economical both in terms of size and cost with increasing complexity of the operations to be performed. This follows from the fact that the stored program leads to a more efficient use of components, particularly because of the possibility of exploiting the increasingly greater speed of the available components through serial operation. In the second place, they provide much greater flexibility, because the same equipment can be used to perform radically different operations by simply changing its program. This flexibility can be a great asset in communication systems, as it permits the adjustment of the rate and mode of transmission to existing channel conditions. Furthermore, it permits one to modify quickly and easily the operation of a system without any equipment changes, in response to suggestions arising from operating experience and from new technical developments.

A third additional advantage of stored-program computers deserves to be mentioned. It is a subtle advantage which has to do with mental attitude in the design of communication systems. When the use of computers is not envisioned, the operation of a system is usually conceived from the beginning in terms of functions that can be performed by known devices (black boxes) such as amplifiers, modulators, shift registers, delay lines, etc. This approach automatically excludes from consideration modes of operation that cannot be implemented in terms of such devices, even if they do not require any greater total amount of equipment. On the other hand, if one assumes from the start that a suitable digital computer is available, one is naturally led to consider a much broader class of solutions, being free to envision any logically possible operation. Compromises between performance and equipment complexity are then made on the basis of the overall characteristics of the computer required rather than piecemeal on the basis of partial information. A better design is likely to result even if in the end implementation with non-programmable circuitry turns out to be more appropriate.

III. NEW THEORETICAL TOOLS

The availability of stored-program computers together with the more exacting transmission requirements that we can foresee in the future suggests a trend toward more complex terminal equipment in long-distance communication systems. This trend is already evident in some of the recently developed systems such as the Rake system

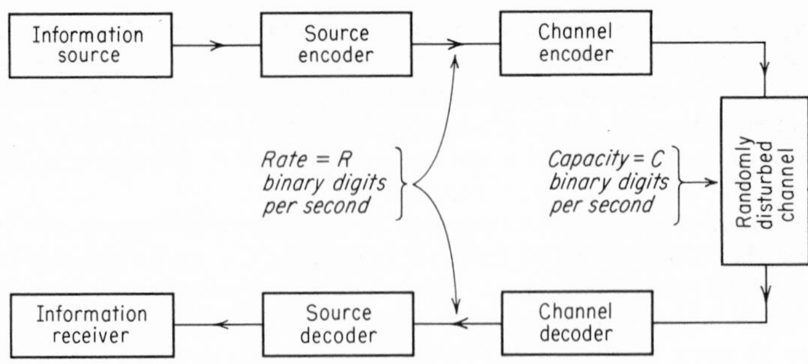

Fig. 1. Model of communication system

discussed in Chapter 12. The successful exploitation of decision theory in Rake and in other systems raises the question of how much more can be achieved at the expense of even greater equipment complexity. This question is answered in principle by Shannon's coding theorem,[1] as refined by Shannon himself,[9,14] Feinstein,[13] and Elias.[4,5] More recent work by Wozencraft[8] indicates that the mode of transmission suggested by the theorem can be implemented, at least in certain special cases, with the help of a computer of reasonable size.

It is convenient for our purposes to think of a simple, unidirectional communication system in terms of the block diagram of Fig. 1. The information source, the information receiver, and the channel providing a link between them are regarded as specified. The source might be an individual generating spoken or written messages, a television camera, a measuring instrument, or a digital computer. The information receiver might be accordingly either a second individual or a second machine. It is understood that the specification of the source and of the receiver includes some fidelity criterion for deciding whether the message input to the receiver is a satisfactory reproduction of the message output from the source.

The first part of Shannon's theorem states that, under rather general conditions, an *information rate* R can be assigned to the source-receiver combination, representing the number of binary digits per second that must be transmitted through the channel in order for the received message to be a satisfactory reproduction of the message generated by the source. The physical implication of this statement is that it is possible to construct a source encoder that transforms the source output into binary digits occurring with an average rate of R digits per second, and a source decoder that can transform back the same binary digits into a satisfactory reproduction of the source output.

The second part of Shannon's theorem states that, under similarly general conditions, an *information capacity* C can be assigned to the channel, representing the maximum average number of binary digits per second that can be transmitted through the channel with perfect accuracy, that is with an arbitrarily small probability of error. This statement implies that it is possible to construct a channel encoder that transforms continuously the input sequence of binary digits into a signal appropriate for transmission through the channel, and a corresponding decoder that can reproduce the original sequence of binary digits from the signal output from the channel.

The essence of Shannon's theorem is that the output from the source can be reproduced at the receiver with the specified fidelity whenever R is smaller than C. Conversely, satisfactory reproduction cannot be achieved when R is equal to or greater than C. It is important to note, in this regard, that R and C are determined independently of each other; in other words C is a characteristic of the channel, and it has the same value for all source-receiver pairs, and R is a characteristic of the source-receiver pair, and has the same value for all channels. In addition, the significance of R and C in terms of binary digits indicates that binary digits can be used to provide an intermediate, common message representation for all sources and all channels without restricting in any way the communication process. In other words, transmission links can be designed to accept and reproduce binary digits, on the assumption that the information sources and receivers are provided with their own binary encoders and decoders as shown in Fig. 1. This does not imply, however, that binary transmission is employed in the links themselves.

It is not surprising that the output of a given source can be represented by means of binary digits while meeting a specified fidelity criterion, and that a certain minimum number of binary digits per second are required for this purpose. It is rather surprising, on the other hand, to find that it is possible to transmit binary digits with as low a probability of error as desired, as long as their rate of transmission is smaller than the information capacity of the available channel. This implies that the presence of random disturbances in the channel does not, by itself, limit the obtainable transmission accuracy, but it limits instead the maximum transmission rate for which the probability of error can be made as small as desired by proper encoding. As one might expect, the price of reducing the probability of error for a fixed transmission rate and a fixed channel capacity is an increase of complexity of the encoding and decoding operations. Perfect transmission accuracy is approached only as a limit with an encoding scheme of infinite complexity.

The block diagram of Fig. 2 illustrates the nature of the encoding and decoding operations involved in the second part of Shannon's theorem. The encoder stores, at any given time, N of the digits to be transmitted. The signal generated by the encoder for transmission is, at that time, a specified function of the N digits stored. Thus, on the average, each of the digits influences the signal transmitted over a time interval T equal to the number N divided by the transmission rate R. We might also say, from a different point of view, that the encoder builds into the signal a dependence on its own past whose extent is measured by the time constant T.

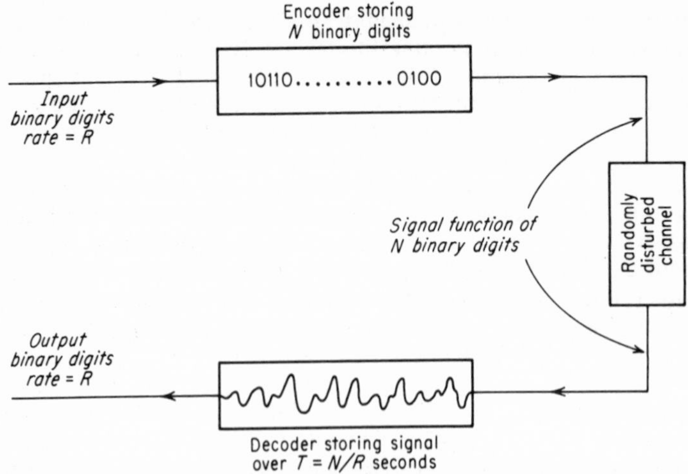

Fig. 2. Channel encoding and decoding

The decoder stores, at any given time, a segment of the received signal of length equal to T. On the basis of this segment it decides, in view of the statistical characteristics of the channel disturbances, whether the digit that influenced the corresponding segment of transmitted signal was a zero or a one. The more probable alternative is assumed to be the correct one. Thus, each of the transmitted digits is decoded in succession from the received signal. It can be shown that the logarithm of the probability P_e that any particular digit be incorrectly decoded is asymptotically proportional to the number N that characterizes the complexity of the encoding scheme, *i.e.*

$$\lim_{N \to \infty} \ln P_e = -EN$$

The quantity E depends on the transmission rate and on the characteristics of the channel, but is independent of N. For any fixed channel, E is positive for $R < C$, it decreases when R increases, and vanishes with a zero derivative for $R = C$. Thus, the probability of error decreases exponentially with increasing N for any fixed transmission rate smaller than the channel capacity.

The asymptotic exponential decay of the probability of error with N is, roughly speaking, a consequence of the law of large numbers; the number that has to be large in order for the necessary statistical convergence to become appreciable is just N. It follows that a reasonably large value of N (such as 50 or 100) must be used in order to make the transmission accuracy substantially better than that obtained for the same transmission rate by conventional modulation techniques. This fact raises the very important practical question of how fast the complexity of the required terminal equipment increases with N.

Our present knowledge of specific encoding and decoding techniques is rather limited. Wozencraft[8] has developed, for a particularly simple type of channel (the binary symmetric channel), a technique for which the complexity of the encoding operation (measured in terms of a suitable unit of computation) grows linearly with N, and that of the decoding operation grows in proportion to $N \ln N$. His results have been confirmed experimentally by simulating the entire communication process on an IBM 704 computer. There are reasons to believe that this technique can be generalized for use in connection with other channels and that the same moderate growth of the complexity with N will result. In any case, it appears that the complexity of the necessary terminal equipment does not present an unsurmountable barrier to the practical exploitation of Shannon's theorem.

IV. CONCLUSIONS

The new requirements, physical tools, and theoretical tools mentioned above indicate a new trend in the design of communication systems. While in the past most communication systems have been designed and developed piecemeal, as aggregates of special-purpose links, we can expect for the future a greater emphasis on integrated, general-purpose communication networks, with automatic traffic routing and control. Binary digits appear to provide an appropriate representation for input and output messages in such general-purpose networks, with transmission facilities being assigned to users in multiples of a basic binary rate, rather than in multiples of a basic bandwidth.

We can also expect a continuing trend toward more complex terminal equipment in the individual links, to perform the operations required for automatic traffic control and routing and for complex encoding. It seems clear that both the equipment and the theoretical knowledge necessary to obtain in practice the accuracy and efficiency of transmission indicated by Shannon's theorem are either available or will be in the near future, at the present rate of progress. The main factor involved in the decision of whether or not to use complex encoding is an economic one. The transmission accuracy required for machine-to-machine communication can be achieved through a given channel by either making the rate of transmission sufficiently low, or by encoding with a sufficiently large value of N and a relatively large transmission rate. These are the only two ways of obtaining a large product EN and a correspondingly small probability of error. Conventional modulation techniques employ in effect small values of N and large values of E, and provide a rate of transmission substantially smaller than the channel capacity. This exchange relation between E, which decreases with increasing rate of transmission, and the coding length measured by N reflects itself in practice in a corresponding exchange relation between cost of terminal equipment and cost of transmission facilities, *i.e.* cables, transmitters, antennas, etc. Looking at the future, the cost of transmission facilities per unit channel capacity is likely to remain, at best, fairly constant because such facilities involve primarily material and special-purpose labor, *i.e.* power equipment, large structures, and laying of cables or waveguides. The digital equipment required for complex encoding, on the other hand, is highly mass producible because of its very structure and because of its general-purpose character. For this reason its cost is likely to decrease substantially with time. These economic factors indicate a trend toward a more efficient use of transmission facilities at the expense of more complex terminal equipment.

In conclusion, this writer believes that the use of digital computers for traffic control, encoding, and decoding will characterize future communication systems. The trend in that direction has not yet gained momentum, primarily because of the small common membership of the fraternities of communication engineers and of computer engineers. The future of long-distance communications will be shaped by engineers who are willing and able to join both fraternities.

SELECTED REFERENCES ON CODING THEORY

1. C. E. Shannon, "A Mathematical Theory of Communications", *Bell System Tech. J.*, vol. 28, July and October 1948. Also: University of Illinois Press.
2. E. N. Gilbert, "A Comparison of Signaling Alphabets", *Bell System Tech. J.*, vol. 31, pp. 504-522, May 1952. Also: Bell Tel. Monograph 1958.
3. I. S. Reed, "A Class of Multiple-Error-Correcting Codes and the Decoding Scheme", *Trans., I.R.E.* PGIT-4, pp. 38-49, September 1954.
4. P. Elias, "Coding for Noisy Channels", I.R.E. Convention Record, Part 4, pp. 37-46, 1955.
5. P. Elias, "Coding for Two Noisy Channels", *Information Theory* (Third London Symposium) edited by C. Cherry, pp. 61-76, Butterworth Scientific Publications, London, 1955.
6. D. Slepian, "A Class of Binary Signaling Alphabets", *Bell System Tech. J.*, vol. 35, pp. 203-234, January 1956. Also: Bell Tel. Monograph 2563.
7. D. Slepian, "A Note on Two Binary Signaling Alphabets", *Trans., I.R.E.* PGIT-2, June 1956. Also: Bell Tel. Monograph, 2733.
8. J. M. Wozencraft, "Sequential Decoding for Reliable Communication", I.R.E. National Convention Record, Part 2, March 1957. Also: Technical Report 325, Research Laboratory of Electronics, M.I.T., 1957.
9. C. E. Shannon, "Certain Results in Coding Theory for Noisy Channels", *Information and Control,* vol. 1, no. 1, pp. 6-25, September 1957. Also: Bell Tel. Monograph 2982.
10. A. B. Brown and S. T. Meyers, "Evaluation of Some Error Correction Methods Applicable to Digital Data Transmission", I.R.E. National Convention Record, Part 4, pp. 37-55, March 1958.

11. A. B. Fontaine and W. W. Peterson, "On Coding for the Binary Symmetric Channel", Transactions Paper No. 58-925, A.I.E.E. Summer General Meeting, June 1958.
12. M. A. Epstein, "Algebraic Decoding for a Binary Erasure Channel", I.R.E. Convention Record, Part 4, pp. 56-69, 1958
13. A. Feinstein, *Foundations of Information Theory*, McGraw-Hill, New York, 1958
14. C. E. Shannon, "Probability of Error for Optimal Codes in a Gaussian Channel", *Bell System Tech. J.*, vol. 38, pp. 611-656, May 1959.

Index